Date Due

Fundamentals of Mathematics from an Advanced Viewpoint

Volumes 1 and 2

Algebra and Analysis:
Evolution of the Number Concept
and
Determinants – Equations – Logarithms

Fundamentals of Mathematics from an Advanced Viewpoint:

Fundamentals of Mathematics from an Advanced Viewpoint

Algebra and Analysis:

Evolution of the Number Concept
and
Determinants – Equations – Logarithms

by

E. G. KOGBETLIANTZ

The Rockefeller University

GORDON AND BREACH SCIENCE PUBLISHERS

NEW YORK · LONDON · PARIS

Editorial office for the United Kingdom:

Gordon and Breach Science Publishers Ltd
8 Bloomsbury Way
London W.C. 1

Editorial office for France:

Gordon & Breach
7–9 rue Emile Dubois
Paris 14e

Distributed in Canada by:

The Ryerson Press
299 Queen Street West
Toronto 2B, Ontario

TO MY WIFE EUGENIA

Contents

Volume 2   Algebra and Analysis: Determinants – Equations – Logarithms

Contents of other volumes

Volume 3   Geometry and Geometric Analysis

Introduction

Human society is not the unique collectivity on the Earth: it is only one of many similar societies of fishes, birds, mammals and insects living on the same planet.

Some of the fundamental characteristics of human society are found in all groups of living creatures. For example, ants have their own types of cattle breeding and agriculture. Like human beings, they have armies, wage wars and practice slavery. Elephants worship the moon: assembling by the thousands from all parts of India, they perform their rites at full moon. Religious rites in the form of daily howling prayers to the rising and setting sun are observed also by Bellowing Apes living in the forests near the Amazon River. In the same way it may be shown that law and ethics are characteristics of many societies other than human. For instance, members of a stork society will try an unfaithful spouse and punish her by death. Finally, tactile or spoken language is widely used for communication of thoughts and emotions by many collectivities other than human society.

But, on the other hand, there are specific traits such as transmission by written language of collective experience (including science), exchange of goods, and mining and manufacturing, which are distinctive features of human society. The common foundation of these specifically human traits is the extensive use of symbols. It is plain, for example, that without written language no accumulation of experience could be possible. Other types of symbols no less important are mathematical symbols, which can be considered as an extension of written language.

This symbolic character of human civilization is, as we will see, the true basis of the facility with which mankind is transforming the environment, adapting it to human needs. Here we have another distinctive trait of human society, because all other societies transform the individual, adapting him to the environment. To transform the environment, mankind has developed complicated and powerful tools, such as electronic computers. It is interesting to study the ways by which the evolution of human thinking has achieved this mastery of environment, organizing industry and world-wide exchange of goods.

It is not an exaggeration to say that the concept of number is a fundamental condition of exchange. Exchange of goods presupposes estimates of relative value based on the idea of magnitude expressed in numbers (money). One must confess that numbers are not specifically a human creation. Birds, for instance, are not unfamiliar with the first integers and they use them in counting their fledglings. Wasps, too, know perfectly well how many paralysed victims must be buried in the nest together with the egg to insure the life of the future larva. But only mankind has created arithmetic, without which there would never be exchange of goods nor its important consequences, the specialization of work and division of labor.

The exchange of goods and Arithmetic are very old, while technology and industry are of recent origin. During many thousands of years until the last three centuries the evolution of human society was relatively slow. Then came a sudden explosion of modern technology with its ever-accelerating tempo of new inventions which is brutally and pitilessly transforming our environment, sometimes with such rapidity that we are lost and bewildered by new possibilities. Precisely now, when we are approaching the miraculous goal of completely taming atomic energy, the most powerful source of energy we know in nature, its discovery is a source of trouble in our time.

What is the profound reason for this turning-point in the evolution of mankind? What is the origin of modern technology? Why did it not occur a thousand years earlier? Or later?

The production and transportation of food, raw materials and energy in the form of coal, oil, electricity, in general all our highly industrialized way of life, our material culture, are based on the use of innumerable machines.

To invent, design and build them, a profound and thorough study of environment, of natural laws in their physical and chemical aspects, a study of the structure of matter and energy was a necessary prerequisite. Physics and chemistry did not exist as developed sciences three hundred years ago.

That is why for fifteen thousand years of human culture man made little progress in the transformation of environment, and it is only during the last three centuries that mankind has learned with increasing rapidity how to master natural forces.

Theoretical physics and chemistry, with all their laws on which are based our industrial machines and methods of mass production, were created only during the past three centuries. If one asks "Why so late?", the answer is very simple: physics and chemistry are impossible without mathematics, since the natural laws can be formulated and expressed only as relations between numbers and their aggregates.

But mathematics is a very old science. Why then does the development of physics and chemistry characterize only the last three centuries?

Here we come to an important discrimination between ancient and modern mathematics. If we want to understand the profound reason why only modern mathematics, the mathematics of Newton and Leibnitz, made possible the development of physics and chemistry, thus creating technology and industry, we must examine more closely the relation between man and his natural environment, environment not as it is in itself, but as it is perceived by man.

The human frame of time and space in which our brain localizes all events, i.e. all its perceptions, is *finite* in all its practical applications. Nature, such as we perceive it, appears to us a *finite* collection of *finite* events which can be characterized by *finite* magnitudes.

More than two thousand years ago Archimedes pointed out that the total number of grains of sand on the shores of all oceans and seas of the earth is enormous but necessarily finite, just as is finite the total number of drops of water in all oceans, seas and rivers. In his letter to King Gelon, Archimedes even says that a mass of sand equal in size to the universe (as bounded by the fixed stars sphere) would contain a finite number of sand grains (about 10^{63}). This thought is remarkably in tune with the modern view of a finite universe.

From our Milky Way to the most remote nebulae astronomers observe and measure there are distances so incredibly vast that light, which travels 186,000 miles per second, takes 500 million years to cover these distances, and still they are finite!

Likewise the amount of heat developed by an atomic explosion is such that the temperature reached is expressed by two million degrees, a number which is meaningless to us in a human scale, but this amount of heat is finite.

In short, nature as we know and perceive it, is finite. Man is a finite being too, for he is only an infinitesimal part of nature. But strangely enough, the mind of this finite being, with his finite brain, has conceived the idea of Infinity.

Infinity first appeared to man in the idea of God. God, by definition, is an infinite being. God personifies infinity since God is Almighty-omnipotent, omnipresent, omniscient, eternal. Then the same idea manifested itself in the first naive image of the earth as an infinite flat surface. We find it again in the concept of an infinite universe, a concept which is still deeply rooted in all of us. When we speak of an "infinite universe" we mean a three-dimensional space extending infinitely in all directions and lasting eternally.

The old mathematics, mathematics elaborated by mankind during the last five thousand years, was finite in the sense that only finite reasoning's chains were admitted as logically existing and true, infinite chains of syllogisms being prohibited as a source of errors (Zeno of Elea). Such finite mathematics, beautiful systems though they were, cannot be applied to the study of nature.

Only after the realization of the true nature of mathematics as the science of Infinity, after the introduction and use of absolute infinity (in a disguised form) by Cavalieri, Fermat, Newton, Leibnitz and others, was modern mathematics born, and with it physics, technology, and industry.

The mysterious power of applied science to master the forces of nature is based in the last analysis on the introduction and use of absolute infinity in mathematics. The prodigious development of theoretical and applied physics began only after the introduction by Newton and Leibnitz of infinitely small numbers in mathematics, and the concept of limit is simply another form of the idea of absolute infinity.

How could it happen that nothing more than the manipulation of mathematical symbols, the use of mathematical language, brought to mankind such a magnificient result as the almost achieved and soon complete mastery of Nature?

Human thought in its struggle with a finite Nature is using as a tool the idea of infinity embodied in mathematical symbols and methods. The success of this struggle is due to the fundamental fact that the finite can easily be understood, studied, and subjugated when the thought uses infinity as a tool against it. The very importance of mathematics in our life is due to this most characteristic trait of modern mathematics, which is the practical use of the infinity concept.

If one studies our environment, mathematics appears as the very basis of our culture. Sir James Jeans, in his book *The Mysterious Universe*, says: "The Great Architect of the Universe now begins to appear as a pure mathematician", and this thought is not new: Plato (429–347 B.C.) said: "God ever geometrizes". And this juxtaposition of two forms of the idea of Infinity is not a coincidence.

Mathematics permeates all our life and in the last analysis one will find the number everywhere. The measurements of the ever-flowing world in its variations are an everyday necessity for our society with its highly complicated economical structure. Every phase of human activity now must be planned and the planning is based on statistical computations which are pure mathematics. The modern trend in biology and psychology is also towards the introduction of numerical characteristics and mathematical methods. It is sufficient to cite as an example the mathematical proof of the fundamental fact that the famous law of heredity, discovered in the beginning of the nineteenth century by Mendel, is not only true but unique and cannot be replaced by another law. This proof was achieved by a Russian mathematician, S. Bernstein, with the aid of purely algebraical methods.

In this book, which describes the fundamental ideas and methods of modern mathematics, the elementary branches of this science: arithmetic, algebra, geometry (plane and solid) and trigonometry (plane and spherical) are studied from a new point of view. This study has been done in an unorthodox way which, it is hoped, will help to orient the readers in the contemporary world and facilitate a basic understanding of our environment.

The text does not include all the theorems but only some important ones. The proofs sometimes are omitted, and the classical division of elementary mathematics into separate branches, arithmetic, algebra, geometry, trigonometry, which in our opinion is artificial, is not always respected; rather, the fundamental unity of mathematics is stressed.

Moreover, the idea of absolute infinity is chosen as the principal axis of exposition, and this in some cases eliminates the possibility of a rigorous proof. These features are intentional and they are introduced with the purpose of facilitating the study of mathematical ideas by an unprepared reader.

Notwithstanding the limitation to four elementary branches we have tried to acquaint the reader with the basic ideas of mathematics in general, since they appear in the foundations of mathematics and can easily be traced through the elementary branches, too.

In such a society as ours, a society still too artificial for the majority of mankind because it is too technical, it is necessary to become aware of the implications of science in our lives. To this end, mathematical thinking and mathematical culture are imperative. If this book can contribute towards such an understanding its appearance will be justified.

The author is grateful to Dr. Clara Mayer of the New School for Social Research. Her insistence and moral help were decisive in the preparation of this book which is the outgrowth of a course on Fundamentals of Mathematics given at The New School during the years 1944 to 1954.

CHAPTER 1

The Infinite Set of Natural Numbers; Mathematical Induction; Prime Numbers; Decimal Numeration

Number rules the Universe
Pythagoras (569–500 B.C.)

The Great Architect of the Universe
now begins to appear as a pure mathematician
Sir James Jeans (1877–1947)

It is a well-known fact that all the mathematical definitions, theorems, and propositions could be formulated using only the so-called *natural numbers*

$$1, 2, 3, 4, \ldots, n - 1, n, n + 1, \ldots, \tag{1}$$

the symbol n denoting any integer, so that $n - 1$ and $n + 1$ mean the integers immediately preceding and following the integer n.

In the final analysis all the mathematical propositions appear as statements about natural numbers. Therefore, these numbers must be considered as the foundation on which mathematics is built. This fact caused the German mathematician Kronecker to say: "God made the integers, all the rest is the work of man".

Integers appear in the history of human thought as the first mathematical concepts created by the human mind. This creation was an extremely slow and painful process; it took many thousands of years. Only at a rather advanced stage of intellectual evolution does the abstract character of the number concept become clear.

Even now, there is in British Columbia a primitive people whose language has seven different names for every number. One set serves to count the days and is associated with the idea of time; the second is for animals; the third men; the fourth long thin objects such as trees; the fifth boats; the sixth, associated with spatial extension, serves for measurements of lengths (counting of units of length); and the seventh, which is unknown to the common people, is used only by sorcerers.

The last-named is the most interesting. It represents the beginning of abstraction since it serves to count the undefined or unknown objects. It is clear that for this people the evolution of the number concept has not yet reached the final stage of the abstract number. Only in the seventh set, the sacred form, is there a first approach to our number concept.

The history of this evolution shows us another important point: in most cases only a few first numbers are formed and used. The counting stops with a "last" number, the word "many" being used to denote any quantity that exceeds this "last" number. For instance, the bushmen of South Africa use words only for the first three numbers 1, 2, 3. They have not yet reached the stage when the idea of number "four" becomes crystallized, and a word for this idea therefore created. All the collections of four or more objects appear to the mind of this primitive people as equally vague in quantity, and therefore are characterized by the same word, which means "many".

The English language preserves a reminiscence of the first steps of the number story in the double meaning of the word "thrice". Thrice originally denoted "many times" and then came to mean "three times". The first meaning remains in such combinations as thrice-blessed and thrice-favored.

With the development of human culture, larger and larger numbers were defined and used, and now we can observe the repetition of this historical process in our children when they slowly learn how to count, first up to three, then up to five, twenty, one hundred, *etc.*

For us, the progressive formation of the sequence of natural numbers is now terminated, and the natural sequence of positive integers appears to us as infinite. Using the symbol n to denote any arbitrary integer, regardless of its value, after any number n we conceive the next to be $n + 1$, then $n + 2, n + 3, \ldots$, and there is no end, no last integer.

Here, at the first step in mathematics, we meet *infinity* in its two fundamental aspects: *potential infinity* and *actual, absolute infinity*. The concept of potential infinity expresses the everlasting, unlimited growth of integers by endlessly repeated additions of a unit, so that a particular number n being given, as large as we please in value, but fixed, an integer greater than n can always be found.

Thus, the concept of potential infinity is a dynamic notion: it involves a variation of ever-growing magnitude. Instead of unit jumps, we may consider finite jumps of arbitrary magnitude, but again their number must be infinitely large, that is unbounded, unlimited.

Actual, absolute infinity, on the contrary, is a *static* concept of the whole set, the collection of *all* the integers considered together at one time as a single entity. We will see later that there are many different actual infinities. This first one we encounter, the infinite set of all the integers, has a special name, *denumerable* infinity, and a special symbol, aleph-null $\aleph_0$.

The aleph-null itself is not an integer, since every integer is necessarily a finite number. Moreover, the addition of a unit to aleph-null cannot change it, since the possibility of increasing a number by adding a unit to it characterizes finite numbers and their progressive formation. The possibility of further increase must be considered as exhausted in the formation of the collection of all the integers, if we want to consider this infinite collection as a perfectly determined, static entity.

The symbol of this entity, aleph-null $\aleph_0$, represents by definition the totality of all the integers which can be formed and were actually formed by repeated additions of one, so that the process of their formation is already terminated. Considered as a number, aleph-null comes after all the finite integers, and it is the first *transfinite* number.

The effect of the addition of a unit on the magnitude of an integer n decreases as n runs through the sequence of natural numbers (1), increasing without limit. Adding one to one, we double it. But, adding one to a thousand, we increase its magnitude by only one-thousandth. In general, adding one to n, we increase n by one n-th part, $1/n$. When n becomes larger, $1/n$ decreases and if n becomes infinite, the effect of adding a unit to it vanishes because $1/n$ becomes zero.

Thus, with respect to actual infinity, the number one (as well as any other finite number) plays the same role as zero plays with respect to the number one or any other integer. Adding zero to one, we do not change it:

$$1 + 0 = 1$$

Likewise, the addition of one to aleph-null has no effect and does not increase it, in symbols

$$\aleph_0 + 1 = \aleph_0$$

We can never reach $\aleph_0$ if we keep adding one. Thus, by creating the concept of a totality of all the integers and its symbol $\aleph_0$, that is, considering the set of all the integers as a single entity, we jump in our imagination over the infinite sequence (1), and must therefore consider the effect of endless additions of units as exhausted.

The general mathematical symbol of actual infinity, without specifying its nature and rank in the classification of infinities, is ∞. Denoting an integer by the letter n, we can express the concept of potential infinity by writing $n \to \infty$, or more precisely $n \to \aleph_0$ (read "n tends towards infinity" or "n approaches infinity"). In this notation the integer n is variable, it becomes infinite, and the arrow expresses the idea of its growth. In $n \to \infty$ or $n \to \aleph_0$, the letter n together with the arrow $\to$ represent potential infinity, whereas ∞ or $\aleph_0$ denote actual infinity.

To clarify the concept of potential infinity, its variable character must be emphasized. The letter n used alone, without the arrow, can denote any integer, as large as we choose, but fixed. Any particular integer is always a *fixed* number; it does not vary even though it may be very large. Potential infinity $n \to \infty$ exceeds any fixed number N, however large it may be: if $n \to \infty$, then $n > N$, however large we choose N. The symbol $>$ means "greater than," while $<$ means "smaller than."

The set of natural numbers 1, 2, 3, ... is the simplest and most natural example of mathematical infinity, and it is the fundamental concept on which is based another form of mathematical infinity, the infinitely small number, which will be studied later.

The set of all the integers is an infinite collection, and there is nothing in our environment or in human experience which has this infinite characteristic. Thus, a new process of thinking is introduced when one considers the infinite collection of all the integers as a single entity, and, doing so, jumps over the infinite sequence of all the integers.

The creation of the infinite sequence of integers is based on the fundamental axiom of mathematical thinking which could be formulated as follows:

AXIOM: *An operation which can be performed once may be repeated indefinitely.*

Having stated that the addition of one unit to a group of units forming an integer n creates the next integer $n + 1$, we have only to repeat this operation indefinitely, that is an infinite number of times, to create all the integers.

Infinite collections have special properties which distinguish them from our familiar finite collections. We know, for example, that a part of a finite collection is always less than the whole collection. Let us analyze this statement. We compare two finite collections by trying to establish the so-called *one-to-one correspondence* between their elements. This one-to-one correspondence consists in pairing off the members of both collections. Each pair thus formed comprises an element chosen from the first collection and an element of the second collection. The process of pairing stops when all the elements of at least one collection are exhausted, and two conditions are possible:

If the collections become exhausted simultaneously, so that all the elements of both collections are grouped in pairs, and there are no free, unpaired elements, the two collections are said to be in one-to-one correspondence. We say also that these two collections are equal: they have the same number of elements, though this number may remain unknown if we have not applied counting.

If, on the contrary, some elements of the second collection remain unpaired when all the elements of the first collection are already exhausted, we say that the second collection has more elements, is richer in elements than the exhausted first collection, it being impossible to establish one-to-one correspondence between two unequal collections.

We observe that these statements do not imply counting and are independent of the number concept. Thus, for instance, if the first collection consists of seats and the other of men, we say that there are more people than seats if every seat is taken and some men still remain standing. This statement does not imply that we know the number of seats.

By definition, two finite collections are said to be equal if it is possible to establish a one-to-one correspondence between them. If the attempt to establish this correspondance fails, the collections are said to be unequal, the one which becomes exhausted while the other is not being defined as the smaller of the two. Therefore, when we say "a part is less than the whole", it can mean only one thing, namely that a part of a finite collection cannot be put into one-to-one correspondence with the total collection.

This law "a part is less than the whole" is deduced from the observation of finite collections and it does not apply to infinite parts of an infinite collection. A finite part of an infinite collection is indeed smaller than the whole collection, because it cannot be put into one to-one correspondence with it. But an infinite collection possesses infinite subsets which are parts of the total set and nevertheless *can* be put into one-to-one correspondence with the total collection.

Pick out, for instance, the even integers from the set (1) of all the integers, even and odd, and consider the infinite sequence thus obtained,

$$2, 4, 6, 8, \ldots, 2n, \ldots$$

where $2n$, the general term of this sequence, is a symbol for any even number. In general, the product of two numbers m and n is denoted by mn. Here $2n$ is the double of n, and therefore it is even. This set of even integers – call it the first set—is part of a second set, the set (1) of all the integers.

One and only one element in the first set corresponds to each element n of the second set, since there can be only one integer $2n$ which is the double of n. Conversely, one and only one element in the second set corresponds to each element $2m$ of the first set since there can be only one integer m which is the half of an even integer $2m$. The one-to-one correspondence between the two sets is thus established, though the first set is a part of the second set.

Denoting the correspondence by the symbol $\updownarrow$ we have therefore

First set: 2, 4, 6, 8, ... , $2n$, ...

                $\updownarrow$ $\updownarrow$ $\updownarrow$ $\updownarrow$ ... $\updownarrow$ ...

Second set: 1, 2, 3, 4, ... , n ...

so that a part and the whole have the same transfinite number of elements, the adjective "transfinite" emphasizing the infinitude of the number.

We use here a generalization of the process of pairing off, originally defined for finite collections only. It is now extended to the pairing off of infinite collections and leads to the following definition: *Two collections whose members can be put into one-to-one correspondence have the same number—finite or transfinite—of elements.*

In other words, there are as many even integers as there are even and odd integers together. This example is important because it proves that in dealing with infinite sets we cannot rely on classical logic. It was founded to deal with finite collections, and consequently some of its laws hold only for such collections.

It is interesting to recall that the profound difference between finite and infinite collections was studied for the first time in the history of human thinking by Galileo. In his *Dialogues,* which appeared in 1636,

Galileo considered the infinite set of perfect squares

$$1, 4, 9, 16, 25, \ldots, n^2, \ldots$$

A number is a perfect square if it is a product of two *equal* factors, as for instance, $25 = 5 \cdot 5 = 5^2$. The number 25 is thus the square of 5, and as such may be denoted by 5^2, the *exponent* 2 indicating the number of equal factors. In general, the square, nn, of any number n is denoted by n^2.

The set of squares is a part of our set of all the integers, but it can be put into one-to-one correspondence with the set of all the integers, (1), since to each square n^2 there corresponds one and only one integer n whose square it is, and conversely to each integer n there corresponds one and only one perfect square, namely n^2. Thus, there are as many perfect squares as there are integers:

$$
\begin{array}{cccccc}
1, & 2, & 3, & 4, & 5, \ldots, & n, \ldots \\
\updownarrow & \updownarrow & \updownarrow & \updownarrow & \updownarrow & \updownarrow \\
1, & 4, & 9, & 16, & 25, \ldots, & n^2 \ldots
\end{array}
$$

and again the whole is equal to one of its parts. This time, the distribution of elements of the partial set of squares among a section of the first N^2 integers of the set of all integers (1) depends on the length of the section considered. The density of distribution decreases, when the number N^2 of first elements of the set of all the integers (I) making up the section considered increases.

If we consider a finite collection of first N^2 integers (for instance, one million of them, N being equal to one thousand), it contains exactly N perfect squares (one thousand). Thus, the ratio of the number N of perfect squares (one thousand) among all the members of this finite collection with N^2 elements (one million of elements) is equal to N divided by N^2, that is $N/N^2 = 1/N$ (one thousandth in our numerical example), and this fraction $1/N$ approaches zero when N increases without limit: $1/N \to 0$ as $N \to \infty$.

The property of a whole of being equal to one of its parts characterizes infinite collections, because it does not belong to finite collections. It can therefore be taken (Bolzano, Dedekind) as the basis for a *positive* definition of infinite sets, that is of absolute infinity:

DEFINITION: *A set (collection) which can be put into one-to-one correspondence with one of its parts is infinite.*

So far, speaking about integers, we have implicitly assumed that we know them. But, what is an integer? The human mind, observing in its environment collections or sets of different objects, and trying to compare them, has elaborated the idea of quantity and formed ideal collections of one, two, three, *etc.* abstract units, units which are devoid of all properties except that of representing a unit of quantity. For instance, the number five is for us a set of five abstract units, each of which is absolutely identical to the others and devoid of any characteristic properties.

The process of counting is possible only if such ideal collections actually exist in the mind, and a child must first form the *concepts* of successive integers as ideal collections of abstract units, before he is actually able to see a quantity in a group of concrete objects and count it. Counting itself is performed by establishing a one-to-one correspondence between the members of a concrete collection of real things and the units of ideal sets ever-present in our minds and called integers.

In counting, we try to assign to each member of a concrete collection an abstract unit in one of our ideal set. In doing so, we try successively different ideal sets. If the units of an ideal sets are exhausted before all the members of the real collection have been considered and have received their assigned abstract units, we pass on to the next, richer set of ideal units, until finally we reach the particular ideal set which fits the concrete collection.

We say that an ideal set fits the concrete collection, when one and only one member of the collection corresponds to one and only one unit of the set, all members of the collection having their assigned units and all the units of ideal set being used. Thus, a one-to-one correspondence between the collection of things and the units of this particular ideal set is established, the pairing-off stops and we have "counted" the collection of concrete things.

Example:

We say, for example, that this group of real things comprizes eight members, because the ideal set ensuring the one-to-one correspondence is the set of eight abstract units, (Fig. 1.1).

In this description of the counting process the idea of order is absent. The order in which we correlate the members of a real group with the units of a number has no importance. What we have been describing as ideal sets of units are the so-called *cardinal* numbers. For our pur-

poses it is quite sufficient to define a cardinal number as an ideal collection of abstract units. It is interesting to note that the efforts to find
a better logical definition of the number concept failed (see Appendix I).

If, in addition to the idea of quantity, the idea of order is introduced,
the so-called *ordinal* numbers are obtained. Ordinal numbers are
integers which assign a relative position to each element of a collection,

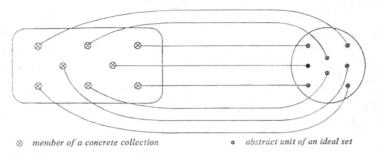

⊗   *member of a concrete collection*   ◦   *abstract unit of an ideal set*

Fig. 1.1

thus transforming an amorphous collection into an ordered *sequence*
of elements: first, second, third, fourth *etc.* The idea of order is a more
complex notion than the idea of quantity. All primitive people have
some cardinal numbers, but the ordinal numbers are often lacking.
The fact that ordinal numbers are formed at a later stage of evolution
than the cardinal numbers suggests that the idea of quantity appears
at an earlier stage of development of human thinking than the idea of
order. While the idea of quantity is suggested by the environment
(observations of different collections), the idea of order can be formed
only by a self-observing mind, able to analyze its own perceptions and
actions in their succession.

A sequence of the elements of an ordered set is noted in mathematics
by using the same letter for all the elements, but with different subscripts. If, for instance, the elements of a set are denoted by the
letter a, then the first, second, third, *etc.* and the last, the n-th, element
of a finite set of n members are denoted respectively by $a_1, a_2, a_3,$
$\ldots, a_n$.

The process of counting is independent of the process of ordering.
If we know, for example, that the number of chairs in a room is equal
to the number of guests, we may be sure that every guest will find a

chair, without knowing which chair he will use. But the process of ordering presupposes counting: the chairs in a theater are ordered, their ordinal numbers correspond to those on the tickets of the audience members in one-to-one correspondence, and this correspondence is counting.

Trying to apply the idea of order to infinite collections, we must make an *a priori* distinction between two cases, namely that in which the ordering is possible and that in which it is impossible. If an infinite collection (A) can be put into one-to-one correspondence with the set of all the integers, we say that the ordering of (A) is possible. In this case the pairing off of the two collections (A) and the set of all the integers (I) necessarily gives all the members of A a numerical order. The infinite collection (A) is then called *denumerable* and its members are denoted by subscripts

$$a_1, a_2, a_3, a_4, \dots, a_n, \dots$$

The subscripts run through the set (1) of all the integers, thus establishing a definite order between the elements of the set (A). The dots are used to denote the members of (A) which have not been explicitly written down. So the dots between a_4 and a_n and those after a_n stand for members following a_4 but preceding a_n and for those following a_n, respectively.

But it can also happen that, in trying to establish a one-to-one correspondence between the set (1) of all the integers and a given infinite collection B, we fail to achieve it. This failure can mean only one thing: one of the two collections has become exhausted, while the other has not. This can happen only if the set of all the integers becomes exhausted before all the members of the other collection B were considered, since the second possibility, namely the exhaustion of B, would mean that B was a finite collection, and we are dealing here with infinite collections.

In such a case, we cannot assign an ordinal number to every member of an infinite collection, and we call the collection *non-denumerable*. An example of a non-denumerable collection is presented by the set of all the points of the interval **AB** on a straight line between two given points A and B. As we shall see later, an attempt to put this infinite collection of points into one-to-one correspondence with the set of all the integers fails.

Number-Axis

Both aspects of the number concept, cardinal and ordinal, are illustrated in the geometrical representation of integers by points on a straight line which are equidistant from each other. This representation is possible only because the ideal straight line, as defined in Euclidian Geometry, is another form of infinity in mathematics: it can be indefinitely extended (potential infinity), and it is therefore of infinite length (actual infinity). Here again, in the concept of an infinite straigth

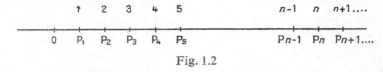

Fig. 1.2

line, we have a wonderful generalization of our finite experimental concepts: all the straight lines in our experience have finite length, but for our mind they are only finite segments of an ideal straight line of infinite length, considered in its wholeness as a static entity.

Let us choose an arbitrary segment of straight line as our unit of length. Applying it to a straight line, we define by its two extremities two points O (origin) and P_1 (first point) such that P_1 ist to the right from O and the distance OP_1 equals a unit of length: $OP_1 = 1$. Applying our unit again, this time with its left end at P_1, we define a third point P_2 such that $P_1P_2 = 1$ and $OP_2 = 2$. Repeating the same operation an infinite number of times (it cannot be done effectively, but we can imagine it), we find as many equidistant points, $P_1, P_2, P_3, \ldots$, $P_n, \ldots$, on our line as there are natural numbers $1, 2, 3, \ldots n, \ldots$, members of the set of all the integers.

This straight line with an infinity of points P_n ($n = 1, 2, 3, \ldots$) on it is called a number-axis. The "next" point P_{n+1} being to the right of its predecessor P_n, the number-axis is said to be *oriented* and the direction to the right is considered as positive. The opposite direction on the number axis, namely that to the left, is then, by definition, the negative direction. For the moment we will consider only the positive half of the line, to the right of the origin O, as we have not yet defined and introduced negative numbers.

A point P_n can be considered as an image of the integer n since its distance, OP_n, from the origin O is equal to n units of length. In this representation, the geometrical intuition of an actually infinite straight line strengthens the abstract idea of an infinite set of all natural numbers. It is indeed easier to consider an infinite straight line as an entity than to grasp all the integers at one time as a perfectly defined infinite set. The points P_n form an ordered sequence of points, and in their order they give us a geometrical picture of the ordinal numbers.

Between any two points on the number axis we perceive a very familiar spatial relation of order: one of the two points precedes (is to the left of) the other, which follows (is to the right of) the first. So, for instance, P_6 is to the right of P_3, and P_3 is to the left of P_6. It is easy to recognize in this spatial relation of order the fundamental relation of *relative magnitude* between two integers represented by the two points: five is greater than three ($5 > 3$), and P_5 is to the right of P_3, which can be paraphrased also by saying that three is less than five and P_3 is to the left of P_5. Thus, on the number-axis, the numerical relation of magnitude becomes a relation of order. In general, if of two given integers n and m, the first, n, is greater than the other ($n > m$), then P_n is to the right of P_m and *vice versa*.

Between any three points P_k, P_m, P_n, which exhibit the relations of order P_n is to the right of P_m, and P_m is to the right of P_k, there is a third relation, which follows necessarily from the given two relations, namely P_n is to the right of P_k. Thus, we have a rule: if P_n is to the right (left) of P_m which, in its turn, is to the right (left) of P_k, then P_n is to the right (left) of P_k. We express this fact in symbols as follows: if $n > m$ and $m > k$, then $n > k$, and also, inverting the order, if $n < m$ and $m < k$, then $n < k$.

Operations with Integers

Among three direct operations with integers, namely addition, multiplication, and exponentiation (raising to a power), the first one, addition, is the most fundamental, because the other two are only particular cases of the first. Any example of addition, for instance

$$5 + 3 = 3 + 5 = 8$$

shows that the result is always an integer and, consequently, addition is always possible. Thus, the addition of integers does not necessitate the extension of the number concept and the introduction of numbers other than integers. We state moreover that the order in which the addition of two *terms* is performed is irrelevant, their *sum* in both cases being the same.

The word "term", as used in mathematics, has three different meanings. In addition, it denotes any part of a sum. So, for instance, in $5 + 3 = 8$, both the numbers 5 and 3 are terms of their sum 8. In the general case, the notation $a + b + c = s$ means that every one of three numbers a, b, c is a term of their sum s.

The same word is also used to denote the numerator and the denominator of a fraction. Thus, the fraction seven-elevenths, 7/11 has two terms, 7 and 11, which are its numerator and denominator, respectively. The value 7/11 itself is also called the *ratio* of two integers 7 and 11. A *proportion* which states the equality of two ratios, such as $3/8 = 15/40$, has therefore four terms, here 3, 8, 15 and 40.

The third meaning of the word term is not specifically mathematical: in mathematics as in other sciences the word term is also used in its customary sense, equivalent to "word", "phrase", or "expression". Multiplication, fraction, aleph-null, exponent, *etc.* are mathematical terms.

To express in symbols the independence of the sum from the order of its terms, which constitutes the essence of the *commutative law of addition*, we must extend our notation. Since this law concerns all the integers, we need a notation that will cover all possible choices of two terms, of which there are an infinite number. Such a notation consists of the use of letters *(algebraic notation)* instead of numerals.

In antiquity, the letters were used to denote *fixed*, specific numbers, as we use now the arabic numerals 3, 7, 9, *etc.* But we will use letters in another way. If we write $m + n$, we express a general case of the addition of *any* two integers. In the sum $m + n$ the letter m, as well as n, stands for any one of the infinite set of all the integers, so that the symbol $m + n$ covers all possible cases of addition of two integers, the case of addition of two equal integers being included because in particular we may choose $n = m$. With this meaning in mind, we can symbolize the commutative law of addition as follows:

$$m + n = n + m$$

The addition of two numbers m and n is represented geometrically by two successive displacements or steps (directed segments of a straight line) along the number-axis, the first, OP_m, having a length m

and the second, OP_n, having a length n. It is plain that these two displacements in the same, positive, direction (defined as to the right of the origin) are equivalent to a single resultant displacement of length $m + n$, irrespective of the order in which the two component displacements were performed. Thus, $OP_{m+n} = OP_{n+m}$:

We have indeed $OP_m = P_nP_{n+m}$ as well as $OP_n = P_mP_{m+n}$, so that

$$m + n = OP_m + OP_n = OP_m + P_mP_{m+n} = OP_{m+n}$$

and, inverting the order, also

$$n + m = OP_n + OP_m = OP_n + P_nP_{n+m} = OP_{n+m}$$

the result being the same, namely $OP_{m+n} = OP_{n+m}$.

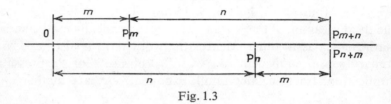

Fig. 1.3

When we have to perform the addition of three or more terms, another question arises. Since *we can add only two terms at a time*, we have many different ways in which we can perform the addition of three integers a, b, c. We may first form the sum $(a + b)$ of a and b, and then add c to it, denoting this double addition by $(a + b) + c$. Or we can proceed by forming the sums $(b + c) + a$ and $(c + a) + b$, each of which represents also a result of addition of three terms a, b, and c, their association being different in each case.

For instance, to add 3, 5, and 7, we can form first the sum $3 + 5 = 8$ and then add 7 to 8, denoted by $(3 + 5) + 7 = 15$. Or we can perform the same addition by forming the sums $(3 + 7) + 5 = 10 + 5 = 15$ and $(5 + 7) + 3 = 12 + 3 = 15$.

The parantheses, in both the general case with a, b, c or in any numerical case such as the above, are used to indicate that the addition of the two enclosed terms is already performed, so that the two terms enclosed in the parentheses are considered as a single term, namely as a number representing their sum. Therefore the parentheses in such an expression, as for instance, $(a + b) + c$ prescribe the *order* in which the two additions are to be performed: first $a + b$ and then $(a + b) + c$.

Thus, the addition of three terms a, b, and c leads to three sums $(a + b) + c$, $(b + c) + a$, and $(c + a) + b$. The numerical examples show immediately that the three results thus obtained are equivalent: the three sums are equal. The same holds in the general case of the addition of any three integers and the second law of addition, the *associative law*, states that there is only one sum of three terms, the three different procedures described above giving equal results. Therefore the parentheses can be dropped and the unique sum of a, b, and c is denoted simply by $a + b + c$:

$$(a + b) + c = (b + c) + a = (c + a) + b = a + b + c$$

as, for example, $(3 + 5) + 7 = (5 + 7) + 3 = (7 + 3) + 5 = 3 + 5 + 7$.

And, in general, in the addition of any number of terms $a, b, c, \dots, k$ the order in which the terms are added has no effect on the sum. For this reason the sum is written without parentheses: $a + b + c + \dots + k$. The parentheses were dropped precisely because of the fact that in the case of addition the order of operations does not affect their result. The parentheses are needed only in cases when the result of a set of operations depends on the order in which they are performed. They are used to fix the order in which the successive operations are to be performed.

Besides the commutative and associative laws, there is a third rule of addition called the *monotonic law*. Given two numbers b and c with b greater than c, the addition of any number a to b and to c preserves the inequality, so that the sum $a + b$ is greater than that $a + c$: if $b > c$, then

$$a + b > a + c$$

EXAMPLE: $11 + 7 > 11 + 3$, because $7 > 3$.

Multiplication

When, in an addition, the special case arises in which all the terms of a sum are equal, the addition is called multiplication. Thus, multiplication, as a particular case of addition, is always possible. Take, for instance, the sum of five terms $3 + 3 + 3 + 3 + 3$, all of them equal to 3. In it the number 3 is repeated five times as term and we express this sentence in symbols by a *product* of two numbers $5 \cdot 3$, where the first *factor* from the left, 5, indicates the number of equal terms, while the second factor, 3, denotes the common value of these five terms.

In mathematics the term *factor* is used only in relation to the operation of multiplication. It designates each of the components which make up a number or an algebraic expression by multiplication. The result of multiplication, computed (15 in our example) or only indicated $(5 \cdot 3)$, is called the *product*. In a product of two factors, for instance ab, the second factor denotes the common value of all the terms (here b), while the first factor (here a) indicates their number in the sum of equal terms. The sign of multiplication is a centered dot between the two factors. However, in the case of letters the sign of multiplication is usually omitted. Thus, the symbol ab is the product of a and b.

The two factors of a product do not play the same role, so that ab and ba are by definition two different expressions. The first, ab, is a sum of a terms each term having the value b, while the second, ba, results from the addition of b equal terms, whose common value is a:

$$ab = b + b + b + \cdots + b + b \qquad (a \text{ terms})$$

$$ba = a + a + a + \cdots + a + a \qquad (b \text{ terms})$$

However, the *commutative law of multiplication* states that the value of a product of two factors does not depend on their order. Thus, the two sums are equal and represent the same number:

$$ab = ba.$$

Recalling that integers are the ideal collections of abstract units, the law can easily be justified. Thus, if $a = 3$ and $b = 5$.

$$5 \cdot 3 = \cdots = 3 \cdot 5$$

As with addition, multiplication also obeys an *associative law* which applies to the products of three or more factors. In the case of three factors, the associative law of multiplication states that the order in which the two operations of multiplication necessary to form a product of three factors are performed, does not affect the value of the product:

$$(ab)\, c = (bc)\, a = (ca)\, b = abc$$

EXAMPLE: If $a = 3$, $b = 5$, and $c = 7$, then

$$(3 \cdot 5) \cdot 7 = 15 \cdot 7 = (5 \cdot 7) \cdot 3 = 35 \cdot 3 = (7 \cdot 3) \cdot 5$$
$$= 21 \cdot 5 = 3 \cdot 5 \cdot 7 = 105$$

To these two laws, again as with addition, we add the *monotonic law*. Given the inequality $b > c$, it is preserved if multiplied by any number a:

$$ab > ac \quad (\text{if } b > c)$$

EXAMPLE: $5 \cdot 9 > 5 \cdot 7$ because $9 > 7$, as well as $7 \cdot 5 < 7 \cdot 9$ because $5 < 9$.

We finally come to the *distributive law* which governs the combination of addition and multiplication. It concerns the multiplication of a sum $a + b$ by a factor c, as well as the multiplication of a number c by a sum $a + b$ of two numbers. These two operations which combine an indicated but *not performed* addition $a + b$ with a multiplication differ only by the order of two factors involved and the commutative law of multiplication states that their results are necessarily equal: $c(a + b) = (a + b)\, c$. But it does not indicate how these multiplications $c(a + b)$ or $(a + b)\, c$ are to be performed if we do not want to or cannot compute first the sum $a + b$, eliminating thus the combination of addition and multiplication.

The distributive law states that, to multiply a sum $a + b$ by a factor c, it is sufficient to multiply separately each term of this sum by c, and then to add the partial products ca and cb:

$$(a + b)\, c = c(a + b) = ca + cb$$

EXAMPLE:

$$15(7 + 3) = 15 \cdot 7 + 15 \cdot 3 = 105 + 45 = 150 = 10 \cdot 15 = (7 + 3)\, 15$$

Now every mathematical formula can and must be read in both directions. Reading the distributive law from the right to the left, we obtain a new rule: if both terms of a sum (here ca and cb) are products, and if they have a common factor (here c), this common factor can be

Kogbetliantz 2

picked out and the sum transformed into a product. The operation of picking out a factor common to all the terms of a sum each time will necessarily introduce parentheses. It is called *factoring* and is of extreme importance in algebra. The distributive law expresses the fact that addition and multiplication are commutative: the result of an addition and a multiplication performed successively does not depend on the order in which they were performed. The expression $c(a + b)$ is obtained, performing the addition first and then the multiplication, while $ca + cb$ results from the addition of two products ca and cb, so that the addition follows the multiplication. As an example of factoring consider the sum $24 + 15$:

EXAMPLE:

$$24 + 15 = 3 \cdot 8 + 3 \cdot 5 = 3(8 + 5) = 3 \cdot 13 = 39$$

The simplest geometrical representation of the laws of multiplication is based on the concepts of area and volume. We define the unit of area as the area of a square whose side is a unit of length (unit square) and the unit of volume as the volume of a cube whose edge is a unit of length (unit cube).

The *commutative law* $mn = nm$ now becomes the expression of the simple geometrical fact that the area of a rectangle with sides of length m and n units (fig. 1.4) can be measured in two different ways. To show this, we subdivide the rectangle's area into unit squares by two sets of equi-

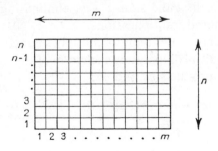

Fig. 1.4

distant parallel lines, one set (horizontal) being parallel to the base and the other (vertical) to the height of the rectangle, with the distance between the parallels equal to a unit of length.

The area is expressed in units of area by the number of unit squares into which it is subdivided. To count them we observe that all the horizontal rows of unit squares are identical with respect to the number of unit squares which they contain and the same is true for the vertical columns of unit squares. Since the base and the height of our rectangle are equal to m and n units of length respectively, there are m unit squares in a row and n unit squares in a column. On the other hand,

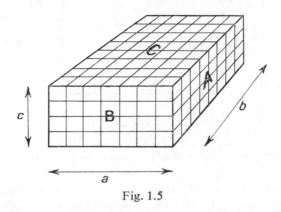

Fig. 1.5

there are n rows and m columns. Assembling first the unit squares belonging to the same row, we find that the area of a single row is measured by the number m, so that the area of the whole rectangle is equal to nm because it contains n rows. But, assembling now the unit squares belonging to the same column, we state that the area of a column is equal to n, so that the rectangle's area is measured by the number mn because it contains m columns. Thus, the products nm and mn being two measures of the same area, we have necessarily $nm = mn$ which is the commutative law.

The *associative law* of multiplication is exemplified in the same way by the measurements of the volume of a rectangular box (parallelepiped with rectangular faces), whose edges are of lengths a, b, and c (fig. 1.5). Subdividing its volume into unit cubes by three sets of equidistant (distance = unit of length) planes, parallel to the faces of the box, we state that the volume of the box is measured by the number of unit cubes composing it. The unit cubes may be assembled in slices parallel to each one of three pairs of parallel faces.

Thus, each slice of the thickness one unit, parallel to the face A of area bc, has a volume also expressed by the same number bc. There are a such slices in the box. Therefore, its volume V is equal to $a(bc)$:

$V = a(bc)$. But let us consider the slices parallel to the face B whose area is ca. Each of them has a volume equal to ca, and there are b such slices in the box, so that this time, $V = b(ca)$. Finally, considering the slices parallel to the face C, we obtain a third expression for the volume V, namely $V = c(ab)$. Thus, the three different expressions for V

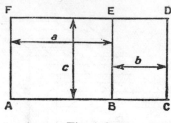

Fig. 1.6

are equal: $a(bc) = b(ca) = c(ab) = abc$, which gives the associative law.

The *monotonic law* simply states that, if the two rectangles $ABEF$, $BCDE$ have the same altitude c but different bases $a = \mathsf{AB}$ and $b = \mathsf{BC}$ with $a > b$, then the area of $ABEF$ with larger base a is greater than the area of the shorter rectangle $BCDE$:

$$ac > bc,$$

if $a > b$, (fig. 1.6).

Finally, the *distributive law* expresses the fact that the sum of two areas $ABEF + BCDE$ is equal to the total area of the rectangle $ACDF$, whose base AC is equal to $a + b$, so that the area $ACDF$ is equal to the product $c(a + b)$. Thus, the relation $ABEF + BCDE = ACDF$ becomes $ac + bc = c(a + b)$ and this is precisely the distributive law.

Ordinary computations with integers consist of repeated use of these fundamental arithmetic laws. Take, as an example, the multiplication of 43 by 45. The factor 45 is conceived as a sum $40 + 5$, and to multiply 43 by this sum, we multiply 43 first by 5, then by 40, and finally add the two products, applying thus the distributive law. But the multiplication of 43 by 5 itself is based again on this law, since 43 must be treated as $40 + 3$, 40 and 3 being multiplied separately by 5. Adding partial products, we again use commutative the law of addition.

Cancellation

The monotonic laws lead to the operation of cancellation which consist in the striking out of equal terms or factors from two sides of an equation expressing the equality of two sums or of two products. Suppose that the two sums $a + b$ and $a + c$, having a common term a, are equal: $a + b = a + c$. The two numbers b and c cannot be different, otherwise the monotonic law of addition would contradict the equation $a + b = a + c$. Therefore, the equality $a + b = a + c$ leads necessarily to the simpler equality $b = c$ which can be obtained from the given equality $a + b = a + c$, by striking out on both sides of it the equal terms a. The same reasoning holds for two equal products $ab = ac$, which have a common factor a. The equality $ab = ac$ laeds necessarily to the simpler one $b = c$, because its negation would contradict the monotonic law of multiplication. If $b \lessgtr c$, then $ab \gtrless ac$ according to this law. Therefore, given $ab = ac$, we deduce from it $b = c$, which can be obtained from the given equality $ab = ac$ by cancelling on both sides the equal factor a.

EXAMPLES: If $7a = 7b$, then $a = b$, as well as: if $7 + x = 7 + y$, then $x = y$.

Number One as Factor

The number one plays a special role in multiplication. The operation of multiplication always results in a product which is different from the multiplicand, except the case when the multiplier used in the multiplication is equal to one. Multiplication by one does not change the number which was multiplied by one and the number one is the only factor such that multiplication by it does not modify the value of the multiplicand. Thus, for any number N we have $N \cdot 1 = N$ and, if $Nx = N$, where the second factor x is unknown, we conclude immediately that $x = 1$.

The laws of addition and multiplication may seem trivial when applied to natural integers, and their formulation with the aid of letters may appear at first sight as an exercise of formal algebra. This impression is wrong: the evolution of the number concept was possible only because at every step of its generalization, the rules of the operation for the new kinds of number thus created were defined in accordance with the fundamental laws. The development of mathematical thinking has been so thoroughly conditioned by these laws that their importance cannot be exaggerated.

The fundamental laws cannot be checked for very large numbers which we can define and imagine but with which we cannot operate. How can we be sure that those laws remain true for *all* integers, that they do not change when the numbers approach actual infinity?

The question is important since mathematical statements are useful only if they are general and apply to all the members of an infinite set without exception, in this case to *all* the integers. The validity of a proposition for an infinite number of cases can be established by the process of reasoning called *mathematical induction*.

This process is entirely different from reasoning by simple induction, which proceeds from the particular to the general, and which is widely used in sciences other than mathematics. Simple induction is used even by animals.

But simple induction cannot be relied upon in mathematics. To show this let us study the following example.

From the point of view of multiplication, integers fall into two different categories and display two different behaviors. Most of them, such as 15 and 72 can be obtained by multiplying two or more other integers, that is, they are products of other integers. Thus $15 = 3 \cdot 5$ and $72 = 2 \cdot 2 \cdot 2 \cdot 3 \cdot 3$.

Such integers are called *composite numbers*. Others, such as 2, 3, 5, 7, 31, 101 cannot be considered as products of smaller integers and consequently are called *prime numbers*. Formally, of course, we can represent these too as products by using as factors the prime integer itself and the number 1, as for instance $5 = 5 \cdot 1$. For this reason their definition must be framed as follows: *an integer which has no other factors than* 1 *and itself is a prime number*.

Consider now a variable integer n which takes the successive values 1, 2, 3, 4, ... , running through the set of all natural numbers, and form, for each value of n, the corresponding integer N, defined as follows:

$$N = n^2 - n + 41$$

It is plain that the value of N depends on the value of n. Giving to n the first eight values, $n = 1, 2, 3, 4, 5, 6, 7, 8$, and substituting them in the expression of N, $(n^2 - n + 41)$, we find the following corresponding values for N:

n	1	2	3	4	5	6	7	8
N	41	43	47	53	61	71	83	97

To our surprise all eight happen to be prime numbers. If we increase n further, the phenomenon persists, and simple induction suggests that for all values of n, the expression $N = n^2 - n + 41$ will represent prime numbers. But this conclusion reached by simple induction is wrong; if n does not exceed 40, that is for the first forty values of n, the corresponding values of N are indeed prime numbers, but for $n = 41$ the sequence of prime numbers stops, and we obtain a composite number; if $n = 41$, then $N = 41^2 - 41 + 41 = 1681$, which being the square of 41 is, by definition, composite. Thus, we see that simple induction is an inadequate form of reasoning because it does not possess the generality which characterizes mathematical statements.

Mathematical induction is entirely different from simple induction and it is a characteristic feature of human thinking.

In its essence mathematical induction is a process of reasoning by recurrence extended to an *infinite* sequence of propositions and therefore it forms and uses an infinite chain of syllogisms. To explain the mechanism of mathematical induction, suppose that we want to investigate whether or not a certain property P (defined and given) belongs to all the terms of an infinite sequence (s)

$$a_1, a_2, a_3, \dots, a_n, \dots \tag{s}$$

and let us denote by A_n the proposition stating that the n-th term, a_n, of this sequence (s) possesses the said property P. If for instance, a_1 has the property P, then A_1 is true. The problem is thus reduced to the proof of existence, in the sense of logical truth, of an infinite sequence of propositions (A)

$$A_1, A_2, A_3, \dots, A_n, \dots \tag{A}$$

A finite number of first terms $a_1, a_2, a_3, \dots$ of the sequence (s) can be directly checked to see whether they have or have not the property P. Suppose that, after having checked the first N terms $a_1, a_2, \dots, a_n$ we find that they all possess the property P, which means that a certain number N of first terms A_n (for $n = 1, 2, 3, 4, \dots, N$) of (A) are true. That is all that can be established by direct study of the terms of the sequence (s). An infinite number of operations cannot be effectively performed by human mind, and therefore to extend the proof to *all* the A_n in (A) we need a more powerful method of reasoning, well adapted to include an infinitude of cases.

The existence of such a method is based on the axiom already mentioned: "What was done once can be repeated indefinitely". Suppose that we can prove the so-called "hereditary" character of the property P, that is, suppose that the fact that P belongs to some term a_n of the sequence (s) implies that P belongs to the *next* term a_{n+1}. In other words, suppose that the validity of a proposition A_n implies the logical existence of the next proposition A_{n+1} (in symbols: $A_n \rightarrow A_{n+1}$). Then the sequence (A) generates a kind of infinite logical chain reaction: the truth of A_1 implies the validity of A_2, $A_1 \rightarrow A_2$; then $A_2 \rightarrow A_3$, $A_3 \rightarrow A_4$ and so on indefinitely, so that we are sure than any particular proposition A_n is finally reached by this logical chain reaction and its truth is established.

Therefore, if the property P belongs to the first term of the sequence (s), by applying the method of reasoning by endless recurrence, we can justify the truth of all the terms of the sequence (A), and thus perform the extension of the property P to all the terms of the sequence (s).

Thus, we assume that through the aid of mathematical induction based on the hereditary character of the property P as well as on the fact that P belongs to the first term a_1 of the sequence (s), we can master an infinite number of cases and prove that the property P belongs to *all* the terms of the infinite sequence (s). The hereditary character of P and the truth of A_1 are necessary and sufficient conditions for our mind to insure the transmission of the property P to and through *all* the terms of this ordered sequence (s) notwithstanding the fact that it is an infinite sequence and has no end.

In this intuitive assumption lies the mysterious power of mathematics in dealing with infinite collections, that is, with infinity. This fundamental assumption is not and cannot be a result of experience, since it concerns infinite collections, and human experience has to deal with finite collections only. Thus, we are obliged to recognize that the entire structure of mathematics rests upon intuition and not upon experience; mathematical induction is an intuitive truth, and it appears as fundaemntal structural trait of human thought.

In the description given above, we do not find the process of simple induction at all. Its use is limited to cases where the characteristic property P of all the terms of the sequence (s) is unknown, in which case the problem is slightly different from that studied above. Suppose that we want to find out whether or not there is an *unknown* property P common to *all* the terms of a certain given sequence (s). If P is unknown, we cannot study whether or not it possesses the hereditary character, before having found what it is, and the first step is necessarily the determination of the property P. This is done by simple induction. Studying the structure of the first terms of the sequence (s), we try to find their common property P by simple induction, and then we check to see whether P does or does not belong to some other terms of the sequence. If it does, then we can study whether or not P is hereditary, and apply mathematical induction, if the hereditary character of P is proved. Thus, simple induction often participates in the first steps of mathematical induction.

Let us now study some examples of mathematical induction. Let us call s_n the sum of the first n *odd* numbers, thus $s_1 = 1, s_2 = 1 + 3 = 4$, $s_3 = 1 + 3 + 5 = s_2 + 5 = 9, s_4 = 1 + 3 + 5 + 7 = s_3 + 7 = 16$, $s_5 = 1 + 3 + 5 + 7 + 9 = s_4 + 9 = 25 \cdots$, a general definition of s_n being

$$s_n = 1 + 3 + 5 + 7 + 9 \cdots + \text{the } n\text{th add integer}$$

To write down the expression of s_n, we must find a formula which expresses the value of the n-th odd integer, and to do this we will use first simple and then mathematical induction. Compare some first odd integers, denoting then by $N_1, N_2, N_3 \cdots$

$$N_1 = 1, \quad N_2 = 3, \quad N_3 = 5, \quad N_4 = 7, \quad N_5 = 9 \ldots \quad (T)$$

If we double the numerical order (the subscript n in N_n) of any one of the above, we obtain an even number which exceeds by one unit the corresponding odd number, symbolized by N_n. For example $N_3 = 5$, and doubling the subscript 3, we obtain 6, that is $5 + 1 = N_3 + 1$. Simple induction suggests that the general expression of the n-th odd integer, N_n, must be $2n - 1$. But this formula, found by induction, was checked only for some first terms of the infinite sequence of odd integers (T). To extend its validity to *all* the terms of the sequence (T), we must study its hereditary character. Suppose that the k-th odd number N_k has this form, that is, the formula $N_k = 2k - 1$ is true. Now form the next odd number N_{k+1}, whose order is $k + 1$. To pass from any odd number to the next larger odd number, we add two units and therefore $N_{k+1} = N_k + 2 = 2k - 1 + 2 = 2k + 1$. The value $2k + 1$

thus obtained for N_{k+1} verifies our rule since doubling the subscript $k + 1$ we get $2k + 2$ which is reduced to $2k + 1$ by subtracting one unit: $N_{k+1} = 2(k + 1) - 1 = 2k + 1$.

Having shown that the structural law expressed by the formula $N_k = 2k - 1$ must be true for N_{k+1} if it holds for N_k, that is, having proved the hereditary character of this law, and knowing that it is true specifically for $k = 1$ (because $N_1 = 2 \cdot 1 - 1$), we apply the mathematical induction and are sure that the formula $2k - 1$ is a general expression for all the odd integers arranged in an ordered infinite sequence. Thus, the value of the k-th odd integer is equal to $2k - 1$ for all values of $k = 1, 2, 3, 4, 5 \ldots$, and we write down the general expression for the sum s_n of the first n odd integers as follows:

$$s_n = 1 + 3 + 5 + 7 + \cdots + (2n - 1)$$

Computing a few first terms of the infinite sequence

$$s_1, s_2, s_3, s_4, \ldots, s_n, \ldots$$

of the sums s_n, we observe a strange fact: they are perfect squares. We have indeed for the first fives terms

$$s_1 = 1 = 1^2 \quad s_2 = 1 + 3 = 4 = 2^2 \quad s_3 = s_2 + 5 = 4 + 5 = 9 = 3^2$$

$$s_4 = s_3 + 7 = 9 + 7 = 16 = 4^2 \quad s_5 = s_4 + 9 = 16 + 9 = 25 = 5^2$$

Simple induction immediately suggests a common property (P) of sums s_n: each s_n—sum of the first n odd integers—is a perfect square, namely the square of its subscript n:

$$s_n = n^2 \qquad\qquad (n = 1, 2, 3, \ldots)$$

To prove this guess we must find out whether or not this property P of the first terms is hereditary. To do this we suppose that it was checked for some s_k, so that $s_k = k^2$ is true. Now let us see whether $s_k = k^2$ implies $s_{k+1} = (k + 1)^2$. We pass from the sum $s_k = 1 + 3 + 5 + \cdots + (2k - 1)$ of the first k odd integers to the sum s_{k+1} of the first $k + 1$ odd integers by adding to s_k the next $(k + 1)$-th odd integer N_{k+1}. We saw already that its value is $2k + 1$. Therefore, $s_{k+1} = s_k + (2k + 1)$. But here we can replace s_k by k^2 since we have assumed that $s_k = k^2$ is true. Thus, using fundamental laws, we obtain

$$s_{k+1} = k^2 + 2k + 1 = k^2 + k + k + 1 = (k^2 + k) + (k + 1)$$

$$= (k + 1)k + (k + 1)1 = (k + 1)(k + 1) = (k + 1)^2$$

This proves the hereditary character of P. Then, since we know that the property P holds for $k = 1$ ($s_1 = 1 = 1^2$), by applying mathematical induction, we arrive to the following conclusion: the sum of the first n odd integers is equal to n^2 regardless of the value of the number n. Thus, for instance, we are sure that the sum of the first 185, 655, 974 odd integers is equal to the square of the number 185, 655, 974:

$$1 + 3 + 5 + 7 + \cdots + 371\,311\,947 = 185\,655\,974^2$$

though the verification of this numerical equality by direct addition would take years of work, even if a calculating machine were used.

This arithmetical result has a sinple geometrical representation. Suppose that the depth of each step of a staircase, except the uppermost, is two units, while the height of each step and the depth of the uppermost is one unit. Such a staircase can be built by laying planks one unit thick one below the other, planks whose lengths are one, three, five, seven, etc. units:

Imagine now that we have two such staircases, each containing planks increasing in length from one to $2n - 1$ units, the value of n being fixed. Overturn either one (shaded on fig. 1.7) and apply is to the other one in such a way that together they form a rectangle of height n and base $2n$. The area of the rectangle thus formed is $2nn = 2n^2$.

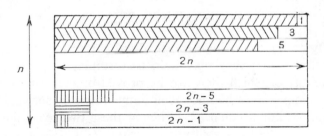

Fig. 1.7

Both staircases being equal, the area of one staircase is half the rectangle's area, that is equal to n^2. Thus, remembering the dimensions of the steps, we can write down the following equation, both members of which express the area of one whole staircase:

$$1 + 3 + 5 + 7 \cdots + (2n - 1) = n^2$$

The illustration above (fig. 1.7) is useful in that it enables us to have a geometrical image of the arithmetical statement involved, but by this very fact it is invalid as a proof because it presupposes a fixed value of n. Indeed, as soon as one wants to use this picture, he must necessarily imagine the staircase to be of a given length, thus fixing a definite value for n. To justify in this way a general statement valid for all the integers n an infinite set of such pictures would be necessary.

This geometrical illustration could be replaced by the arithmetic addition of two sums s_n written in opposite order as follows:

$$s_n \qquad 1 \quad + \quad 3 \quad + \quad 8 \quad + \cdots + (2n - 1)$$
$$s_n = (2n - 1) + (2n - 3) + (2n - 5) + \cdots + \qquad 1$$

Adding, we obtain:

$$2s_n = \quad 2n \quad + \quad 2n \quad + \quad 2n \quad + \cdots + 2n$$

There are n terms in the expression of $2s_n$ and each is equal to $2n$. Hence, their sum is equal to the product $2nn = 2n^2$ and $s_n = n^2$. Both of these illustrations are valid for any fixed value of n, but they are effectively performable only for a finite number of values of n: we cannot draw rectangles or write down sums of the type $s_n = 1 + 3 + 5 + 7 + \cdots + (2n - 1)$ for *all* the values of n. In this respect there is a flaw in such concrete proofs: insofar as they use effective concrete representation of sums, they presuppose fixed values of n, and therefore they cannot replace mathematical induction.

In general, reasonings such as these are incapable of having the universality attained in a mathematical induction, but they are nevertheless useful in that they may help to formulate an expression the general validity of which then can be proved by mathematical induction. For example, if we had not seen immediately by simple induction that the sum s_n might equal n^2, either of these two reasonings would have pointed out that possibility.

To give another example of this type of reasoning let us evaluate the sum S_n of the first n integers

$$S_n = 1 + 2 + 3 + \cdots + (n - 1) + n$$

Adding two S_n written down in opposite order

$$S_n = \quad 1 \quad + \quad 2 \quad + \quad 3 \quad + \cdots + (n - 1) + n$$
$$S_n = \quad n \quad + (n - 1) + (n - 2) + \cdots + \quad 2 \quad + 1$$
$$\overline{2S_n = (n + 1) + (n + 1) + (n + 1) + \cdots + (n + 1) + (n + 1)}$$

we express $2S_n$ in terms of the number n of integers composing S_n. The sum of two terms in the same vertical line is always equal to $(n + 1)$, and since the number of terms in S_n is n, we have $(n + 1)$ repeated n times, so that $2S_n$ is equal to $n(n + 1)$, and therefore our tentative formula for S_n is as follows:

$$S_n = n(n + 1)/2$$

EXAMPLE: $1 + 2 + 3 + \cdots + 9 = 9 \cdot 10/2 = 45$

To apply mathematical induction we must prove that the property of S_n, according to which S_n is equal to $n(n + 1)/2$, is hereditary. We therefore suppose that the property holds for some n say for $n = m$ $S_m = m(m + 1)/2$, and form $S_{m+1} = S_m + (m + 1)$:

$$S_{m+1} = S_m + (m + 1) = m(m + 1)/2 + (m + 1)$$

$$= (m + 1)(m/2) + (m + 1)1 = (m + 1)(m/2 + 1)$$

But, $m/2 + 1 = m/2 + 2/2 = (m + 2)/2$, and therefore

$$S_{m+1} = (m + 1)(m + 2)/2$$

The expression obtained for S_{m+1} obeys the law, being its particular case for $n = m + 1$. Thus, we see that if S_m is assumed to be equal to $m(m + 1)/2$, S_{m+1} must also obey the same law and the expression $S_{m+1} = (m + 1)(m + 2)/2$ is true. And since we know that the law applies to the case $n = 1$ ($s_1 = 1 = 1 \cdot 2/2$), we conclude by mathematical induction that this law is true for all values of the integer n. Once the hereditary character of the law is established, its validity for all the integers n follows from $S_1 = 1 \cdot 2/2$.

As the last example, let us study the sum of the "cubes" of the first n integers. The volume of a cube with edges of length n units is obtained by multiplying the area of its base $nn = n^2$ by the height n. Therefore it is measured by the product nnn. Such products of three equal factors are called cubes and denoted n^3. So for instance, the cube of 5 is a product of three factors all equal to 5, and it is denoted by 5^3; $5 \cdot 5 \cdot 5 = 125 = 5^3$, which is read "cube of five" or "five cubed". We form the cubes $1^3 = 1$; $2^3 = 8$, $3^3 = 27$, $4^3 = 64$, etc., until n^3, and denote their sum by T_n

$$T_n = 1^3 + 2^3 + 3^3 + \cdots + n^3$$

Studying the first sums $T_1, T_2, T_3, \ldots$, we note that they are perfect squares:

$$T_1 = 1 = 1^2; T_2 = 1^3 + 2^3 = 1 + 8 = 9 = 3^2;$$

$$T_3 = T_2 + 3^3 = 9 + 27 = 36 = 6^2$$

Simple induction suggests that T_n, in general, for all values of n must be a perfect square. To justify this conjecture we must first find a formula which expresses T_n as the square of a number t_n, $T_n = t_n^2$, where t_n—unknown for the moment—depends on n and consequently must be expressed in terms of n. All that we know is that $t_1 = 1$, $t_2 = 3$, $t_3 = 6$, because $T_1 = 1^2; T_2 = 3^2; T_3 = 6^2$. Computing T_4, we find $T_4 = 1^3 + 2^3 + 3^3 + 4^3 = 100 = 10^2$, so that $t_4 = 10$. We now note that the numbers t_n are sums S_n of the first n integers. Thus, for $n = 1, 2, 3, 4$, we have established that $T_n = S_n^2$ and this result suggests (simple induction) that the relation

$$T_n = 1^3 + 2^3 + 3^3 + \cdots + n^3 = (1 + 2 + 3 + \cdots + n)^2 = S_n^2$$

holds for all values of the integer n. In other words: *the sum of the first n cubes is equal to the square of the sum of the first n integers.*

To justify this statement for all values of n, we again apply mathematical induction. It is sufficient to prove that the truth of $T_n = S_n^2$ implies that of $T_{n+1} = S_{n+1}^2$. Now

$$T_{n+1} = T_n + (n + 1)^3 = S_n^2 + (n + 1)^3$$

Replacing S_n by its value $n(n + 1)/2$, we have to verify that the expression of T_{n+1}, namely $T_{n+1} = [n(n + 1)/2]^2 + (n + 1)^3$, is equal to S_{n+1}^2, that is to $[(n + 1)(n + 2)/2]^2$. Now we have

$$T_{n+1} = [n(n + 1)/2]^2 + (n + 1)^3 = n^2(n + 1)^2/4 + 4(n + 1)^3/4$$

and, picking out the common factor $(n + 1)^2/4$, we find that T_{n+1} is equal to $[(n + 1)^2/4] [n^2 + 4(n + 1)]$. But $(n + 1)^2/4 = (n + 1)^2/2^2$ $= [(n + 1)/2]^2$, while $n^2 + 4(n + 1) = (n^2 + 2n) + (2n + 4) = n(n + 2)$ $+ 2(n + 2) = (n + 2)^2$. Therefore, finally we check that

$$T_{n+1} = [(n + 1)/2]^2 (n + 2)^2 = [(n + 1)(n + 2)/2]^2 = S_{n+1}^2$$

This proves the hereditary character of the law and thus extablishes its validity for all $n = 1, 2, 3, \ldots$

It is important to mention that the fundamental idea of mathematical induction is already contained in the recurrent definition of the infinite sequence of natural numbers. To deduce the existence of the infinite sequence of all natural numbers with the aid of mathematical induction it is sufficient to state with Peano that (1) one is a natural number; (2) every natural number has a successor which is also a natural number; (3) no two natural numbers can have the same successor. Denoting the successor of n by $n + 1$, we first form $1 + 1$, call it two, and denote it by 2. Having formed 2, we obtain $2 + 1 = 3$, then $3 + 1 = 4$, and so on *ad infinitum*. This fact caused Russell to say that mathematical induction is nothing else but the definition of the infinite sequence of natural numbers; there is a kind of numbers (natural numbers) to which mathematical induction can be applied, and the sequence of the same numbers is necessarily involved when mathematical induction is used. In our opinion, Russell's observation does not eliminate the fact that we build and use an infinite logical chain in applying mathematical induction, as we build an infinite sequence of natural numbers. Poincare emphasized the same characteristic feature of mathematical induction by saying that the final conclusion obtained with its aid is a typical synthetic judgment *a priori*. Felix Klein expressed the same idea when he qualifiied mathematical induction as an *intuitive* law of human thinking.

It is interesting to observe that the same infinite recurrence which characterizes mathematical induction can be applied to definitions. If we want to avoid any reference to our physical experience, and to build arithmetics as a purely logical structure, we must eliminate the usual definition of addition as the result of mixing together the elements of two collections into one collection. It can be done by using the axiom of the existence of a successor $n + 1$ to every natural number n, and building an infinite chain of recurrent definitions. We begin by stating that the addition of one to a is possible because it is a definition of the successor $(a + 1)$ to a. In symbols: $a + 1 = (a + 1)$. Now we define the addition of the "successor to one" that is of the number 2 to a as the addition of one to the successor $(a + 1)$ to a:

$$a + 2 = (a + 1) + 1$$

Having defined the addition of 2, we pass to the addition of its successor $3 = 2 + 1$, and again we define the sum $a + 3$ as the result of the addition of 1 to the sum $a + 2$:

$$a + 3 = (a + 2) + 1$$

This chain of recurrent definitions is an infinite one, and the formula

$$a + (n + 1) = (a + n) + 1$$

where n runs through the infinite sequence of all natural numbers, appears now as a recurrent definition of the operation of addition in the domain of natural numbers.

It is known that all basic laws are deduced with the aid of the mathematical induction, from the recurrent definition of addition and the axiom of the existence of a successor.

It is not our purpose here to study these deductions. We define now another important mathematical operation.

Exponentiation

Exponentiation is a particular case of multiplication, namely multiplication of equal factors. Thus, since multiplication is always possible, we conclude immediately that exponentiation is also always possible. A product is called a "power of a" (which means power of the base a) if all its factors are equal to a, which is then the *base* of the power. The number of equal factors a involved in such a product is called the *exponent* of the power. Thus, a square $a^2 = aa$ is a power of base a with exponent 2; a cube $a^3 = aaa$, is a power of a, too, but with exponent 3. A general definition of a power with the base a and exponent n is therefore

$$a^n = \underbrace{a \cdot a \cdot a \cdots a}_{n}$$

where the exponent n denotes the number of equal factors. Two numbers a and b, not equal, involved in a power, such as a^b, do not play symmetrical roles, and therefore there is no commutative law of exponentiation.

Using the sign of inequality $\neq$, we have

$$a^b \neq b^a \qquad\qquad \text{(for } a \neq b)$$

For example $3^2 = 9$, but $2^3 = 8$, so that $3^2 \neq 2^3$. The definition of exponentiation leads to the following three *laws of exponents:*

$$a^n \, a^m = a^{n+m}; \quad a^m \, b^m = (ab)^m; \quad (a^m)^n = a^{mn}$$

In a power with the exponent equal to 1, the exponent is dropped, and a^1 is written always simply as a, thus for example $a^n a = a^{n+1}$. Note that the product of two powers with different bases and different exponents cannot be simplified. Finally, any integral power of one is equal to one: $1^n = 1$, and any integral power of 0 is equal to 0, $0^n = 0$.

Infinite Set of Primes

We have seen that the natural integers belong to two different groups: there are prime and composite integers. It can be proved that the decomposition of a given composite integer N into a product of primes is unique. Let us denote the different prime factors of N by $p_1, p_2, p_3, \dots \dots, p_n$. In general, the product N may involve the same prime factor, say p_k, many times. If t_k denotes the number of prime factors of N all equal to p_k, the product involves as a factor the power $p_k^{t_k}$ of p_k, and the general formula of decomposition can be written

$$N = p_1^{t_1} \cdot p_2^{t_2} \cdot p_3^{t_3} \dots p_n^{t_n}$$

Thus, if $N = 10,348,065,000$, then by trial we find that the number n of different primes is 6, and they are $p_1 = 2$, $p_2 = 3$, $p_3 = 5$, $p_4 = 7$, $p_5 = 13$, $p_6 = 19$ with the exponents $t_1 = 3$, $t_2 = 2$, $t_3 = 4$, $t_4 = 2$, $t_5 = 1$, $t_6 = 2$, so that

$$10,348,065,000 = 2^3 \cdot 3^2 \cdot 5^4 \cdot 7^2 \cdot 13 \cdot 19^2.$$

The prime integers appear as fundamental elements of the sequence of natural numbers, since all the composite integers can be built by multiplication, if the set of prime integers is given. We mention that only primes not exceeding $20,000,000$ are determined and tabulated.

A very interesting question now arises: is the set of primes a finite or an infinite one. Greek mathematicians solved this question and found that the number of all the primes is infinite.

They used the *indirect method of reasoning.* This method consists of the study of logical corollaries of a hypothesis which is contrary to what is to be proved. If such a contrary hypothesis leads to a logical contradiction, it is necessarily wrong, and the proof is obtained.

Such ist the famous Euclid's proof of the fact that there are infinitely many prime integers. Suppose, to the contrary, that the number of different primes is finite, say n; we can then write their sequence in the order of increasing magnitude:

$$p_1 = 2, p_2 = 3, p_3 = 5, p_4 = 7, \dots, p_{n-1}, p_n$$

p_n being the last and at the same time the *largest* prime number possible. Thus, the hypothesis of a finite set of primes leads us to the conclusion that there must be a last and largest prime p_n.

Consider now a number N obtained by adding one to the product $p_1 p_2 \cdots p_n$ of all the primes. Since each prime is a finite number and, by hypothesis, the number of primes is finite, this product must be a finite number, and therefore the number N is finite too:

$$N = p_1 p_2 p_3 \cdots p_n + 1$$

Only two cases are logically possible, and they are mutually exclusive: N is either prime or composite, and there is no third possibility. Now N cannot be prime since it is greater than p_n, and p_n, by hypothesis, is the last and greatest prime. But N cannot be composite either. For, to be composite, it would have to be divisible by some of our n primes, $p_1, p_2, \dots, p_n$, but trying to divide N by any one of these primes, we always find a remainder equal to one, since the product $p_1 p_2 \cdots p_n$ is divisible by any prime, but the second term, 1, is not.

This contradiction with the logical principle of the *excluded middle* proves that our initial hypothesis of a finite set of primes is wrong, and therefore this set must be an infinite one. If one objects by saying that N may be a composite number divisible by primes other than $p_1, p_2, \dots p_n$, then we again obtain a contradiction to the initial assumption that there are n and only n primes, for if N is composite, then there must exist more than n primes.

The domain of prime numbers is filled with interesting and as yet unsolved problems, the law of their distribution among the integers being unknown. It is known, however, that prime numbers occur with rapidly diminishing frequency as we ascend the scale of integers.

Representation of Integers

Our decimal system of numeration, with its nine symbols 1, 2, 3, 4, 5, 6, 7, 8, 9 for the first nine integers and the tenth symbol, zero 0 for the representation of nothing, is so familiar to us that it seems quite simple. But history proves that it is a highly refined product of a slow and long evolution which lasted more than four thousand years, from 4000 B.C. to 100 A.D. Remember that the Greeks and Romans did not know it. They could not represent large numbers, and this circumstance alone stopped the development of arithmetics and algebra, thus precluding for the Greek and Roman civilizations the study and mastery of laws of nature.

Our system of numeration is based first on the principle of *positional value* of the symbols used, and second, on the introduction of such a contradictory symbol as zero, which represents nothing.[1]) How can nothing be represented by a symbol? The philosophers of antiquity pointed out the logical difficulty inherent in the use of zero: they argued that the fact of representing a thing by a symbol is equivalent to the affirmation that this thing does exist, but the concept of nothing is precisely a negation of any existence, and as such it cannot be symbolized by zero. And indeed, the introduction of zero by Hindu mathematicians in 100 A.D. was a bold and daring innovation.

The principle of positional value was discovered some 2500 years ago by the Phoenicians. They ascribed, as we do, different values to the same digit according to the relative position it occupied in the sequence of digits representing a number, and used letters to denote these values. Thus they would write the number 702935 as

$$7h\,2T \mid 9h\,3t\,5$$

where the vertical bar (our comma) marks the two periods, the second one being a period of thousands and t, h, and T standing for tens, hundreds and thousands. It was the lack of a symbol for a position for which there was no significant digit (in our example, tens of thousands) which obliged the Phoenicians to use letters.

Both the principle of positional value and the use of zero were known

---

[1]) The word *zero* ist an abbreviation of the Italian form *zephiro*, for the Arabic *zifr* which means empty, nothing. The Arabic *zifr* is an exact translation of the Hindu word *sunya*, which is used in India to denote zero.

to the Maya civilisation in 500 B.C. Their numbers were written on steles vertically, and only three symbols were used; a symbol for zero, a dot for one, and a horizontal bar for five. In our system of numeration, the number ten is the base, ten units of a class forming a unit of the next higher class. This is why our system is called decimal. In the Maya numeration two bases, namely 20 and 18, are used alternately: twenty units of the first order and, in general, of any odd order form a unit of the next—even—order, but eighteen units of the second order and of any even order are sufficient to form a unit of the next—odd—order. Thus the number 38,533 may be written in Maya numeration as

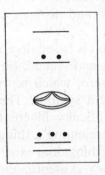

Fig. 1.8.

follows: The values of the units of the second, third, and fourth class are respectively equal to 20, 360 and 7200. Thus

$$38,533 = 5 \cdot 7200 + 7 \cdot 360 + 0 \cdot 20 + 13 \cdot 1$$

The symbol zero may be characterized by two important properties, which are unique to zero:

$$N + 0 = N \quad \text{and} \quad 0 \cdot N = 0$$

Zero is the only number such that, first, its addition to any number N does not change this number N, and, second, multiplication by it always generates a vanishing product, regardless of the value of the first factor N. The second property can be justified by observing that the extension of the number field we perform by adding a new element, zero, to the sequence of integers, must be done in harmony with the fundamental laws. Therefore $0 \cdot N = N \cdot 0$ and the right member is an abbreviation for a sum of N zeros whose value can only be zero. The left member $0 \cdot N$ could be interpreted as a sum of equal terms of value N each, the number of terms in this sum being zero. A sum of zero terms is empty and is equivalent to nothing. Therefore its value is zero.

The result $0 \cdot N = 0$ read from right to left may be stated as follows:

If the value of a product is zero, at least one of its factors must be equal to zero.

To justify this, observe that a product of two factors, both different from zero, cannot be zero. On the other hand, the product of two zeros is zero: $0 \cdot 0 = 0$, hence the need for inserting "at least" in the statement of this rule.

The introduction of zero also obliges us to study powers with the base zero or with exponent zero. It is plain that any power of zero with an exponent different from zero is, by definition of such a power, zero: $0^n = 0$ if $n \neq 0$. But the notation 0^0 has no meaning, and we therefore eliminate its use.

If zero is used as the exponent, the value of such a power a^0 must be defined in agreement with the law $a^n a^m = a^{n+m}$. Putting $n = 0$, we obtain $a^0 a^m = a^{m+0} = a^m$. Therefore multiplication by a^0 does not change the multiplicand a^m. On the other hand, we know that there is only one factor such that multiplication by it has no effect on the multiplicand, and this special factor is one. Therefore, we must fix the value of a^0 as equal to one, and thus any number N, except zero, raised to a power with the exponent zero is equal to one: $N^0 = 1$, if $N \neq 0$.

All three direct operations, addition, multiplication and exponentiation, are used in decimal notation of numbers. Let us call the position of a digit, counting from the right towards the left, its "rank". Thus, a unit of the first rank denotes the simple unit $1 = 10^0$, the value of a unit of the second rank is ten, 10^1; of the third rank, one hundred, 10^2; and in general a unit of the $(n + 1)$-th rank denotes 10^n for $n = 0, 1, 2, 3, \ldots$ Thus, 14,507 is an abbreviation for

$$1 \cdot 10^4 + 4 \cdot 10^3 + 5 \cdot 10^2 + 0 \cdot 10^1 + 7 \cdot 10^0;$$

since
$$10^4 = 10,000, \, 10^3 = 1000, \, 10^2 = 100, \, 10^1 = 10, \, 10^0 = 1$$

Generalizing the decimal notation we can use any integer x as the base of a system of numeration, so that now the group of x units of a certain rank will form a unit of the next rank. Then the number of symbols for groups of $0, 1, 2, \ldots, x - 2, x - 1$ units, needed in such a system of numeration, is equal to x. If x is less than 10, familiar Arabic numbers from zero to $(x - 1)$ will suffice. Thus, with the base eight $(x = 8)$ the symbols 0, 1, 2, 3, 4, 5, 6, 7, are sufficient to represent all integers. Let us write, as an example, the number three hundred seventy-one in the system of numeration with the base 8. The values of units of successive ranks being $8^0 = 1$, $8^1 = 8$, $8^2 = 64$, $8^3 = 512$, *etc.*, we see that no units of the fourth rank are needed since $371 < 512$. Dividing 371 by 64, we find five units of the third rank and a remainder 51, so that $371 = 5 \cdot 8^2 + 51$. But $51 = 6 \cdot 8 + 3$, so that finally $371 = 5 \cdot 8^2 + 6 \cdot 8^1 + 3 \cdot 8^0 = (563)_8$, the subscript 8 denoting the base for which the notation $(563)_8$ has the required meaning.

But if the base x of numeration is greater than ten, we must introduce new symbols for groups of ten, eleven, twelve, thirteen, *etc.* units, the last symbol to be used denoting the group of $(x - 1)$ units, which is one unit less than the base x. Choosing, for example, $x = 13$ we will use the symbols ϕ, †, and ‡ to represent ten, eleven and twelve respectively. To rewrite the number represented in this tredecimal system of numeration by $(† 20\ ‡7)_{13}$ in our decimal system, it is sufficient to read its notation as follows:

$$(†20\ ‡7)_{13} = 11 \cdot 13^4 + 2 \cdot 13^3 + 0 \cdot 13^2 + 12 \cdot 13^1 + 7 \cdot 13^0$$

$$= 11 \cdot 28{,}561 + 2 \cdot 2197 + 0 \cdot 169 + 12 \cdot 13 + 7 \cdot 1$$

$$= 314{,}171 + 4394 + 156 + 7 = 318{,}728$$

Operations with numbers represented in a system of numeration with a base different from 10 are performed with the aid of tables of addition and multiplication. We give as an example the tables for the base 8:

Addition

	1	2	3	4	5	6	7
1	2	3	4	5	6	7	10
2	3	4	5	6	7	10	11
3	4	5	6	7	10	11	12
4	5	6	7	10	11	12	13
5	6	7	10	11	12	13	14
6	7	10	11	12	13	14	15
7	10	11	12	13	14	15	16

Multiplication

	1	2	3	4	5	6	7
1	1	2	3	4	5	6	7
2	2	4	6	10	12	14	16
3	3	6	11	14	17	22	25
4	4	10	14	20	24	30	34
5	5	12	17	24	31	36	43
6	6	14	22	30	36	44	52
7	7	16	25	34	43	52	61

In general in a system of numeration with any base x a number represented by $n + 1$ digits $a_n a_{n-1} a_{n-2} \cdots a_3 a_2 a_1 a_0$ has the value $a_n x^n + a_{n-1} x^{n-1} + a_{n-2} x^{n-2} + \cdots + a_3 x^3 + a_2 x^2 + a_1 x + a_0$, where all the digits a_n, a_{n-1}, $\ldots a_3$, a_2, a_1, a_0 are positive integers less than x or equal to zero. In algebra such an expression, a sum of many terms, is called a *polynomial* (a Greek word meaning "of many terms") or more precisely "*a polynomial in x*". The factors a_n, a_{n-1}, $\ldots$, a_1, a_0 multiplying the different powers of x are called the *coefficients* of the polynomial.

Thus, the value of a number represented in our decimal system of numeration by digits $a_n a_{n-1} a_{n-2} \ldots a_2 a_1 a_0$ is a polynomial of n-th order (involving as the highest power of x the power x^n) in $x = 10$, and the representation consists of the symbolic notation of the value of a polynomial by the sequence of its coefficients, omitting the powers of the base and the signs of addition of terms.

The choice of base 10 was without doubt motivated by the fact that fingers are used in counting, and there are ten fingers on our hands. Roman numeration is fingerlike: I, II, III, and V is an abbreviation for the hand image. Ten, X, is composed of two fives. The word digit preserves the double meaning of finger and cipher up to this very day.

It is to be noted that there were many other systems of numeration. The base twenty, for example, was widely used, and is reflected in the English *score* and the French *quatre-vingt* (four times twenty) for eighty. The origin of the base twenty is probably the use of all our fingers and toes in counting. We note finally the use of the binary system by the most primitive tribes of Australia: they have different words for the first two integers, one and two, which they combine to form subsequent numbers 3, 4, 5, 6 by the addition of one and two. So for instance, three is named "two-one". The vague concept of many is represented by the word *heap*, and it is applied to all numbers exceeding the "last" integer six.

CHAPTER 2

Evolution of the Number Concept; Negative Integers

So far we have defined three direct operations: addition, multiplication, and exponentiation. Each of them can be inverted, and there are inverse operations corresponding to each direct operation. Subtraction, as an operation inverse to addition, is defined by the equation

$$a + x = b$$

where a and b are two given and known numbers such that b (the sum) is greater than a (one of two terms of the sum) and the symbol x stands for the unknown second term of the sum b, the first term of which, a, is known.

We ask what the value x of the unknown term must be, if it is known that, added to the number a, it generates a sum equal to b. To take an example, consider the equation $7 + x = 11$. It is of the same type $a + x = b$ with $a = 7$ and $b = 11$. We find by trial that the only value of x is 4 since $7 + 4 = 11$.

This solution of the equation $7 + x = 11$ is now stated in the form $x = 11 - 7 = 4$, and we say that the subtraction of 7 from 11 gives 4. Note that the meaning of a subtraction such as $11 - 7 = 4$ is derived from the corresponding addition $7 + 4 = 11$, whose inversion it represents. Each addition generates two corresponding subtractions. Thus, $7 + 4 = 11$ gives not only $11 - 7 = 4$, but also $11 - 4 = 7$. We observe moreover that in $11 - 7 = 4$ and $11 - 4 = 7$ the minus sign is used as symbol of an operation (operation of subtraction) and not as a part of a number symbol.

In the same way any addition $a + b = c$ can be inverted into two subtractions: if $a + b = c$, then $a = c - b$ as well as $b = c - a$. An algebraic equation $a + x = b$, where $b > a$, is solved by subtracting a from b, so that its solution is $x = b - a$, under the condition $b > a$. The definition of subtraction can be extended to include the operation

$a - a$. We know indeed that the addition of zero to a number a does not change this number, so that $a + 0 = a$. Therefore, $x = 0$ appears as the solution of the equation $a + x = a$.

On the other hand, extending the validity of the rule $x = b - a$ for the solution of the equation $a + x = b$, obtained under the condition $b > a$, to the case of the equation $a + x = a$ in which $b = a$, we express the solution of this equation $a + x = a$ in the same form $x = a - a$, as for the equation $a + x = b, b > a$.

Comparing now the two forms $x = 0$ and $x = a - a$ of the solution, we obtain the relation

$$a - a = 0 \tag{1}$$

which expresses an important property of subtraction. Thus, the condition $b > a$, necessary for performing the operation of subtraction, is now replaced by a less stringent one, namely $b \geqslant a$ (read: b greater than or equal to a).

But there is still a third possibility, namely when the number b is *less* than a, $b < a$. What happens in this case to our equation $a + x = b$ and its solution $x = b - a$? If we are conservative and decide to limit ourselves to old, known ideas, we must say that in the case when $b < a$ the equation $a + x = b$ has no sense because the sum b of two (positive) numbers a and x cannot be less than the first term a of the sum and therefore its solution is an impossible operation. Such an attitude eliminates the expansion of knowledge.

Before generalizing the number concept and introducing the negative numbers which solve the equation $a + x - b$, when $b < a$, let us consider as a preliminary example of an impossible operation the addition of two numbers in the field of natural *odd* integers $1, 3, 5, 7, 9, \dots, 2n + 1, \dots$, etc.

Imagine that we do not know yet of the existence of even integers 2, 4, 6, *etc.* so that only odd integers do exist for us. A "number" is for us, by definition of this concept, necessarily a positive and odd integer. In such a limited field multiplication and exponentiation are always possible operations, since a product of two or more odd integers is again another odd integer. It belongs to the field of our "numbers" and therefore does exist for us. The addition of three or five and, in general, of an odd number of terms is possible too, as for instance, $3 + 5 + 7 = 15$, since the sum of an odd number of odd integers is itself an odd integer.

But, the addition of two or four or any even number of terms appears as an impossible operation because its result, an even integer, does not exist for us, does not belong to our "numbers". We could not ascribe a meaning to the operation $3 + 5$ since the number 8, by definition of our numbers, is unknown to us.

To transform this impossible operation into a possible one, to allow addition of our odd numbers in all cases, irrespective of the number of terms to be added, we must remove the barrier and invent, create a new kind of number, namely even integers. Generalizing our narrow number concept and extending it to include all the integers, odd and even, we achieve a development of mathematical thinking and increase its power. Such is the general way of the evolution of human thought through the ages, and in particular the way of the development of mathematics.

In the sixteenth century the Italian mathematician Cardan considered the equation $x + 1 = 0$ which was then said to have no sense and no solution. To solve it Cardan introduced in mathematics a new kind of unit, the negative unit (-1), and defined it as the solution of the equation $x + 1 = 0$, where x is a symbol for an unknown number which, when added to a positive unit, will produce zero as a result of this addition.

At this time, equations of the general type $x - n = 0$ with the positive known term n (such as $x - 5 = 0$ or $x - 11 = 0$) were said to have the solution $x = n$, but all the equations of the type $x + n = 0$, again with n positive, were rejected as contradictory and impossible to solve since—as it was argued before Cardan—the sum of two numbers cannot vanish. This argument proves that the contemporaries of Cardan did not yet have at their disposal the concept of the negative number, and for them "number" meant "positive number".

Negative numbers, invented in India in the early centuries A.D., are now used extensively and we are quite familiar with them, but in mediaeval Europe the first attempt to introduce negative numbers aroused a vehement protest and strong opposition. Italian mathematicians refused to follow Cardan and declared negative numbers to be fictitious and imaginary. How could the symbol $(-n)$ be used, they argued, if it had to be increased by $+n$ to form zero, and therefore had to mean something which was less than zero, that is, less than nothing? There could be no quantity less than nothing, and therefore the equation $x + n = 0$ was thought to have no sense, and its solution was considered impossible.

The opposition to negative numbers caused by the belief that they were fictitious and imaginary was based on a naive and fallacious idea that positive numbers were real. Positive integers (cardinal numbers) seem to participate in the environment, to be a part of reality: we have *five* fingers on our hand. But Nietzsche was right, when he said: "No more fiction for us: we calculate; but that we may calculate, we had to make fiction first."

In other words, if we know that there are five fingers on our hand, we know it only because thousands of years ago the human mind formed the abstract concept of the number five. Otherwise we would never be able to understand that our hand possesses five fingers. In fact we would not be able even to see *five* fingers.

In general it can be said that we remain blind to facts and do not perceive them at all unless and until our mind is well prepared to receive the perceptions of these facts. The positive integers are fictions, *ideal* collections of *abstract* units created by the human mind and existing only in our imagination. They have nothing real in them. Thus, positive as well as negative numbers and any other kind of numbers are pure abstractions and are equally fictitious and imaginary, if opposed to perceptions of reality.

The state of mind of Cardan's contemporaries is characteristic of all the steps in the development and evolution of human thinking. Every new concept whose introduction will enlarge knowledge and increase the power of thought meets, at first, with very strong opposition from all sides since the extension of the field of knowledge cannot be achieved without a generalization of ideas and concepts deeply rooted in human thinking. That generalization always means a profound transformation of human thinking. What was impossible yesterday becomes possible today when a new tool is used by human thought. Mathematicians are often confronted with the impossibility of performing a mathematical operation, and it is a fundamental fact in the evolution of mathematical thinking that it is precisely this impossibility which is the principal source of progress and refinement of mathematical thought.

The history of the evolution of the number concept, which is important for us from the viewpoint of the study of mathematical thinking and culture, is also interesting as a particular example of a more general phenomenon in the evolution of the human thought. It is an exceedingly clear and simple illustration of a kind of Hegelian triad which in mathematics takes the form

$$possible \rightarrow impossible \rightarrow synthesis$$

and we will try to study the evolution of the number concept from a more general point of view, namely that of conquering the impossible.

It may seem at first glance that the conquest of the impossible is a contradictory proposition since the logical definition of impossible precludes its conquest by human thought. However, the concept of the impossible has two aspects. There is the theoretical, logical concept of the impossible which transcends any temporal consideration and by definition precludes its conquest forever. We may call this aspect absolute impossibility.

And there is also the concept of a relative impossibility, the impossibility to act in a given situation. Such is the case of every action which appears to us as impossible to realize in human life. There are supposedly some barriers which hinder this action. Remove the barriers, change the conditions by extending knowledge, create new tools and the action becomes possible: a relative impossibility is transformed into a possibility.

But the creation of new tools, the extension of knowledge, necessitates new acts of thinking, an evolution and development of human thought. This is why absolute freedom of action in the domain of thought is a prerequisite for such a development, and the evolution of scientific ideas in general gives us the best example of such a removal of barriers, of the conquest of the impossible.

From this point of view the best slogan for mathematics and for science in general would be: there is nothing impossible for mankind; what appears as impossible today will be transformed into the possible tomorrow.

Going back to the equation $a + x = b$, where $b < a$, the impossibility of solving it is seen to be a relative impossibility, the "given situation" being here the assumption of the existence of positive integers only.

Let us adopt, with Cardan, a revolutionary way of thinking and systematically introduce new ideas and tools. In this case we will say that the general form of the solution $x = b - a$ *must* have a meaning in all cases, so that the number $b - a$ *must* exist even, if $b < a$. We call this new kind of number a negative integer, and its creation re-moves the impossibility of subtraction when, in $b - a$, the integer b is less than a, $b < a$.

Studying the definition of this new object of thought, we observe that, the number a being greater than b, the difference $a - b$ exists in the field of positive integers. Denoting it by c, so that $a - b = c$, we deduce that $a = b + c$. Therefore, if $a > b$, our equation $a + x = b$ may be written also, replacing a by $b + c$, as:

$$b + c + x = b \qquad\qquad (c = a - b > 0)$$

Cancelling b on both sides, it takes the final form

$$x + c = 0 \qquad\qquad (c > 0)$$

This equation $x + c = 0$ is equivalent to the equation $a + x = b$, and the unknown x is the same in both equations. Applying the general form of solution to the equation $x + c = 0$, we obtain $x = 0 - c$.

In this representation of x, zero can be dropped since it is a symbol for nothing. Thus, $x = -c$ is a new form of our negative number $x = b - a$. The minus sign in $-c$ expresses the *negative character* of x, and it must be incorporated in the concept of the negative number $-c$. Thus, the symbol $-c$ ceases to be a result of subtraction, and is con-sidered as an entity, as a new kind of number. Substituting $-c$ for x back into the equation $x + c = 0$, we obtain the relation

$$(-c) + c = 0 \qquad\qquad (2)$$

which is in fact a *definition* of the negative number $-c$.

It states that, to every natural integer c, we associate a corresponding negative integer $(-c)$ such that their sum $(-c) + c$ is zero. Two numbers such that their sum is zero are called *symmetrical* numbers. For example, 5 and -5 are two symmetrical numbers. Moreover, the natural integers now acquire a new characteristic: they become *positive* as opposed to negative integers.

The negative integers form a new infinite sequence

$$\ldots, -n, -(n - 1), -(n - 2), \ldots, -4, -3, -2, -1 \qquad (3)$$

which is written down and read from the right to the left, and in which the minus signs are an inseparable part of the notation for negative numbers.

The introduction of negative numbers thus creates the possibility of the subtraction $b - a$ even when a is greater than the number b from which it must be subtracted. The solution $x = -c$ of the equation $x + c = 0$ is at the same time the solution $x = b - a$ of the equivalent equation $a + x = b$, so that $b - a = -c$. But $c = a - b$ by definition and thus the negative number $-c$ can be written also as $-(a - b)$. Therefore, if $a > b$, we obtain finally

$$b - a = -(a - b) \tag{4}$$

This relation is a rule of subtraction. It can be formulated as follows: to perform the subtraction $b - a$, where a is greater than b, subtract b from a and prefix a minus sign. Thus, for instance,

$$7 - 11 = -(11 - 7) = -4$$

Defining with Cardan the negative unit -1 as the solution of the equation $x + 1 = 0$, we obtain $(-1) + 1 = 0$, which is a particular case of (2) for $c = 1$. Now the negative integers (3) are also collections of negative units. To show this, we multiply both members of the relation

$$(-1) + 1 = 0$$

by a positive integer n. The principle of permanency of fundamental laws demands that our newly created negative numbers must obey the fundamental laws. Thus, applying the distributive law of multiplication, we obtain

$$n[(-1) + 1] = n(-1) + n \cdot 1 = n(-1) + n = n \cdot 0 = 0$$

By definition of multiplication, the product $n(-1)$ represents a collection of n negative units

$$n(-1) = \overbrace{(-1) + (-1) + (-1) + \cdots \cdots + (-1)}^{n \text{ terms}}$$

On the other hand, adding to both sides of the equality $n(-1) + n = 0$ the negative number $(-n)$, we have with the aid of the commutative law

$$[n(-1) + n] + (-n) = n(-1) + [n + (-n)] = 0 + (-n) = (-n)$$

But the sum in brackets, $n + (-n)$, is equal to zero and therefore $n(-1) = (-n)$, which shows that the negative integer $(-n)$ is a collection of n negative units: $-n = n(-1)$. Applying now the commutative law of multiplication to the product $n(-1)$, we deduce the following rule for the multiplication of a positive number n by the negative unit:

$$(-1)\, n = n(-1) = -n$$

Thus, the multiplication of a positive number n by minus one transforms it into its symmetrical number $-n$.

EXAMPLE: $(-1) \cdot 17 = -17$.

If we want to ascribe a concrete interpretation to negative numbers, it will be sufficient to find such an interpretation for the negative unit -1 since any negative integer $-n$ appears as a collection of negative units.

Addition of two natural (positive) numbers was illustrated on the number-axis by the fact that two successive displacements or "steps" taken in the

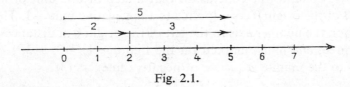

Fig. 2.1.

same direction, such as for example steps of two and three units, are equivalent to one resultant step whose length is the sum of lengths of two component steps, here $2 + 3 = 5$. We emphaszie that both component steps are directed in the same *positive* sense of the number axis.

To interpret a subtraction, such as for example $5 - 3 = 2$, we observe that on the number axis the subtraction of 3 corresponds to a step of length three, but in the opposite direction, which we will call the negative direction:

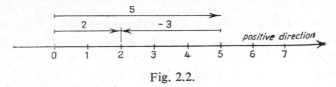

Fig. 2.2.

Suppose now that our negative displacement to the left is greater in length than the first positive displacement to the right, say $5-6$ instead of $5-3$. The first term represents a step beginning at the origin 0 and ending at the point "5". The subtraction of the number 6 corresponds to a step of six units but directed to the left, this second step beginning at the point "5" and ending to the left of the origin at a distance of one unit from it:

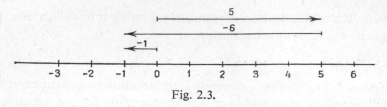

Fig. 2.3.

On the other hand, applying the rule (4), we can see that the difference $5 - 6$ is equal to the negative unit -1:

$$5 - 6 = -(6 - 5) = -1$$

Thus, we come to the conclusion that a step of one unit of length *to the left* of the origin 0 corresponds to the negative unit -1. Therefore, points on the number axis to the left of the origin 0 at distances of one, two, three, *etc.* units, marked on the figure -1, -2, -3, *etc.* correspond to the infinite sequence of negative integers (3):

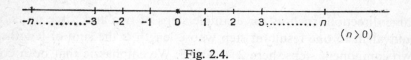

$$(n > 0)$$

Fig. 2.4.

These "negative" points are symmetrical to the corresponding "positive" points: the point image of -4 is at the same distance from the origin 0 to the left as the point image of $+4$ is to the right. The steps leading from the origin 0 to $+4$ and to -4 are equal, but their directions are opposite.

The points representing all negative and positive integers are separated by intervals of a unit length and they cover the whole infinite straight line. We may say that the infinite sequence of all integers, negative and positive, extends from minus infinity at the left to plus infinity at the right, having neither a first nor a last term.

The fact that on the number axis the points 4 and -4 are symmetrical with respect to 0 is the reason why 4 and -4 are called symmetrical numbers. The sum $4 + (-4)$ is zero and indeed, if we add two displacements of the same length but pointing in opposite directions, the resultant displacement is seen to vanish since we come back to the origin 0:

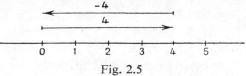

Fig. 2.5

The representation of displacements in a negative direction by negative numbers is only one of many familiar uses of negative numbers. Thus, the temperatures below zero are called negative and represented by negative numbers such as $-3°$ in opposition to temperatures above zero which by definition are represented by positive numbers. The altitudes above and below sea level are again examples of the simultaneous use of positive and negative numbers to represent vertical displacements in two opposite directions.

"Ago" *versus* "hence" corresponds to the negative measure of time intervals, negative since the natural direction of the time flow is reversed. We illustrate this application of negative numbers to the solution of arithmetical problems dealing with time by the following example. Let us find out when the father's age will be equal to twice the sum of the ages of his two children, if he is now 61 years old and has a boy of 19 and a girl of 13?

To solve this problem let us denote the answer by x, which means that the condition stated in the problem will be fulfilled in x years from now. But in x years the children's ages will be equal to $19 + x$ and $13 + x$, while the father's age will be equal to $61 + x$. Computing the sum of children's ages, we find $(19 + x) + (13 + x) = 32 + 2x$. Doubling it we obtain $64 + 4x$. At the moment the desired event takes place the doubled sum $64 + 4x$ becomes equal to the father's age $61 + x$, so that

$$64 + 4x = 61 + x$$

This equation formulates our problem. Consequently, in solving it we will find the answer to the problem, that is the numerical value of the unknown number x. Subtracting $61 + x$ from both sides, we obtain

$$64 + 4x - (61 + x) = (64 - 61) + (4x - x) = 3 + 3x$$

$$= (61 + x) - (61 + x) = 0$$

so that our equation is replaced by the equivalent equation $3 + 3x = 0$. Picking out the common factor 3, we have a vanishing product $3(x + 1) = 0$. Now, in Chapter 1, we saw that, if a product is equal to zero, then at least one of its factors must be equal to zero. In $3(x + 1) = 0$ the first factor 3 does not vanish. Therefore, the second factor $x + 1$ must be equal to zero which gives the equation $x + 1 = 0$. Solving it, we get for x a negative solution, namely $x = -1$, instead of the expected positive solution.

A positive number obtained for x would mean that the expected event would take place in the future and therefore the negative answer $x = -1$ means that the event already took place one year *ago*. In fact, one year ago the children's ages were 18 and 12 and their sum (30) doubled was equal to the father's age, 60, at that time.

The introduction of negative numbers is also an example of a general phenomenon in the evolution of human knowledge, namely the quantification of qualities. Qualitative differentiations between two perceptions (such as red and blue) or between two behaviors (such as cowardice and courage) can sometimes be reduced to quantitative differences and expressed in numbers, notwithstanding the logical definition (Aristotle) of quality as a category opposed to quantity. It is this transformation of quality into quantity that we call quantification of qualities and it is a characteristic feature of the evolution of human thinking.

Thus, the colors which were first considered as intrinsic qualities of objects are now interpreted as effects of different wave*lengths* of light on our retina. They are expressed in and reduced to numerical, quantitative characteristics. Now, when we know the action of adrenalin on the human brain, cowardice and courage appear simply as exterior manifestations of different proportions of adrenalin in the blood, the vehicle for internal secretions. A coward becomes courageous and ready to fight, if the *quantity* of adrenalin in the cerebrospinal fluid increases. On the contrary, if the suprarenal capsules (adrenals) slow down and cease to pour necessary quantities of adrenalin into the blood, a bold man becomes a coward.

Therefore, with the development of our knowledge, the qualitative aspect of phenomena is transformed into a quantitative picture and the introduction of negative numbers is a typical example of this general process. We first considered natural numbers without qualifying them as positive, since we did not combine with the number concept the idea of two opposite qualities. Now the introduction of negative numbers as characterizing a definite direction in space and in time, or a definite direction of variation in general, obliges us to ascribe the character of positiveness to natural integers as representing the opposite direction. In these two sets of numbers—negative and positive—we have expressed in quantitative form the existence of two opposite qualities.

The signs plus and minus affixed to positive and negative numbers such as $+4$ and -7, must be incorporated into the number concept for they are a part of the number. But usually in the notation of positive numbers the plus sign is omitted and is to be understood. Thus 5 means $+5$.

Negative and positive numbers have thus two characteristics: magnitude and sign. The magnitude of a number is called in mathematics the *absolute value*. It is denoted by two vertical bars, such as $|-5| = 5$, and for a positive number the absolute value is equal to the number: $|+5| = 5$. Two symmetrical numbers have necessarily the same absolute value, but opposite signs.

Operations with Negative Numbers

Having introduced negative integers, we must now study the rules for operating with them. Here we touch a very important question. An extension of the number concept or of any other concept cannot be entirely arbitrary. To be useful, it must satisfy the principle of permanency of the laws governing the use of the concept before it was generalized. In our case the fundamental laws we have studied must be respected as we develop our rules for operating with negative numbers.

The addition of two negative numbers is reduced to the addition of their absolute values, that is to the addition of two positive numbers. Consider the sum $(-m) + (-n)$, where $m > 0$ and $n > 0$. Since $-m = (-1)m$ and $-n = (-1)n$, we have, by applying the distributive law of multiplication and the rule (5)

$$(-m) + (-n) = (-1)m + (-1)n = (-1)(m + n) = -(m + n)$$

Thus, to add two negative numbers it is sufficient to add their absolute values and then prefix the minus sign. Example:

$$(-7) + (-11) = -(|-7| + |-11|) = -(7 + 11) = -18$$

The addition of a negative number is performed by subtracting its symmetrical positive number. This can be shown by using the relations (1) and (2):

$$m + (-n) = m + (-n) + 0 = m + (-n) + (n - n)$$
$$= m + [(-n) + n] - n = m + 0 - n = m - n$$

Reading this result $m + (-n) = m - n$ from right to left, we see that, inversely, the subtraction of a positive number is equivalent to the addition of its symmetrical negative number:

$$A - B = A + (-B) \qquad (6)$$

This relation is thus established on the assumption that A and B are two positive numbers, but it also holds when either A or B or both of them are negative. It shows that to subtract a number, positive or negative, it is sufficient to add its symmetrical number.

EXAMPLE: $(-3) - (-11) = (-3) + 11 = 11 + (-3) = 11 - 3 = 8$

We emphasize the important fact that the introduction of negative numbers, caused by the impossibility of subtraction in some cases, not only removes this impossibility, but completely *abolishes* the inverse operation of subtraction, reducing it ot the direct operation of addition: we do not need to consider the operation of subtraction, if we have at our disposal the concept of symmetrical numbers, because any subtraction is an addition of the symmetrical number. This is why only the sums of numbers are considered in algebra.

With the aid of (6) we can now deduce an algebraic rule concerning the transfer of a term (positive or negative) from one member of an equality to the other. This transfer is called *transposition*, and it obeys the rule: *transposition of a term changes its sign.* Suppose that we are given an equality $A + B = C$ and want to transpose B to the right-hand member. Adding to both sides of the equality the symmetrical number $(-B)$, and using the relation $B + (-B) = 0$, which is a corollary of (6) for $A = B$, we obtain

$$A + B + (-B) = A + 0 = A = C + (-B)$$

But the relation (6) gives $C + (-B) = C - B$, so that finally $A + B = C$ is equivalent to $A = C - B$ and the rule of transposition is justified.

The same reasoning can be applied to $A - B = C$. Using (6), we have $A - B = A + (-B) = C$ and, adding B to both sides,

$$A + [(-B) + B] = A + 0 = A = C + B \text{ since } B + (-B) = 0.$$

Multiplication

We study now the four rules of sign for multiplication. Given two numbers $(-a)$ and b, where a and b are positive, so that $(-a)$ is negative, we want to find the sign of the product $(-a)b$ one factor of which is negative while the other factor is positive. The parentheses in $(-a)$ are necessary to avoid the confusion between the two different meanings with which the minus sign is used in mathematics. In the notation $N - 1$, for instance, the minus sign denotes an operation, that of the subtraction of a positive unit from the number N, while in $(-a)b$ the minus sign is a part of the notation of the negative factor $(-a)$.

It was shown that it is sufficient to multiply a positive number n by the negative unit (-1) to obtain its symmetrical number $(-n)$. Thus, $(-a) = (-1)a$ and, returning to the product $(-a)b$, we can write
$$(-a)b = (-1)ab = (-1)(ab) = -(ab) = -ab$$
since the positive number ab is transformed into its symmetrical associate $-ab$ by the multiplication by (-1). Thus, a product of a negative and a positive factor is negative:

$$(-a)b = b(-a) = -ab \qquad\qquad (a > 0, b > 0)$$

EXAMPLE: $(-4)3 = -12 = 4(-3)$.

But there remains the important case when both factors of a product are negative numbers. What will the sign of such a product be? We must fix it in agreement with our basic laws, in particular with the distributive law
$$ab + ac = a(b + c)$$

Let b (positive) and c (negative) be two symmetrical numbers, so that $c = -b$ and $b + c = 0$. Choosing further a negative value for the first factor a, say $a = -n$ with $n > 0$, we obtain, using the distributive law:

$$(-n)b + (-n)(-b) = (-n)[b + (-b)] = (-n)0 = 0$$

In this application of the distributive law the right member is zero since the sum of two symmetrical numbers $b + (-b)$ vanishes and thus $(-n)$ is multiplied by zero. But we know that the product $(-n)b$ of a positive and negative factor is negative: $(-n)b = -(nb)$ and therefore the final result is as follows

$$(-nb) + (-n)(-b) = 0$$

This shows that the product $(-n)(-b)$ and the negative number $(-nb)$ are two symmetrical numbers. But the positive number nb and $(-nb)$ are also two symmetrical numbers. Since there is only one number symmetrical to a given number we conclude that $(-n)(-b)$ and nb represent one and the same number, that is

$$(-n)(-b) = nb$$

Thus, the rule of multiplication of two negative numbers states that their product is positive.

EXAMPLE: $(-4)(-5) = 4 \cdot 5 = 20$

The four rules of sign

$$(+)(+) = +; (+)(-) = -; (-)(+) = -; (-)(-) = +$$

follow from the definition of negative numbers and the principle of permanency of basic laws.

For the negative unit we have in particular $(-1)(-1) = (-1)^2 = 1$.

To illustrate the sign rule $(-1)(-1) = +1$ we restate the algebraic relation (distributive law):

$$(a + b)(c + d) = ac + bc + ad + bd \tag{7}$$

in terms of areas, interpreting a, b, c, d, as lengths of four segments: $AB = a$, $BC = b$, $AD = c$, and $DE = d$.

Plotting them on two perpendicular lines AX and AY (the reader should draw the figures) and drawing through the points B and C parallels to AY and through D and E parallels to AX, we form four rectangular areas equal to ac, bc, ad and bd. Together, they form a large rectangular area $ACFE$ equal to $AC \cdot AE$, that is to $(a + b)(c + d)$, so that (7) is obtained.

Now suppose that in (7) b and d are two negative numbers $b = -m$, $d = -n$, where m and n are positive. Then we must use oriented segments instead of lengths, and we see that the direction of $BC = b$, and $DE = d$ is opposite to that of $AB = a$ and $AD = c$ respectively: $AC = a + b = a - m$, $AE = c + d = c - n$, $AB = a$, $AD = c$. Therefore, the sums $a + b = a - m$, and $c + d = c - n$ represent the lengths of the segments AC and AE. The area of the rectangle $ACKE$ is equal to $(a + b)(c + d)$, while that of the large rectangle $ABFD$ is now equal to ac. For the areas of the three other rectangles we obtain:

$$\text{area } CBFM = |b| \cdot c = mc$$
$$\text{area } ELFD = |d| \cdot a = na$$
$$\text{area } KLFM = |b| \cdot |d| = mn$$

Here we use for the lengths **BC** $= |b|$, and **ED** $= |d|$ of oriented segments **BC** and **ED**, represented by negative numbers b and d, their absolute values $|b| = |-m| = m$ and $|d| = |-n| = n$.

The five areas we are considering verify the following relation:

$$ACKE = ABFD - CBFM - ELFD + KLFM$$

which gives

$$(a + b)(c + d) = ac - mc - na + nm \tag{8}$$

But in the first member we can replace b by $-m$ and d by $-n$, thus, applying the distributive law of multiplication, we also obtain

$$(a + b)(c + d) = [a + (-m)][c + (-n)]$$
$$= ae + (-m)c + a(-n) + (-m)(-n) \tag{9}$$
$$= ac - mc - na + (-m)(-n)$$

since, as we have already seen, $(-m)c = -mc$ and $a(-n) = -na$. Thus, comparing the second members in (8) and (9) we come to the conclusion that

$$(-m)(-n) = mn$$

Now, $-m = m(-1)$, $-n = n(-1)$ and applying the commutative law we have

$$(-m)(-n) = mn(-1)(-1) = mn$$

Therefore, cancelling mn on both sides of $mn(-1)(-1) = mn$:

$$(-1)(-1) = +1$$

and the sign rule is illustrated.

The relations (greater and less than) between negative numbers must be defined in agreement with the geometrical principle of order which states that a number b is greater than a, if the point image of b on the number axis is to the right of the point image of the number a. Therefore we have the inequalities

$$0 > -1 > -2 > -3 > -4 > -5 \cdots > -n > -(n + 1) > \cdots$$

and so on. In other words *a negative number decreases when its absolute value increases.*

Multiplication by a negative number has another important geometrical meaning which is related to the rotation and stretching of segments. In mathematics we distinguish between segments characterized uniquely by their length and oriented and directed segments (arrows) which are called *vectors* and which possess not only length but also direction.

A segment of a straight line defined by two points A and B on this line can be oriented in two opposite directions: from A towards B or from B towards A. The two corresponding vectors are denoted by **AB** and **BA** respectively.

An oriented segment such as **AB** has its own direction which is reflected in its notation, the first letter denoting the beginning (tail) and the second, the end (head) of an oriented segment (vector). To compare the orientations of different vectors we need a frame of reference in which to locate them. For instance, if we have to deal only with different segments of the same line (number axis), we orient the line, choosing as our frame of reference a "positive" direction on the line and ascribing a plus sign to segments having the same orientation as the whole straight line, and a minus sign to segments oriented in the opposite ("negative") direction.

If we consider vectors in a plane and want to characterize their directions, the concept of angle must be used. This concept is analogous to the concept of length, for as a length is the measure of a distance between two points on a line, so an angle is the measure of a distance between two lines through a point, which is their intersection point. Just as a length **AB** can always be considered as generated by the motion of the point M on the line supporting the segment **AB**, the motion beginning at A and ending at B, so an angle AOB is generated when an infinite half-line **OM** rotates around the point O, starting at **OA** and stopping at a new position **OB**, (fig. 2.6).

It is clear that the angular distance between two half-lines with a common origin O can be oriented in two different ways and thus between the two infinite *rays* (half-lines) **OA** and **OB**, we may have two oriented angles AOB and BOA. We can ascribe to them plus and minus signs if we choose a definite sense of rotation as positive. Let us call counterclockwise rotations positive. Thus, AOB will be a positive angle and BOA a negative angle of the same magnitude (absolute value) as AOB. We can now measure any rotation by a positive or negative angle of rotation, its magnitude being expressed for example in degrees, a right angle being by definition equal to $90°$.

A vector **OB** in a plane can be represented by an arrow with its tail at O and its head at B. It is characterized by two numbers: its length $l = |\mathbf{OB}|$, which expresses the magnitude or absolute value $|\mathbf{OB}|$ of the vector **OB**, and the angle $\alpha = AOB$ which represents its direction. The angle α is computed with respect to an arbitrary, fixed direction **MN**, so that **OA** is parallel to **MN**. The angle AOB is often

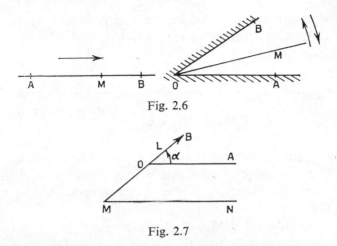

Fig. 2.6

Fig. 2.7

called the *azimuth* of the line **MOB**, the direction **MN** being the origin of azimuths and corresponding to an azimuth zero.

Choosing the number axis OX as the origin of azimuths, we consider on it a vector **OM** pointing to the right. Its length is represented by a positive number m and the azimuth is zero, $\alpha = 0$, fig. 2.8. The point M, head of the arrow **OM**, is the geometric image of the number m. We can also say that the vector **OM** is represented by the positive number m. Rotating **OM** through 180° around the origin O, we obtain a new vector **ON** whose endpoint N is the point image of the negative number $-m$. The azimuth of the vector **ON** is equal to 180°, $\alpha = 180°$, and we can say also that the negative number $-m$ represents the vector **ON** because this vector is on the number axis and is pointing to the left:

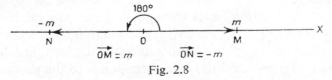

Fig. 2.8

But $-m = (-1) m$, so that **ON** $= (-1)$ **OM**. On the other hand, **ON** is equal to **OM** rotated through 180°. We see therefore that the multiplication by the negative unit rotates the vector **OM** through 180°:

The negative unit may be called the *"rotation-factor* through 180°" because multiplication by it produces a rotation of the vector through 180°.

Now let us consider the product 5*m*. This product is represented by a vector **OP**, pointing in the same direction as **OM** $= m$ (to the right), but five times longer:

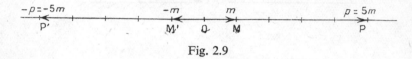

Fig. 2.9

Thus, the multiplication of a vector by a positive number k corresponds to a stretching of that vector to k times its original length, and it leaves the direction of the vector unchanged. In symbols: 5**OM** = **OP**.

Let us now multiply **OM** by -5. Since $-5 = 5(-1)$ we can perform this operation in two steps: first we multiply **OM** by 5 and then the product by (-1). Thus, (-5) **OM** $= (-1) (5$**OM**$) = (-1)$ **OP** = **OP**', where **OP**' is directed to the left and has the same length as **OP**. If we represent **OP** by $p = 5m$, then **OP**' $= -p = -5m$.

Thus, the multiplication of a vector by a negative number $-n$ ($n > 0$), both rotates the vector through 180° and stretches it $|-n|$ $= n$ times.

It is not difficult to find now the geometric meaning of the sign law $(-1)^2 = 1$. Using the square of the negative unit $(-1)^2$ as a factor in a multiplication, we have $(-1)^2$ **OM** $= (-1) [(-1)$ **OM**]. But we saw that the multiplication by (-1) rotates a vector through 180°. Therefore two successive multiplications by (-1) rotate **OM** through 180° + 180° = 360° and $(-1)^2$ appears as a rotation factor through 360°. But rotation through 360° brings a vector back into its initial position and thus, as a final result, leaves its position unchanged.

Therefore the rotation-factor through 360° can only be the positive unit 1, the number 1 being the only factor multiplication by which has no effect at all on the multiplicand and leaves it unchanged. Thus, we must have $(-1)^2 = 1$ and this rule corresponds to the geometric fact that two successive rotations through 180° have no effect on the direction of a vector. The operation which corresponds to the addition of two angles of 180° of the successive rotations is the multiplication of their rotation-factors.

All the fundamental laws hold for the multiplication of negative numbers with one important complement: multiplication by a negative factor of both members of an inequality changes the sense of this inequality. Thus $5 > 3$, but the multiplication by (-1) changes the sign of inequality since $-5 < -3$. In general, if $a > b$, multiplying this inequality by a negative number c $(c < 0)$, we obtain an important complement to monotonic law of multiplication:

$$ac < bc \qquad \text{(if } a > b, c < 0)$$

EXAMPLE: The inequality $7 > 5$ multiplied by -6 becomes $-42 < -30$.

We observe that all *even* powers of negative numbers are positive, while all *odd* powers are negative. It is sufficient to prove this for the negative unit -1. Multiplication by -1 changes the sign of the multiplicand. Therefore

$$(-1)^{n+1} = (-1)(-1)^n = -(-1)^n$$

as well as

$$(-1)^{n+2} = (-1)^2(-1)^n = 1(-1)^n = (-1)^n$$

The addition of 2 in the exponent of a power of (-1) does not change its value. Thus, since $(-1)^1 = -1$, all the odd powers of -1 are equal to -1, while all the even powers of -1 are equal to $(-1)^2$, that is to 1:

$$(-1)^{2n} = +1, \quad (-1)^{2n+1} = -1.$$

$2n$ standing for any even number and $2n + 1$ for any odd number.

Negative Digits

At the end of the first chapter, we saw that the representation of integers in our decimal system of numeration is a particular case of the representation of an algebraic polynomial

$$a_n x^n + a_{n-1}x^{n-1} + a_{n-2}x^{n-2} + \cdots a_2 x^2 + a_1 x + a_0$$

by the sequence of its coefficients $a_n a_{n-1} a_{n-2} \cdots a_2 a_1 a_0$, where this time the juxtaposition of a's does not mean multiplication, but simply their relative order (positional notation), zeros being used as coefficients of lacking terms.

In an algebraic polynomial coefficients may be negative numbers as well as positive, and very often we use such generalized representation of integers also. Take, for instance, the use of a short cut in a subtraction: $2032 - 889$ can be computed more easily as follows

$$2032 - 889 = 2032 - (1000 - 111) = 2032 - 1000 + 111$$
$$= 1032 + 111 = 1143$$

In such a case, what we use in fact is a generalized decimal numeration in which the number 889 is represented as $1\bar{1}\bar{1}\bar{1}$, the minus signs placed above the units of first, second and third rank indicating their negativeness, while the unit of fourth rank is positive. This use of negative digits in the generalized decimal representation of integers is of great help in numerical computations for it simplifies them, often enormously. The use of negative digits $\bar{4}, \bar{3}, \bar{2}, \bar{1}$ instead of positive ones 6, 7, 8, 9 eliminates the operations with these four largest digits.

To persons not well acquainted with the technique of negative digits and with the negative numbers in general, this simplification may seem at first to be a complication, but it is sufficient to practice the use of the negative digits $\bar{4}, \bar{3}, \bar{2}, \bar{1}$ a while to become aware of the fact that their use is much more economical and easy than the use of the positive digits 6, 7, 8, 9.

We give here only one example where the multiplication of 7849 by 872 is performed with the aid of negative digits. Write 7849 and 872 as follows: $1\,\bar{2}\,\bar{2}\,5\,\bar{1}$ and $1\,\bar{1}\,\bar{3}\,2$ and then apply the rules of sign in their multiplication

$$
\begin{array}{r}
1\;\bar{2}\;\bar{2}\;5\;\bar{1} \\
1\;\bar{1}\;\bar{3}\;2 \\
\hline
2\;\bar{4}\;\bar{3}\;0\;\bar{2} \\
\bar{3}\;6\;5\;\bar{5}\;3 \\
\bar{1}\;2\;2\;\bar{5}\;1 \\
1\;\bar{2}\;\bar{2}\;5\;\bar{1} \\
\hline
1\;\bar{3}\;\bar{2}\;5\;5\;\bar{5}\;7\;3\;\bar{2}
\end{array}
$$

$$7\,8\,4\,9 \times 8\,7\,2 = 6\,8\,4\,4\,3\,2\,8$$

The table of multiplication used with such a generalized representation of integers is a much smaller table than the one normally used, with positive digits only. It reduces to the following table:

	1	2	3	4	5
1	1	2	3	4	5
2	2	4	6	8	10
3	3	6	9	12	15
4	4	8	12	16	20
5	5	10	15	20	25

CHAPTER 3

Evolution of the Number Concept;
Rational Numbers;

In Chapter 2 we saw that to eliminate the impossibility of subtracting a number from a smaller number negative integers had to be introduced. Another inverse operation, division (the inverse of multiplication) is also not always possible in the number field of positive and negative integers. Just as the operation of subtraction necessitated the introduction of negative integers, the operation of division leads us to define a new kind of numbers which are called *rational* numbers.

Given two integers a and b, the purpose of multiplication is to find the value N of their product ab: the unknown element in $N = ab$ is N. To invert this operation we suppose that among the three numbers N, a, b such that $N = ab$, the value N of the product and one of two factors, say a, are known numbers, while the second factor is unknown. Denoting the unknown factor b by x, we formulate the problem of division as follows: to find a number x such that, N and a being two given and known integers, $N = ax$.

The use of the symbol x for the unknown is the usual procedure in mathematics. The choice of the letter x itself is conventional. It is the idea of symbolizing the unknown and treating its symbol x, as though it were a symbol for a known number, which is of extreme importance. Operating with the unknown x, as if it were known, can be justified by the fact that the symbol x stands for some number upon which operations are performed. The first thing to do therefore, when one is trying to find an unknown, is to denote it by a symbol and operate with this symbol, expressing in formulas the conditions of the problem. Our problem is to solve the equation

$$N = ax$$

Let us find, for instance, a solution of the numerical equation $2091 = 123x$. The only way to do it is to try different values for x, substituting them in the equation and checking whether it is satisfied or not. The value $x = 10$, for example, is too small since $123 \cdot 10 = 1230$ is less than 2091, while $x = 20$ is too large a value because $123 \cdot 20 = 2460$ is greater than 2091. Substituting various numbers for x into the product $123x$, we finally find that the product of 123 and 17 is precisely equal to 2091. We state this fact by saying that $x = 17$ is the solution of the equation $2091 = 123x$. The trial process just described is what we call division. Denoting it by the symbol of operation $\div$, we express our result as follows:

$$x = 2091 \div 123 = 17$$

This result can be found by applying the well-known process of long division but this customary operation itself is nothing else than a convenient and standard form of our trial process, with the aid of which we perform more easily the inverse operation called division, because it subdivides the trial process into many steps, each of which is performed by trial too.

We saw that subtraction also necessitates a trial process, and—as we will see later—no inverse operation can be performed except by trial. Direct operations, on the contrary, are performed without trial, by applying definite precise rules of operation.

To solve the general equation $N = ax$, in which by hypothesis the number a is a factor of N, so that $N = ab$, we observe that substituting for x into $N = ax$ any value other than b, we do not obtain an equality between the two members, N and ax, of our equation. Thus, no number other than b can be solution of this equation. But, if $x = b$, then the equation is satisfied. Since the relation $N = ab$ is equivalent to $b = N \div a$, we state that $x = N \div a = b$ is solution of the equation $N = ax$.

In the division $N \div a = b$, the value b of the unknown factor $x = N \div a$ is called the *quotient* of the *dividend* N divided by the *divisor a*. Thus, in any division, dividend is equal to divisor times quotient, in symbols: $N = ab$, where a and b are divisor and quotient.

This property of division, when applied to integers, shows immediately that division is not always possible. Given an integer N (dividend), the integral quotient $x = N \div a$ can exist, if and only if the integer a (divisor) is one of the factors of the integer N. Thus, taking $N = 66$, to make the numerical equation $66 = ax$, where a denotes a known and given integer, solvable in integers, we must choose as a

one of the six factors of the number 66, namely choose as a one of numbers 2, 3, 6, 11, 22, 33. Only if this condition is fulfilled, the quotient $66 \div a$ will exist for us since it will be an integer and as such will be one of our numbers.

Suppose, however, that we choose $a = 17$, so that we have to solve the equation $66 = 17x$. Since 17 is not one of the factors of 66, it is plain that there is no integer x such that the product $17x$ will be equal to 66. Therefore, we are obliged to conclude that in the field of integers, the division of 66 by 17 is an impossible operation: 66 being not divisible by 17, the quotient $66 \div 17$ does not exist for one who knows only integral numbers.

In such a case most of the textbooks of arithmetic say that to divide 66 by 17 we must find the largest integer M such that 17 times M is less than 66, but 17 times the next integer $M + 1$ is greater than 66. In the case of our equation $66 = 17x$ this number M is equal to 3, since $17 \cdot 3 = 51 < 66 < 68 = 17 \cdot 4$. These textbooks, using improper terminology, again define the number $M = 3$ thus found as a quotient in the division of 66 by 17, adding that this time there is also a *remainder* 15, since $66 = 17 \cdot 3 + 15$. Thus, it is stated frequently that 66 divided by 17 yields a quotient 3 and a remainder 15. Such statement is incorrect: there is no quotient at all and 66 is not divisible by 17 because the remainder 15 is different from zero. In such a case division, if it is defined correctly, appears as an operation impossible to perform. We will see later that the quotient does exist, if we generalize the number concept and introduce fractions, but its value (3 plus 15/17) is *not* an integer.

The use of an improper terminology is always a source of confusion. For the moment, since the only numbers we know are integers, we can have only integral quotients and therefore, if there is a remainder different from zero, we are obliged to conclude that the division is impossible. In cases, where there is a remainder, we propose to use the term "improper quotient". Thus, in general, when the division is impossible and the proper quotient does not exist, one can state the definition of an improper quotient obtained in a long division as follows:

DEFINITION: *Dividend is equal to divisor times improper quotient plus remainder.*

But again, we can remove the barrier and, respecting the principle of permanency of the basic laws, extend the number concept in such a way that the division of integers becomes possible in all cases. To achieve this, we postulate the existence of an exact quotient for all divisions, included such cases as $66 \div 17$, thus introducing and defining a new kind of number other than integers. Such non-integral quotients are called *rational* numbers, since they always express the *ratio* of two integers. For instance, the quotient of the division $66 \div 17$ expresses the ratio of 66 to 17. We denote this ratio by a letter

$$66 \div 17 = Q$$

to emphasize the fact that such a quotient is a single number, an *entity*.

Although Q is related in a definite way to the two integers 66 and 17, whose ratio it expresses, this entity Q has its own independent existence as a mathematical concept. It is precisely because we postulate the existence of the rational number Q that we can define and use the division $66 \div 17$. Otherwise, this operation would be meaningless, the expression $66 \div 17$ itself being an empty symbol.

A rational number such as $66 \div 17 = Q$ admits of many different representations. Our decimal system of numeration can be extended in such a way as to include all rational numbers. For instance, we have $3 \div 4 = 0.75$. The representation of rational numbers by decimal fractions however is only one of many possible representations. Another way of representing rational numbers, namely by *continued fractions*, is also studied in this chapter.

Among different representations of rational numbers, their expression by ordinary *fractions*, m/n where both m and n are integers, is the most important. The fractions were invented and used long before the concept of rational number was elaborated and the rules of operating with rational numbers were found in working with fractions. In such an expression as, for instance, 66/17 the bar separating 66 and 17, as well as the symbols 66 and 17 remind us that the rational number represented by 66/17 is also the quotient of the division $66 \div 17$, and thus express the ratio of 66 to 17.

The introduction of rational numbers achieves the extension of the set of integers into a richer field consisting of integers and rational numbers, and it solves the problem of division for all possible choices of integral dividend and divisor. We can now say that the operation $m \div n$, where m and n are any two integers, is always possible:

$m \div n = m/n$. In other words, given any equation $nx = m$, where m and n are integers, we can find the unknown x by division: $x = m \div n$ $= m/n$, so that the rational number $x = m/n$ is the solution of the equation $nx = m$.

Thus, the concept of divisibility is a relative one and it is related to the nature of numbers considered. Whereas in the domain of integers most of divisions are impossible to perform, in the field of rationals by definition any integer m is always divisible by any other integer n, their quotient m/n being a rational number. But the word "divisible" as used in arithmetic means divisible in the domain of integers and will be used in what follows only in this sense.

A long division with a non-vanishing remainder and an improper integral quotient yields in fact a proper quotient equal to a sum of an integer plus a rational part. Dividing 66 by 17, we can use the fact that $66 = 51 + 15$ and divide each part separately. Now the quotient $51 \div 17$ is an integer, namely 3, while $15 \div 17 = 15/17$ is a fraction. Therefore, $66 \div 17 = 3 + 15/17$ and thus the improper quotient 3 is simply the integral part of the exact quotient $3 + 15/17$.

The two terms m and n of a fraction m/n are called *numerator* and *denominator* respectively. The value of the fraction m/n is defined by the relation $(m/n) n = m$, because in a fraction considered as quotient in a division, the numerator m corresponds to the dividend and the denominator n to divisor. We obtain the relation $n(m/n) = m$, observing that in a division dividend is equal to divisor times quotient.

In particular cases, the denominator n can be equal to one, and then the fraction $m/1$ represents the integer m since for $n = 1$ the general relation $(m/n) n = m$ becomes $(m/1) 1 = m/1 = m$. Therefore the concept of rational number includes that of integer as a particular case.

Another particular case $m = 1$ is also important. Two numbers related so that their product is equal to one are called *reciprocal* numbers. Rational numbers of the particular type $1/n$, that is with the numerator 1, are reciprocals of integers. So, for instance, $^1/_2$ and 2, $^1/_3$ and 3, $^1/_4$ and 4 and in general $1/n$ and n are pairs of reciprocal numbers. Given $1/n$, we have indeed by definition $n(1/n) = 1$. Hence $1/n$ and n are reciprocal numbers.

Moreover, the relation $n(1/n) = 1$ proves that the reciprocal $1/n$ of an integer n can be considered as the nth part of the unit since $n(1/n) = 1$ means that the sum of n terms, each of which is equal to $1/n$, is one:

$$\overbrace{1/n + 1/n + 1/n + \cdots + 1/n + 1/n}^{n \text{ terms}} = 1.$$

EXAMPLE: $1/7 + 1/7 + 1/7 + 1/7 + 1/7 + 1/7 + 1/7 = 1$

The infinite decreasing sequence of reciprocals of integers

$$1/1,\ 1/2,\ 1/3,\ 1/4,\ \ldots,\ 1/n,\ 1/(n + 1)\ \ldots$$

has as many terms as there are integers.

To study the cases, where in m/n either m or n or both m and n are zero, we observe that if one of two factors of a product is zero, then the product is also zero regardless of the value of the second factor. Thus, from $0 \cdot N = 0$, where N is arbitrary but does not vanish $N \neq 0$, we can deduce $0/N = 0$. Denoting the value of $0/N$ by x, $0/N = x$, we have indeed $(0/N)\,N = xN = 0$. Since the product xN is zero, one of its factors must vanish; but N does not vanish, therefore x must vanish and $x = 0/N = 0$.

The symbol $0/0$ is meaningless since its value cannot be determined: denoting its value by x, we deduce from $0/0 = x$ the condition $0 \cdot x = 0$. But any number satisfies this condition and thus $0/0$ can be equal to an arbitrary number which proves that its value cannot be determined. For this reason the symbol $0/0$ is never used. A more general symbol $a/0$, where the number a does not vanish, has no meaning either, but for another reason than $0/0$. The numerator of a fraction is, by definition, the value of a product, one of whose factors is the denominator. If the denominator (factor) is zero, then also the value of the numerator (product) must necessarily be zero, because a product vanishes if one of its factors is zero. Therefore, if $a \neq 0$, the symbol $a/0$ is meaningless since it contradicts its own definition. The result of this discussion is that *division by zero is impossible.*

As might be expected paradoxes arise, if we use division by zero. Let us for example consider three numbers 2, 3 and 5, denoting them by $a = 2$, $b = 3$ and $c = 5$ respectively, so that $a + b - c = 0$. Here is now a logical chain of arguments beginning with $c = a + b$. Multiplying both members of this relation by the sum $a + b$, we have

$$(a + b)\,c = (a + b)\,(a + b)$$

Applying twice the distributive law of multiplication, we open the parentheses and multiply out:

$$ac + bc = a^2 + ab + ab + b^2$$

Transposing b^2 and one of two terms ab from the righthand member to the lefthand member, as well as ac from the left to the right of the equality sign, gives

$$-ab - b^2 + bc = a^2 + ab - ac$$

Now, using the rules of sign, we observe that $-ab = (-b)\,a$, $-b^2 = (-b)\,b$, $bc = (-b)\,(-c)$ and $-ac = a(-c)$. Moreover, a^2 means aa and thus, our relation can be written as follows

$$(-b)\,a + (-b)\,b + (-b)\,(-c) = aa + ab + a(-c)$$

Picking out the common factor $(-b)$ in the lefthand member, and the common factor a in the righthand member, we obtain

$$(-b)\,(a + b - c) = a(a + b - c)$$

Each member of this relations is a product of two factors one of which is their common factor $a + b - c$. The two products are equal and they have the same first factor $(a + b - c)$. Therefore, their second factors must be equal, that is we must have $-b = a$, a result which is manifestly wrong since $-b = -3$ cannot be equal to $a = 2$.

The fallacy is caused by the division by zero: to conclude from $M = N$, where $M = (-b)\,(a + b - c)$ and $N = a(a + b - c)$, to $-b = a$, we have in fact divided two equal numbers M and N by the same number $(a + b - c)$ and concluded as follows: $M = N$ and therefore

$$M/(a + b - c) = -b = a = N/(a + b - c)$$

But the divisor we used was zero, since $a + b - c = 2 + 3 - 5 = 0$, and the division by zero is the source of the paradoxe $-3 = 2$.

In cancelling the common factor $a + b - c$, we have applied the rule: if the second factors of two equal products of two factors are equal, then their first factors are equal, too. We see now that this rule implies an important limitation, namely the products which are equal by hypothesis must not vanish. From the fact that $5 \cdot 0 = 7 \cdot 0$ we cannot conclude that 5 equals 7, and in this case the two products are equal without having their second factors (5 and 7) equal. The exact formulation of this important cancellation rule is as follows:

if the second (or first) factors of two equal non-vanishing products of two factors are equal, then their first (second) factors are equal too.

Fractions were introduced by the Egyptians more than thirty-six

centuries ago, but they used only the reciprocals of integers, that is •
fractions of the special type $1/n$ with the numerator one.[1]) Therefore,
their principal preoccupation was to express the ratio m/n of any two
integers in terms of a sum of such special fractions. While all the books
on arithmetic written during many centuries in different civilized coun-
tries treat extensively many examples of this arithmetical problem and
emphasize its importance, it is now completely obsolete and forgotten.
This problem is meaningless for us. This is a good example of the rela-
tivity of intellectual values.

Ordinary fractions, as we know and use them, were introduced some
fifteen centuries ago by Hindu mathematicians. They were unknown to
Greeks. We will now deduce and define the rules of operating with
fractions, applying the principle of permanency of basic laws. We begin
with the sign rule for division.

From the sign rule for multiplication

$$(-1) \cdot (-1) = +1; \ (-1)(+1) = -1;$$
$$(+1)(-1) = -1; \ (+1)(+1) = +1$$

where the second members appear as the products of two factors, we
deduce the *sign rule for division:*

$$(+1) \div (+1) = +1; \ (+1) \div (-1) = -1;$$
$$(-1) \div (+1) = -1; \ (-1) \div (-1) = +1$$

This deduction is based on the definition of division: if P is a product
of two factors, $P = uv$, then $P \div u = v$, as well as $P \div v = u$.

The sign rule for division is the same as for multiplication and,
applying it to fractions (which are quotients too), we state that a fraction, whose both numerator and denominator are negative integers,
represents a positive rational number, as for instance

$$(-3)/(-4) = 3/4,$$

but if the numerator and denominator have opposite signs, then the
value of the fraction is a negative rational number:

$$(-3)/4 = 3/(-4) = -(3/4) = -0.75$$

---

[1]) Ahmes Papyrus, *circa* 1650 B. C.

Reducing to Lowest Terms

It is not necessary to consider fractions which have the same numerical value and express the same ratio, as distinct rational numbers. Thus, for example, any term of the infinite sequence of different fractions $1/2, 2/4, 3/6, \ldots, m/2m, \ldots$ represents the same rational number 0.5 which is the common value of all terms of the sequence.

If $m/n = h$, where h denotes the rational number represented by the fraction m/n, then by definition $m = nh$. This equality can be multiplied on both sides by any integer G without destroying it.

$$(mG) = nhG = (nG)\,h \qquad\qquad (G \gtrless 0)$$

Applying the definition of rational number, we deduce from $(mG) = (nG)\,h$ that

$$h = (mG)/(nG) \qquad (G = \pm 1, \pm 2, \pm 3, \ldots)$$

which means that one can multiply both terms of a fraction by any integer G, without changing its value. Thus each rational number is represented by an infinite number of equal fractions since it appears as the quotient in an infinite set of different divisions all of which lead to the same ratio.

In this infinite sequence of equal ratios, all except one are ratios of two integers which have a common factor. Take our example: the value of all fractions $m/2m$ is the same, namely one-half, regardless of the values taken by the arbitrary integer m. In all cases, except the case when $m = 1$, the numerator m and the denominator $2m$ have the common factor m. The case of $m = 1$ stands alone and this representation of one-half as $1/2$ is the most valuable because it cannot be simplified by cancelling the common factor of its two terms. This case is important, and fractions expressed in such a way that the numerator and the denominator are *relatively prime numbers* (that is numbers which have no common factor), are said to be *reduced to their lowest terms*. Such is the case with $3/5$ and $7/8$: these fractions are reduced to their lowest terms, while $6/10$ or $21/24$ are not.

If the numerator and the denominator of a fraction have a common factor, one can divide both terms of such a fraction by their common factor without changing the value of the fraction. To show this let us consider $mG/nG = h$, were G is the common factor of two terms mG

and nG of the fraction h. By definition, we have $mG = nGh = (nh)\,G$, where the two equal products of two factors mG and nhG have the same first factor G. Since they do not vanish we can apply the cancellation rule which gives the equality of their second factors: $m = nh$ and, thus, $h = m/n$. Therefore, $mG/nG = m/n$.

To reduce a fraction to lowest terms, it is sufficient to divide both terms of that fraction by their *greatest common factor*. This greatest common factor of two numbers is also called the *greatest common divisor* (and is denoted by the abbreviation GCD) since it is the largest number by which both the numerator and denominator can be divided exactly, that is without a remainder.

If both terms of a fraction are small numbers it is easy to find their GCD. Such is the case for instance, with $126/168$: since $126 = 42 \cdot 3$ and $168 = 42 \cdot 4$, the GCD of 126 and 168 is equal to 42 and thus $126/168$ is easily seen to be equal to $3/4$. But, if the terms of a fraction M/N are very large numbers, how can their GCD, denoted for the sake of brevity by GCD $(M; N)$, be found?

Euclid's Algorithm

Greek mathematicians devised a regular process called Euclid's algorithm, which enables one to find the GCD of any two given numbers in a finite number of steps. An *algorithm* is a set of operations performed in prescribed order. Thus, long division is an algorithm which yields a proper or improper quotient. Euclid's algorithm is a chain of successive and *interlocked* divisions, of which all but the last are improper divisions and produce a remainder. This sequence of divisions stops when there is no remainder, the last non-vanishing remainder yielding the GCD.

Let us study a numerical example before expressing this algorithm as a set of algebraical formulas. Supposed that we must find GCD $(25{,}515; 7819)$. We begin by dividing the larger number 25,515 by the smaller one 7819. The improper quotient and remainder of this first division are 3 and 2058 respectively. Applying the definition of improper division, we state that the dividend 25,515 is equal to the divisor 7819 times the improper quotient 3 plus the remainder 2058:

$$25{,}515 = 7819 \cdot 3 + 2058$$

With the aid of this relation we can prove that each common divisor of two numbers 25,515 and 7819 is at the same time a divisor of 2058 and therefore a common divisor of two numbers 7819 and 2058. *Vice versa*, a common divisor 7819 and 2058 is also a common divisor of 25,515 and 7819, so that the set of common divisors of 25,515 and 7819 is identical to the set of common divisors of 7819 and 2058. Suppose indeed that the number n divides 25,515 and 7819 exactly. Then we have $25,515 = np$ and $7819 = nq$, where p and q are integers. Thus, transposing the product $7819 \cdot 3$ to the left and permuting left and right,

$$2058 = 25,515 - 7819 \cdot 3 = np - 3nq = n(p - 3q)$$

where $p - 3q$ is an integer, so that n divides 2058 exactly, the proper quotient being equal to $p - 3q$. If now conversely a number m divides 7819 and 2058 exactly, we have on one hand $7819 = mr$, $2058 = ms$, where r and s are integers, and on the other hand,

$$25,515 = 7819 \cdot 3 + 2058 = 3mr + ms = m(3r + s)$$

which proves that m divides 25,515 too and therefore is a common divisor of 7819 and 25,515.

The sets of common divisors of pairs 25,515 and 7819 on one hand, and 7819 and 2058 on the other hand being identical, their greatest divisors are equal and thus we have

$$GCD(25,515; 7819) = GCD(7819; 2058)$$

The problem is thus reduced to finding the GCD (7819; 2058), a simpler problem insofar as we have to deal with smaller numbers. This reduction can now be repeated. We have established, indeed, a general fact, namely that the GCD of two given numbers is at the same time GCD of the smaller number and the remainder obtained in the division of the larger number by the smaller. To repeat the reduction we now divide 7819 by the remainder of the first division 2058. This second division yields an improper quotient 3 and the remainder 1645 since $7819 = 2058 \cdot 3 + 1645$. Again we conclude

$$GCD (7819; 2058) = GCD (2058; 1645)$$

To continue the reduction we have only to extend the chain of successive and interlocked divisions, in which each divisor and remainder of one division become dividend and divisor in the next division. Thus, we obtain successively:

$$25,515 = 7819 \cdot 3 + 2058$$
$$7819 = 2058 \cdot 3 + 1645$$
$$2058 = 1645 \cdot 1 + 413$$
$$1645 = 413 \cdot 3 + 406$$
$$413 = 406 \cdot 1 + 7$$
$$406 = 7 \cdot 58 + 0$$

We come to the conclusion that GCD (25,515; 7819) is 7 because the reduction yields step by step: GCD (25,515; 7819) = GCD (7819; 2058) = GCD (2058; 1645) = GCD (1645; 413) = GCD (413; 406) = GCD (406; 7) = 7, the last division establishing the fact that 406 is divisible by 7 *without remainder*. In practice the arrangement of the divisions chain is as follows:

$$
\begin{array}{r}
3 \\
\hline
7819 \mid 25515 \\
23457 \qquad 3 \\
\hline
2058 \mid 7819 \\
6174 \qquad 1 \\
\hline
1645 \mid 2058 \\
1645 \qquad 3 \\
\hline
413 \mid 1645 \\
1239 \qquad 1 \\
\hline
406 \mid 413 \\
406 \qquad 58 \\
\hline
7 \mid 406 \\
406 \\
\hline
\end{array}
$$

The successive remainders are thus 2058; 1645; 413; 406; 7 and 0. They are divisible by the last non-vanishing remainder 7 which is the GCD of two given numbers 25,515 and 7819. The quotients are 3; 3; 1; 3; 1; 58, all except the last 58 being improper.

To formulate Euclid's algorithm in its algebraic form we will use letters to symbolize the elements of the division and also subscripts to indicate to which step of the algorithm they belong. The remainders will be denoted by R and we write R_1 instead of saying "remainder of the first division". Likewise R_2, R_3, *etc.* will denote the remainders of the second, third, *etc.* divisions. The quotients will be identified by the letter Q and again Q_1, Q_2, Q_3, *etc.* represent the quotients of the first, second, third, *etc.* divisions. If there are in all $n + 1$ divisions in the chain, the remainder R_{n+1} of the last, the $(n + 1)$-th, division is zero: $R_{n+1} = 0$. The symbol R_n then denotes the last *nonvanishing* remainder which is the desired GCD $(M; N)$, M and N denoting the two given numbers. Any division of the chain will be called the j-th division, the variable ordinal integers j having any one of the $n + 1$ values from 1 to $n + 1$: $1 \leqslant j \leqslant n + 1$.

Given two numbers N and $M > N$, to find their GCD we divide the greater number M by the smaller one N, the improper quotient and remainder being Q_1 and R_1, so that

$$M = NQ_1 + R_1$$

because in an improper division the dividend M is equal to the improper quotient Q_1 times the divisor N plus the remainder R_1.

Building the chain of interlocked divisions, we apply the rule that the divisor and remainder of one division become dividend and divisor in the next division. Thus, in the second division, the divisor of the first division, N, becomes the dividend and it is divided by R_1, the remainder of the first division. Denoting the improper quotient and remainder of the second division by Q_2 and R_2 respectively, we obtain

$$N = R_1Q_2 + R_2$$

In the third division R_1 and R_2 become dividend and divisor, so the third division yields the relation

$$R_1 = R_2Q_3 + R_3$$

where the quotient and remainder of the third division are denoted by Q_3 and R_3 respectively. Using the general notation Q_j and R_j for the quotient and remainder of the j-th division, we express the result of the j-th division as follows

(*) $$R_{j-2} = R_{j-1}Q_j + R_j \qquad (1 \leqslant j \leqslant n + 1)$$

where j can assume all the integral values from 1 to $n + 1$.

This formula condenses in one line all the $n + 1$ different relations which may be derived from it by giving to the variable integer j its $n + 1$ values. For the first two values of j, namely $j = 1$ and $j = 2$, it involves the symbols R_{-1} and R_0 which can represent only M and N $(R_{-1} = M; R_0 = N)$ because they denote the dividends of the first two divisions.

Euclid's Algorithm is a finite chain of divisions and there is a last step which is a proper divisions with no remainder. In our notation this is the $(n + 1)$-th division, so that the last quotient Q_{n+1} is a proper quotient and the last remainder R_{n+1} is zero: $R_{n+1} = 0$. Writing down explicitly the relations (*) for $j = 1, 2, 3, ..., n, n + 1$ we obtain:

$$
\begin{array}{ll}
M = NQ_1 + R_1 & j = 1 \\
N = R_1Q_2 + R_2 & j = 2 \\
R_1 = R_2Q_3 + R_3 & j = 3 \\
\quad\quad \cdots & \cdots \\
R_{k-2} = R_{k-1}Q_k + R_k & j = k \\
\quad\quad \cdots & \cdots \\
R_{n-2} = R_{n-1}Q_n + R_n & j = n \\
R_{n-1} = R_nQ_{n+1} + 0 & j = n + 1
\end{array}
\tag{1}
$$

EXAMPLE: Applying the Euclid's algorithm to $M = 39,767$ and $N = 4301$ and writing down for this case the relations (*), we obtain $(n = 3)$:

$$
\begin{array}{rl}
39,767 = & 4301 \cdot 9 \; + 1058 \\
4301 = & 1058 \cdot 4 \; + \quad 69 \\
1058 = & 69 \cdot 15 + \quad 23 \\
69 = & 23 \cdot \; 3 + \quad\; 0
\end{array}
$$

The sequence of remainders is: $R_1 = 1058$; $R_2 = 69$; $R_3 = 23$ and $R_4 = 0$. The last non-vanishing remainder 23 divides each of the others: $69 = 23 \cdot 3$ and $1058 = 23 \cdot 46$. The fact that the first remainder is divisible by the last remainder is a corollary of the law of our inter-locked divisions: $R_3 = 23$ is the remainder in the division of $R_1 = 1058$ by $R_2 = 69$ and the relation $R_1 = R_2Q_3 + R_3$ proves that R_1 is a sum of two terms R_2Q_3 and R_3 each of which is divisible by R_3 since the first factor R_2 of the product R_2Q_3 is a multiple of R_3. We have, indeed, $R_2 = R_3Q_4$.

From this we gather that each one of the successive remainders is divisible by the last remainder. This fact is general and we proceed to prove it in the general case of remainders in (1). The last line namely $R_{n-1} = R_nQ_{n+1}$, shows that R_{n-1} is a multiple of R_n, hence is divisible by R_n. Reading the relations (1) upwards, we examine now the second from the end, namely $R_{n-2} = R_{n-1}Q_n + R_n$. It shows that R_{n-2} is a sum of two terms each of which is divisible by R_n. The first term $R_{n-1}Q_n$ indeed is a product whose first factor R_{n-1} is a multiple of R_n. There-fore, the sum R_{n-2} itself is divisible by R_n. .

At this point we use mathematical induction. Consider the sequence of remainders written in a reverse order

$$R_n, R_{n-1}, R_{n-2}, ..., R_{k+1}, R_k, R_{k-1}, ..., R_3, R_2, R_1 \qquad (R)$$

The divisibility by R_n of the third term R_{n-2} was deduced from that of the first two terms R_n and R_{n-1}. To apply mathematical induction we have to prove that, in general, for any group of three successive terms R_{k+1}, R_k, R_{k-1}, where k is any integer, the divisibility by R_n of two first terms R_{k+1} and R_k entails the same property for the third term R_{k-1}. Suppose that R_{k+1} and R_k are divisible by R_n, then R_{k-1} is a sum of two terms each of which is divisible by R_n because $R_{k-1} = R_k Q_{k+1} + R_{k+1}$. Thus, the transmission of the divisibility by R_n along the sequence (R) is assured. We come to the conclusion that all the terms of the sequence (R), and in particular R_2 and R_1, are divisible by the last non-vanishing remainder R_n.

Examine now in (1) the relation $N = R_1 Q_2 + R_2$. In it each term of the righthand member is divisible by R_n. Therefore, their sum N is also divisible by R_n. Finally, the relation $M = N Q_1 + R_1$ again shows that M is a sum of two terms of which is divisible by R_n since R_1 and N are. Thus, M is divisible by R_n and this completes the proof that the last non-vanishing remainder is a common divisor of M and N.

It remains to prove that R_n is not only a common divisor of M and N, but their *greatest* common divisor. Using the indirect method, we suppose that M and N have another common divisor P which is greater than R_n, $P > R_n$. Any common divisor of M and N is at the same time a divisor of R_1 since (1) for $j = 1$ gives $R_1 = M - N Q_1$. Writing the second ($j = 2$) relation (1) as $R_2 = N - R_1 Q_2$, we conclude further that any common divisor of M and N divides also R_2 since it divides N and R_1. Solving the third relation ($j = 3$) for R_3, we have $R_3 = R_1 - R_2 Q_3$ which shows that P divides R_3 because it divides R_1 and R_2. Thus, the divisibility by P of R_3 is deduced from that of R_1 and R_2.

Wee apply now mathematical induction to the sequence of remainders

(R*) $R_1, R_2, R_3, R_4, ..., R_{k-1}, R_k, R_{k+1}, ..., R_{n-1}, R_n$

first three terms of which are divisible by P. In any group of three successive terms R_{k-1}, R_k, R_{k+1} the third term R_{k+1} is related to the first two terms by

$$R_{k+1} = R_{k-1} - R_k Q_{k+1}$$

so that the divisibility of R_{k-1} and R_k by P entails the same property for the third term R_{k+1}. In other words, this sequence (R*) is characterized by the fact that any common divisor of a pair of two adjacent terms (R_{k-1}, R_k) is also common divisor of the next pair (R_k, R_{k+1}).

Since P by hypothesis divides the first two terms R_1 and R_2, applying the mathematical induction, we conclude that P divides all the terms of the sequence (R*). Thus, if P divides M and N, it necessarily divides R_n. Since P divides R_n, it cannot exceed it and therefore the hypothesis of existence of a common divisor of M and N which is greater than R_n leads to a contradiction. We conclude that R_n is the greatest common divisor of M and N:

$$R_n = \text{GCD}(M; N)$$

Our proof presupposes that the chain of divisions is finite, that there is a last division with no remainder. To prove this point, it is sufficient to observe that the sequence (R*) is a decreasing sequence: any term R_{k+1} is a remainder in a division with the divisor R_k. Since in any division the remainder is always less than the divisor we have $R_{k+1} < R_k$. Thus, the integers R_k verify the system of inequalities

$$R_1 > R_2 > R_3 > \cdots > R_k > R_{k+1} > \cdots > R_n \geqslant 1$$

A sequence of *decreasing* integers cannot be an infinite one: if it begins with R_1, it is plain that there can be at most R_1 successive decreasing integers, and therefore at most $R_1 + 1$ successive divisions in our chain. Euclid's algorithm solves the question of how to reduce a fraction to its lowest terms and therefore we can always suppose that the numerator m and the denominator n of a fraction m/n are relatively prime numbers, that is have no common factor, so that GCD $(m; n) = 1$.

Addition of Rational Numbers

The study of addition includes that of the subtraction because a subtraction $g - h$ is equivalent to the addition of the symmetrical number: $g - h = g + (-h)$. Considering the addition of positive and negative fractions, we have four cases $(+) + (+), (+) + (-), (-) + (+)$ and $(-) + (-)$, where $(+)$ and $(-)$ stand for positive and negative term respectively. But these four cases form only two distinct operations since, picking out (-1) as a common factor, we reduce the last two cases to the first two:

$$(-) + (+) \equiv -[(+) + (-)]; (-) + (-) \quad -[(+) + (+)]$$

Thus, we only have to study the addition of two positive fractions and the addition of a positive and a negative fraction. We begin by viewing this question historically and explaining how the rules for adding fractions were found and justified in the past.

The origin of fractions is different from that of integers. They were not needed in the process of counting and appeared in the history of human thinking as a device for measurements of lengths thousands of years later than the integers. These measurements are based on the choice of a unit of length and this choice is completely arbitrary.

In the universe in which we live, as it is revealed to us in our perceptions and mapped by our science, there may be an absolute unit of length (radius of curvature of the universe, if the universe is finite), but as yet we are not sure of this unit's existence and continue to use arbitrary units of length.

Incidentally, the best one seems to be very old, a remnant of a remarkably advanced civilization which perished many thousands of years ago. This is the "sacred cubit" carved in the Egyptian Great Pyramid and discovered by the famous English astronomer William Hershel at the beginning of nineteenth century. Very recently its length was found to be *exactly* equal to one ten-millionth part of the polar axis of the Earth (that is of the distance between the North and South poles). This fact was proved only recently not because the length of the "sacred cubit" was unknown, but because the measurement of the Earth's polar axis is a difficult enterprise and the precision with which its length was known until 1925 was not sufficient to achieve the comparison.

It is to be noted that the length of the polar axis is the only terrestrial magnitude which can be perfectly defined. The length of a meridian, for example, gives an illusory definition of the unit of length called the meter as representing one forty-millionth of a "meridian", since terrestrial meridians have different lengths and, thus, such a thing as "length of a meridian" does not exist at all. To the contrary, the length of the polar axis is given in our environment as a perfectly determined magnitude and its ten-millionth part defines a length.

It is amazing to find carved in the Great Pyramid of Cheops, built forty-eight centuries ago, a perfect unit of length, a much better unit than those we now use, and this is a meaningful illustration of the fact that great civilizations are perishable and disappear.

Returning to fractions, let us suppose that we want to measure a given length L with the aid of a unit of length chosen arbitrarily but fixed once for all. In general, if we want to count how many times this unit is contained in the length L, we apply the unit n times until we find a remainder whose length l is shorter than our unit, so that we cannot continue.

But the intervals of space and time can be divided, and we believe that we can use arbitrarily fine subdivisions. To measure the length l of the remainder, we divide our unit into a sufficiently great number m of equal parts and try to measure the length l by using them. If we can find such m that there is exactly an integral number p of the m-th parts of our unit in the length l, then we consider the length l as containing p m-th parts of the unit and say that L is measured and is found to contain n units plus p m-th parts of a unit:

$$L = (n + p/m) \text{ units}$$

Here the notation p/m means "p equal parts of the fundamental unit, m such parts forming a unit". Each one of them, called one m-th part of the unit, plays therefore the role of a new, smaller unit. The measurement of L is achieved through the choice of this new sufficiently small unit and through the use of the process of counting units: L contains $nm + p$ new units.

Thus, in the history of mathematics fractions first appeared as collections of units smaller than the original unit and thus were really conceived as integers, the only distinction between integers and fractions being the relative size of the units whose collections they represented.

The fact that the problem of measurement of physical quantities such as lengths, intervals of time, *etc.* can be reduced to the process of counting is based first on the fundamental hypothesis of infinite divisibility of space and time, and second, on the concept of fractions as collections of equal parts of a unit. Later we will see that, even if we assume the infinite divisibility of our units, the choice of an integer m such that the m-th part of a unit is contained exactly an integral number of times in a given length (or any other physical quantity), is *not always possible*. In practice, however, we have to take into account the approximate character of all our measurements which are always affected by unavoidable errors. In actual measurement therefore, we always find some m such that p/m of our unit seems to coincide exactly with the length to be measured.

The parts of a fundamental unit may have special names. Thus, a meter has a hundred *centimeters*; a centimeter, ten *millimeters*; a millimeter, a thousand *microns*; a micron, ten thousands *Angstroms* (an Angstrom is the microscopic unit of length in which physicists express the wavelengths of light. There are 10^8 Angstroms in a centimeter, so that light travels $3 \cdot 10^{18}$ Angstroms in a second).

Now let us add two positive fractions p/m and q/n. Interpreting them as collections of m-th and n-th parts of a unit, we realize that their addition must be prepared for, that they must be converted into collections of the same parts of a unit. In general, addition of two concrete collections is possible only if their members belong to the same category. We cannot, for example, add five inches squared and ten inches cubed, addition of area and volume having no sense at all.

To compare one n-th part with one m-th part of the same unit, it is sufficient to find a new, smaller part of that unit such that it is contained an integral number of times in the n-th as well as in the m-th part of the unit. An easy solution which always works consists of the use of one (nm)-th part which is contained exactly m times in one n-th, and n times in one m-th part of the unit. So, for instance, if $n = 3$, $m = 7$, to compare $1/3$ with $1/7$ we may use $1/21$ and write $1/3 = 7/21$ and $1/7 = 3/21$. But in the case of $1/96$ and $1/30$ it is not necessary to use $1/2\,880$, although $1/96 = 30/2\,880$, and $1/30 = 96/2\,880$, for 96 and 30 have a common factor which is equal to 6, and we can use $1/480$ as a common measure for $1/96$ and $1/30$. Thus, $1/96 = 5/480$, and $1/30 = 16/480$.

The process described above is called *reduction to the common denominator* and we see that there are two different cases. Sometimes the common denominator is simply the product of the denominators of two fractions we want to compare, but sometimes it is smaller. The second case arises when the denominators of two fractions are not relatively prime numbers and have a common factor. In both cases common denominator is the *least common multiple* of the denominators of the two fractions.

Let us now study how the least common multiple 480 of 96 and 30 was found. Decomposing 96 and 30 into prime factors, we have $96 = 32 \cdot 3 = 2^5 \cdot 3$ and $30 = 2 \cdot 3 \cdot 5$. The common multiple must include all the factors of 96 in order to be divisible by 96, and all the factors of 30 to be divisible by 30. The product $2^5 \cdot 3 \cdot 5 = (2^5 \cdot 3)\,5$

$= 2^4(2 \cdot 3 \cdot 5) = 480$ fulfills this condition and thus it is a multiple of 96 and of 30. It is the *least* common multiple of these two numbers, because if we omit any one of its factors, it ceases to be a multiple of *both* 96 and 30.

Denoting the least common multiple of two numbers m and n by LCM $[m; n]$, we have LCM $[96; 30] = 480$. It is less than the product $96 \cdot 30 = 2880$ of 96 and 30 because these two numbers are not relatively prime, their greatest common divisor being equal to 6. We observe that this number $6 = \text{GCD}(96; 30)$ is the product of all *common* factors of 96 and 30; GCD $(96; 30) = 2 \cdot 3 = 6$. Moreover, if we multiply GCD $(96; 30) = 6$ by LCM $[96; 30] = 480$, we obtain 2880 which is the product of two numbers 96 and 30. This fact

$$\text{LCM}[96; 30] \cdot \text{GCD}(96; 30) = 96 \cdot 30$$

is general, and for any two integers m and n we have the same relation

$$\text{LCM}[m; n] \cdot \text{GCD}(m; n) = mn \tag{2}$$

As we have shown, the GCD $(m; n)$ can be found by applying Euclid's algorithm. Hence, to find LCM $[m; n]$ it is sufficient to divide mn by GCD $(m; n)$ since the relation (2) solved for LCM $[m; n]$ gives:

$$\text{LCM}[m; n] = mn/\text{GCD}(m; n)$$

The proof of the relation (2) can be deduced from the fact that the decomposition of a composite number into its prime factors is unique. Denoting for the sake of brevity GCD $(m; n)$ simply by G, we consider the quotients m^* and n^* obtained by dividing m and n respectively by their greatest common divisor G: $m^* = m \div G = m/G$ and $n^* = n \div G = n/G$, so that $m = m^*G$ and $n = n^*G$.

The two integers m^*, n^* cannot have a common factor (except 1), because G, as the greatest common divisor of m and n, is the product of all the common prime factors which can be found in decompositions of m and n. Therefore, m^* and n^* are relatively prime and their greatest common divisor is equal to one: GCD $(m^*; n^*) = 1$.

A multiple of a number, by definition, is a product of this number and of some other integer, so that any multiple of m is of the form km, where k is some integer. Similarly, any multiple of n is of the form rn, where r is some integer. But, $m = m^*G$, $n = n^*G$ and, thus, a number N which is a common multiple of m and n is simultaneously of the form km^*G and of the form rn^*G for some integer k and r. Dividing both members of the equality $km^*G = rn^*G$

by G, we transform it into

$$km^* = rn^*$$

which proves that km^* is a multiple of n^* and must therefore be divisible by n^*. But GCD $(m^*; n^*) = 1$, which means that m^* and n^* have no common factor. Therefore, the integer k must be divisible by n^*, that is k must be a multiple of n^* and, thus, be of the form k^*n^*, where k^* denotes the quotient $k \div n^*$.

On the other hand, the relation $rn^* = km^*$ proves that rn^* is a multiple of m^*, so that the product rn^* must be divisible by m^*. Again GCD $(m^*; n^*) = 1$ and therefore the integer r must be divisible by m^*, since n^* and m^* have no common factor. Thus, r as a multiple of m^* is of the form r^*m^*, where $r^* = r \div m^*$. Substituting these values $k = k^*n^*$ and $r = r^*m^*$ of k and r into the relation $km^* = rn^*$, we obtain $k^*n^*m^* = r^*m^*n^*$, so that $k^* = r^*$ and thus, finally, a common multiple of m and n is necessarily of the form cm^*n^*G, if $m = m^*G$ and $n = n^*G$, the integer c denoting the common value of $k^* = r^* = c$.

Therefore, all common multiples of $m = m^*G$ and $n = n^*G$ are represented by the formula cm^*n^*G, where c denotes an arbitrary integer: $c = 1, 2, 3, 4, ...$ The *least* common multiple, LCM $[m; n]$, corresponds naturally to the least value of this integer c, that is to $c = 1$:

$$\text{LCM } [m; n] = m^*n^*G = mn^* = m^*n$$

Multiplying it by GCD $(m; n) = G$, we form the product

$$\text{LCM } [m; n] \cdot G\text{CD } (m; n) = m^*n^*G \cdot G = m^*G \cdot n^*G = mn$$

and this completes the proof of the relation (2). We add another numerical example of this important relation. Take $m = 30,030 = 2 \cdot 3 \cdot 5 \cdot 7 \cdot 11 \cdot 13$ and $n = 67,890 = 2 \cdot 3 \cdot 5 \cdot 7 \cdot 17 \cdot 19$, so that GCD $(m; n) = G = 2 \cdot 3 \cdot 5 \cdot 7 = 210$, $m^* = m/G = 11 \cdot 13 = 143$ and $n^* = n/G = 17 \cdot 19 = 323$. On the other hand, LCM $[m; n] = m^*n^*G = mn/G = 2 \cdot 3 \cdot 5 \cdot 7 \cdot 11 \cdot 13 \cdot 17 \cdot 19 = 9,699,690$.

Addition and Subtraction

Given two fractions p/m and q/n, we have in general GCD $(m; n) > 1$. Let GCD $(m; n) = G$, then the common denominator d of p/m and q/n is the least common multiple of their denominators m and n:

$$d = \text{LCM } [m; n] = mn^* = m^*n$$

where $m = m^*G$, $n = n^*G$. Thus, reducing the fractions p/m, q/n to their common denominator, we find that $p/m = pn^*/mn^* = pn^*/d$ and $q/n = qm^*/m^*n = qm^*/d$.

To perform now the addition $p/m + q/n$ we need only to add the numerators pn^* and qm^* in the sum $pn^*/d + qm^*/d$ since they express the number of equal parts of the unit which are to be added:

$$p/m + q/n = pm^*/d + qn^*/d = (pn^* + qm^*)/d$$

EXAMPLE: $3/5 + 4/7 = 21/35 + 20/35 = (21 + 20)/35 = 41/35$

In particular, when $G = \mathrm{GCD}\,(m; n) = 1$, that is, when m and n are two relatively prime numbers, we obtain $d = \mathrm{LCM}\,[m; n] = mn$ since in this case $m^* = m$, $n^* = n$. Thus, if $\mathrm{GCD}\,(m; n) = 1$, then $d = mn$ and

$$p/m + q/n = pn/d + qm/d = (pn + qm)/mn$$

The addition of a positive and a negative fraction is performed in the same way. In general, if $q/n > 0$, we have

$$p/m - q/n = pn^*/d - qm^*/d = (pn^* - qm^*)/d$$

and in particular, if $\mathrm{GCD}\,(m; n) = 1$, $p/m - q/n = (pn - qm)/mn$.

EXAMPLE: $3/5 - 4/7 = 21/35 - 20/35 = (21 - 20)/35 = 1/35$

Since G and the common denominator are always positive, the sign of the difference $p/m - q/n$ is that of the expression $(pn^* - qm^*)$. $LG = pn - qm$. Thus, we say that the fraction p/m is greater than, less than or equal to the fraction q/n, according as $pn > qm$, $pn < qm$ or $pn = qm$ respectively:

$$p/m \gtreqless q/n, \text{ if } pn \gtreqless qm$$

The deduction of the rule for adding two fractions

$$p/m \pm q/n = (pn^* \pm qm^*)/d$$

given above represents an example of old mathematical thinking and was studied as such. Nowadays, this rule is deduced from the definition of rational number and is based on the principle of permanency of fundamental laws.

To apply this principle we denote the rational numbers represented by p/m and q/n by g and h respectively: $g = p/m$, $h = q/n$. Therefore, by definition, we have

$$mg = p, \quad nh = q \tag{3}$$

Multiplying these equalities by n and m, we transform them into

$$nmg = np, mnh = mq$$

Adding or subtracting them, we apply the distributive law (principle of permanency of fundamental laws) to terms with *rational* factors g and h:

$$np \pm mq = nmg \pm mnh = (mn)(g \pm h)$$

In the equality $np \pm mq = mn(g \pm h)$ thus obtained the lefthand member is an integer because it is a sum (or difference) of two integers np and mq. The first factor mn of the product $(mn)(g \pm h)$ standing in the righthand member is an integer too, so that the second factor $g \pm h$ may be represented by the ratio of two integers

$$g \pm h = (np \pm mq)/(mn)$$

If m and n have G as their GCD, then $np \pm mq = G(n^*p \pm m^*q)$ as well as $mn = Gd$. Reducing the fraction $(np \pm mq)/(mn) = G(n^*p \pm m^*q)/Gd$ to its lowest terms, we find the general rule

$$g \pm h = p/m \pm q/n = (pn^* \pm qm^*)/d \qquad (4)$$

as a corollary of the definition of rational number.

Multiplication

To find the value of the product gh of two rational numbers $g = p/m$, $h = q/n$ it is sufficient to multiply member by member the two equalities (3):

$$(mg)(nh) = (mn)(gh) = pq$$

so that the product gh of two rational numbers is a rational number too, namely $(pq)/(mn)$:

$$gh = (p/m)(q/n) = (pq)/(mn)$$

EXAMPLE: $(3/5)(4/7) = (3 \cdot 4)/(5 \cdot 7) = 12/35$

Note that the commutative law was used as well as the associative when we wrote $(mg)(nh) = mngh = mgnh = (mn)(gh)$.

Thus, the multiplication of two fractions is performed by multiplying their numerators and denominators separately.

Division

We pass now to the study of division in the field of rational numbers. We have considered the reciprocals of integers and seen that the reciprocal of n, $1/n$, verifies the condition $(1/n)\, n = 1$. Now we define the reciprocal x of a rational number $h = q/n$ by the same condition $hx = 1$. The definition of the rational number h gives $nh = q$, so that we can transform the equation $hx = 1$ into $qx = n$ by multiplying both members by n. We have indeed $nhx = n$ and $nhx = n(hx) = (nh)x = qx$, so that $qx = n$.

But, if $qx = n$, then x is a rational number and $x = n/q$, which means that the reciprocal x of q/n is n/q. This result is consistent with the multiplication rule since indeed $(q/n)\,(n/q) = (qn)/(nq) = 1$.

EXAMPLE: $3/5$ and $5/3$ are two reciprocal numbers: $(3/5)\,(5/3) = 1$.

We state that of two reciprocal numbers one is greater than 1, while the other is less than 1.

Consider now the division of $g = p/m$ by $h = q/n$ and denote the quotient by $Q : Q = g \div h$. When we write $g = p/m$, $h = q/n$ it is assumed that m and n do not vanish: $m \neq 0$, $n \neq 0$. Since the division by zero is meaningless, we must have also $h \neq 0$, that is q cannot vanish either: $q \neq 0$. Finally, we assume $p \neq 0$ because the case $g = 0$ is not interesting at all. Thus, all four integers m, n, p, q are different from zero. They verify the relations (3) and moreover $Q = g \div h$ entails $hQ = g$.

Multiplying both members of this last relation by the product mn, we obtain $mn(hQ) = mng$. But, $mnhQ = mQ(nh) = (mQ)\,q = (mq)Q$ and, on the other hand, $mng = n(mg) = np$, so that we obtain, using (3), the relation $(mq)Q = pn$. This relation shows that the quotient of two rational numbers is also a rational number, namely

$$Q = g \div h = (p/m) \div (q/n) = (pn)/(mq) \tag{5}$$

Furthermore, by definition of multiplication the righthand member can be interpreted as a product:

$$(pn)/(mq) = (p/m)\,(n/q)$$

and we conclude that

$$(p/m) \div (q/n) = (p/m)\,(n/q)$$

Hence we see that the division by q/n is reduced to the multiplication by the reciprocal n/q of the divisor q/n:

Division by any rational number (integers included) is nothing else than multiplication by the reciprocal of the divisor.

EXAMPLE: To divide 2/3 by 5/7, multiply 2/3 by 7/5:

$$(2/3) \div (5/7) = (2/3)(7/5) = (2 \cdot 7)/(3 \cdot 5) = 14/15$$

It is important to emphasize that the introduction of rational numbers (fractions) not only extends the operation of division to all integers, but in fact completely *abolishes* division as an operation, reducing it to multiplication, just as the introduction of negative numbers abolishes subtraction, reducing it to addition.

The rules for operating with fractions were formulated by applying the fundamental laws to rational numbers. It remains to show that with the rules thus construed the rational numbers obey the fundamental laws. Thus, for example, we easily verify that the rational numbers obey the commutative law for addition. By (4) we have on one hand

$$g + h = p/m + q/n = (pn^* + qm^*)/d$$

and, on the other hand,

$$h + g = q/n + p/m = (qm^* + pn^*)/d$$

so that $g + h = h + g$.

Similarly, we may verify the same fact for the distributive law as follows. Given three rational numbers $g = p/m$, $h = q/n$, $k = r/s$, we have

$$k(g + h) = (r/s)\,[(pn + qm)/mn] = r(pn + qm)/(smn)$$

$$= (rpn + rqm)/(smn)$$

while, on the other hand,

$$kg + kh = (r/s)(p/m) + (r/s)(q/n) = rp/sm + rq/sn$$

$$= rpn/smn + rpm/smn$$

so that indeed

$$k(g + h) = (rpn + rqm)/smn = rpn/smn + rqm/smn = kg + kh$$

which expresses the distributive law for rational numbers.

The importance of the principle of permanency for generalization of the number concept is emphasized by the fact that the rules of operating with a new kind of number, here rational numbers, obtained by applying this principle are exactly the same, as those imposed by the use of fractions as the result of measurements.

If, in defining such rules, we disregard the principle of permanency, we destroy the possibility of measuring physical quantities. Suppose, for instance, that the rule of addition is defined arbitrarily by the formula

$$p/m + q/n = (p + n)/(q + m)$$

First of all such a rule breaks the commutative law of addition

$$q/n + p/m = (q + m)/(p + n) \neq (p + n)/(q + m) = p/m + q/n$$

and secondly, it cannot be used for measurement, as may be seen from the particular case $p = 2, m = 4, q = 3, n = 6$. In this case $p/m = q/n = 1/2$ and, applying the false rule of addition, we would obtain many different values for the same sum, namely

$$2/4 + 3/6 = 8/7; 3/6 + 2/4 = 7/8; 1/2 + 1/4 = 5/3;$$

$$2/4 + 1/2 = 4/5, etc.$$

The above example amply illustrates the impossibility of working with such a rule and trying to measure lengths or other physical quantities.

Having stated the rules of operation, we now apply them to the equation

$$ax + b = c$$

where a, b, c are any three given and known rational numbers, and x is the unknown. Subtracting b from both members and dividing by the coefficient a of x, we obtain as the solution for x a rational number too:

$$x = (c - b) \div a = (c - b)/a$$

EXAMPLE: Given the equation $53x/9 - 7/4 = 8/3$, find the value of x. Here $a = 53/9, b = -7/4, c = 8/3$, and thus $x = (8/3 + 7/4) \div (53/9) = (53/12)(9/53) = 9/12 = 3/4$.

Negative Exponents

The operation of exponentiation was defined for positive (natural) integers, but now, having defined negative integers, we can use them as exponents or bases of powers, thus extending the exponentiation to the larger field of positive and negative integers.

To fix the meaning of negative exponents, we must first complete the law of exponentiation $a^m a^n = a^{m+n}$ which concerns the multiplication of powers with the same base and study the division of such powers. Let us form the quotient $a^m \div a^n = a^m/a^n$, where m and n are two positive integers such that $m > n$. Since $m = (m - n) + n$, applying the law, we can write a^m as $a^{m-n+n} = a^{m-n}a^n$, so that the fraction a^m/a^n can be reduced to its lowest terms:

$$a^m \div a^n = a^m/a^n = a^{m-n} \cdot (a^n/a^n) = a^{m-n}/1 = a^{m-n}$$

But $m - n = m + (-n)$, and therefore, applying the principle of permanency, we also obtain

$$a^m/a^n = a^{m-n} = a^{m+(-n)} = a^m a^{-n}$$

On the other hand, we have

$$a^m/a^n = a^m \div a^n = a^m(1/a^n)$$

since $1/a^n$ is reciprocal to a^n and multiplication by $1/a^n$ is equivalent to division by a^n. The relation thus obtained

$$a^m(1/a^n) = a^m a^{-n}$$

proves that there is only one meaning which can be ascribed to the new symbol a^{-n}, and this meaning is $a^{-n} = 1/a^n$.

The same conclusion can be deduced from the law $a^m a^n = a^{m+n}$, if we recall that $a^0 = 1$. Substituting $-m$ instead of n, we obtain immediately

$$a^m a^{-m} = a^{m+(-m)} = a^0 = 1$$

Therefore, $a^{-m} = 1/a^m$, that is *the symbol a^{-m} denotes the reciprocal of a^m*.

EXAMPLES: $4^{-2} = 1/4^2 = 1/16$; $1/3^{-3} = 1 \div (1/3^3) = 3^3 = 27$

As we have shown, any quotient can be transformed into a product since a division, say by q as for instance $p \div q$, is equivalent to the multiplication by the reciprocal $1/q$ of q. Using the negative exponent, we write now this reciprocal $1/q$ as q^{-1}, so that finally

$$p \div q = pq^{-1}$$

This relation is useful in the study of the question how to raise a rational number to a power. Consider $(p/q)^m$ and substitute pq^{-1} instead of p/q:

$$(p/q)^m = (pq^{-1})^m = p^m(q^{-1})^m = p^m q^{-m} = p^m(1/q^m) = p^m/q^m$$

Hence, to raise a fraction to a power it is sufficient to raise to the same power the numerator and the denominator separately. We postpone the study of powers with rational (fractional) exponents to Chapter 4.

Let us consider now a power with negative base, say $(-N)^m$ with $N > 0$. The negative base $-N$ can be considered as a product $(-1)N$ and the law of exponentiation gives $(-N)^m = (-1)^m N^m$, so that it is sufficient to study the powers $(-1)^m$ of the negative unit. When the integral exponent m is even, $m = 2k$, then the value of $(-1)^m$ is plus one since $(-1)^{2k} = [(-1)^2]^k = 1^k = 1$. But if m is odd, $m = 2k + 1$, then the value of $(-1)^m = (-1)^{2k+1}$ is minus one because $(-1)^{2k+1} = (-1)^{2k}(-1) = 1 \cdot (-1) = -1$. Therefore, $(-N)^m = \pm N^m$, where the plus sign corresponds to even exponent $m = 2k$ and minus sign to odd exponent $m = 2k + 1$, k being any integer.

Combining the negative base and the negative exponent, we have

$$(-N)^{-m} = (-1)^m N^{-m} = (-1)^m/N^m - \pm 1/N^m \ (N > 0, m > 0)$$

because

$$(-1)^{-m} = 1/(-1)^m = (-1)^m/(-1)^{2m} = (-1)^m = \pm 1$$

EXAMPLE: $(-5)^{-3} = (-1)^3/5^3 = -1/125 = -0.008$

Decimal Fractions

We shall describe now an important extension of the decimal system of numeration the purpose of which is to represent rational numbers. Observe that $10^{-1} = 1/10$, $10^{-2} = 1/100$, $10^{-3} = 1/1000$, etc. and compare this with the fact that in our decimal numeration the value of a digit decreases ten times, if this digit is shifted one position to the right. So 50 becomes 5 when the digit 5 is shifted one position to the right.

We ask now what happens, if we shift the digit of the *first* rank to the right? To characterize the new position thus created, we must use a dot between it and the simple units. Thus, shifting 1 to the right, we obtain 0.1. The symbol 0.1 means 1/10 of the unit since the value of 1 was diminished ten times by shifting it one position to the right. Thus, 31.5 denotes the sum of 31 units plus 5/10 of the unit: $31.5 = 31 + 0.5 = 31 + 5/10$.

In exactly the same way we obtain an infinite sequence of new positions to the right of the dot, which correspond to all negative powers of 10: $10^{-1} = 1/10 = 0.1$, $10^{-2} = 1/100 = 0.01$, $10^{-3} = 1/1000 = 0.001$, *etc.* and in general, for any integral and negative exponent $--n$ (with $n > 0$),

$$10^{-n} = 1/10^n = 1/\underbrace{100 \cdots 00}_{n \text{ zeros}} = 0.\underbrace{00 \cdots 001}_{n \text{ zeros}}$$

It is a very important fact that this sequence of negative powers of 10 is an *infinite* sequence: n can take all integral values and therefore the decimal system of numeration extends towards the right *without limit*.

Introducing the positions to the right of the position occupied by simple units (units of the first rank), we have achieved an important step which extends decimal numeration to include decimal *fractions*. The number 1073.573, for instance, is an abbreviation for

$$1 \cdot 10^3 + 0 \cdot 10^2 + 7 \cdot 10^1 + 3 \cdot 10^0 + 5 \cdot 10^{-1} + 7 \cdot 10^{-2} + 3 \cdot 10^{-3}$$

and this symbol represents the sum of the integer 1073 plus the *decimal fraction* $0.573 = 573/1000$.

Decimal fractions, when written as ordinary fractions, have as denominators positive integral powers of 10. Conversely, any ordinary fraction (rational number) whose denominator is of the form 10^n, $n > 0$, is a decimal fraction. Thus,

$$2013/1,000,000 = 0.002013$$

since $1,000,000 = 10^6$ and $2013 = 2 \cdot 10^3 + 0 \cdot 10^2 + 1 \cdot 10^1 + 3 \cdot 10^0$, so that $2013/10^6 = 2 \cdot 10^{-3} + 0 \cdot 10^{-4} + 1 \cdot 10^{-5} + 3 \cdot 10^{-6}$.

The digits 2, 0, 1, 3 occupy the third, fourth, fifth, and sixth positions to the right of the dot, respectively. Since there are no significant digits for the first and second positions to the right of the dot, we use zeros in these two positions, completing the decimal notation of $2013/10^6$ by the two terms $0 \cdot 10^{-1}$ and $0 \cdot 10^{-2}$.

The extension of decimal numeration to the right is due to François Viète who introduced it in 1579. It raises many problems which are studied in the next chapter. For the moment, we note that decimal fractions are obtained using negative exponents with the base 10. Therefore analogues of decimal fractions can be formed in any system of numeration, using the powers of any given base with negative exponents. Thus, in the binary system of numeration with the base 2, the number $(10,101.0111)_2$ means

$$1 \cdot 2^4 + 1 \cdot 2^2 + 1 \cdot 2^0 + 1 \cdot 2^{-2} + 1 \cdot 2^{-3} + 1 \cdot 2^{-4}$$

$$= 16 + 4 + 1 + 1/4 + 1/8 + 1/16$$

This number when written in our system of numeration is equal to $21.4375 = 343/16$. The denominator $16 = 2^4$ is a power of 2 and, transforming any analogue of a decimal fraction in the binary system of numeration (any *binary fraction*) into an ordinary fraction we always obtain a power of the base 2 in the denominator. Since $10 = 2 \cdot 5$, multiplying both numerator and denominator of the fraction $343/16$ by $5^4 = 625$, we transform it into a decimal fraction and thus establish the equality

$$(10,101.0111)_2 = 21.4375$$

Number-Axis

Any rational number m/n can be represented on the number-axis by a point whose distance from the origin is equal to the absolute value $|m/n|$ of this number. The point is located to the right of the origin 0, if m/n is positive, and to the left, if m/n is negative. This statement is a corollary of the infinite divisibility of space.

To find the point-image of m/n we first divide the unit of length into n equal parts of length $1/n$, and then count m such parts in the appropriate direction, beginning at the origin 0. Thus P is the point-image of $33/7$, the distance OP being equal to $4 + 5/7$ units of length, (fig. 3.1).

The question now arises of how the point-images of all rational numbers are distributed on the number axis? To answer this question it is sufficient to consider only one interval of unit length between any two

consecutive integers such as the interval (0,1) between the origin 0 and
the image of 1. Any other interval $(n, n + 1)$, where n denotes any
integer (positive or negative), is similar to (0,1) with respect to the distribution of rational points. Any rational number between n and $n + 1$
indeed can be represented as $n + p/q$, its fractional part p/q being positive and less than one: $0 < p/q < 1$. Therefore, if we shift the interval

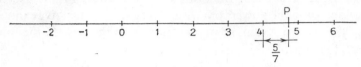

Fig. 3.1

$(n, n + 1)$ n units and thus bring it into coincidence with the interval
(0, 1), the point-image of the rational number $n + p/q$ will coincide with
that of the pure fraction p/q in the interval (0, 1). We conclude that the
distributions of rational points in the intervals $(n, n + 1)$ and (0, 1) are
identical. Here we call a "rational point" the point-image of a rational
number.

Now there are an infinite number of rational points between any
two rational points in (0, 1). To prove this let us consider two different
rational points A and B in (0, 1) which are the images of two unequal
rational numbers p/q and m/n, so that $\mathbf{OA} = p/q < 1, \mathbf{OB} = m/n < 1$:

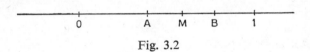

Fig. 3.2

Denoting by M the midpoint of the interval $\mathbf{AB}$, we shall prove that the
distance $\mathbf{OM}$ is measured again by a rational number. We have $\mathbf{OA}$
$= \mathbf{OM} - \mathbf{AM}$ and $\mathbf{OB} = \mathbf{OM} + \mathbf{MB}$, as well as $\mathbf{AM} = \mathbf{MB}$. Adding
$\mathbf{OA}$ and $\mathbf{OB}$, we obtain

$$\mathbf{OA} + \mathbf{OB} = 2 \cdot \mathbf{OM} + (\mathbf{MB} - \mathbf{AM}) = 2 \cdot \mathbf{OM}$$

since $\mathbf{MB} - \mathbf{AM} = 0$. Thus

$$\mathbf{OM} = (\mathbf{OA} + \mathbf{OB})/2 = (p/q + m/n)/2 = (pn + qm)/(2nq)$$

where m, n, p, q are integers. Therefore, both terms of the ratio expressing $\mathbf{OM}$ are integers too and *the midpoint of an interval with rational
extremities is rational also.*

In other words: between any two rational numbers there is always at least a third rational number at an equal distance from each of them. This dichotomy (division into two equal parts) can be repeated. Applying it to both half-intervals AM and MB, we obtain two more rational points, one between A and M and another between M and B. The dichotomy of an interval between two rational numbers always produces a rational number. Since we can repeat this indefinitely (note the postulate of infinite divisibility of space), we come to the conclusion that there are an infinite number of rational numbers between any two rational numbers p/q and m/n. We express this property of rational numbers by saying that the *rational points are everywhere dense on the number-axis.*

This geometric picture of the distribution of rational numbers is based, as is the infinite divisibility of space, on the assumption that a "point" has no length. If it were otherwise, a point having a length, an infinite length would correspond to the infinite number of rational points in $(0, 1)$, which is impossible the length of the interval $(0,1)$ being manifestly finite and equal to one.

It is important to note that space and time—contrary to matter and energy (light, electricity), which are known to be discrete, that is composed of last non-vanishing elements—are conceived as continuous, notwithstanding the idea that the element of space, the point, has no length and the element of time, the instant, has no duration.

There are protons, electrons, and quanta which are considered as final elements of matter, light, electricity and energy and which—as they are revealed to us in our perceptions—though microscopic in the human scale, are nevertheless of a definite and fixed, non-vanishing magnitude.

But the elements of space and time, the point and the instant, have no extension (length, duration), no magnitude at all. Space and time do not possess discrete atomic structure which characterizes physical environment, object of our perceptions. This continuity of space and time which entails—as we shall see later—important corollaries for mathematical thinking, is another intuitive element in the foundations of geometry and the theory of motion to which nothing in our experience corresponds.

On the other hand, space and time could not play their fundamental role of that frame of reference with respect to which we localize matter and energy, would they lack continuity. Thus, the continuity of space and time appears as their necessary attribute which allows the human mind to build up a synthesis of all perceptions, to weld together all discrete manifestations of discontinuous matter and energy into a coherent and unified picture of the universe around us.

We saw that the totality of rational numbers forms an infinite collection. Integers are a part of this collection because our definition of rational number $h = p/q$, namely $hq = p$ (where p and q are integers and $q \neq 0$), includes the integers as a special case when $q = 1$. For example, the integer 5 is also equal to $5/1$ and belongs therefore to rational numbers.

Is the infinity of all rational numbers, integers and fractions, the same as that of integers only? In other words, are the rational numbers denumerable? The answer is yes, and to prove this we shall establish a one-to-one correspondence between the totality of all positive fractions and the set of natural numbers $1, 2, 3, \ldots, n, n + 1, \ldots$

To bring the two infinite sets into one-to-one correspondence, it is sufficient to order the totality of all rational numbers, ascribing to each rational number its numerical order and thus arranging them in a well ordered sequence.

The sequence of integers $1, 2, 3, 4, \ldots$ is ordered in the sense of increasing magnitudes: $1 < 2 < 3 < 4 \cdots$ This can be done, since between N and $N + 1$ there is no other integer: with every given integer N we can associate one and only one other, greater integer $N + 1$, such that it is the *least* integer among all the integers greater than N. With respect to a given rational number p/q we can also classify all other rational numbers in two mutually exclusive categories: there are rationals which exceed p/q and there are rationals which are smaller than p/q. But we can find neither the *least* rational number among all rationals greater than p/q nor the *largest* among all rationals smaller than p/q. This impossibility is a corollary of the fact that between any two rational numbers, there is an infinity of other rational numbers.

Therefore the ordering of all rational numbers cannot be performed in the sense of increasing magnitude, but this does not stop us. All that we want to establish is the existence of a one-to-one correspondence between all the rationals and all the integers. In such a correspondence the set of integers is ordered in the sense of increasing magnitude, but the set of rational numbers is necessarily ordered without considering their relative values.

An ordering of all rational numbers can be performed in many different ways. Here is one of them. First we group together all rationals m/n such that for each one of them, the sum $m + n =$ numerator plus denominator is equal to the same fixed number. For example, the fractions 1/5, 2/4, 3/3, 4/2 and 5/1 form a group for which $m + n = 6$. The sum $N = m + n$ varies from 2 to infinity, $N \geqslant 2$ running through all integers, and we denote by G_N the group for which the sum $m + n$ is equal to N. Thus, in G_2 there is only one term 1/1; in G_3 two terms, 1/2 and 2/1; and so on. In general G_{N+1} includes N terms:

$$1/N, 2/(N - 1), 3/(N - 2), \ldots , (N - 2)/3, (N - 1)/2, N/1$$

and the ordering of terms *within each group* is done in the sense of increasing magnitude (increasing numerators). Ordering now the groups G_N in the sense of increasing N, we obtain an ordered sequence of all rational numbers (positive):

$$1/1 \, ; 1/2, 2/1 \, ; 1/3, 2/2, 3/1 \, ; 1/4, 2/3, 3/2, 4/1 \, ; 1/5, 2/4, 3/3, 4/2 \text{ etc.}$$

Given any rational number m/n, let N_{mn} represent the ordinal number which expresses the order of m/n in this sequence. To express N_{mn} in terms of m and n we observe that m/n belongs to the group G_{m+n} and is the m-th term in this group. Hence $N_{mn} = S + m$, where S represents the number of terms which precede the first term of G_{m+n}. Thus, the number S is equal to the sum of terms in G_2, G_3, ..., G_{m+n-1}, that is $S = 1 + 2 + 3 + 4 + \cdots + (m + n - 2)$.

To compute S we recall that the value S_k of the sum of the first k integers is $k(k + 1)/2$, as was shown in Chapter 1:

$$S_k = 1 + 2 + 3 + 4 + \cdots + (k - 1) + k = k(k + 1)/2$$

Therefore, S as the sum of the first $(m + n - 2)$ integers is equal to

$$S = S_{m+n-2} = (m + n - 2)(m + n - 1)/2$$

and the other of m/n is then:

$$N_{mn} = (m + n - 2)(m + n - 1)/2 + m$$

For example, the fraction 7/19 with $m = 7$, $n = 19$ occupies in our sequence the 307-th place, since $m + n - 2 = 24$, $m + n - 1 = 25$ and thus $N_{7;16} = 307$.

To each rational number, therefore, there corresponds one and only one integer N_{mn}, denoting its order, and inversely to each integer there is one and only one perfectly defined rational number whose order is expressed by this integer. Therefore, the totality of rational positive numbers is countable or denumerable. Here again we come across the characteristic property of infinite collections: the set of integers is only a part of the set of rational numbers, but there are as many integers as there are rational numbers.

The point-images of integers as marked on the number-axis are separated from one another by intervals of unit length. If we limit the concept of number to integers only, we can find no numbers which correspond to the points interior to these intervals.

It may seem, at first glance, that now that we have defined rational numbers and introduced an infinite set of rational points on the number-axis which is everywhere dense on this straight line, we have exhausted all points of the line. It may seem that for any point on the line its distance from the origin could now be expressed by a rational number of the general type m/n.

Such a conclusion would be wrong, and we will see later that all rational points do not exhaust, do not fill up the line, that there are other points on the line whose distances to the origin O cannot be expressed by ratios of the type m/n. These points, which are not rational—they are called *irrational*, which means precisely "not rational"—also form an infinite set. They are infinitely more frequent on the line than the rational points. As we will see in Chapter 4, the intuitive assumption that point has no length carries with it as a logical corollary the astonising conclusion that all the rational points of the infinite line, if tightly compressed after the expulsion of irrational points, would not even form a length.

The continuous character of the straight line, which finds its tangible expression in the concept of length, is due therefore uniquely to the existence on the line of irrational points which fill all the lengthless gaps between rational points, forming the continuous line and giving to any segment its property of having a length.

There is another useful geometric representation of rationals based on the idea of the system of coordinates in the plane. To locate a point P on a straight line (number-axis) it is sufficient to give its distance from the origin O and prefix a plus sign if the point is to the right of O, and a minus sign—if it is to the left of O. Such an oriented distance **OP** is called the *abcissa* of the point P. The positive or negative number expressing the abscissa is denoted by x and called x-coordinate of P. The use of one of the last letters x, y, z always stresses the *variable* character of the denoted quantity, and here the abscissa x varies from minus infinity to plus infinity as the point P describes the infinite straight line moving from left to right.

But to locate a point M in the plane we need two coordinates measured on two number-axes which we call OX and OY. Both axes pass through the origin O and in the special coordinate system which we shall use, they are perpendicular to each other.

Given a point M, we draw two straight lines through M parallel to OX and OY respectively: $MP//OY$ and $MQ//OX$. The two intersection

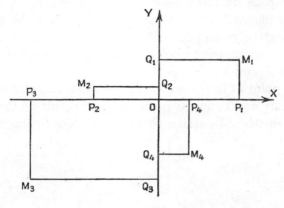

Fig. 3.3

points P (on OX) and Q (on OY), are called projections of the point M on the lines OX and OY respectively. The coordinate $x = \mathsf{OP}$ of P and the coordinate $y = OQ$ of Q are considered as coordinates (x, y) of the point M in the plane XOY. The second number axis OY is oriented upwards, so that $y = \mathsf{OQ}$ is positive when Q is above O, and negative when Q is below O.

The coordinate axes OX, OY divide the plane into four *quadrants* (Fig. 3.3). The subscripts 1, 2, 3, 4 of points M correspond to quadrants, so that M_3 for instance belongs to the third quadrant. The locations of points P and Q with respect to the origin O show that the different quadrants are characterized by various combinations of signs of x and y: in the first quadrant both, x and y, are positive; in the second quadrant x is negative, but y remains positive; in the third quadrant both coordinattes are negative and, finally, in the fourth quadrant x is positive and y negative.

This system of coordinates was invented by the French mathematician

Descartes (in 1637). It is called a rectangular coordinate system because the two axes are perpendicular to each other. The introduction in geometry of numbers as coordinates of points was one of the most important and decisive steps in the evolution of mathematics. Descartes, in his system of coordinates created a bridge between numbers and figures, between algebra and geometry, and this bridge, now called analytic geometry, is one of the foundations of pure and applied mathematics.

The system of plane coordinates (x, y) can be extended to three-dimensional space by using as a frame of reference three mutually perpendicular planes XOY, YOZ, ZOX which divide the whole space into eight *octants* (trirectangular trihedral angles). These three coordinate planes intersect along three coordinate-axes OX, OY, OZ oriented as shown on the figure.

Given any point M in space (see fig. 3.4 where M belongs to the first octant), we may now define its position by constructing three planes I, II, III through M and parallel to the three coordinate-planes XOY,

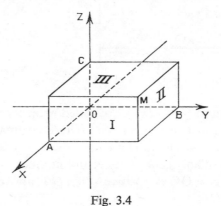

Fig. 3.4

YOZ, ZOX and by marking on OX, OY, OZ the points A, B, C where these planes I, II, III intersect the three coordinate-axes. The position of A on the number-axis OX is characterized by its coordinate $x = \text{OA}$ which at the same time is considered as the first coordinate of the point M. Likewise, we define $y = \text{OB}$ and $z = \text{OC}$ as the second and the third coordinates of the point M. Therefore, the location of M in space is fully characterized by the triplet (x, y, z).

Conversely, given a triplet of numbers (a, b, c), one and only one point in space corresponds to it, since the three planes passing through the points A, B, C on axes OX, OY, OZ such that $\mathsf{OA} = a$, $\mathsf{OB} = b$, $\mathsf{OC} = c$ and perpendicular to them intersect in one and only one point M.

The further development of the same idea is of fundamental importance in modern physics: an event is localized in the four-dimensional universe (space plus time) by its four coordinates (x, y, z, t). The first three among them indicate the point of space, *where* the event took place, and the fourth, t, denotes the moment in time, *when* the event happened.

In the geometric representation of rational numbers which we want to describe, the numerator m and the denominator n of a fraction m/n are interpreted as cartesian coordinates $y = m$ and $x = n$ of a point in the plane XOY, so that one and only one point corresponds to each fraction and *vice versa*. The terms m, n of a fraction are integers and therefore only points with integral coordinates correspond in this picture to rational numbers.

Though to each point with integral coordinates there corresponds one and only one rational number, an infinite sequence of points corresponds to every rational number. We know indeed that to each rational number there corresponds an infinite sequence of fractions, whose common value is equal to this number. Thus, m and n being relatively prime integers, we have

$$m/n = (-m)/(-n) = \pm 2m/(\pm 2n) = \pm 3m/(\pm 3n = \cdots$$

$$= \pm km/(\pm kn) = \cdots \tag{6}$$

If a straight line through the origin O meets one of the point images of the rational number (6) represented by the sequence of equal fractions, it meets all of them. In fig. 3.5 the rational number, equal to the common value of all fractions corresponding to points marked on a line, expresses the common ratio of two sides of all similar triangles with parallel sides which are drawn by dropping perpendiculars from the points to the OX axis.

So, for instance, all the points marked on the line HOK represent the different fractions having the common value $1/2$, and this rational number $1/2$ is the common ratio of the vertical side y to the horizontal side x of all similar triangles.

The operation of reducing a positive fraction to its lowest terms corresponds in this picture to the replacement of a point marked on a line through the third and the first quadrants by the point on that line nearest the origin O and in the first quadrant. Thus, on all lines such as GOL, HOK, SOT only their first points, those nearest the origin O and in the first quadrant, represent fractions reduced to their lowest terms.

Again, the point images of fractions (6) with $m = 3$, $n = 5$ are all located on the straight line SOT and represent different fractions all of

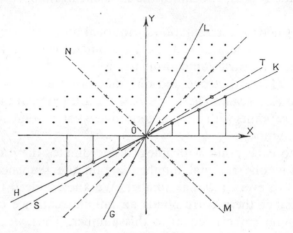

Fig. 3.5

which have the same value 3/5. Therefore, it is more natural to associate the rational number 3/5 with the *position* of the line SOT rather than with any particular point on the line SOT. Thus, the common value 3/5 of fractions corresponding to points marked on the line SOT, is the measure of the inclination of this line with respect to the axis of reference OX, and as such it is called the *slope* of the straight line. Likewise, the slopes of the lines HOK and GOL are equal to 1/2 and 2 respectively, while the slope of NOM is negative and equal to -1.

The sign of the slope is plus, if the line belongs to the first and third quadrant, and minus, if the line passes through the second and fourth quadrants. By definition of the slope concept two parallel lines have equal slope, so to fix the slope of a line which does not pass through the origin O, a parallel to it through O can be drawn.

An interesting question now arises: Are there lines through O that do not pass through a single point-image of rational numbers? We will see in Chapter 4 that the answer is yes, and it means that, although the slopes of many lines are represented by fractions. The slopes of *all* lines through O cannot be expressed as rational numbers.

Continued Fractions

Rational numbers can also be represented by continued fractions, and we proceed to define and describe them. An ordinary fraction m/n is the result of a division. A chain of interlocked divisions, as for instance Euclid's algorithm, generates a chain of interlocked fractions. Such chains of fractions are called *continued fractions*, and they play an important role in mathematics.

Let us first study a numerical example. Applying Euclid's algorithm to the numbers 1393 and 972, we obtain a chain of divisions:

$$\begin{aligned}
1393 &= 1 \cdot 972 + 421 & 130 &= 4 \cdot 31 + 6 \\
972 &= 2 \cdot 421 + 130 & 31 &= 5 \cdot 6 + 1 \\
421 &= 3 \cdot 130 + 31 & 6 &= 6 \cdot 1 + 0
\end{aligned} \qquad (7)$$

which incidentally proves that the numbers 1393 and 972 are relatively prime, their greatest common divisor being equal to one. Reading (7) upwards, the second line from the end is $31 = 5 \cdot 6 + 1$. Dividing both members of this equality by the improper quotient 6, we obtain

$$31/6 = 5 + 1/6$$

Taking now the reciprocals of both members, we get a continued fraction with two links only:

$$6/31 = 1/(5 + 1/6) = \tfrac{1}{5} + 1/_6$$

Now take the third line from the end $130 = 4 \cdot 31 + 6$, divide both sides by 31, and again invert, taking the reciprocals. This gives

$$31/130 = 1/(4 + 6/31) = \tfrac{1}{4} + 6/_{31}$$

which includes the fraction 6/31 obtained in the first operation. Replacing 6/31 by its representation as continued fraction, we obtain for 31/130 a continued fraction with three links:

$$31/130 = \tfrac{1}{4} + \tfrac{1}{5} + 1/_6$$

We continue, applying the same operations to the remaining three lines in (7). The final result is a new representation of the rational number 972/1393 by a continued fraction with six links:

$$972/1393 = \frac{1}{1} + \frac{1}{2} + \frac{1}{3} + \frac{1}{4} + \frac{1}{5} + \frac{1}{6}$$

We see that Euclid's algorithm not only allows us to find the greatest common divisor of two given integers, but at the same time generates a finite continued fraction which involves the sequence of improper quotients and represents the ratio of these two integers. The improper quotients (in our example 1, 2, 3, 4, 5, 6) are called denominators of the continued fraction, and the sequence of ones (which are always obtained, if the continued fraction is derived by Euclid's algorithm) is the sequence of its numerators.

Suppose now that a finite continued fraction is given, and its value is asked. The computation must begin at the end of the fraction and we will order the links by reading the continued fraction from the end upwards. Thus, in our case we begin by adding the first link 1/6 to the denominator 5 of the second link: $5 + 1/6 = 31/6$. Therefore, the first two links represent $1/(31/6) = 6/31$, and the third link now can be written as $1/(4 + 6/31)$. Adding the two terms of the denominator, $4 + 6/31 = 130/31$, and taking the reciprocal, we obtain the value of the first three links:

$$\frac{1}{4} + \frac{1}{5} + \frac{1}{6} = 31/130$$

Passing to the fourth link which is now $1/(3 + 31/130) = 1/(421/130) = 130/421$, we use its value 130/421 in the denominator of the fifth link and get $1/(2 + 130/421) = 1/(972/421) = 421/972$. The value of the continued fraction is finally obtained:

$$1/(1 + 421/972) = 1/(1393/972) = 972/1393 \qquad (8)$$

Successive Convergents

In general, a continued fraction may have numerators other than one. Let us consider two finite sequences of positive numbers: sequence (A) of numerators $a_1, a_2, a_3, \ldots, a_n$ and a sequence (B) of denominators $b_1, b_2, b_3, \ldots, b_n$. They must have the same number n of terms, but are otherwise arbitrary. We call a continued fraction the expression

$$W = a_1 \,|/|\, b_1 + a_2 \,|/|\, b_2 + a_3 \,|/|\, b_3 + \cdots a_n \,|/|\, b_n \qquad (9)$$

where the vertical bars are used to distinguish a continued fraction from the sum of n ordinary fractions of the type a_k/b_k. If the sequences (A), (B) are known, the value W of the continued fraction (9) can be computed in the same way as was of our numerical example (8).

But there is another, better way for finding the value W of (9). It consists in the formation of a sequence of n ordinary fractions

$$P_1/Q_1, \, P_2/Q_2, \, P_3/Q_3 \cdots, \, P_n/Q_n \qquad (10)$$

called *successive convergents* of the continued fraction (9). These convergents represent the values of different continued fractions which are sections of the given fraction (9), the k-th section with the value P_k/Q_k being defined as the aggregate of k links beginning with a_1/b_1 up to and including a_k/b_k:

$$P_k Q_k = a_1 \,|/|\, b_1 + a_2 \,|/|\, b_2 + \cdots a_k \,|/|\, b_k = a_1/b_1 + a_2/b_2 + a_3/b_3 + \cdots /b_k$$

All the n convergents are represented by this formula, the subscript k taking the values 1, 2, 3, 4, $\ldots$ $(n - 1)$, n. The last convergent P_n/Q_n is identical with the continued fraction (9), so that $W = P_n/Q_n$. The terms of the sequence (10), read from left to right, approach the last term, so that the absolute value $|P_k/Q_k - W|$ of the difference $P_k/Q_k - W$ between the k-th convergent and W decreases as k increases, and vanishes when k reaches n. We describe the behaviour of the absolute value of the difference $P_k/Q_k - W$ because this difference changes its sign when k varies, oscillating about zero.

There would be no advantage in using the sequence (10), if its terms had to be computed directly, but they can and must be computed by recurrence: in any group of three successive convergents

$$P_{k-1}/Q_{k-1}, \, P_k/Q_k, \, P_{k+1}/Q_{k+1}$$

their numerations and denominators satisfy the same recurrence relation:

$$P_{k+1} = P_k b_{k+1} + P_{k-1} a_{k+1} \qquad Q_{k+1} = Q_k b_{k+1} + Q_{k-1} a_{k+1} \qquad (11)$$

This important relation (11) enables us to compute the elements P_{k+1} and Q_{k+1} of a convergent, if the elements $P_{k-1}, Q_{k-1}, P_{\kappa}, Q_{k}$ are known. Thus, the computation of the value W of (9) can be done in the following way: we have $P_1/Q_1 = a_1/b_1$ and $P_2/Q_2 = a_1/(b_1 + a_2/b_2)$ by definition. Therefore, we know the first two convergents and obtain P_1, P_2 and Q_1, Q_2:

$$P_1 = a_1, Q_1 = b_1, P_2 = a_1 b_2, Q_2 = b_1 b_2 + a_2$$

Thus, the first two terms of sequences (P_k) and (Q_k) are computed directly. But P_3 and Q_3 are deduced from them with the aid of (11). Knowing P_2, P_3 and Q_2, Q_3 we again apply (11) and obtain P_4, Q_4 and so on until we reach P_n and Q_n. Having computed P_n and Q_n by recurrence, we know the value $W = P_n/Q_n$ of (9).

To illustrate the general procedure just described let us take up again our continued fraction for 972/1393. In this example $n = 6$ and $a_k = 1, b_k = k$ for all six values of $k = 1, 2, 3, 4, 5, 6$. The first two convergents are 1/1 and 2/3, so that $P_1 = a_1 = 1, Q_1 = b_1 = 1$, $P_2 = a_1 b_2 = 2$ and $Q_2 = b_1 b_2 + a_2 = 3$. Now (11) gives us successively:

$$P_3 = b_3 P_2 + a_3 P_1 = 3 \cdot 2 + 1 \cdot 1 = 7$$
$$Q_3 = b_3 Q_2 + a_3 Q_1 = 3 \cdot 3 + 1 \cdot 1 = 10$$
$$P_4 = b_4 P_3 + a_4 P_2 = 5 \cdot 7 + 1 \cdot 2 = 30$$
$$Q_4 = b_4 Q_3 + a_4 Q_2 = 4 \cdot 10 + 1 \cdot 3 = 43$$
$$P_5 = b_5 P_4 + a_5 P_3 = 5 \cdot 30 + 1 \cdot 7 = 157$$
$$Q_5 = b_5 Q_4 + a_5 Q_3 = 5 \cdot 43 + 1 \cdot 10 = 225$$
$$P_6 = b_6 P_5 + a_6 P_4 = 6 \cdot 157 + 1 \cdot 30 = 972$$
$$Q_6 = b_6 Q_5 + a_6 Q_4 = 6 \cdot 225 + 1 \cdot 43 = 1393$$

The final result of this computation P_6/Q_6 coincides with the value $W = 972/1393$ obtained by direct computation. This recurrent procedure is not only simple to perform, but also it has important applications in all questions of pure mathematics, where finite or infinite continued fractions are used.

Given any ordinary fraction m/n, we can expand it into a continued fraction with the aid of Euclid's algorithm. On the other hand, given a finite continued fraction, all the terms P_k, Q_k of its successive convergents are integers and therefore its value, found with the aid of a recurrent procedure based on the relations (11), is a rational number. Thus, we come to the conclusion: *Any rational number can be expressed in the form of a finite continued fraction with integral terms and, inversely, any finite continued fraction with integral terms represents a rational number.*

Reverting to the continued fraction

$$972/1393 = 1/1 + 1/2 + 1/3 + 1/4 + 1/5 + 1/6$$

we form the sequence of its six convergents, denoting the value of the k-th convergent by V_k:

$$V_1 = 1, \ V_2 = 2/3, \ V_3 = 7/10, \ V_4 = 30/40, \ V_5 = 157/225,$$

$$V_6 = 972/1393$$

First, we find the inequalities $V_1 > V_3 > V_5$ which mean that the sequence of convergents of *odd order* is a *decreasing* sequence. On the other hand, we have $V_2 < V_4 < V_6$, so that the sequence of convergents of *even order* is an *increasing* sequence. Moreover, $V_5 > V_6$ since $157 \cdot 1393 - 225 \cdot 972 = 218{,}701 - 218{,}700 = 1$. Therefore, if we plot on the number-axis the point-images of all six convergents V_1 through V_6 (the figure represents only the order of the points, and is out of scale),

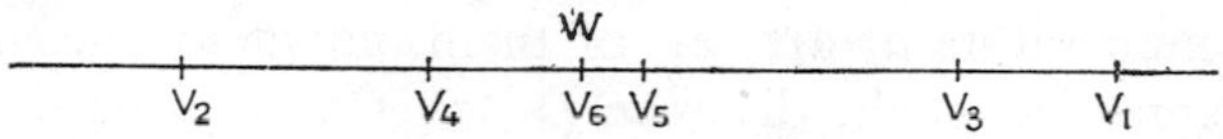

Fig 3.6

we observe a peculiar phenomenon: the convergents approach their ultimate value $W = V_6$ alternately from both sides. This phenomenon is general, and it characterizes the way in which the convergents of any finite (or infinite) continued fraction (9) with $a_k > 0$, $b_k > 0$ approach its value (represented, in the case of a finite continued fraction, by the last convergent).

It is easy to show that the distance D_k between the point-images of two consecutive convergents P_k/Q_k and P_{k+1}/Q_{k+1} decreases when k increases. This distance D_k is equal to the absolute value of the difference $P_k/Q_k - P_{k+1}/Q_{k+1}$

$$D_k = |P_{k+1}/Q_{k+1} - P_k/Q_k| = |P_{k+1}Q_k - P_kQ_{k+1}|/Q_kQ_{k+1}$$

On the other hand, relations (11) entail

$$|P_{k+1}Q_k - P_kQ_{k+1}| = |P_kQ_{k-1} - P_{k-1}Q_k| a_{k+1}$$

so that, by repeated application of this formula, we obtain

$$|P_{k+1}Q_k - P_kQ_{k+1}| = a_1a_2a_3 \cdots a_ka_{k+1}$$

and therefore

$$D_k = a_1a_2a_3 \cdots a_{k+1}/Q_kQ_{k+1}$$

Forming the difference $D_k - D_{k+1}$ and using (11), we get

$$D_k - D_{k+1} = a_1a_2 \cdots a_{k+1}b_{k+2}/Q_kQ_{k+2} > 0$$

which proves that the difference in question is positive and thus $D_k > D_{k+1}$, that is

$$D_1 > D_2 > D_3 > \cdots > D_k > D_{k+1} > \cdots$$

The same inequality $D_k > D_{k+1}$ can be deduced from the fact that the ratio D_{k+1}/D_k is less than one. We have, indeed, with the aid of (11)

$$D_{k+1}/D_k = a_{k+2}Q_k/Q_{k+2} = a_{k+2}Q_k/(b_{k+2}Q_{k+1} + a_{k+2}Q_k) < 1$$

For example, in our numerical example we find

$$D_1 = 1/3, D_2 = 1/30, D_3 = 1/430, D_4 = 1/9675, D_5 = 1/313,425.$$

For the continued fractions obtained with the aid of Euclid's algorithm the numerators a_k are, all of them, equal to one, $a_k = 1$, so that the expression of the distance D_k takes a very simple form: $D_k = 1/Q_kQ_{k+1}$, and our example illustrates this particular fact.

Concluding this chapter, we note that a rational number admits of three different representations: (a) as a ratio m/n of two integers (fraction), (b) as a finite continued fraction, and (c) as a decimal fraction. The study of this last representation will be continued in Chapter 4.

Infinite decimal Fractions; Geometric Series

Any fraction m/n can be transformed by direct division of its numerator by the denominator n into a decimal fraction having the same value and therefore representing the same rational number. Thus $1/8 = 1.000/8 = 0.125$. To perform the division we write the dividend m with as many zeros after the dot as are needed to finish the division by n. In so doing we use an important property of extended decimal numeration: *there is an infinite number of positions to the right of the dot*.

In most cases we need all of them to be able to find the decimal representation of even the simplest rational numbers. So, for instance, to transform $1/3$ we divide $1.000 \cdots$ by 3, picturing in our imagination the unit as the digit 1 with a denumerable infinity of zeros after the dot. The process of division is an endless one: it could stop only if at some step there was no more remainder. But, dividing 1 by 3, we have to divide ten by three at each step, and according to the relation $10 = 3 \cdot 3 + 1$ the same remainder 1 appears at each step. It is transformed in the next step into ten units of the next lower rank and the cycle continues indefinitely.

Therefore the division cannot stop, and the *infinite* decimal fraction $0.3333\cdots$ is generated. Considered in the process of growth, with an ever-increasing number of digits, this is a variable number since as long as n continues to increase, its value is not a fixed and definite number, but increases with n. Therefore the infinite decimal fraction $0.3333\cdots$ must be considered and defined as an entity, an entity obtained as the final result of the process of successive divisions, when the process is completed and there is no more change.

This can mean only one thing: introducing infinite decimal representation of a rational number m/n, we must consider the infinite chain of successive divisions, which develops when we perform the division of m by n, as *completed*. Thus our thought *jumps over and beyond* the set of all integers which are here used as ordinal numbers to mark the order of all successive divisions as well as the order of the consecutive digits involved in the notation of an infinite decimal fraction resulting from the successive divisions.

On the other hand we may be given an infinite expression such as the infinite decimal fraction 0.3333··· considered as a whole, as an entity. Although it has an infinite number of digits we know all of them because they are all equal to 3. But how can we be sure that its value is exactly one third? What do we mean when we use the term "value" in this case, when the number of digits as well as the number of additions to be performed is infinite and therefore the expression can never be effectively computed or explicitly written down? Does the "value" exist and, if so, in what sense?

We cannot of course consider 0.333··· as a *sum* of terms: if we try to apply the definition of decimal numeration and write

$$0.3333\cdots = 0.3 + 0.03 + 0.003 + 0.0003 + \cdots \qquad (1)$$

we have to perform an endless operation of successive additions, and since the number of terms is infinite we will never be able to finish the addition of *all* terms. Nevertheless we have an intuitive feeling that the division of one by three which generates this infinite decimal fraction *must* give, as a final result, an expression which represents one third, that the "value" of the infinite decimal fraction *must* be equal to the fraction 1/3 which is its origin. How can we prove that our intuition does not deceive us?

Any infinite mathematical expression such as an infinite decimal fraction (an infinite sum) or an infinite continued fraction (an infinite sequence of interlocked divisions) raises two different questions: first, does it represent a number, does its value exist or is it an empty symbol devoid of any meaning, and, second (which has a meaning only if the first question is answered affirmatively), *what* is the number thus represented, what is its *value?*

Suppose for a moment that the first question, the question of the *existence* of a value, was solved and the answer to it was yes. To find the unknown value we first denote it by x. The very introduction of a symbol such as x for a quantity whose existence is not yet established, is equivalent to the tacit assumption that the quantity denoted by it does exist. Operating with such a symbol we may find a numerical value for it, but this purely formal, operational result does not prove the existence of the value it is supposed to represent and therefore the symbol may be devoid of any meaning.

Having stressed this important point, let us denote by x the unknown value of the infinite decimal fraction 0.333···

$$x = 0.333 \cdots = 0.\dot{3}$$

using the abbreviated notation $\dot{3}$ for an infinite sequence of digits 3. The hypothesis that the value of $0.\dot{3}$ exists is thus used and expressed in the introduction of a symbol for it, x.

To find x we will use the fact that the decimal fraction 0.333··· is not only infinite, but is also *periodic* (sometimes such decimal fractions are called *recurrent*) which means that the digit 3 is repeated indefinitely. The fact that we effectively known *all* the digits, notwithstanding their infinite number, is a corollary of this periodicity.

Since we cannot perform an infinite number of operations the numerical value of the unknown x can be found only by operating with the equation $x = 0.\dot{3}$ in such a way that the infinite expression will be eliminated. This can be done by using the periodicity of $0.\dot{3}$ and the fact that infinity does not change if we subtract one from it. If we multiply both sides of the equation $x = 0.\dot{3}$ by 10, we do not change the infinite part $\dot{3}$ of the decimal fraction $0.\dot{3}$ which follows the dot. The multiplication by 10 simply shifts all its digits one position to the left and there are after the multiplication exactly as many digits 3 after the dot as there were before the multiplication. Thus the only effect of the multiplication is the appearance of the integer 3:

$$10x = 3.\dot{3} = 3.333... = 3 + 0.\dot{3}$$

But $0.\dot{3} = x$ and therefore

$$10x = 3 + x$$

Solving this equation for x, we first obtain $9x = 3$ and then

$$x = 3/9 = 1/3$$

This result means that, if $0.\dot{3}$ has a meaning and therefore a numerical value, this value can only be 1/3. In the same way dividing 1 by 7 we obtain for 1/7 a representation by an infinite periodic decimal fraction whose period 142857 involves six digits:

$$1/7 = 0.142857\,142857\,142857\cdots = 0.\dot{1}4285\dot{7} \tag{2}$$

using the customary notation $\dot{1}4285\dot{7}$ for the period.

In this case to find the numerical value y of $0.\dot{1}4285\dot{7}$ we must multiply the equation $y = 0.\dot{1}4285\dot{7}$ by a million since the purpose of the multiplication is to shift the whole first period 142857 to the left of the dot. Thus $1\,000\,000 \cdot y = 142857.\dot{1}4285\dot{7}$ and the equation for y is:

$$10^6 y = 142857 + y$$

Therefore $0.\dot{1}4285\dot{7} = y = 142857/999999$. Now the composite numbers 999999 and 142857 can be written as products of primes

$$999999 = 3^3 \cdot 7 \cdot 11 \cdot 13 \cdot 37; \; 142857 = 3^3 \cdot 11 \cdot 13 \cdot 37$$

and the GCD $(999999;\; 142857) = 142857$ since $999999 = 142857 \cdot 7$. Thus, finally $0.\dot{1}4285\dot{7} = 1/7$.

In general an infinite periodic decimal fraction involves an aperiodic part which precedes the periodic part. Such are, for instance, the fractions

$$0.103\,575\,7575\cdots = 0.103\dot{5}\dot{7} \text{ and } 0.210\,151\,010\cdots = 0.210\,1\dot{5}\dot{1}\dot{0}$$

Consider now a general periodic decimal fraction whose aperiodic part has m digits and is equal to $0.a_1 a_2 \cdots a_m$ while its period has n digits and is noted by $b_1 b_2 b_3 \cdots b_n$. Denoting the value of this fraction by x, we now derive a rule for the transformation of a general decimal periodic fraction into an ordinary fraction. To shift the first period to the left of the dot we multiply the equation

$$x = 0.a_1 a_2 a_3 \cdots a_m \dot{b}_1 b_2 \cdots \dot{b}_n \tag{3}$$

by 10^{m+n} and obtain

$$10^{m+n} x = 10^n (a_1 a_2 a_3 \cdots a_m) + (b_1 b_2 \cdots b_n) + 0.\dot{b}_1 b_2 \cdots \dot{b}_n \tag{4}$$

where $(a_1 a_2 \cdots a_m)$ and $(b_1 b_2 \cdots b_n)$ are two integers represented by their digits in the usual decimal system of numeration.

Denoting these integers $(a_1 a_2 \cdots a_m)$ and $(b_1 b_2 \cdots b_n)$ by M and N

respectively, we rewrite (4) as

$$10^{m+n}x = 10^n M + N + 0.\dot{b}_1 b_2 \cdots \dot{b}_n \qquad (5)$$

Now (3) multiplied by 10^m can be written as

$$10^m x = (a_1 a_2 \cdots a_m) + 0.\dot{b}_1 b_2 \cdots \dot{b}_n = M + 0.\dot{b}_1 b_2 \cdots \dot{b}_n$$

so that

$$0.\dot{b}_1 b_2 \cdots \dot{b}_n = 10^m x - M$$

Using this expression in (5), we obtain finally an equation for the unknown x:

$$10^{m+n}x = 10^n M + N + 10^m x - M$$

To solve this equation we transpose $10^m x$ to the left which gives $10^m 10^n x - 10^m x = 10^n M - M + N$, that is, picking out $10^m x$ and M as common factors

$$10^m(10^n - 1) x = (10^n - 1) M + N$$

and thus, dividing by $10^n - 1 = \overset{n \text{ digits}}{\overbrace{999 \ldots 9}}$ and by 10^m

$$x = M/10^m + N/999 \cdots 99000 \cdots 0 \qquad (n \text{ digits } 9, m \text{ zeros})$$

$$x = (999 \ldots 9M + N)/999 \ldots 900 \ldots 0$$

EXAMPLES: (a) In $0.130\dot{5}\dot{7}$ we have $m = 3$, $n = 2$, $M = 103$ and $N = 57$.

Therefore: $0.103\dot{5}\dot{7} = (103 \cdot 99 + 57)/99000 = 10254/99000$ $= 1709/16500$.

(b) In $0.210\,15\dot{1}\dot{0}$ we have $m = 5$, $n = 2$, $M = 21015$ and $N = 10$. Therefore

$$0.210\,15\dot{1}\dot{0} = (21015 \cdot 99 + 10)/9900000$$

$$= 2080495/9900000 = 416099/1980000$$

Some rational numbers, such as $3/4 = 0.75$ may be represented by finite decimal fractions. The reason for this is simple: fractions with a denominator of the form $2^m \cdot 5^n$ (in general $m \neq n$) admit of finite decimal expression, because multiplying $2^m \cdot 5^n$ by $2^n \cdot 5^m$, we transform the denominator into 10^{m+n}, an integral power of 10. But all the fractions whose denominators have factors other than 2 and 5 are transformed into *infinite* but *periodic* decimal fractions. The periodicity is always present since, dividing the numerator by a finite number, the denominator, we can have only a *finite* number of different remainders (at most $n - 1$, if the denominator is denoted by n) and therefore when the endless division is continued one of the possible remainders necessarily reappears, after which the cycle is completed and the sequence of remainders as well as the sequence of digits of the quotient are repeated.

On the other hand, we already saw that an infinite periodic decimal fraction can represent only a rational number because, using its periodicity, we can express its value in the form of a ratio of two integers. Therefore, we come to the conclusion that the totality of all *rational* numbers and the totality of all *periodic* decimal fractions are one and the same infinite collection. To avoid a possible misunderstanding, we add that integers and finite decimal fractions are included in the totality of all infinite periodic decimal fractions since we can insert an infinite number of zeros to the right of the last significant digit of a finite decimal fraction without changing its value. Thus, $0.75 = 0.750000\cdots = 0.75\dot{0}$ with a period $\dot{0}$, or also $0.75 = 0.74\dot{9}$ with a period $\dot{9}$, as well as $1 = 1.\dot{0}$, or $1 = 0.\dot{9}$. The last expression for 1 can be obtained by multiplying by 3 both members of the equality $1/3 = 0.\dot{3}$.

This representation of all rational numbers by the totality of infinite periodic decimal fractions suggests an important question. It is plain that an infinite decimal fraction is not necessarily periodic. A general infinite decimal fraction can be conceived as any given infinite sequence of digits to the right of the dot, the only restriction being that the n-th digit to the right, a_n, for all values of n must be a natural integer less than ten, or zero. This expression can be periodic or aperiodic and we saw that the collection of all infinite periodic decimal fractions is identical with the set of all rational numbers. Therefore an infinite aperiodic decimal fraction

$$0.a_1 a_2 a_3 \cdots a_n a_{n+1} \cdots$$

cannot represent a rational number. If it has a meaning, its value is a number of a new kind which does not belong to the class of rational numbers.

We consider the points of a straight line (number-axis) as images of numbers. On this line the point-image of an aperiodic infinite decimal fraction is not a member of the set of rational points. Here again we come across a suggestion of the same kind we encountered, when we saw that the gaps between the point-images of integers indicated the existence of numbers other than integers.

If there are points on the line other than rational points, the latter ones being, as we know, everywhere dense on the number axis, they must separate rational points. Thus their existence is equivalent to the recognition of the fundamental fact that the rational points do not fill up the line, that there are gaps between rational points notwithstanding the fact that they are everywhere dense so that there are an infinite number of rational points in any interval, regardless of how small we chose this interval. The straight line thus appears to our mind as populated densely but imperfectly by rational points.

All this discussion is based on the assumption that infinite decimal fractions, periodic and aperiodic, are not meaningless symbols and have definite numerical values. We now pass to the study of this fundamental question, the question of the existence of infinite decimal fractions as numbers having definite values.

The existence of an infinite mathematical expression, such as an infinite decimal fraction, cannot be analysed with the aid of classical logic. The Greek philosophers systematically precluded the use of infinite chains of syllogisms and, in particular, the use of infinite chains of mathematical operations. They realised perfectly well that a step of thought necessarily corresponds to each link of such a chain of mathematical operations. Thus, ascribing a meaning to an infinite mathematical expression, we accept in substance the possibility of reaching a definite logical conclusion with the aid and "at the end" of an infinite, endless chain of steps of thought. Having no confidence in such a transcendental infinite logical chain, Greeks limited scientific, and, in particular, mathematical thinking to *finite* logical chains. Thus, eliminating the use of infinity in mathematics, they not only precluded the application of the number concept to the study of Nature but also prevented the development of mathematical thinking.

Take for instance the four famous Arguments of Zeno of Elea, sometimes also called Zeno's Paradoxes. They exerted enormous influence on human thinking. The "Arguments of Zeno of Elea," says Bertrand Russell, "have, in one form or another, afforded grounds for almost all the theories of space and time and infinity which have been constructed from his day to our own".

And again the most characteristic feature of the four Arguments is *"horror infiniti"*, fear of infinity. Therefore it is not at all surprising that at the very first steps in arithmetic, the steps dealing with such familiar things as decimal fractions, we meet the same problems which were treated by Zeno of Elea in his Arguments and which present themselves to us in the form of the existence of infinite decimal fractions.

First Argument: Dichotomy

We begin with the first Argument (Dichotomy) which is related to the infinite divisibility of space intervals and which states that motion as a *logical concept* is non-existent (Aristotle, *Physica*): "The first is the one of non-existence of motion, on the ground that what moves must always attain the middle point sooner than the end point".

Let us translate this into mathematical language. It seems as clear to us as anything can be, that a moving point M, starting at the origin O, can reach a fixed point A at a unit-distance $OA = 1$ from O. Now Zeno says that to reach A, that is to move one unit of length, the variable point M must first reach the mid-point A_1 of the interval OA, which is at a distance $OA_1 = 1/2 = 2^{-1}$ from O. We agree with Zeno and mark the point A_1 as our first goal, Fig. 4.1.

But the argument is repeated: to reach A_1 the point M must first reach the mid-point A_2 of the new interval OA_1, at a distance $OA_2 = 1/4 = 1/2^2 = 2^{-2}$ from O. This corresponds to a second step of thought and it is again inconclusive since to reach A_2 another third mid-point A_3, mid-point of OA_2, at a distance $OA_3 = 2^{-3}$ from O must first be attained—third step of thought. The argument is continued indefinitely, the dichotomy cannot be stopped and an infinite sequence of points $A_1, A_2, A_3, \dots A_n, A_{n+1}\dots$ is constructed such that at the n-th step of thought we state the necessity of first reaching the point A_n at a distance $OA_n = 1/2^n = 2^{-n}$ from the origin:

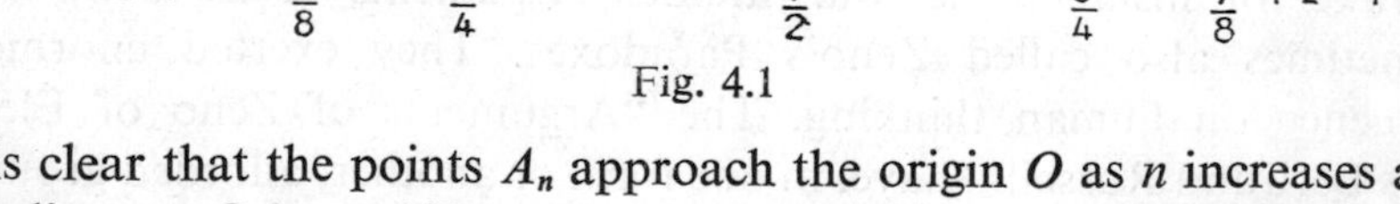

Fig. 4.1

It is clear that the points A_n approach the origin O as n increases and the distance $OA_n = 1/2^n$ can be made as small as we want by choosing a sufficiently large value for the integer n.

If we prefer not to use the concept of absolute infinity in our thinking we cannot understand how a fixed point A_n, corresponding to a given *fixed n*, can ever be reached by a motion starting at O since an infinite chain of events and therefore an infinite chain of steps of thought precede the desired event. But n can be chosen as large as we want, which means that we cannot understand how a point A_n as near to the origin as we want can ever be reached. We cannot understand therefore how motion *starts*.

On the other hand, if we decide to introduce infinity but do it timidly, refusing to consider the actual infinity and using with Zeno only the potential infinity, there again cannot be a *first* phase of motion because there is no *last* integer and only the existence of a last integer could correspond in our chain of thought to the first phase of motion, to its beginning.

In other words, what Zeno says in his first Argument is that the human mind cannot understand motion, cannot analyse it logically. He tries to prove this by combining the fact of motion (which of course he accepts as a physical fact) with the assumption of the infinite divisibility of space intervals. Zeno wants to show that infinite dichotomy based on infinite divisibility precludes the understanding of motion.

But we do move and Zeno always completed the statement of his first Argument by getting up and walking, which proves that the meaning of "non-existence" in the wording of the first Argument has no relation to the physical fact of motion. Motion is indeed there, before our eyes, a certainty for us. It is a real fact. It is our thinking, if we agree with Zeno, which cannot explain it, cannot analyse and measure it. Zeno's first Argument is a classical example of fear of *actual* infinity, with its inescapable consequence: impossibility of understanding the environment.

Modern mathematics solves the first paradox of Zeno. Accepting Zeno's construction and using the infinite dichotomy as he did, we nevertheless can understand and explain the fact of motion because human thinking has expanded and is now much stronger than Greek thinking was. Zeno's logic is a *finite one* and as such it was useless in the analysis of the *infinite* divisibility of space. Zeno refused to introduce and use actual infinity and his attitude is characteristic of all Greek thinkers, except, perhaps, Archimedes who justifiably is now considered as the precursor of Newton and Leibniz. We have in the aleph-null of Georg Cantor a new powerful tool of thinking. Our mathematical logic is based on the study of infinity, and it uses actual infinity. This fact explains our success where Zeno failed.

Let us now study the infinite dichotomy, first slightly modifying Zeno's argument, and then analyzing it as it is. The fact of motion being accepted as a fundamental datum of the environment as we perceive it, our problem consists of creating new methods of thinking which make the conceptual description of motion compatible with the infinite divisibility of space.

Consider a motion beginning at O and ending at A. In the first step of thought (first dichotomy) we state with Zeno that before reaching A, the point M must first reach the mid-point $A_1 = B_1$. Since we accept the existence of motion as a fundamental postulate, let us suppose that M does reach B_1, having covered in its first phase of motion the first distance $OB_1 = 1/2 = 2^{-1}$. An equal distance $B_1A = 2^{-1}$ remains to be covered after this first step. Now to reach A starting at B_1, the point M again must pass through the mid-point B_2 of the remaining interval B_1A. A second distance covered by the moving point M, distance $B_1B_2 = 1/4 = 2^{-2}$ corresponds to this second step of thought and the remaining distance to be covered, B_2A, is again equal to the last distance covered: $B_2A = B_1B_2 = 2^{-2}$. Now, when the point B_2 is reached, the variable point M must again (third step of thought) reach the mid-point B_3 of the remaining interval B_2A before arriving at A, and thus it covers in its motion third distance B_2B_3 equal to $1/8 = 2^{-3}$. Again an equal distance $B_3A = 2^{-3}$ remains to be covered. The argument is repeated indefinitely and again the dichotomy cannot stop, for at the end of the n-th phase of motion (n-th step of thought) we arrive at a point B_n such that the n-th distance $B_{n-1}B_n$ covered during the n-th phase of motion, as well as the remaining interval B_nA, both are equal to 2^{-n}, so that a next $(n + 1)$-st step is necessary. It is easy to check that the total distance D_n covered in the first n steps is equal to

$$D_n = 1/2 + 1/2^2 + 1/2^3 + 1/2^4 + \dots 1/2^n = 1 - 1/2^n$$

since the remaining distance B_nA is equal to $2^{-n} = 1/2^n$.

In this case the logical difficulty discovered by Zeno has changed its form, but it is still present. Even disregarding the question of how a motion begins, we see that the point A at unit distance from the origin O cannot be reached in a finite number of phases of motion. If we do not admit an actually infinite chain of reasoning we cannot understand how the point A can be reached in general: after the n-th step of thought where n is arbitrarily large but finite, the distance covered $D_n = 1 - 1/2^n$ is still *less* than 1 and the distance $B_n A$, which remains to be covered and which separates M from A, is equal to $1/2^n$ and *does not vanish*. If we prohibit the use of actual infinity all what we can use is the unlimited growth of n: for a sufficiently large n the fraction $1/2^n$ becomes as small as we want and the point B_n will be as near to A as we want. But the integer n, no matter how large we choose it, always remains a *finite number*. If n is finite, the number 2^n is finite too and its reciprocal $1/2^n$, which represents the remaining distance $B^n A$, exceeds zero for any n.

Thus, if we use potential infinity only, point M will never reach the point A and the simplest physical fact, namely that a moving body *does* reach a predetermined point, remains impossible to understand. It is useless to introduce potential infinity and say that when n, and with it 2^n, tend to infinity the variable quantity $1/2^n$ tends to zero. Such *variable* quantities, which tend to zero and approach as near to it as we choose, are called "infinitely small quantities". It is true that the distance $B_n A = 1/2^n$ which separates B_n from A is infinitely small, because in our reasoning n is variable and, running through the sequence of all natural numbers, increases without limit. But the same logical obstacle is still there: $2^{-n} > 0$ for all integers n.

If actual infinity, aleph-null, is excluded, we cannot understand how M reaches A: the infinitely small $1/2^n$ being a variable quantity by definition, cannot stop its variation. Although it approaches zero, it cannot become and remain zero since its vanishing would contradict its definition. The definition of infinitely small in the realm of classical finite logic is based on the existence of two logical categories: the category of constant, *invariable* quantities and the opposite category of changing, *variable* quantities. They are mutually exclusive categories, which means that a variable cannot become fixed. In particular the infinitely small, forever variable, cannot vanish, for, becoming zero, it would become a constant.

Greek philosophers studied very closely the infinitely small in its geometric form. Thus, Antiphon of Athens (about 480–411 B.C.) in his attempts to define the area and length of the circumference of a circle, invented the famous construction of an infinite (potentially infinite) denumerable sequence

$$P_1, P_2, P_3, \dots, P_n \dots$$

of regular polygons inscribed in a circle, the n-th inscribed regular polygon P_n having 2^{n+1} equal sides.

He knew and stated explicitly that the difference (in area and in the length of perimeter) between the circle and the n-th polygon P_n decreases when the integer n increases and that this difference is an infinitely small quantity. But he refused to mix two mutually exclusive logical categories. At the end of his analysis he concluded that although the difference between the circle and the inscribed regular polygon is an infinitely small, it is present at every step of thought, it never vanishes and therefore the circle cannot be considered as a regular polygon with an infinite number of sides.

This negative conclusion eliminated the logical possibility of ascribing an area and a length to the circle, because as we shall see in Chapter 16, length and area can be defined and measured directly only for straight line segments and polygons respectively. Lengths and areas of curves and figures bounded by curves can be defined and measured only, if the ultimate vanishing of the infinitely small through the use of actual infinity is accepted as a basic postulate. They are nonexistent in the logical and mathematical sense, if the contrary assumption, namely the negation of the ultimate vanishing of the infinitely small is made.

How could the ancient Greeks study nature, if their best thinkers refused to understand motion and were unable to ascribe the logical existence to perimeter and area of the simplest curve possible, the circle? Greek thought was also unable to invent zero, the symbol of nothing, which was introduced and used by the Hindus and Mayas. Such facts throw a new light on the universally accepted superiority of Greek thinking.

The situation becomes entirely different if the transfinite number aleph-null is defined and introduced. The concept of actual infinity as something fixed, invariable and in the same time greater than all integers, something which is beyond potential infinity, allows the introduction of a new act of thought which we can characterize as a jump into actual infinity and which is associated in mathematics with the concept of *limit*. In this *new act of thought* a variable integer n, running through the set of all integers and increasing without limit, changes its nature, when it reaches aleph-null. First its variation is stopped, it becomes a fixed number (transfinite number aleph-null), secondly it loses its fundamental character of being an integer since aleph-null is not an integer, there being no last integer.

This new act of thought allows therefore a fundamental transformation of a quantity and its passage from one logical category into another which is its opposite: at the limit variable quantity becomes *fixed*. The expression "at the limit" means the jump beyond all integers into the aleph-null. This jump is equivalent to the introduction of an infinite chain of syllogisms considered in its wholeness as an entity, and its use in a reasoning yields a final, definite conclusion, exactly as the use of a finite chain of syllogisms does.

In our case this passage to the limit explains completely how M reaches A. The infinitely small variable distance $B_n A$ which remains to be covered in the motion of M and is measured by $1/2^n$ at the n-th step of thought, becomes a fixed quantity and vanishes when n ceases to be variable and attains its ultimate value aleph-null. Formulating this result in mathematical language, we say that an infinitely small quantity has a fixed limit. The value of this fixed limit can only be zero since the infinitely small approaches zero in its variation and surely becomes smaller than any fixed quantity different from zero. Thus, using the customary notation "lim" for limit, we state that

$$\lim_{n=\infty} B_n A = \lim_{n=\infty} (1/2^n) = 0$$

where $n = \infty$ reminds us that the variation of n has stopped because n has reached aleph-null. The distance $B_n A$ *disappears*, when n reaches aleph-null and thus at the limit point M *is* at A, having reached the

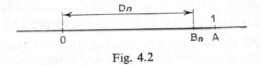

Fig. 4.2

end-point of the interval OA. If we consider the distance D_n covered in the first n phases of motion and corresponding to n steps of thought,

$$D_n = 1 - 2^{-n} \qquad OB_n = D_n = 1 - 1/2^n$$

and ask what is the ultimate value of D_n when n reaches aleph-null, this question is equivalent to asking what is the ultimate conclusion at the end of our actually infinite chain of reasoning. To obtain the answer we must "pass to the limit", and thus the ultimate value of D_n is

$$\lim_{n=\infty} D_n = \lim_{n=\infty} (1 - 1/2^n) = 1 - \lim_{n=\infty} (1/2^n) = 1$$

since $\lim_{n=\infty} (1/2^n) = 0$. Therefore, we have not only found in the concept of actual infinity the solution to Zeno's first paradox, but have also formulated a new mathematical operation, *passage to the limit*, which, in its general form, states that

$$\lim_{n=\infty} \varepsilon_n = 0$$

if ε_n is an infinitely small quantity, when $n \to \infty$. This ultimate vanishing of an infinitely small quantity is the mathematical counterpart and description of the natural phenomenon of motion.

The solution of the problem we just found can be expressed in another form which is also important to study. The ultimate value $D_\infty = 1$ of D_n, attained after the growth of n has exhausted all integers and n has jumped beyond potential infinity into actual infinity and reached aleph-null, is represented by the infinite periodic binary fraction $(0.\dot{1})_2$ with the period $\dot{1}$:

$$D_\infty = 1 = (0.111 \cdots) = (0.\dot{1})_2 = 1/2 + 1/2^2 + 1/2^3 + 1/2^4 + \cdots 1/2^n + \cdots$$

The fraction $(0.\dot{1})_2$ is to be considered not as a *process*, as a growth of ever increasing sequences of digits, but as a *static* entity, the result of a *completed* process. We denote the ultimate distance 1 by the symbol D_∞ to express the essential feature of finality characterising infinite mathematical expressions which have a perfectly determined and fixed, static value.

The logical difficulty inherent in the infinite divisibility of space and time intervals now takes a new mathematical form: what is the meaning of the infinite periodic binary fraction $(0.\dot{1})_2$? Does it exist? Does it have a perfectly determined value, or is it a meaningless and empty symbol?

We have solved the problem of its existence by introducing passage to the limit, and this mathematical operation, which is the most characteristic feature of modern mathematics, is the only foundation on which the use of decimal periodic fractions rests. It is relatively easy to justify the value one obtained for $\lim_{n=\infty} D_n$ by the passage to the limit, if its existence is proved: denoting $\lim_{n=\infty} D_n$ by x and multiplying both sides of the expression

$$x = \lim_{n=\infty} D_n = (0.\dot{1})_2 = 1/2 + 1/2^2 + 1/2^3 + 1/2^4 + \cdots 1/2^n + \cdots$$

by 2, we form an equation for the unknown x

$$2x = 1 + 1/2 + 1/2^2 + 1/2^3 + \cdots = 1 + (0.\dot{1})_2 = 1 + x$$

so that $2x = 1 + x$, and $x = 1$, as we have previously established, by using passage to the limit in the expression $1 - 1/2^n$ of D_n.

We cannot emphasize too strongly that the contrary assumption, namely the refusal to ascribe the ultimate fixed value zero to an infinitely small variable quantity, is equivalent to the assumption that the human mind will forever remain unable to understand how a variable point M, which by definition approaches a fixed point A as near as we want $(1/2^n \to 0)$, can ultimately reach it and stop at this point M ($\lim_{n=\infty} 1/2^n = 0$).

The ultimate vanishing of the infinitely small imperatively demands a jump into actual infinity (aleph-null) over and beyond the potential infinity of ever increasing integers n since the infinitely small $1/2^n$ remains variable and different from zero as long as the integer n, running through the infinite sequence of integers, continues to increase.

The fear of actual infinity characterizes not only ancient Greek thinking, but also mathematical thinking of the nineteenth and twentieth centuries. The introduction of passage to the limit with the ultimate substitution of zero for an infinitely small quantity is even today justified in terms which thoroughly avoid the use of the word infinity, an infinite set of inequalities being used to hide the fundamental idea underlaying this new act of thinking.[1]

The first use of passage to the limit, in substance equivalent to ours, is implicitly contained in the work of Archimedes (about 287–212 B.C.), in his method of exhaustion, and his introduction of π as a perfectly determined and *fixed* number. The work of this genius and its fate is the most illuminating example of a general fact characterizing the evolution of human thinking and culture. Among all discoveries made by Archimedes only those for which humanity was prepared were accepted, developed, and used. His greatest achievement, the creation of a new and extremely powerful act of thought, passage to the limit, was not understood. It was completely disregarded and forgotten until nineteen centuries later, when it was revived in the work of an English mathematician. Passage to the limit was discovered for the second time

---

[1] See Appendix II where the usual definition of the passage to the limit is discussed.

in the history of human thinking by John Wallis in 1665, though his work was published thirty years later (*opera* I, p. 382).

Reverting to Zeno's first Argument we shall see now, after having studied how motion *stops*, how the fact that motion *starts* from rest can be mathematically described. To analyze and explain from our point of view Zeno's first Argument, as he framed and phrased it, it is sufficient to reverse in our thought the sense of variation of the parameter n and imagine that, starting with the initial non-integral value aleph-null n decreases, running back through all integers. We introduce therefore the jump back from the transfinite number aleph-null to integers, so that the variable point M, moving continuously to the right from O towards A is always first at the midpoint of each interval OB_n before it reaches the end B_n of this interval, as was prescribed by Zeno in his first argument. We are not studying here the continuity of motion, but are limiting our problem to the analysis of the possibility of a motion starting. In the last analysis it is the introduction of the jump beyond the set of integers to aleph-null *and back* which allows us to understand motion and thus apply numbers, that is mathematics, to the study of nature. Considered in itself, this jump beyond the finite chain of syllogisms is a new and extremely bold act of thinking. It introduces infinity in human thinking and uses it as a tool. As we will see later, all the mysterious power of modern mathematics is based on it.

Geometric Series

Reverting back to the first Argument of Zeno, we state that we will be able to describe motion, to correlate it with numbers, if we first make certain the mathematical existence of such infinite expression, as for instance

$$(1.\dot{1})_2 = 1 + 1/2 + (1/2)^2 + (1/2)^3 + (1/2)^4 + \cdots + (1/2)^n + \cdots \quad (6)$$

ascribing a meaning to a sum of an infinite number of terms, though in fact we are unable to achieve their addition.

Generalizing (6) let us now consider the sum of an infinite number of terms which are the consecutive powers of any positive or negative but non-vanishing number $q \neq 0$

$$1 + q + q^2 + q^3 + q^4 + q^5 + \cdots q^n + q^{n+1} + \cdots \quad (7)$$

instead of the sum of powers of the particular number $1/2$ in (6). The infinite expression (7) is called a geometric series and its characteristic property is that the ratio of any of its terms to its predecessor is constant, namely equal to q: $q/1 = q^2/q = q^3/q^2 = q^4/q^3 = \cdots = q$. The value q of the ratio is called the *standard ratio* of the geometric progression $1, q, q^2, q^3, \ldots$

The infinite expression (7) has no meaning, if the standard ratio q is equal to or greater than one. In mathematics we have to operate with finite numbers and therefore we can use only expressions which represent fiinite numbers. If $q = 1$, all the terms of (7) become equal to one and since their number is infinite the expression (7) cannot represent a finite number and is therefore useless. We may say that its value is infinite, but this does not change the fact that it is of no use to us. If $q > 1$ each term, except the first one, is greater than one, and again the expression (7) has an infinite value. We state this fact by saying that for $q \geqslant 1$ the geometric progression *diverges*, its "sum" being infinite. Such infinite and *divergent* expressions are not used in mathematics.

But for $q = 1/2$ the geometric series reduces to the infinite periodic binary fraction (6) and it can be easily shown that it represents the number two. We saw indeed that

$$1/2 + 1/2^2 + 1/2^3 + 1/2^4 + 1/2^5 + \cdots = 1 \tag{8}$$

Therefore, adding 1 to both sides:

$$1 + 1/2 + 1/2^2 + 1/2^3 + 1/2^4 + \cdots = 1 + 1 = 2 \tag{9}$$

The infinite series (9) can also be obtained as a result of passage to the limit in

$$2D_{n+1} = 1 + 1/2 + 1/2^2 + 1/2^3 + \cdots + 1/2^n$$

$$= 2(1 - 1/2^{n+1}) = 2 - 1/2^n$$

An infinite sequence can be constructed

$$2D_1, 2D_2, 2D_3, \ldots, 2D_n \ldots \tag{10}$$

such that its terms $2D_n$ approach the number two when n increases and moreover $\lim\limits_{n=\infty} (2D_n)$ exists and is equal to two, a fact expressed by the equality (9). An infinite sequence of terms such that its terms converge, to a limit, in our example $2D_n \to 2$, is called a *convergent* sequence.

There may be *divergent* sequences whose terms do not approach a finite and perfectly determined limit, when $n \to \infty$. Such are, for instance, the sequences

$$1, \quad 2, \quad 3, \quad 4, \quad 5, \quad 6, \ldots n, \ldots$$
$$1, \quad -1, \quad 1, \quad -1, \quad 1, \quad -1, \ldots (-1)^{2n}, (-1)^{2n+1} \ldots$$

The first one diverges because its terms increase without limit; the second one diverges because its terms forever oscillate between $+1$ and -1 without approaching any limit.

We deduce from the example of a geometric series (9) that to study the existence of the number represented by a geometric series and to find its value we must transform the series into an infinite *sequence* of type (10). If the sequence is convergent the series has a meaning and its value is given by the limit to which tend the terms of the corresponding infinite sequence. If the sequence is divergent the series is meaningless.

Now it may be shown that the series (7) has a meaning and represents a finite number, its "sum", for all values of its standard ratio q (positive) less than one, $0 < q < 1$. To prove this we first transform the series (7) into an infinite sequence $S_1, S_2, S_3, S_4, \ldots, S_n, \ldots$ defined as follows: $S_1 = 1$, $S_2 = 1 + q$, $S_3 = 1 + q + q^2$, $S_4 = 1 + q + q^2 + q^3$ and so on. Thus, S_n denotes the sum of the first n terms of (7) and is obtained by cutting off the series after the n-th term q^{n-1} and omitting all the other terms beginning with q^n:

$$S_n = 1 + q + q^2 + q^3 + q^4 + q^5 + \cdots q^{n-2} + q^{n-1}$$

The successive values of S_n for $n = 1, 2, 3, 4, 5 \ldots$ form an infinite sequence of so-called *partial sums*

$$S_1, S_2, S_3, S_4, \ldots S_n, S_{n+1} \ldots \tag{11}$$

which now replaces the series. If this sequence is convergent, the series has a meaning and its value is the limit to which tend the terms of the convergent sequence (11). It is obvious that at the limit, when n reaches aleph-null, the partial sum S_n is transformed into the sum of *all* terms. Denoting this sum of the entire geometric series by S, we formulate this fact by writing

$$S = \lim_{n = \infty} S_n$$

provided that (11) is a convergent sequence. Here we use the passage to the limit as a tool for *computing* the number S represented by (7), when $q < 1$, implying that the series (7) converges if $q < 1$ (which is yet to be proved), the $\lim\limits_{n=\infty} S_n$ having a meaning and representing a finite and perfectly determined number. Thus, in the case of convergence the operation of addition is extended to include its most important case, when the number of terms to be added is infinite, but their sum is nevertheless a finite number. Such sums can be computed only with the aid of passage to the limit because an infinite number of additions cannot be performed effectively. Therefore, to find S we must first form the partial sum S_n of the first n terms, where n is any integer, but for the moment a *fixed* integer. Multiplying S_n by the standard ratio q and adding and subtracting one on the right side, we obtain

$$qS_n = q + q^2 + q^3 + \cdots q^{n-1} + q^n$$

$$= (1 + q + q^2 + q^3 + \cdots q^{n-1}) + q^n - 1$$

But the sum of terms between the parentheses is manifestly equal to S_n, which gives us the following equation for the unknown S_n:

$$qS_n = S_n + q^n - 1$$

Transposing S_n to the left member and factoring it out, we have

$$qS_n - S_n = S_n(q - 1) = q^n - 1$$

Dividing both sides by $q - 1$, we finally form the expression of S_n:

$$S_n = 1 + q + q^2 + q^3 + \cdots + q^{n-1} = (q^n - 1)/(q - 1) \qquad (12)$$

The same result may be obtained by direct algebraic division of the difference $q^n - 1$ by $q - 1$:

$$
\begin{array}{r}
q^{n-1} + q^{n-2} + \cdots q^2 + q + 1 \\
\hline
q - 1 \,\big|\, q^n - 1 \\
q^n - q^{n-1} \\
\hline
q^{n-1} - 1 \\
q^{n-1} - q^{n-2} \\
\hline
q^{n-2} - 1 \text{ etc.}
\end{array}
$$

The algebraic identity thus obtained

$$1 + q + q^2 + q^3 + \cdots + q^{n-1} = (q^n - 1)/(q - 1)$$

holds for all finite values of q except the value $q = 1$ (division of zero by zero being meaningless). If, for instance, $q = 2$ it gives

$$1 + 2 + 4 + 8 + 16 + \cdots + 2^{n-1} = (2^n - 1)/(2 - 1) = 2^n - 1$$

and the numerical result for $n = 64$

$$1 + 2 + 4 + 8 + 16 + \cdots + 2^{63} = 2^{64} - 1$$

represents, according to an old tale, the number of grains of wheat asked as reward by the Hindu inventor of chess, Sissa ben Dahir, from his King Shirham: a grain to be placed on the first square, twice as much on the second, and so on, multiplying each time the number of grains on the previous square by 2 and covering all 64 squares of the chess board. The King granted his demand, exclaiming "And this is all you wish, Sissa?", but when it came to paying Sissa, His Majesty was unable to amass such a huge quantity of grain and Sissa was decapitated.

The division of $q^n - 1$ by $q - 1$ shows that the algebraic division of a polynominal by another polynominal of lower degree is performed exactly in the same way as a long division of two numbers. This is not surprising because, as we know, numbers are polynomials. To find the successive terms of the algebraic quotient $q^{n-1} + q^{n-2} + \cdots + q + 1$ we always divide the term with greatest exponent in the dividend and in the successive remainders by the term with greatest exponent in the divisor.

Reverting to the expression (12) of S_n we observe that it can be split into two parts. Multiplying in the algebraic fraction $(q^n - 1)/(q - 1)$ by minus one the numerator and the denominator, we transform it first into the equivalent fraction $(1 - q^n)/(1 - q)$. Now to perform the division of the sum $1 - q^n = 1 + (-q^n)$ by the divisor $(1 - q)$ we divide each of the two terms separately by $(1 - q)$, so that

$$S_n = 1/(1 - q) - q^n/(1 - q)$$

The first term $1/(1 - q)$ does not depend on the number n of terms involved in the sum S_n, but the second one, which contains q^n in the numerator, changes its value when n varies.

The ultimate value S of S_n for $n = \infty$ depends therefore on the limit of the second term, that is on the limit of q^n. As we will prove, the value of $\lim_{n=\infty} q^n$ is zero, if q is less than one and positive. The final result is therefore the existence of the limit

$$\lim_{n=\infty} S_n = 1/(1-q) \qquad (0 < q < 1) \tag{13}$$

because

$$\lim_{n=\infty} [q^n/(1-q)] = (\lim_{n=\infty} q^n)/(1-q) = 0/(1-q) = 0$$

To prove that $q^n \to 0$ for $n \to \infty$, if $q < 1$, we need the inequality

$$(1+p)^n > 1 + np \qquad (p > 0) \tag{14}$$

found by Bernoulli, which holds for all integral values of $n \geqslant 2$, p being any positive number. We will use mathematical induction to prove this inequality. For $n = 2$ we obtain, performing the multiplication of $1 + p$ by itself and omitting p^2

$$(1+p)^2 = (1+p)(1+p) = 1 + p + p + p^2$$

$$= 1 + 2p + p^2 > 1 + 2p$$

since p^2 is obviously positive. Thus, $1 + 2p + p^2$ is greater than $1 + 2p$ and the inequality (14) is proved for $n = 2$.

To justify its validity for all values of n we must now prove its hereditary character. Let us suppose that it holds for $n = k$, that is let us assume that the inequality

$$(1+p)^k > 1 + pk$$

is true. Forming $(1+p)^{k+1}$ for the next value $n = k + 1$ of n, we obtain

$$(1+p)^{k+1} = (1+p)^k (1+p) > (1+pk)(1+p)$$

where we have replaced the first factor $(1+p)^k$ by $1 + pk$ which has been assumed smaller. Now, performing the multiplication and omitting p^2k, we obtain

$$(1+pk)(1+p) = 1 + pk + p + p^2k = 1 + (k+1)p + p^2k$$

$$> 1 + (k+1)p$$

Therefore, $(1+p)^{k+1} > 1 + p(k+1)$, and (14) is justified for $n = k + 1$, if it is true for $n = k$. Since (14) holds for $n = 2$, it is true for $n = 3$, hence for $n = 4$ and so on $ad\ infinitum$.

Having proved Bernoulli's inequality (14), we can show that $\lim_{i=\infty} q^n = 0$ for $0 < q < 1$. The reciprocal $1/q$ of the number $q < 1$ must be greater than one since by definition the product of two reciprocal numbers is equal to one. Therefore, we can denote the reciprocal of q by $1 + p$, p being some positive number, so that $1/q = 1 + p$ is greater than one. Now, q being the reciprocal of $1 + p$, we have $q = 1/(1 + p)$ and

$$q^n = [1/(1 + p)]^n = 1/(1 + p)^n$$

But $(1 + p)^n > 1 + pn$ and since by decreasing the denominator one increases the value of the fraction, we conclude that

$$0 < q^n = 1/(1 + p)^n < 1/(1 + pn) < 1/pn$$

But the fraction $1/pn$ is infinitely small for $n \to \infty$; it tends to zero and $\lim_{n=\infty} q^n = 0$, too.

In particular we have justified our assertion that $(1/2)^n = q^n$ for $q = 1/2$ is infinitely small for $n \to \infty$. Having proved the formula (13), we can now use the equality

$$1 + q + q^2 + q^3 + q^4 + \cdots q^n + \cdots = 1/(1 - q) \qquad (15)$$

for any positive value of q less than one, $0 < q < 1$.

EXAMPLE: If $q = 0.1$ we have

$$1.1111 \cdots = 1 + 0.1 + 0.001 + 0.0001 \cdots$$

$$= 1 + 0.1 + (0.1)^2 + (0.1)^3 + \cdots + (0.1)^n + \cdots$$

$$= 1/(1 - 0.1) = 1/0.9 = 10/9$$

and, subtracting one from both sides, we deduce that

$$0.111 \cdots = 0.\dot{1} = 1/9$$

Multiplying both sides by 9, we obtain

$$0.999 \cdots = 0.\dot{9} = 1$$

It is important that from the existence of this particular decimal fraction we can deduce the existence of all possible infinite decimal fractions. The most general one $0 \cdot a_1 a_2 \cdots a_n \cdots$ is formed with the aid of positive (or zero) digits $a_1, a_2, a_3, \ldots a_n, \ldots$, all of them being at most equal to nine. Since the sum

$$9/10 + 9/100 + 9/1000 + \cdots + 9/10^n + \cdots = 1 \qquad (16)$$

does exist and has a meaning, all possible sums

$$a_1/10 + a_2/100 + a_3/1000 + \cdots + a_n/10^n + \ldots \tag{17}$$

whose terms are all less than or, at most, equal to corresponding terms of the sum (16), exist as perfectly determined and fixed numbers.

Although all recurrent, that is infinite and periodic, decimal fractions are in fact geometric series, aperiodic infinite decimal fractions have nothing in common with them. An infinite aperiodic decimal fraction such as (17), where $0 \leqslant a^n \leqslant 9$, is an infinite convergent expression belonging to a general class of infinite sums called *infinite series*.

Let us now suppose that the standard ratio q of a geometric series is a negative number whose absolute value $|q|$ is less than one so that q exceeds minus one $-1 < q < 0$. The algebraic formula for S_n

$$S_n = 1 + q + q^2 + \cdots + q^{n-1} = 1/(1-q) - q^n/(1-q) \tag{18}$$

holds also for negative q. We have $|q^n| = |q|^n$, where $|q| < 1$, and therefore, as it was proved above:

$$\lim_{n=\infty} |q^n| = \lim_{n=\infty} |q|^n = 0.$$

We see therefore that the absolute value of the second term in the expression (18) of S_n is infinitely small for $n \to \infty$ also in the case, when $-1 < q < 0$:

$$\lim_{n-\infty} |q^n/(1-q)| = (\lim_{n=\infty} |q^n|) = 0.$$

Therefore a geometric series has a meaning for negative as well as positive q, provided the absolute value of q remains less than one. The number represented by a geometric series with a negative standard ratio q is equal to the reciprocal of $1 - q$, because the formula

$$\lim_{n=\infty} S_n = 1/(1-q)$$

holds for $q \gtrless 0$, provided that $|q| < 1$. For instance, if $q = -1/2$, we obtain as a final result of an infinite number of additions and subtractions, a finite number $1/(1 + 1/2) = 1/(3/2) = 2/3$:

$$1 - 1/2 + 1/4 - 1/8 + 1/16 - 1/32 + \ldots + (-1)^n/2^n + \cdots = 2/3 \tag{19}$$

The geometric picture of the approach to the point 2/3 exhibited by the sequence of partial sums of (19) is the following one:

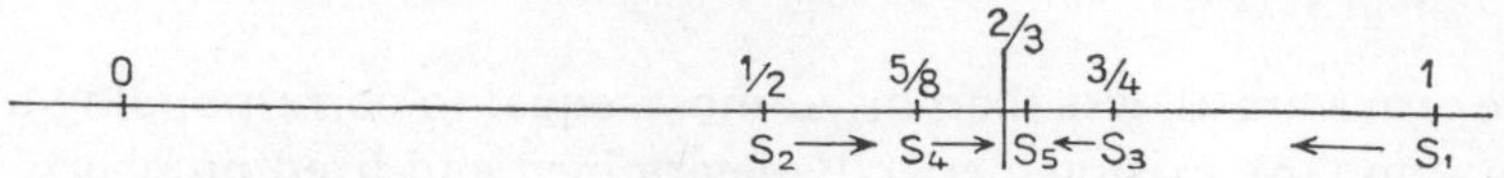

Fig. 4.3

and the point 2/3 appears as a cut separating two infinite sequences of points

$$S_1 > S_3 > \cdots > S_{2n+1} > \cdots > 2/3 > \cdots > S_{2n} > \cdots > S_4 > S_2$$

which approach it from two opposite directions. The sequence of partial sums S_{2n} of an *even* number $2n$ of terms is an *increasing* sequence and the points S_{2n} approach 2/3 from the left. The sequence of partial sums S_{2n+1} of an odd number $2n + 1$ of terms is a *decreasing* sequence and the points S_{2n+1} approach 2/3 from the right:

$$S_2 = 1/2 = (2/3)(1 - 2^{-2}) \qquad S_1 = 1 = (2/3)(1 + 2^{-1})$$
$$S_4 = 5/8 = (2/3)(1 - 2^{-4}) \qquad S_3 = 3/4 = (2/3)(1 + 2^{-3})$$
$$S_6 = 21/32 = (2/3)(1 - 2^{-6}) \qquad S_5 = 11/16 = (2/3)(1 + 2^{-5})$$

These expressions are particular cases of general formulas

$$S_{2n} = (2/3)(1 - 2^{-2n}) \qquad S_{2n+1} = (2/3)(1 + 2^{-2n-1})$$

which show that the distance $S_{2n+1} - S_{2n}$ between the points S_{2n+1} and S_{2n} decreases when n tends to infinity: $S_3 - S_2 = 1/4$; $S_5 - S_4 = 1/16$; $S_7 - S_6 = 1/64$ *etc.* In general

$$S_{2n+1} - S_{2n} = (2/3)(2^{-2n-1} + 2^{-2n}) = 4^{-n} = 2^{-2n}$$

The point of accumulation, 2/3, is the common limit for points of both sequences S_{2n+1} and S_{2n}. It is interior to all the intervals (S_{2n}, S_{2n+1}). These intervals form such an infinite sequence that each one of them is interior to its predecessor and contains in its interior the next interval. Such a sequence is called sequence of *nested* intervals.

The length of the *n*-th interval, $S_{2n+1} - S_{2n}$, is equal to $4^{-n} = 1/4^n$. It is an infinitesimal small and tends to zero, when n increases without limit. Thus, our sequence of nested intervals shrinks to the point 2/3 and it can be considered as a definition of the number 2/3 represented by a point which is interior to all the intervals of a sequence of nested intervals.

The algebraic counterpart of this geometric definition of a rational number as the limit of a sequence of nested intervals which shrink to zero consists of an infinite set of numerical inequalities

$$S_2 = 1/2 < 2/3 < 1 = S_1$$
$$S_4 = 5/8 < 2/3 < 3/4 = S_3$$
$$S_6 = 21/32 < 2/3 < 11/16 = S_5$$
$$\dotsb$$
$$S_{2n} = (2/3)(1 - 2^{-2n}) < 2/3 < (2/3)(1 + 2^{-2n-1}) = S_{2n+1}$$

In these inequalities the difference $S_{2n+1} - S_{2n} = 1/2^{2n}$ between the upper and the lower bounds for 2/3 given by the n-th inequality approaches zero when $n \to \infty$. We will see later how important is this method of defining a number by an infinite set of inequalities in the study of numbers in general.

To complete the study of the geometric series let us consider its particular cases for (a) $q = -1$, (b) $q = 1$, and (c) $q > 1$. The last case (c) is very simple; if $q < -1$ or $q > 1$, we have in both cases $|q| > 1$ and $|q^n|$ increases with n. It is easy to show that $|q^n|$ increases without limit. Since by hypothesis $|q| > 1$, we can write $|q|$ as $1 + p$, where $p > 0$ is some positive number: $|q| = 1 + p$. Thus, applying Bernoulli's inequality:

$$|q^n| = |q|^n = (1 + p)^n > 1 + pn > pn$$

But $pn \to \infty$, if $n \to \infty$, and therfore $|q^n| \to \infty$, if $|q| > 1$. We conclude that the second term $q^n/(1 - q)$ in the expression (12) of S_n tends to infinity, when $n \to \infty$, if $|q| > 1$. For a positive q, $q > 1$, we have $\lim_{n=\infty} S_n = \infty$ because

$$\lim_{n=\infty} [-q^n/(1 - q)] = \lim_{n=\infty} [q^n/(q - 1)] = +\infty$$

For a negative q, $q < -1$, q^n increases in absolute value, but is alternatively positive and negative, according to n being even or odd. Therefore, if $q < -1$, S_n increases in absolute value without limit and forever oscillates between $-\infty$ and $+\infty$ without approaching a definite and finite limit. We formulate our findings by stating that a geometric series with $|q| > 1$, $(q < -1$, or $q > 1)$, is a *divergent* series and as such has for us neither meaning nor value.

If $q = 1$, the terms of the geometric series are equal to 1 and it diverges since $S_n = n$ and $\lim_{n=\infty} S_n = +\infty$.

The case (a), $q = -1$, corresponds to the infinite expression

$$1 - 1 + 1 - 1 + 1 - 1 + 1 - \cdots + (-1)^n \cdots \qquad (20)$$

which again is a divergent series since the sequence of its partial sums

$$1, 0, 1, 0, 1, 0, \ldots$$

diverges: it oscillates from one to zero and back indefinitely. We will have more to say about (20) later. For the moment, summing up our findings, we come to the conclusion that a geometric series converges, has a meaning and represents a number if and only if its standard ratio q remains between -1 and 1.

The convergence of a geometric series for $|q| < 1$ is due without doubt to the extremely rapid decrease of the absolute value $|q|^n$ of q^n, when n runs through all the integers: the terms decrease so rapidly that accumulating and adding an infinite number of them we obtain nevertheless a *finite* sum. But the mere fact that the terms of a series form a decreasing sequence is not sufficient in itself to insure convergence and to yield a finite sum. The simplest example of this fact is the so-called *harmonic series*

$$1 + 1/2 + 1/3 + 1/4 + 1/5 + \cdots + 1/n + \cdots$$

which may be defined as the result of adding the reciprocals of all integers taken in their natural order. The harmonic series is a *divergent* series and the sum of the reciprocals of all integers is infinite. The *partial sums* s_n of the first n terms of the harmonic series

$$s_n = 1 + 1/2 + 1/3 + 1/4 + \cdots + 1/n \qquad (n = 1, 2, 3, \ldots)$$

increase without limit: $s_n \to \infty$, if $n \to \infty$, notwithstanding the fact that its *terms* decrease and tend to zero, $\lim_{n=\infty} (1/n) = 0$.

The use of a divergent series which represents infinity is a source of error and we give here an exemple of such an erroneous conclusion caused by the introduction of, and operations with symbols devoid of any meaning. Suppose that, disregarding the fact that for the harmonic series $s_n \to \infty$, if $n \to \infty$, we introduce a symbol S for the infinite sum of reciprocals of all integers and write the equality

$$S = 1 + 1/2 + 1/3 + 1/4 + \cdots + 1/n + \cdots \qquad (21)$$

This sum S whose existence as a finite and perfectly determined number is fallaciously postlated by introducing a symbol for it, must be positive since all its terms are positive. Dividing S by two

$$S/2 = 1/2 + 1/4 + 1/6 + 1/8 + \cdots + 1/(2n) + \cdots \qquad (22)$$

we obtain the sum of the reciprocals of all *even* integers. Subtracting (22) from (21) we have a third infinite sum

$$S - S/2 = S/2 = 1 + 1/3 + 1/5 + 1/7 + \cdots + 1/(2n + 1) + \cdots \quad (23)$$

which is the sum of reciprocals of all *odd* integers. Finally, subtracting (22) term by term from (23), we get a contradiction:

$$S/2 - S/2 = 0 = (1 - 1/2) + (1/3 - 1/4) + (1/5 - 1/6) + \cdots$$

This result is a contradiction since a sum of *positive* terms such as $(1 - 1/2) = 1/2$, $(1/3 - 1/4) = 1/12$, $(1/5 - 1/6) = 1/30$ *etc.* cannot be equal to zero. All the steps of our reasoning are simple and there is no error in them except the initial hypothesis implied by ascribing a symbol S to the sum (21). The final conclusion being absurd, we must have committed an error somewhere. The logical chain being valid, the error can only be at its beginning and we see even if we did not know that the harmonic series is divergent—that our initial step must have been wrong. There is no finite number S which could be equal to the sum of the harmonic series. Therefore the harmonic series is a meaningless expression; it does not represent a number, and the source of our fallacious conclusion that $0 = 1/2 + 1/12 + 1/30 + \cdots$ is the introduction and use of the meaningless symbol S. This result is an indirect proof of the divergence of the harmonic series because the statement that a sum of *positive* terms is not a finite number is equivalent to the assertion that it is infinite. Since the sequence of partial sums of the harmonic series is an increasing infinite sequence there are only two alternatives: either this sequence increases without limit and the series represents infinity or it increases towards a finite limit.

Here is the direct proof of divergence of harmonic series. Consider a finite sum of 2^n terms

$$T_n = 1/(2^n + 1) + 1/(2^n + 2) + \cdots + 1/2^{n+1}$$

which are reciprocals of successive integers beginning with $2^n + 1$ and ending with 2^{n+1}. Each of these 2^n terms is greater than the last one. Therefore their sum T_n is greater than 2^n times 2^{-n-1}, that is greater than one-half: $T_n > 1/2$. Now we can find such groups T_1, T_2, *etc.* in the harmonic series. It can be written, indeed, as follows:

$$1 + 1/2 + (1/3 + 1/4) + (1/5 + 1/6 + 1/7 + 1/8) + \cdots$$

which is nothing else but

$$1 + 1/2 + T_1 + T_2 + T_3 + T_4 + \cdots + T_n + \cdots$$

all the groups T_n being present. Therefore, the numerical value of the sum of reciprocals of all integers exceeds the sum of an *infinite* number of terms equal to one-half and this proves that the sum in question is infinite.

We will now give some important applications of convergent geometric series. Archimedes, who was the first to discover and use geometric series, is responsible for our first illustration. In his computation of an area bounded by a curve (parabola) and a straight line he summed up the geometric series

$$1 + 1/4 + 1/16 + 1/64 + \cdots + 1/4^n + \cdots$$

ascribing to it the value 4/3. Here $q = 1/4$ and $1/(1 - q) = 1/(3/4) = 4/3$.

It is easy to show that any infinite periodic decimal fraction is a geometric series and thus its value can be computed by using the formula $S = 1/(1 - q)$. Take, for instance, the fraction

$$x = 0.23\dot{1}4285\dot{7} = 0.23 + 0.00\dot{1}4285\dot{7}$$

The second term $0.00\dot{1}4285\dot{7} = 0.\dot{1}4285\dot{7}/100$ is a fraction and its numerator $y = 0.\dot{1}4285\dot{7}$ can be written as a geometric series with $q = 1/10^6$. Picking out the common factor 0.142857 in

$$y = 0.\dot{1}4285\dot{7} = 0.142857 + 0.142857/10^6 + 0.142857/10^{12} + \cdots$$

we obtain

$$y = 0.142857[1 + q + q^2 + q^3 + \cdots + q^n + \cdots]$$

where $q = 1/10^6$. Therefore, since $10^6 - 1 = 999999$

$$y = 0.142857/(1 - q) = 0.142857/(1 - 1/10^6) = 142857/999999,$$

that is $y = 1/7$. Thus, the second term is equal to 1/700, so that

$$y = 23/100 + 1/700 = 161/700 + 1/700 = 162/700 = 81/350$$

We have seen that the rational points are everywhere dense on the number axis and have added without proof that nevertheless, if they are condensed, they do not form a finite length. Now with the aid of geometric series it can be proved. Suppose that if there are points on the line other than rational points (later we will see that there are such "irrational" points on the line), all such points are dropped and rational points only remain on the line with gaps between them instead of "irrational" points. As we have proved, the set of all rational numbers can be ordered and, as a result of this fact, each rational point-image of a rational number receives an ordinal number as its index of order. Choosing a fixed length h (note that h is arbitrary and can be chosen *as small as we want*), we associate an interval of length $h/2$ with the first rational point P_1, an interval of length $h/4 = h/2^2$ with the second, P_2, and so on, associating with the n-th point P_n, the image of the n-th rational number, an interval of length $h/2^n$. Let this process be considered as completed for all rational points, that is for all values of $n = 1$, 2, 3, 4 ...

In associating the rational points and the intervals we enclosed each point P_n in the interior of the corresponding n-th interval. Instead of

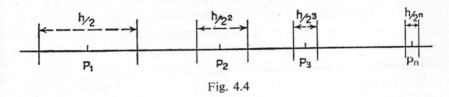

Fig. 4.4

condensing all the rational points on the line, we juxtapose the intervals which surround them.

The total length L obtained after the addition of *all* intervals is clearly the sum of the geometric series

$$L = h/2 + h/2^2 + h/2^3 + h/2^4 + \cdots + h/2^n + \cdots$$

The first term is a common factor of all terms. Picking it out, we write L as

$$L = (h/2) [1 + 1/2 + (1/2)^2 + (1/2)^3 + (1/2)^4 + \cdots + (1/2)^n + \cdots]$$

and since the sum of the infinite number of terms in the parenthesis is $1/(1 - 1/2) = 2$, we obtain $L = h$ which proves that all the rational points can be imprisoned in a length h, where h is as small as we want.

If, after being condensed, they were to form an interval of some non-vanishing length a, we could never imprison them in as small an interval as we want. The inequality $a < h$ is impossible if its first member is a *fixed* quantity different from zero, while the second member can be chosen as small as we want. It becomes possible only, when $a = 0$ and therefore proves that, if we condense the rational points of an infinite straight line as close to each other as all the points of the line are, we do not obtain a length. The continuity itself of the straight line and its tangible expression in the length of its segments are due uniquely to the existence on the line of points other than rational.

This important fact means that there are points on the line whose distances from a fixed point 0, chosen as the origin of the distances, cannot be measured and expressed by rational numbers. It becomes clear to us that, before trying to apply the number concept to the study of nature, we must first generalize it in such a way that we will be able to express in numbers all possible distances. In other words we must create a new kind of number, the irrational number, which is capable of expressing the distances of irrational points from the origin 0.

It is important to emphasize that this conclusion is suggested by the concept of length and is therefore an immediate corollary of our intuitive idea of the straight line as a *continuous* structure formed by an infinite collection of simple *dimensionless* elements, its points. We know that point, the fundamental element of geometry, has no length by definition, and we see now that the logical necessity of defining the new kind of number, the irrational number, is a necessary corollary of our assumption that points, elements of length, have themselves no length. We have been able to imprison a rational point in an interval of infinitely small length $h/2^n$ only because a point in general is supposed to have no length.

Are we right in refusing to ascribe an atomic structure to the line? Perhaps point, the atom of the line and therefore also an element of such a necessary attribute of the line as its length, should be considered as having this attribute of length too. Maybe it has a length too small to be perceived, but fixed? This question must be answered before introducing the concept of irrational number based on the definition of point as a dimensionless element.

The proofs that point has no length are necessarily geometric and we will use some simple geometric facts, anticipating the second half of this book which discusses geometry. Here is the first one, based on the one-to-one correspondence of certain infinite collections and on the proportionality of sides of similar triangles. Intersecting both sides of the angle *EOF* by two parallel lines **AB** and **CD**, **AB//DC**,

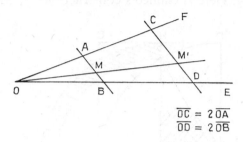

$$\overline{OC} = 2\,\overline{OA}$$
$$\overline{OD} = 2\,\overline{OB}$$

Fig. 4.5

where points *A* and *C* are such that **OC** = 2**OA** we consider two parallel segments **AB** and **CD**. The two triangles *OAB* and *OCD* are similar so that the length **CD** is twice that of **AB**:

$$CD/AB = OD/OB = OC/OA = 2$$

To disprove the hypothesis that a point has a length, let us assume its truth, and then deduce a contradiction. We conclude first that, if a point has a length there must be a finite number of points in **AB** and **CD**, and second that there are twice as many points in **CD** as in **AB** since the length of **CD** is double of that of **AB**. On the other hand the points on **AB** can be put into one-to-one correspondence with the points on **CD** by drawing through O lines such as **OMM'**. There is one and only one point at the intersection of two lines. A line **OM** which intersects **CD** at one and only one point *M'* corresponds to each point *M* on **AB**. Therefore, to each point *M* on **AB** there corresponds one and only one point *M'* on **CD** and *vice versa*, as can be shown by tracing a line through O and *M'*. Two collections have the same number of members, if they can be put into one-to-one correspondence. Therefore there are as many points in **AB** as in **CD** which contradicts our second conclusion, namely that there are twice as many points in **CD** as in **AB**.

The second proof which is more complicated is based on Pythagoras' theorem and on the measure πR^2 of a circle's area, if the circle's radius is *R*. It can be traced back to Galileo who considered it as a paradox. The explanation of this paradox is the work of Bernhard Bolzano who was the first to study the concept of infinity. His little pamphlet "Die Paradoxien des Unendlichen", published posthumously in 1851 but written in 1816, marked an important step in the evolution of mathematical thinking. Here is Galileo's construction:

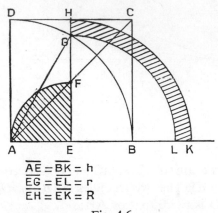

$$\overline{AE} = \overline{BK} = h$$
$$\overline{EG} = \overline{EL} = r$$
$$\overline{EH} = \overline{EK} = R$$

Fig. 4.6

Inscribe in a square $ABCD$ a quarter of a circle with the center at A and the radius R equal to the side $\mathsf{AB} = R$ of the square. Draw the diagonal AC and a parallel EH to the vertical side AD of our square through the point E chosen arbitrarily on the base AB at a distance $\mathsf{AE} = h$ from A.

$$\mathsf{AE} = \mathsf{BK} = h$$
$$\mathsf{EG} = \mathsf{EL} = r$$
$$\mathsf{EH} = \mathsf{EK} = R$$

This parallel meets the diagonal AC, the circular arc DB and the upper side DC at the points F, G, H respectively. Now, with E as center, draw three circular arcs FA, GL, HK with radii $\mathsf{EF} = \mathsf{AE} = h$, $\mathsf{EG} = \mathsf{EL} = r$, and $\mathsf{EH} = \mathsf{EK} = R$ respectively. We proceed now to prove that the two shaded areas AEF (curvilinear triangle) and $LKHG$ (quarter of a circular ring between two circles of radii r and R) are equal areas. Joining G to A we obtain $\mathsf{AG} = R$ and applying the Pythagorean theorem to the triangle AEG we obtain $\mathsf{AG}^2 = \mathsf{AE}^2 + \mathsf{EG}^2$ that is $R^2 = h^2 + r^2$, and multiplying by $\pi/4$,

$$\pi h^2/4 = \pi R^2/4 - \pi r^2/4.$$

The left member is the measure of the shaded area AEF (quarter of the circle with radius h), while the right member is the measure of the shaded area $LKHG$ (quarter of the circular ring). Therefore, the two areas are equal. Now let us shift the point E closer and closer to the point A choosing an infinitely small $h = AE$, so that for $h \to 0$ the first area shrinks into the *point A* and the second area shrinks into the *arc DB*, quarter of the circle of radius R.

The choice of h as an infinitely small number means that, being variable and approaching zero, h runs through an infinite sequence of successive fixed values $h_1, h_2, h_3, ..., h_n, ...$ converging to zero, such that $\lim_{n=\infty} h_n = 0$. At every step, for every fixed value h_n of $h \to 0$, the two areas are equal and therefore they must remain equal at the limit when $h = 0$. But their limits for $h = 0$ are a point A for the first area and a circular arc of finite length DB for the second area. Galileo's paradox consists precisely of the equality of a point A and an arc DB. Its solution, given by Bolzano, states that it is impossible to ascribe any dimensions to a point since this reasoning would then ascribe the same measure to a point A and to a set of many points, elements of the arc BD. Since a point has no area, the equality (24) at the limit, when $h = 0$, is transformed into $0 = 0$, and it proves not only that a point is dimensionless, but also that a line has no area, and hence only one dimension, length.

Let us finally apply the geometric series to the second argument of Zeno, the famous race between Achilles and the tortoise. Zeno says that although Achilles runs much faster than the tortoise he cannot catch it, if the tortoise has an initial head start. Here are his words (Aristotle, *Physica*): "The slower will never be overtaken in its course by the quicker, for the pursuer will always come first to the point from which the pursued had just departed, so the slower necessarily must always be more or less in advance". In this context the words "more or less" are important because their use implies that Zeno realized fully the infinitely small character of the forever decreasing distance separating the pursuer from the pursued. What the Greek thinking was unable to understand and accept was again the final disappearance of this infinitesimal distance which becomes zero only *at the limit*, after the completion of an *actually infinite* sequence of steps of thought.

Zeno was unable to compute *where* and *when* Achilles catches the tortoise because he refused to understand *how* it could happen. We will now apply with Zeno the infinite divisibility of space and time, and, with the aid of passage to the limit embodied in the concept of geometric series, we shall obtain precise numerical answers to these questions of where and when.

To fix our ideas we represent the pursuer and the pursued by two points P and Q respectively and we count the time t in seconds from the moment when the race begins. At this initial moment $t = 0$, the point P (pursuer) is at the origin O, but the point Q (pursued) is at the point P_1, at a distance $OP_1 = 10$ feet from the origin. Let the speeds of P and Q be ten feet and one foot per second, respectively. In the first phase of the race, (first step of thought) P reaches P_1 in one second and at $t = 1$ sec. P is at P_1, but Q has moved to P_2 such that $P_1P_2 = 1$ foot. The distance PQ is now equal to one foot and is ten times smaller than before. Now the second phase begins (second step of thought): P, in 0.1 second, reaches P_2 but Q has moved to P_3 and the distance between P and Q is now 0.1 foot. It has decreased again ten times. We continue with Zeno indefinitely and the number of phases (steps of thought) is infinite. The distance PQ at each step of thought decreases ten times. For Zeno it is always there and never reaches zero. For us it is also different from zero while the number of steps of thought continues to increase, n running through the set of integers (potential infinity). But if we ask ourselves what the *ultimate* value of the distance PQ is, we realize that it is zero since every infinitesimal small quantity vanishes at the limit.

To answer when and where the pursuer P catches the pursued Q we analyze with Zeno the phases of the race:

Phase (Step of thought)	Duration of the phase	Distance covered by P	Distance covered by Q	Distance PQ
First	1 second	10 feet	1 foot	1 foot
Second	0.1	1	0.1	0.1
Third	0.01	0.1	0.01	0.01
...	...	...	...	...
n-th	$\underbrace{0.0 \cdots 01}_{n \text{ digits}}$	$\underbrace{0.0 \cdots 01}_{n-1 \text{ digits}}$	$\underbrace{0.0 \cdots 01}_{n \text{ digits}}$	$\underbrace{0.0 \cdots 01}_{n \text{ digits}}$

Summing up the infinite series of numbers in the second column, it is seen that the whole race takes only 10/9 seconds since

$$1.111 \cdots = 1.\dot{1} = 1 + 1/9 = 10/9$$

During this times the pursuer ran $11.111 \cdots = 11.\dot{1} = 10 + 10/9$ feet, while the pursued covered only $1.111 \cdots = 1.\dot{1} = 10/9$ feet. Thus, the pursuer catches the pursued in $10/9$ seconds at $10/9$ feet from the point P_1 and there is no mystery for us where Greek thinking was completely puzzled.

The application of geometric series to the second Argument of Zeno well emphasizes the importance of this new act of thinking called passage to the limit and in which an actually infinite chain of steps of thought is used. Without this new powerful tool, this bold "jump into aleph-null" embodied in geometric series as well as in all infinite series, derivatives and integrals, human thinking would remain forever as childishly helpless and bewildered before Nature as was Greek thinking two thousand years ago. If today mankind has at his disposal innumerable and wonderful machines, it is a tangible result of the creation of theoretical physics the existence of which is due uniquely to modern mathematics, that is, in the end, to the creation of a new act of thinking called passage to the limit.

CHAPTER 5

Irrational Numbers

Radicals and Fractional Exponents

The introduction of negative integers and of rational numbers was motivated by the extension of the inverse operations of subtraction and division, so as to include all possible cases. We will consider now the operations which are inverse to the direct operation of exponentiation.

There are two such operations since the commutative law does not apply to the exponentiation, the base and the exponent playing two different roles. We have indeed $3^4 = 81 \neq 64 = 4^3$, and in general $a^b \neq b^a$. In exponentiation, three numbers, a, b, and c are involved in the relation $a^b = c$, and in this direct operation a and b are considered as known and it is the value c of the power a^b which is to be computed. To invert this operation we consider c as known. We have then two choices for our unknown. We first ask the value of the unknown *base x* such that, if raised to a power with a known exponent b, it generates a number whose value is c:

$$x^b = c \tag{1}$$

On the other hand we can also ask the value of the unknown *exponent t* such that the power a^t of the known base a with exponent t has the given, prescribed value c

$$a^t = c \tag{2}$$

These equations define two different inverse operations corresponding to the same direct operation of exponentiation. The equation $a^t = c$ falls within the realm of logarithms and we postpone its study until Chapter 11, concentrating our attention on the first equation $x^b = c$.

Sometimes this equation can be solved in terms of rational numbers. Taking for instance $b = 2$ and $c = 25/49$ we have the equation $x^2 = 25/49$,

142

where the second member 25/49 is a perfect square: $25/49 = (5/7)^2$, so that $x = \pm 5/7$. In general, if $x^2 = a^2$, the unknown x is easy to find with the aid of an algebraic *identity*, which is deducible as follows:

Multiplying the sum of any two numbers $a + b$ by their difference $a - b$, we obtain the difference of their squares:

$$(a + b)(a - b) = a^2 + ba - ab - b^2 = a^2 - b^2$$

Thus, for $a = 60$ and $b = 2$ we have $a + b = 62$, $a - b = 58$, and $62 \cdot 58 = (60 + 2)(60 - 2) = 60^2 - 2^2 = 3600 - 4 = 3596$. This important algebraical formula

$$(a + b)(a - b) \equiv a^2 - b^2 \tag{3}$$

is called an *identity* because it holds for all values of a and b. The relations which are true only for the special values of quantities involved are called equations. To distinguish between these two kind of equalities, the signs $=$ and $\equiv$ are sometimes used, the latter denoting an identical equality. Equations are solved to find the unknown numbers which verify certain conditions expressed by these equations. Identities are applied to transform the equations in order to facilitate their solution.

The identity (3) can and must be read and used both ways. Not only is the product of the sum of any two numbers times their difference equal to the difference of their squares, but also the difference of two perfect squares $a^2 - b^2$ can be factored into a product, namely the product of the sum $a + b$ times the difference $a - b$. This interpretation of (3) is obtained reading it from the right to the left. It is easy to check this relation in arithmetic: $13^2 - 7^2 = 169 - 49 = 120$ and also $(13 + 7)(13 - 7) = 20 \cdot 6 = 120$, so that $13^2 - 7^2 = (13 + 7) \cdot (13 - 7)$.

There is also a geometric equivalent of (3). Subtracting the area b^2 of the small square *KDEF* from that, a^2, of a larger square *ACEG*, we obtain the shaded area of the figure 5.1 (page 144).

Cutting off the upper shaded rectangle *HKFG* and juxtaposing it to the rectangle *ACDH* so that its vertices G and F coincide with C and D respectively, we transform the shaded area $a^2 - b^2$ into an equivalent rectangular area *AHKH* with the base $\mathsf{AC} + \mathsf{GH} = a + b$ and the altitude $\mathsf{CD} = a - b$, so that the measure of this area is $(a + b)(a - b)$, and the identity (3) is obtained.

Now to solve the equation $x^2 = a^2$ we write it as $x^2 - a^2 = 0$ and, applying (3), factor the difference of two squares:

$$(x + a)(x - a) = 0$$

A product of two factors $(x + a)(x - a)$ can be zero if and only if one of the factors (or both) is zero. The number a being different from zero the sum $x + a$ cannot be equal to the difference $x - a$. Therefore the equation $(x + a)(x - a) = 0$ means that either one of two factors must be zero. If it is the second factor which vanishes and $x - a = 0$,

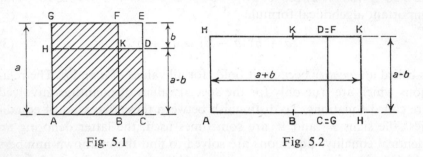

Fig. 5.1   Fig. 5.2

then $x = a$, but if it is the first and $x + a = 0$, then we obtain another value, $x = -a$, for our unknown x. This value is $x = -a$, since $(-a) + a = 0$, and x must verify the equation $x + a = 0$.

Thus $x^2 = a^2$ has two possible solutions: $x = +a$ or $x = -a$. We call each of them the *square root of a^2* and denote the operation of finding a number such that its square is a^2 by $\sqrt{a^2}$. This operation is called extraction of the square root. The square root $\sqrt{a^2}$ of a perfect square such as a^2 has two values, one is positive, the other negative, and both have the same absolute value. Thus, if $x^2 = a^2$, then

$$x = \sqrt{a^2} = \pm a$$

EXAMPLE: Applying to $x^2 = 25/49$ we find $x = \sqrt{25/49} = \pm 5/7$.

To distinguish between different solutions of an equation subscripts are used. Thus, $x_1 = +a$ and $x_2 = -a$ are two solutions of the quadratic equation $x^2 - a^2 = 0$. The name *quadratic* means that the square x^2 of the unknown x is involved, but not its third, fourth, and higher powers.

The operation of extraction of square root is only a particular case of the general operation of extraction of n-th root: given a power x^n of an unknown base with a known *integral* exponent n, we can find the base x, if the value c of the power x^n is known. By definition, a number x such that its n-th power is equal to c, is called n-th *root* of c and is denoted by $\sqrt[n]{c}$. Thus $x^n = c$ is solved by $x = \sqrt[n]{c}$. For instance, we have $3 = \sqrt[4]{81}$, $5 = \sqrt[3]{125}$, $2 = \sqrt[5]{32}$, since $3^4 = 81$, $5^3 = 125$ and $2^5 = 32$. The definition of the symbol $\sqrt[n]{N}$ carries with it the corollary $\sqrt[1]{N} = N$. The symbol $\sqrt[0]{N}$ has no meaning: if N is different from one, $\sqrt[0]{N}$ cannot represent a number since any number raised to the power with exponent 0 is equal to one. But $\sqrt[0]{1}$ is meaningless too, since it has no definite value, *any* number being equal to $\sqrt[0]{1}$. We mention also that the notation $\sqrt{N}$ means $\sqrt[2]{N}$, that is in the particular case of a square root the index 2 in $\sqrt[2]{N}$ is always omitted.

The root of order n, $\sqrt[n]{N}$, of an integer N is also called a *radical*. It is easy to show that radicals are powers themselves, but with fractionary exponents. We have indeed, applying the law of exponentiation:

$$[N^{1/n}]^n = N^{(1/n)n} = N^1 = N$$

Thus the power $N^{1/n}$, whose exponent $1/n$ is the reciprocal of an integer, is equal to the n-th root $\sqrt[n]{N}$ of N:

$$\sqrt[n]{N} = N^{1/n}$$

Raising both sides to the m-th power (m = integer) we obtain:

$$(\sqrt[n]{N})^m = [N^{1/n}]^m = N^{m/n} = (N^m)^{1/n} = \sqrt[n]{N^m}$$

This result shows that the n-th root of the m-th power of N is equal to a power of N with the fractional exponent m/n

$$N^{m/n} = \sqrt[n]{N^m} \qquad (4)$$

Introducing the use of fractional exponents defined by (4), we in fact eilminate radicals and reduce the inverse operation of extraction of roots to the corresponding direct operation of exponentiation.

Fractional exponents are much handier than the obsolete notation of radicals and in general it is advisable to use them instead of radicals. But since in mathematical literature fractional exponents are used concurrently with radicals, we study radicals too. Multiplication and division of radicals as well as their exponentiation become easy when fractional exponents are used. Instead of dividing by $N^{m/n} = \sqrt[n]{N^m}$, we can multiply by its reciprocal $N^{-m/n}$, thus reducing division to multiplication. In the multiplication of two radicals of the *same* number the laws of exponentiation are to be applied. Thus

$$N^{m/n}N^{p/q} = {}^{m/n+p/q} = N^{(mq+np)/nq}$$

which in old times was written awkwardly as

$$\sqrt[n]{N^m}\sqrt[n]{N^p} = \sqrt[nq]{N^{mq+np}}$$

To represent the product of two radicals $\sqrt[n]{N}$ and $\sqrt[m]{M}$ as a single radical we can write:

$$\sqrt[n]{N}\sqrt[m]{M} = N^{1/n}M^{1/m} = N^{m/mn}M^{n/mn} = (N^m M^n)^{1/mn} = \sqrt[mn]{N^m M^n}$$

EXAMPLE: $\sqrt{2}\sqrt[3]{3} = \sqrt[6]{8}\sqrt[6]{9} = \sqrt[6]{72}$

The Square Root of Two as an Irrational Number

In the field of rational numbers the extraction of the n-th root can be performed only if the n-th radical of the corresponding n-th power of rational number is considered. Just as the square root can be extracted only from a perfect square, so $\sqrt[3]{N}$ can be computed only if $N = (p/q)^3$, and so on. Such a simple operation as the extraction of square root of 2 cannot be performed if we limit ourselves to the field of rational numbers. By this we mean that the equality $\sqrt{2} = m/n$ does not hold for *all* possible choices of integers m and n, even though the number of such choices is an infinite one.

This fact was discovered by Pythagoreans and it was a terrific blow to them. They knew that in a right triangle the square of the hypotenuse is equal to the sum of squares of the two sides (Pythagorean Theorem). Therefore, in a square of unit side, the square of its diagonal is expressed by the number 2. On the other hand Greeks used only rational numbers and did not know anything about the existence of irrational numbers. As a result they were obliged to acknowledge the impossibility of expressing the length of the diagonal by a number. This was a complete negation of their fundamental belief, "Number rules the universe".

Let us now see how it can be proved that $\sqrt{2} \neq M/N$ for all integers M and N. Suppose the opposite and denote the two particular integers, such that their ratio is equal to $\sqrt{2}$, by m and n, so that $2 = (\sqrt{2})^2$

$= (m/n)^2 = m^2/n^2$. The fraction m/n may be considered as already reduced to its lowest terms. Hence, we assume m and n to be relatively prime integers, having no common factor by hypothesis. Thus, in particular, m and n cannot be both even, for then they would have the common factor 2. Multiplying both sides of the equation $2 = m^2/n^2$ by n^2 we obtain:

$$2n^2 = m^2$$

This relation $2n^2 = m^2$ proves that m must be even: $2n^2$ is an even number and so is m^2 since they are equal; therefore, m cannot be odd because the square of an odd number is also odd. To prove this we expand the square of any odd number $2s + 1$, where s is any integer,

$$(2s + 1)^2 = (2s + 1)(2s + 1) = 4s^2 + 4s + 1$$
$$= 2(2s^2 + 2s) + 1 = 2K + 1$$

where $K = 2s^2 + 2s$ is an integer. Thus, $(2s + 1)^2$ is odd.

Having proved that m is even, we can write it in the form $m = 2p$, where p is some integer. Therefore, by substitution we obtain $2n^2 = m^2 = 4p^2$. Dividing both sides by 2 we find the same form for n^2, namely $n^2 = 2p^2$ as we have found for m^2. Therefore, applying the same reasoning again, we see that n cannot be odd because its square is even. Thus the hypothesis $\sqrt{2} = m/n$ leads us to the inescapable conclusion that both m and n must be even numbers.

But, if both m and n are even, we have a contradiction: at the very beginning of our reasoning we supposed that m and n had no common factor. Now we see that they have at least one common factor, namely 2. This contradiction proves that something in our reasoning is wrong. All the steps of the logical deduction being valid, the error must have been made at the beginning. We have, indeed, based our deductive reasoning on an unjustified assumption, namely that we *can* find two particular integers m and n, such that the ratio of their squares m^2/n^2 is equal to 2. It becomes clear now that this assumption, as the origin of the contradiction, is fallacious. Therefore we conclude that $\sqrt{2}$ cannot be expressed in the form m/n and it is proved that $\sqrt{2}$ is not a rational number.

We have expounded the proof of the proposition $\sqrt{2} \neq m/n$ as it was found by Greek mathematicians. It is interesting to observe that this ingenious proof becomes superfluous if one uses our decimal system of numeration which was unknown to Greek mathematicians. Observe that, the squares of 0, 1, 2, 3, 4, 5, 6, 7, 8, 9, being 0, 1, 4, 9, 16, 25, 36, 49, 64, 81, the square n^2 of any integer n can have as its digit of the first rank (number of simple units) only 0, 1, 4, 5, 6 and 9, the other four digits 2, 3, 7 and 8 being excluded. Doubling n^2 and forming the number $2n^2$, we obtain as possible digits of the first rank only 0, 2 and 8. Therefore, if $m^2 = 2n^2$, the square m^2 of m can be the square of an integer only, when m terminates by a zero, for $2n^2$ must end in 0, 2 or 8, and m^2 must end in 0, 1, 4, 5, 6 or 9, the *only common* end digit being 0.

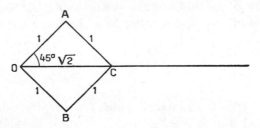

Fig. 5.3

Similarly, since $2n^2 = m^2$, $2n^2$ must terminate by a zero and n^2 can terminate only by 0 or 5, so that n also terminates by 0 or 5. Thus m and n have a common factor equal at least to 5. But, by hypothesis, m and n are relatively prime and we obtain again a contradiction.

This argument can be applied with slight modifications to other numerical cases such as $x^2 = 17$ or $x^3 = 5$. The fact we are studying is general: *when A is not a perfect n-th power of some rational number the equation $x^n = A$ cannot be solved in rational numbers.*

The number $\sqrt{2}$, like the rationals, has a point image on the number-axis. Consider a square with a vertex at O and sides $OA = OB = 1$ so oriented that the number-axis bisects the right angle at O.

It is plain that the diagonal $OC = \sqrt{2}$ is a segment of the number-axis and the distance of the point C from the origin cannot be expressed as a rational number. If we want to apply numbers to the study of nature we must postulate that a number corresponds to each length we can define on a straight line. Therefore $\sqrt{2}$ *must* be a number.

Here we again meet with the necessity of generalizing the number concept, a necessity which is deduced here from purely geometrical considerations. The example of the diagonal OC proves that though the rational points are everywhere dense on the number axis *there are gaps between them* and in these gaps, although they are not intervals and have no length, points other than rational are located because their distances from O cannot be expressed by rational numbers. We call them *irrational* points.

The set of irrational points is also an infinite set, and to prove this we observe that the midpoint of an interval formed by one rational point, m/n, and one irrational, s, is irrational. We have shown that the distance of the midpoint from the origin is expressed by half the sum of the distances m/n and s of both extremities of the interval from the origin 0. Suppose that the midpoint is rational. Then its distance is equal to p/q, where p and q are integers, and we must have

$$(1/2)\,(m/n + s) = p/q$$

Solving for the number s, we obtain for it a *rational* value

$$s = 2p/q - m/n = (2pn - mq)/nq$$

which contradicts our definition of the number s. Therefore, the midpoint of our interval cannot be a rational point: it must be irrational. Therefore, around a given irrational point there are at least as many irrational points as there are rational, that is an infinity of them. Hence, we see that the irrational points too are everywhere dense on the number-axis.

Now we come to the most important question: what is an irrational number? How can it be defined and expressed? Its definition must be based on numbers we know, that is, on rational numbers. Let us begin with the study of a numerical example such as $\sqrt{2}$. To transform an "impossible" operation, $\sqrt{2}$, into a possible one, we first postulate that the symbol $\sqrt{2}$ has a meaning. Thus, we create a new kind of number: the irrational number.

Extraction of a Square Root

We study now the algorithm (process) of extracting square roots, which we will have to apply to $\sqrt{2}$. This algorithm is based on the algebraic identity

$$(A + B)^2 = A^2 + 2AB + B^2 \qquad (5)$$

This identity admits of a simple geometric interpretation. $(A + B)^2$, A^2, B^2 may be considered as areas of square with sides $A + B$, A and B

while AB is the area of a rectangle with sides A and B. Now the square of side $A + B$ can be divided into four parts by two parallels ab, cd to its sides at distance B from the vertex V so that the area $(A + B)^2$ is equal to the sum of the areas of the four parts A^2, B^2, AB, AB. Hence (5) is obtained.

On the other hand, to expand the square $(A + B)^2$ of the sum $A + B$ algebraically, it is sufficient to apply twice the distributive law:

$$(A + B)^2 = (A + B)(A + B) = (A + B)A + (A + B)B$$

$$= A^2 + AB + AB + B^2 = A^2 + 2AB + B^2$$

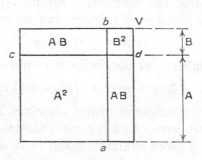

Fig. 5.4

The extraction of a square root, like every inverse operation, is performed by successive trials. Take for instance $N = \sqrt{7383}$. To find the number N whose square is 7383 we first separate the digits of this number into periods of two digits each, beginning with the digits of lower rank: 73'83. The reason for this is the fact that the square N^2 of any integer N contains either twice as many digits as N or one digit less than twice as many, the last, lefthand period sometimes being incomplete and consisting of one digit only. The number of periods fixes the number of digits of the square root and each period in N^2 corresponds to a digit in N. The digits of the root are found one after another and beginning with the second digit the algorithm becomes cyclic, the same operation being applied to find every digit (the first digit of the root is the only exception).To find the first digit, it is sufficient to extract the square root of the largest perfect square contained in the first period. The square root $\sqrt{73'83}$, for instance, is a two digit number and begins with the digit 8, since $8^2 = 64$ is the largest perfect square contained in 73.

To find the second digit of $\sqrt{73'83}$ we represent the square root as $80 + x$ and apply (5) with $A = 80$ and $B = x$, so that

$$7383 = (80 + x)^2 = 6400 + 160x + x^2$$

Subtracting 6400 from both sides we obtain

$$983 = 160x + x^2$$

and this equation for the unknown x will give us the second digit of $\sqrt{7383}$ which is the integral part of the number x. The unknown x is certainly less than 10, so that its integral part does not exceed nine. The first term $160x$ is thus much larger than the second term x^2, so that in the first trial x^2 can be neglected. Replacing the equation $983 = 160 + x^2$ by $983 = 160x$ we try to obtain the integral part of x dividing the remainder 983 by 160, or better 98 by 16. The quotient is less than seven and greater than six, so our first trial is $x = 6$. Forming the value of $160x + x^2$ for $x = 6$, we find 996, a number which is greater than our remainder 983, so that x cannot be equal to six. We try now $x = 5$ and since $160 \cdot 5 + 25 = 825 < 983$, we take 5 as the second digit of $\sqrt{7383}$, leaving a remainder $158 = 983 - 825$.

The successive steps we have performed computing the second digit of the square root can be formulated as follows: subtract the square of the first digit from the first period and complete the remainder by bringing down the *first* digit of the next period; divide the number thus formed (in our case 98) by the *double* of the first digit of the square root (16) and try the integral part of the quotient as the second digit of the square root: write it after the doubled first digit and multiply the number thus obtained by the second digit you are trying. If the product exceeds the remainder obtained by bringing down the whole second period, the second digit is less than the number you have tried and a new trial is needed.

In our case the product, 996, was greater than the remainder 983, and therefore we saw that the integral part 6 of the quotient was greater than the second digit of the square root. Neglecting the term x^2, we increased too much the value of the number x which verifies the equation $983 = 160x + x^2$. Therefore, we did use five, which was one unit less than the integer we tried without success. Sometimes this does not work either; then we continue to diminish by one unit the number n we tried last as x in the expression $160x + x^2 = (160 + x) x$, until the product $(160 + n)\, n$ becomes less than or equal to the remainder. Thus, the second digit of the square root $\sqrt{7383}$ is the largest integer, n, for which the product $(160 + n)\, n$ is less than (or equal to) the remainder 983. To continue the extraction we now add to the right of the dot as many periods, each consisting of two zeros, as we want, and these periods will give us the decimal digits for $\sqrt{7383}$, increasing the accuracy with which $\sqrt{7383}$ is computed. Suppose we add two such empty periods:

$$
\begin{array}{l|l}
 & \quad\ 8 \quad\ 5 \quad\ 9\ \ 2 \\[2pt]
8^2 < 73 < 9^2 & \overline{\ 73'\ \ 83'\cdot\ 00'\ \ 00'} \\
 & -64 \\ \cline{2-2}
\quad\quad\quad\ \ 16'5 & \quad\ 9\ \ 8'3 \\
\quad\quad\quad\quad\ \ 5 & \\ \cline{1-1}
\quad\quad\quad\ \ 825 & -8\ \ 25 \\ \cline{2-2}
166 \cdot 6 = 996 > 983 & \quad 1\ \ 58\ \ 0'0 \\
\quad\quad\ 1\ 70'9 & \\
\quad\quad\quad\quad\ 9 & \\ \cline{1-1}
\quad\quad 15\ 381 & \quad 1\ \ 53\ \ 81 \\ \cline{2-2}
 & \quad\quad\ 4\ \ 19\ \ 0'0 \\
\quad\quad 17\ 18'2 & \\
\quad\quad\quad\quad\ 2 & \\ \cline{1-1}
\quad\quad 34\ 364 & \quad\quad\ 3\ \ 43\ \ 64 \\ \cline{2-2}
 & \quad\quad\ 0\cdot\ 75\ \ 36
\end{array}
$$

To find the first digit of the square root after the dot we subtract $165 \cdot 5 = 825$ from the remainder 983 and obtain the second remainder 158. The cycle is now repeated: completing 158 by the first digit zero of the next period we divide 1580 by the double 170 of the known part of the square root, 85. This gives us nine, as the integral part of the quotient. To try 9 we inscribe 9 after 170 and multiply the number 1709 by 9. The product 15381 is less than the remainder 15800, and thus the third digit of our square root is 9.

Continuing the algorithm, we find that the fourth digit is equal to two, while the remainder is 0.7536. Therefore, what we have found is the square root of 7382.2464, since $(85.92)^2 = 7383 - 0.7536 = 7382.2464$:

$$\sqrt{7382.2464} = 85.92$$

This example suggests that we can compute a square root to any number of decimals by adding twice as many zeros after the dot as we want decimals in the square root. Now, a finite decimal fraction necessarily has a rational value. Therefore, dealing with irrational numbers defined by square roots such as $\sqrt{2}$, $\sqrt{3}$, $\sqrt{5}$ *etc.* we will never be able to finish the extraction of the square root: *irrational square roots are infinite decimal fractions.* We have seen in Chapter 4 that infinite decimal fractions always have a meaning and now, for square roots at least, we find in them a first representation of irrational numbers. To clarify the definition of irrational number we will now study the infinite decimal fraction which is approximated by the extraction of square root of 2.

Assuming an unlimited number of zeros written after 2 and separating them into groups of two, we apply the algorithm of extraction of a square root of $2'00'00'00'00\cdots$ and find thus, one after another, as many decimals as we want:

$$\sqrt{2} = 1.41421356 \cdots$$

With the aid of this infinite decimal fraction we can construct an infinite set of nested intervals such that the irrational point C at the distance $OC = \sqrt{2}$ from the origin O is interior to all these intervals. These nested intervals shrink towards the point C since their lengths approach zero: they are equal successively to 0.1; 0.01; 0.001; ... $(0.1)^n$; .... The point C, point-image of $\sqrt{2}$, appears as the common limit of two sequences of points: the left extremities of our intervals, L_n, approach C from the left and the right extremities, R_n, from the right:

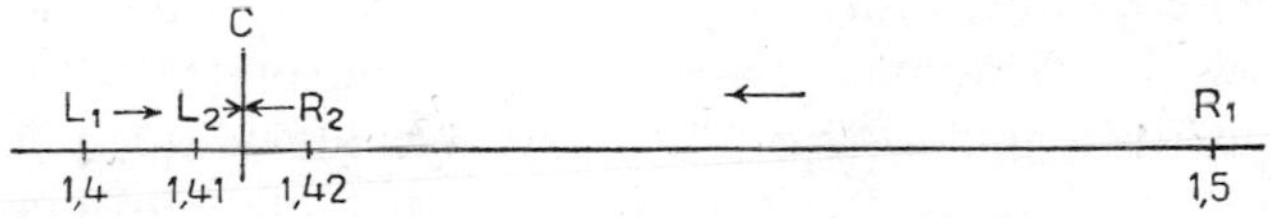

Fig. 5.5

Corresponding to this geometric picture, there are two numerical sequences of *rational* numbers formed by the lefthand members and by the righthand members of an infinite set of inequalities deducible from the infinite decimal representation of $\sqrt{2}$. The difference between the righthand and lefthand members of the n-th inequality is $(0.1)^n = 0.00\cdots$ 01 (n digits after the dot) and it is an infinitesimal small: $\lim_{n=\infty}(0.1)^n = 0$.

Therefore, continuing the extraction of square root we increase the accuracy of our representation of $\sqrt{2}$ as far as we want and at the limit we find $\sqrt{2}$ as represented by an aperiodic *infinite* decimal fraction. Thus, an irrational number can be defined as the common limit of two convergent sequences of rational numbers: the first one (lefthand extremes of successive intervals) being an increasing sequence, the second

n	L_n		R_n	Length of the n-th interval
1	1.4	$< \sqrt{2} <$	1.5	0.1
2	1.41	$< \sqrt{2} <$	1.42	0.01
3	1.414	$< \sqrt{2} <$	1.415	0.001
4	1.4142	$< \sqrt{2} <$	1.4143	0.0001
5	1.41421	$< \sqrt{2} <$	1.41422	0.00001
6	1.414213	$< \sqrt{2} <$	1.414214	0.000001
...	...	...	...	...

(righthand extremes) a decreasing sequence. These two infinite sequences define at the same time an infinite aperiodic decimal fraction which is a representation of the irrational number considered. We have shown this for square roots but the fact is a general one and holds for all irrational numbers regardless of their value.

We have seen that there are an infinite number of rational numbers in any interval (a, b) between two distinct rational numbers a and b, however close we choose them, provided $a \neq b$. We now state that there are an infinite number of *irrational* numbers in every interval (c, d) between any two given numbers c and $d > c$ rational or irrational, because, as we know, the length $d - c$ of this interval is due uniquely to the existence of irrational points and a finite number of them could not be sufficient to generate a length. But also a denumerable infinity of irrational points does not form a length either, because we can apply to this set the same reasoning as one we applied to all rational points of a line. Therefore, not only is the set of irrational points an infinite one, but it is greater than aleph-null. All these irrational points interior to the interval (c, d) are limits of convergent sequences of interior rational points.

At the same time we may consider any irrational number N as a cut, in the sense that it *separates* all the rational numbers into two classes:

the first class consisting of all rational numbers smaller than N, while all the rational numbers greater than N form the second class. The irrational number N is thus a common limit of two rational sequences formed 1) by choosing among the numbers of the first class an infinite sequence $m_1 < m_2 < m_3 < \cdots$ of rational numbers ordered according to their *increasing* magnitude and 2) by choosing among the numbers of the second class another infinite sequence of rational numbers $n_1 > n_2 > n_3 > \cdots$ ordered according to their *decreasing* magnitude.

Take for instance the number $\sqrt{2}$: the corresponding point C of the number axis separates the two infinite classes of rational points which can be defined as being to the left, first class, or to the right, second class, of the point-image C of $\sqrt{2}$. All rational numbers m such that $m^2 < 2$ belong to the first class and all rational numbers n such that $n^2 > 2$ form the second class.

Both classes are infinite, so that we can extract an infinite increasing sequence of numbers m_k from the rationals of the first class

$$m_1 < m_2 < m_3 < m_4 < \cdots < m_k < \cdots < \sqrt{2} \qquad (6)$$

and an infinite decreasing sequence of numbers n_k from the second class

$$n_1 > n_2 > n_3 > n_4 > \cdots > n_k > \cdots > \sqrt{2}. \qquad (7)$$

They are characterized by the conditions $m_k^2 < 2$ and $n_k^2 > 2$ for all $k = 1, 2, 3 \cdots$ We have therefore $n_k^2 > 2 > m_k^2$. Since the rational numbers are everywhere dense on the line we can choose sequences (6) and (7) in such a way that

$$\lim_{k=\infty} m_k^2 = 2 \text{ and } \lim_{k=\infty} n_k^2 = 2$$

which shows that the *inequality* $m_k^2 < n_k^2$ becomes at the limit $k = \infty$ an *equality*

$$\lim_{k=\infty} m_k^2 = \lim_{k=\infty} n_k^2 = 2$$

and therefore

$$\lim_{k=\infty} m_k = \lim_{k=\infty} n_k = \sqrt{2} \qquad (8)$$

On the number axis the point images of rational numbers m_k and n_k tend, as $k \to \infty$, to their common limit point C whose distance from the origin is equal to

$$\lim_{k=\infty} m_k = \lim_{k=\infty} n_k = \text{OC}.$$

Since

$$\lim_{k=\infty} m_k^2 = \lim_{k=\infty} n_k^2 = OC^2 = 2$$

we see that the limit (8) defines the irrational number

$$\sqrt{2} = \lim_{k=0} m_k = \lim_{k=0} n_k.$$

Computation of a Square Root by Successive Approximations:

It is interesting to give a second illustration of this definitition of $\sqrt{2}$ as a common limit of two infinite converging sequences of rational numbers approaching it, one from below and the other from above, an illustration which is not related to the process of extracting the square root. We deduce it from the following algebraic fact: *if p^2 is the double of q^2, then $(p + 2q)^2$ is the double of $(p + q)^2$.* To prove this fact expand the squares in the difference $(p + 2q)^2 - 2(p + q)^2$, applying the formula (5):

$$(p + 2q)^2 = p^2 + 4pq + 4q^2, 2(p + q)^2 = 2p^2 + 4pq + 2q^2$$

Thus

$$(p + 2q)^2 - 2(p + q)^2 = -p^2 + 2q^2 = -(p^2 - 2q^2) \qquad (9)$$

But, if $p^2 = 2q^2$, then $p^2 - 2q^2 = 0$ and (9) proves that

$$(p + 2q)^2 = 2(p + q)^2, \text{ if } p^2 = 2q^2.$$

Now if p and q are two *integers*, then as we saw before $p^2 - 2q^2$ can never be equal to zero. However we can choose such an infinite sequence of pairs of integers, $p_k, q_k, (k = 1, 2, 3 \cdots)$ that the differences $p_k^2 - 2q_k^2$ take alternatively the value $+1$ and -1, when k runs through all the integers, $k = 1, 2 \cdots$ Indeed, choosing $p_1 = 3$, and $q_1 = 2$, we first have

$$p_1^2 - 2q_1^2 = 3^2 - 2 \cdot 2^2 = 9 - 8 = 1$$

From $p_1^2 - 2q_1^2 = 1$ we deduce a first approximation to $\sqrt{2}$, dividing this equality by $q_1^2 = 2^2 = 4$:

$$(p_1/q_1)^2 - 2 = (3/2)^2 - 2 = 1/4 = (1/q_1)^2$$

Thus $3/2$ appears as the first approximate value of $\sqrt{2}$, if we neglect the difference $1/4$ between their squares.

To construct the second pair p_2, q_2, of integers p_k, q_k, we use the recurrent law expressed by the formulas

$$p_{k+1} = p_k + 2q_k, \qquad q_{k+1} = p_k + q_k \qquad (10)$$

and define p_2, q_2 as follows:

$$p_2 = p_1 + 2q_1 = 3 + 2 \cdot 2 = 7, \qquad q_2 = p_1 + q_1 = 3 + 2 = 5$$

Using the identity (9), we conclude that

$$p_2^2 - 2q_2^2 = -p_1^2 + 2q_1^2 = -(p_1^2 - 2q_1^2) = -1$$

From this result $p_2^2 - 2q_2^2 = -1$ we deduce a second approximation to $\sqrt{2}$ in the same way as we deduced the first from $p_1^2 - 2q_1^2 = 1$. Dividing the equality $p_2^2 - 2q_2^2 = -1$ by q_2^2, we obtain

$$(p_2/q_2)^2 - 2 = (7/5)^2 - 2 = -1/q_2^2 = -1/25$$

Neglecting $-1/25$, we can consider $7/5$ as the second and better approximation to $\sqrt{2}$, deduced from the first approximation $3/2$ with the aid of (9). The square $(p_2/q_2)^2 = 49/25$ of the second approximation p_2/q_2 is much nearer to the number 2 than was the square $(p_1/q_1)^2 = 9/4$ of the first approximation. Note also that $(p_2/q_2)^2 = 49/25 < 2$, while $(p_1/q_1)^2 = 9/4 > 2$.

The law (10) is now used again to deduce the third approximation p_3/q_3. First we form p_3 and q_3

$$p_3 = p_2 + 2q_2 = 7 + 2 \cdot 5 = 17, \quad q_3 = p_2 + q_2 = 7 + 5 = 12$$

Then, with the aid of (9), we conclude that

$$p_3^2 - 2q_3^2 = -(p_2^2 - 2q_2^2) = -(-1) = +1$$

Dividing by q_3^2, we obtain

$$(p_3/q_3)^2 - 2 = (17/12)^2 - 2 = 1/q_3^2 = 1/144$$

Again, $p_3/q_3 = 17/12$ is better approximation to $\sqrt{2}$ than $p_2/q_2 = 7/5$ since the square of $17/12$ is nearer to 2 than the square of $7/5$.

We continue this process of successive approximations indefinitely, defining always the next $(k + 1)$-th approximation p_{k+1}/q_{k+1} in terms of the previous, k-th, approximation p_k/q_k with the aid of the same law (10).

As a final result, two infinite sequences (6) and (7) are constructed, where m_k and n_k are defined as follows

$$m_k = p_{2k}/q_{2k}; \; n_k = p_{2k-1}/q_{2k-1}$$

with $k = 1, 2, 3\cdots$ We have indeed, $n_1 = p_1/q_1 > \sqrt{2}$ since $p_1^2 - 2q_1^2 = 1 > 0$ and for all the approximations of *odd* order $2k - 1$, the differences $p_{2k-1}^2 - 2q_{2k-1}^2$ are equal to plus one and thus $p_{2k-1}^2/q_{2k-1}^2 > 2$, so that $n_k = p_{2k-1}/q_{2k-1} > \sqrt{2}$.

On the other hand, $p_2^2 - 2q_2^2 = -1$ and for all approximations of *even* order $2k$, the differences $p_{2k}^2 - 2q_{2k}^2$ are equal to minus one so that $p_{2k}^2/q_{2k}^2 < 2$ and $m_k = p_{2k}/q_{2k} < \sqrt{2}$.

To show that

$$\lim_{k=\infty} p_k/q_k = \sqrt{2}$$

either by odd or by even values of $k \to \infty$, it is sufficient to state that in general

$$\lim_{k=\infty} (p_k/q_k)^2 = 2$$

This last point is easy to prove. We have always

$$p_k^2 - 2q_k^2 = (-1)^{k+1} \qquad (K = 1, 2, 3, \ldots)$$

and, dividing by q_k^2 and transposing to the right, we deduce

$$(p_k/q_k)^2 - 2 = (-1)^{k+1}/q_k^2 \qquad (11)$$

As we will see below, the number q_k is greater than 2^k. Assuming for a moment this fact, we have $q_k^2 > 2^{2k}$, so that

$$0 \leqslant \lim_{k=\infty} |(-1)^{k+1}/q_k^2| = \lim_{k=\infty} (1/q_k^2) \leqslant \lim_{k=\infty} (1/2^{2k}) = 0$$

which proves that $\lim_{k=\infty} (p_k/q_k)^2 = 2$.

It remains to show that $q_k > 2^k$. The law (10) governing the successive formation of the integers p_k, q_k gives

$$p_{k+1} - q_{k+1} = q_k > 0$$

so that $p_k > q_k$ for all values of $k \geqslant 1$. Now $q_{k+1} = p_k + q_k$ and therefore $q_{k+1} > 2q_k$. Using this inequality k times we obtain a chain of inequalities

$$q_{k+1} > 2q_k > 2^2 q_{k-1} > 2^3 q_{k-2} \cdots > 2^{k-1} q_2 > 2^k q_1 = 2^k 2 = 2^{k+1}$$

so that, in general, $q^k > 2^k$.

Here are some first terms of the sequences (6) and (7):

$$7/5; 41/29; 239/169; 1393/985; 8119/5741; 47321/33461$$

$$3/2; 17/12; 99/70; 577/408; 3363/2378; 19601/13860$$

They are formed according to the law (10) in the following order

$$n_1 \rightarrow m_1 \rightarrow n_2 \rightarrow m_2 \rightarrow n_3 \rightarrow m_3 \rightarrow etc.$$

The sixth pair, m_6, n_6 gives the inequality

$$m_6 = 47321/33461 < \sqrt{2} < 19601/13860 = n_6$$

or, written in decimal fractions

$$1.4142135620 \ldots < \sqrt{2} < 1.4142135642 \cdots$$

Hence, the first eight decimals after the dot in the expression of $\sqrt{2}$ as an infinite aperiodic decimal fraction are

$$\sqrt{2} = 1.41421356 \cdots$$

It is important to add that, if we begin with other initial values of m_1 and n_1, the sequence of nested intervals with rational endpoints m_k, n_k changes, but since it shrinks to the same limit point C, the inequalities will give the same infinite decimal fraction for the square root of two.

In Chapter 3 we saw that a rational number $2/3$ is also the common limit of two rational sequences. On the other hand we have defined an irrational number as the limit of rational sequences. We see now that in dealing with infinite convergent rational sequences we must distinguish between two cases: the rational sequences which have rational limits and the rational sequences with irrational limits.

Only irrational numbers can be considered as cuts in the totality of all rational numbers. The definition of irrational numbers as cut in the totality of rational numbers was proposed by Dedekind in 1872 and is known as *Dedekind's cut*.

The decimal representation of an irrational number has an important defect. In principle any decimal having a definite location, say the n-th decimal, can be computed but in practice we can never know *all* the decimals since we cannot compute an infinite number of them. A decimal representation of an irrational number is not only infinite, but aperiodic as well, and this fact precludes the explicit knowledge of all decimals of the infinite decimal fraction representing a given irrational number. We study now two important numbers π and e as examples of irrational numbers.

The fact that the number π is irrational was first proved by Lambert (1728–1777). The best proof, short and elegant, is due to Ivan Niven.[1]) The first method for computing the approximate value of π with any prescribed accuracy was given by Archimedes who, using the regular inscribed polygon with 96 sides proved the inequality

$$3 + 10/70 = 22/7 < \pi < 223/71 = 3 + 10/71$$

This is equivalent to $\pi \sim 3.14\cdots$ with two exact decimals. Before his work, two approximate values, both in excess, were used: the Egyptian value $256/81 \sim 3.160$, which is at least 3600 years old,[2]) and the Hindu value, $\sqrt{10} \sim 3.162...$[3])

About 1579, François Viète (1540–1603), applying the idea of Archimedes to a polygon with 393216 sides, computed π to the first nine exact decimals. A Netherlander, van Ceulen, has devoted his whole life to the computation of π. He died in 1610 after having computed only the first thirty-five decimals, which are engraved on his tombstone at Leyden.

Abraham Sharp, using a new tool, namely the infinite series of Gregory, in 1699 found and published the value of π with 71 exact decimals. Dase, in 1844, worked out 200; Richter, in 1854, 500 and Shanks, in 1873, determined the first 707 decimals. Here are the first twenty of them:

$$\pi \sim 3.141\,592\,653\,589\,783\,238\,46 \cdots$$

In December 1955 an electronic computer of International Business Machines Corporation in New York computed the first 3089 decimals of π in fifteen minutes.

A naturalist, Buffon, found that π is involved in a mathematical formula expressing the ratio r of the number of successes to the number of trials in the so-called needle problem. This problem consists of dropping a needle many times on a plane surface ruled by parallel lines, the distance between the parallel lines being equal to the length of the needle. A toss was considered a success, if the needle fell across

---

[1]) *Bulletin of Amer. Math. Society*, *53*, No. 6, June 1947.
[2]) Ahmes Papyrus (1650 B.C.), based on a still older manuscript (*circa* 2300 B.C.)
[3]) Arya Bhata and Brahmagupta.

a line, and a failure, if the needle fell between two lines. The probability of success is $2/\pi$. The ratio r, obtained in a number N of trials, approximates $2/\pi$ more and more closely as N increases. In 1901, Lazzerini, having made more than 3400 trials gave the value of π to first six exact decimals, namely $\pi \simeq 3.141\,5929$.

The astonishing fact that the number π, first defined as the ratio of the length of a circumference to its diameter, appears in the expression of the probability of an event, emphasizes the importance of the number π for the study and understanding of our environment.

Number e

Another important irrational number was introduced more than two hundred years ago, in 1748, by Euler. It is denoted by the first letter e of its discoverer's name. This important constant, e, is defined as the limit of the convergent sequence of irrational numbers, $r_1, r_2, r_3, \ldots r_n, \ldots$, where

$$r_1 = (1 + 1/1)^1 = 2$$

$$r_2 = (1 + 1/2)^2 = 2.25$$

$$r_3 = (1 + 1/3)^3 = (4/3^2)\,64/27$$

etc. and in general
$$r_n = (1 + 1/n)^n$$

By definition
$$e = \lim_{n=\infty} (1 + 1/n)^n = \lim_{n=\infty} [(n + 1)/n]^n$$

It can be proved that the sequence $r_1, r_2, r_3, \ldots r_n, \ldots$ is an increasing sequence, so that $(1 + 1/n)^n$ approaches e from the left, $(1 + 1/n)^n < e$. Another rational sequence, $R_1, R_2, R_3, \ldots$, where

$$R_n = (1 + 1/n)^{n+1} = (1 + 1/n)\,r_n$$

also has the limit e, but it is a decreasing sequence, so that it approaches e from the right
$$(1 + 1/n)^{n+1} > e$$

Therefore, we again have an infinite sequence of inequalities with rational numbers r_n, R_n as lower and upper bounds of e:

$$r_n = (1 + 1/n)^n < e < (1 + 1/n)^{n+1} = R_n. \tag{12}$$

Kogbetliantz 11

Thus e is defined by the infinite set of nested rational intervals, (r_n, R_n) which shrink towards a point at a distance e from the origin O.

The inequalities (12) allow us to compute as many decimals as we want in the expression of the irrational number e but again, only a finite number of them can be computed, and not all. Here is an approximate value of e with 23 exact decimals given by Euler:

$$e = 2.718\,281\,828\,459\,045\,235\,360\,28\cdots$$

The number e is related to the idea of continuous growth (or continuous decay) which can be illustrated by the example of accumulation of compound interest. Suppose that compound interest is computed n times per year, once every $1/n$ fraction of a year, the rate being 100% per year. Then the principal and the accumulated interest are multiplied every n-th part of a year by $1 + 1/n$, and therefore, in one year, one dollar grows by jumps to $\$\,(1 + 1/n)^n$.

If n is finite, growth is not continuous, and there are n jumps per year. Suppose however that n increases without limit, $n \to \infty$. At the limit for $n = \infty$, the growth becomes continuous and at the end of the first year one dollar is transformed into $\$\,e = \$\,2.718\,28\cdots$ since

$$\lim_{n=\infty} (1 + 1/n)^n = e = 2.718\,28\cdots$$

Note that if the interest were simple (case $n = 1$), at the rate of 100% per year one dollar would be doubled. If the interest is computed and added ten times per year ($n = 10$), at the end of one year one dollar becomes

$$\$\,2.5937\cdots = (1 + 0.1)^{10}$$

For $n = 100$, the result is

$$(1 + 0{,}01)^{100} = \$\,2.7048\cdots$$

and for $n = 1000$,

$$(1 + 0.001)^{1000} = \$\,2.7169\cdots$$

which is already very near to $2.718\,28\cdots = e$.

The idea of continuous decay can be illustrated by the gradual vanishing of a radioactive substance which dissipates its mass by emitting radiation. If such a substance undergoes a discontinuous decay, the rate of decay being 100% per year, it loses say $1/(n + 1)$ part of its actual mass at the end of every $1/(n + 1)$ fraction of a year.

If initial mass was one gram, at the end of the first year, after the $(n + 1)$-th loss of mass, the remaining mass is equal to

$$[1 - (1/n + 1)]^{n+1} = [n/(n + 1)]^{n+1} = 1/[(1 + 1/n)^{n+1}] = 1/R_n$$

grams, where

$$R_n = (1 + 1/n)^{n+1}$$

and consequently $\lim_{n=\infty} R_n = e$. When n increases without limit, the discontinuous decay approaches continuity and at the limit for $n = \infty$, the decay becomes continuous. The rate of decay being 100% per year, the residual mass which remains at the end of one year from one gram is equal to

$$1/e \text{ grams} = 1/2.718 \cdots \text{ grams} = 0.366 \cdots \text{ grams}$$

Representation by Continued Fractions

There are other representations of irrational numbers which do not possess the defect of representation by infinite aperiodic decimal fractions, namely the lack of knowledge of *all* decimals involved in such a representation. They are infinite expressions too, whose irrational values are defined as limits of rational sequences, but all of their elements are known numbers. They give an *explicit* representation of irrational numbers.

To study these representations let us again take as an example the irrational number $\sqrt{2}$. We have by definition $(\sqrt{2})^2 - 1^2 = 1$. Factoring the difference of two squares $(\sqrt{2})^2 - 1^2$ we transform $(\sqrt{2})^2 - 1^2 = 1$ into $(\sqrt{2} + 1)(\sqrt{2} - 1) = 1$. Dividing both sides by $\sqrt{2} + 1$ and adding one, we obtain successively $\sqrt{2} - 1 = 1/(\sqrt{2} + 1)$ and

$$\sqrt{2} = 1 + 1/(1 + \sqrt{2}) \tag{13}$$

Adding again one to both sides, (13) is transformed into

$$1 + \sqrt{2} = 2 + 1/(1 + \sqrt{2}) \tag{14}$$

and thus we have succeeded in expressing the irrational number $1 + \sqrt{2}$ in terms of itself. This allows us to replace in the formula (13) the denominator $1 + \sqrt{2}$ of the fraction $1/(1 + \sqrt{2})$ by the righthand member of (14), thus transforming the simple fraction into a finite continued fraction with two links:

$$\sqrt{2} = 1 + \cfrac{1}{2 + \cfrac{1}{1 + \sqrt{2}}}$$

But, "what was done once can be repeated indefinitely", and repeating the substitution of $2 + 1/(1 + \sqrt{2})$ for the equal number $1 + \sqrt{2}$ an *infinite* number of times, we build up an infinite continued fraction

$$\sqrt{2} = 1 + \cfrac{1}{2 + \cfrac{1}{2 + \cfrac{1}{2 + \cfrac{1}{2 + \ddots}}}} \tag{15}$$

in which all elements are known explicitly: its numerators and denominators are all equal to one and two, respectively. It is to be noted that in the right member $\sqrt{2}$ finally disappears since there is no last integer, and therefore *no last link*. The irrational number $\sqrt{2}$ is now represented explicitly by the infinite continued fraction (15) which involves only the integers 1 and 2.

This expression of an irrational number $\sqrt{2}$ in terms of 1 and 2 is an excellent illustration of the fact that the integers are the foundations on which all mathematics is built.

The fraction (15) also allows the numerical computation of approximate rational values of $\sqrt{2}$ to any prescribed accuracy. We recall that a finite continued fraction is computed by transforming it into a finite sequence of successive convergents P_n/Q_n. Here the continued fraction (15) is infinite and therefore we obtain an infinite sequence of convergents which are to be computed by the same recurrent formulas given by Wallis (1616–1703) which we used in the computation of finite continued fractions:

$$\left. \begin{aligned} P_{n+1} &= P_n b_{n+1} + P_{n-1} a_{n+1} = 2P_n + P_{n-1} \\ Q_{n+1} &= Q_n b_{n+1} + Q_{n-1} a_{n+1} = 2Q_n + Q_{n-1} \end{aligned} \right\} \tag{16}$$

In our case $P_0/Q_0 = 1$, $P_1/Q_1 = 3/2$ and therefore beginning with $P_0 = 1$, $P_1 = 3$, and $Q_0 = 1$, $Q_1 = 2$, we obtain successively as many convergents P_n/Q_n as we want:

Order n	P_n	Q_n	P_n/Q_n
0	1	1	1
1	3	2	1.5
2	7	5	1.4
3	17	12	1.4166 $\cdots$
4	41	29	1.41379 $\cdots$
5	90	70	1.41428 $\cdots$
6	239	169	1.41420 $\cdots$
7	577	408	1.414215 $\cdots$
8	1393	985	1.414213 $\cdots$

We recognize here the same two rational sequences (6) and (7) which were deduced from the first approximation 3/2 with the aid of recurrent relations

$$P_{k+1} = P_k + 2Q_k; \quad Q_{k+1} = P_k + Q_k \tag{10}$$

It is easy to check that (10) is equivalent to Wallis' formulas (16)

$$P_{k+1} = 2P_k + P_{k-1}; \quad Q_{k+1} = 2Q_k + Q_{k-1}. \tag{16*}$$

To deduce (16) from (10) we observe that, according to (10)

$$P_k = P_{k-1} + 2Q_{k-1}$$

so that

$$P_k + P_{k-1} = 2(P_{k-1} + Q_{k-1})$$

But on the other hand

$$Q_k = P_{k-1} + Q_{k-1}$$

too. Therefore

$$2Q_k = P_k + P_{k-1}$$

and substituting $P_k + P_{k-1}$ for $2Q_k$ in the first relation (10), we obtain the first relation (16). Similarly,

$$Q_k + Q_{k-1} = (P_{k-1} + Q_{k-1}) + Q_{k-1} = P_{k-1} + 2Q_{k-1} = P_k$$

so that

$$Q_{k+1} = P_k + Q_k = (Q_k + Q_{k-1}) + Q_k = 2Q_k + Q_{k-1}$$

Therefore, the infinite continued fraction (15) can also be considered as a definition of the irrational number $\sqrt{2}$, because it generates, through the sequence of its successive convergents, an infinite set of nested intervals, which shrink towards the point $\sqrt{2}$.

The convergents of even orders approach $\sqrt{2}$ from below and those of odd orders from above, so that the length L_n of the n-th interval is equal to

$$L_n = P_{2n-1}/Q_{2n-1} - P_{2n}/Q_{2n} = 1/(Q_{2n-1}Q_{2n}) \qquad (n = 1, 2, 3, ...)$$

and is infinitely small for $n \to \infty$:

$$L_1 = 1/2, L_2 = 1/60, L_3 = 1/2030, L_4 = 1/68952, ...$$

These numbers L_n give the upper bounds of the error commited, if $\sqrt{2}$ is replaced by P_{2n-1}/Q_{2n-1} or P_{2n}/Q_{2n}.

The infinite continued fraction

$$\sqrt{2} = 1 + \cfrac{1}{2 + \cfrac{1}{2 + \cfrac{1}{2 + \cdot \cdot}}}$$

represents the $\sqrt{2}$ better than the infinite aperiodic decimal fraction $1.414\cdots$ Both generate an infinite set of nested intervals, defining $\sqrt{2}$ as a Dedekind's cut, but all elements of the continued fraction are known because all the links are the same and it is *periodic* while only a finite number of decimals of the decimal fraction can be computed effectively.

Method of Infinite Descent

The representation of $\sqrt{2}$ by the continued fraction (15) can be deduced by purely geometric considerations related to the incommensurability of the side and diagonal of a square. This method is called the *method of infinite descent* and it is a combination of indirect method and of mathematical induction. In the indirect method a contradiction is deduced as a necessary corollary of an assumption which is contrary to what is to be proved. Thus, disproving the opposite, we obtain the proof.

Applying the method of infinite descent, we begin by assuming a hypothesis which is contrary to the statement we must prove: we postulate the commensurability of the side and diagonal of a square. An infinite chain of squares is then built such that their sides decrease and tend to zero. By hypothesis the side and diagonal of the first square are commensurable and the geometric construction of the next smaller square is defined in such a way that the commensurability of side and diagonal is preserved: it holds for the second square, if it is true for the first, and therefore, by mathematical induction, it must be valid for the whole infinite chain of squares. Here is how the chain is constructed: in the figure 5.6, page 168, $ABCD$ is the first square with which we begin. Its side is chosen as the unit of length: $s_1 = AB = 1$, and it is laid off on the diagonal $d_1 = BD$, defining the point E on it such that $BE = 1$. The difference $BD - BE = ED$ between the diagonal $d_1 = BD$ and the side $s_1 = AB = BE$ is chosen as side $s_2 = DE$ of a second square with a vertex at D. Therefore $d_1 = s_1 + s_2$. Because the angle ADE is equal to 45 degrees, the second square $DEFG$ has its vertex F on the side AD of the first square and its diagonal $d_2 = DF$ is equal to $AD - AF$. Now the three segments AF, FE and ED are equal: the first two because the two right triangles FAB and BEF are equal, having equal hypotenuses and equal sides, $AB = BE$. Thus, $AF = FE = DE = $ side s_2 and the diagonal $d_2 = DF$ of the second square is equal to $DF = AD - AF = s_1 - s_2 : d_2 = s_1 - s_2$.

We shall now prove that, if the side AB and the diagonal BD of the first square are commensurable, then so are the side $s_2 = DE$ and the diagonal $d_2 = DF = s_1 - s_2$ of the square. Suppose that $AB = s_1$ and $d_1 = BD - s_1 + s_2$ are commensurable. This hypothesis is equivalent to the assumption that a segment of fixed length λ exists such that it is a common measure of two segments $AB = s_1$ and $BD = s_1 + s_2 = d_1$, which means that

$$d_1 = s_1 + s_2 = m_1\lambda; \quad s_1 = n_1\lambda \qquad (17)$$

where the two numbers m_1 and n_1 are integers ($m_1 > n_1$).

We have clearly $m_1 < 2n_1$, since the diagonal of a square is shorter than the sum of the two sides: $BD = m_1\lambda < 2AB = 2n_1\lambda$. Thus, $n_1 < m_1 < 2n_1$.

From (17) we deduce that λ is a common measure of two segments s_2 and $d_2 = s_1 - s_2$:

$$s_2 = (s_2 + s_1) - s_1 = (m_1 - n_1)\,\lambda; \quad d_2 = s_1 - s_2 = (2n_1 - m_1)\,\lambda$$

Therefore not only is the commensurability of the side and diagonal preserved, but the common measure does not change and it is the same for DE and DF, as for AB and BD.

Let us now denote the positive integers $2n_1 - m_1$ and $m_1 - n_1$ by m_2 and n_2 respectively so that

and
$$d_2 = s_1 - s_2 = (2n_1 - m_1) \lambda = m_2 \lambda$$

$$s_2 = (m_1 - n_1) \lambda = n_2 \lambda$$

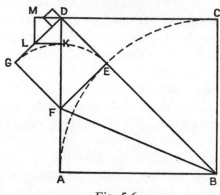

Fig. 5.6

are measures of the diagonal and sides of the second square, and thus, again

$$n_2 < m_2 < 2n_2.$$

Moreover

and
$$m_1 - m_2 = m_1 - (2n_1 - m_1) = 2(m_1 - n_1) > 0$$

$$n_1 - n_2 = n_1 - (m_1 - n_1) = 2n_1 - m_1 > 0$$

so that $m_2 < m_1$ and $n_2 < n_1$, as it must be since $s_1 + s_2 > s_1 - s_2$ and $s_1 > s_2$.

Repeating the same procedure in the second square, we construct a third square, $DKLM$, whose side $s_3 = DK$ is defined as the difference of the diagonal and the side of the second square: $DF - DE = (s_1 - s_2) - s_2 = s_1 - 2s_2$, so that $s_3 = s_1 - 2s_2$, and therefore

$$s_1 = 2s_2 + s_3 \qquad (18)$$

This relation is characteristic for the chain of succesive squares with sides $s_1, s_2, s_3, s_4, \ldots$ and it holds for the sides s_{q-1}, s_q, s_{q+1} of any group of three successive squares. Denoting the length of the side and the length of the diagonal of the q-th square by s_q and d_q respectively, we have for every $q = 2, 3, 4, \ldots$ the relations

$$s_{q-1} = 2s_q + s_{q+1}; \tag{19}$$

$$d_q = s_{q-1} - s_q \qquad (q = 2, 3, 4, \ldots)$$

The diagonal d_q and the side s_q of every one of these squares are commensurable, if the diagonal d_1 and the side s_1 of the first are commensurable. Moreover, the construction insures that they all will have the same common measure, λ that is

$$s_q = n_q \lambda; \tag{20}$$

$$d_q = m_q \lambda$$

where m_q and n_q are integers. The relations (20) must exist for all values of $q = 1, 2, 3, \ldots$ since the chain of squares is infinite. On the other hand, the two sequences

$$m_1 > m_2 > m_3 > m_4 \cdots > m_k > m_{k+1} > \cdots \tag{21}$$

$$n_1 > n_2 > n_3 > n_4 \cdots > n_k > n_{k+1} > \cdots$$

cannot be infinite, because their terms are decreasing integers. Therefore, the assumption of commensurability of the diagonal d_1 and the side s_1 of the first square leads to a contradiction: on one hand, there must be an infinite number of integers m_q, n_q; on the other hand, there can be only a finite number of them because the two sequence of integers (21) are necessarily finite. This contradiction disproves the assumption and thus diagonal and side of a square are incommensurable.

Another way of formulating the same contradiction consists in proving that $\lim_{q=\infty} s_q = 0$, so that a nonvanishing length λ cannot play the role of a common measure of all terms of the infinite sequence $s_1, s_2, s_3, \ldots, s_q, \ldots$: if $\lim_{q=\infty} s_q = 0$, then s_q becomes for sufficiently large values of q *smaller* than λ.

To prove the ultimate vanishing of s_q for $q \to \infty$, it is sufficient to observe that omitting the positive term s_{q+1} in the relation (19) we obtain the inequality $s_{q-1} > 2s_q$. Multiplying both members by 2^{q-1}, we have $2^{q-1}s_{q-1} > 2^{q-1}2s_q$, so that in general $2^{q-1}s_{q-1} > 2^q s_q$. Thus for $q = 2, 3, 4 \cdots$ we prove successively the inequalities:

$$2 = 2s_1 > 2^2 s_2 > 2^3 s_3 > \cdots > 2^q s_q > \cdots$$

Therefore, for any q we have $2^q s_q < 2$, that is $s_q < 2/2^q$, and thus

$$0 \leqslant \lim_{q=\infty} s_q \leqslant \lim_{q=\infty} (2/2^q) = 0$$

Returning to $\sqrt{2}$ we observe that $s_1 = AB = 1$ and $d_1 = BD = \sqrt{2}$. Thus the geometric incommensurability of $AB = 1$ and $BD = \sqrt{2}$ finds its arithmetical counterpart in the impossibility of expressing $\sqrt{2}$ as a ratio of two integers:

$$\sqrt{2} = BD/AB \neq m_1/n_1$$

But the expression for $\sqrt{2}$ can be found, if we succeed in expressing the ratio

$$BD/AB = (s_1 + s_2)/s_1 = 1 + s_2/s_1$$

of two incommensurable lengths BD and AB. This can be done, if the ratio s_2/s_1 can be expressed. Now the relation (18) gives, dividing both members by s_2

$$s_1/s_2 = 2 + s_3/s_2$$

so that, taking the reciprocals of both members,

$$s_2/s_1 = 1/(2 + s_3/s_2) \qquad (22)$$

Likewise the first relation (19) can be written

so that in general

$$s_{q-1}/s_q = 2 + s_{q+1}/s_q$$

$$\frac{s_q}{s_{q-1}} = \frac{1}{2 + \dfrac{s_{q+1}}{s_q}} \qquad (23)$$

We can therefore, using (22), express $\sqrt{2}$ with the aid of the ratio s_3/s_2 instead of s_2/s_1:

$$\frac{BD}{AD} = \sqrt{2} = 1 + \frac{s_2}{s_1} = 1 + \frac{1}{2 + \dfrac{s_3}{s_2}}$$

Now for $q = 3$ the relation (23) gives

$$\frac{s_3}{s_2} = \frac{1}{2 + \dfrac{s_4}{s_3}}$$

Using (23) for $q = 4, 5, 6, 7\cdots$ and repeating endlessly the same substitution, we obtain for $\sqrt{2}$ the infinite periodic continued fraction (15). Thus, we see that the infinite chain of squares we built not only proves that $\sqrt{2}$ is an irrational number, but gives us its best representation (15).

Similar representations are known for irrational π and e. Euler found for the difference $e - 2$ the following continued aperiodic fraction:

$$e - 2 = \cfrac{1}{1 + \cfrac{1}{2 + \cfrac{1}{1 + \cfrac{1}{1 + \cfrac{1}{4 + \cfrac{1}{1 + \cfrac{1}{1 + \cfrac{1}{6 + \cfrac{1}{1 + \cfrac{1}{1 + \cfrac{1}{8 + \cdots}}}}}}}}}}$$

In this fraction all the numerators a_n are equal to 1, $a_n = 1$, and all the denominators $b_n = 1$, except for $n = 3k - 1$ $(k = 1, 2, 3, ...)$, that is except for $n = 2, 5, 8, 11, 14\cdots$ in which case $b_{3k-1} = 2k$. Another infinite continued fraction expressing the same difference, $e - 2$ is:

$$e - 2 = \cfrac{1}{1 + \cfrac{1}{2 + \cfrac{2}{3 + \cfrac{3}{4 + \cfrac{4}{5 + \cdots}}}}}$$

where $a_1 = 1$, $a_n = n - 1$ for $n \geqslant 2$, and $b_n = n$ for $n \geqslant 1$.

It is easy to deduce from this continued fraction the two rational sequences which approach e from above and from below (see Appendix V).

For the number π Lambert, in 1761, proved that

$$\frac{\pi}{4} = \cfrac{1}{1 + \cfrac{1^2}{2 + \cfrac{3^2}{2 + \cfrac{5^2}{2 + \ddots \qquad \cdot + \cfrac{(2n-3)^2}{2 + \ddots}}}}}$$

This representation of $\pi/4$ was communicated without proof by Lord Brouncker (1620–1684) to John Wallis. In it we have $b_n = 2$ for $n = 2, 3, 4 \cdots$ but $b_1 = 1$, and $a_n = (2n - 3)^2$ for all $n = 1, 2, 3, 4 \cdots$ Thus

$$P_{n+1} = 2P_n + (2n - 1)^2 P_{n-1}$$

$$Q_{n+1} = 2Q_n + (2n - 1)^2 Q_{n-1}$$

with $P_1 = 1, Q_1 = 1$ and $P_2 = 2, Q_2 = 3$.

Notice that the infinite continued fraction (15) obtained for $\sqrt{2}$ is periodic while the continued fractions for π and e are aperiodic. We have already seen that an infinite *periodic decimal* fraction corresponds to a special class of numbers, namely the rational numbers. This fact suggests that infinite periodic *continued fractions*, too, represent a special class of irrational numbers.

And indeed irrational numbers which are solutions of quadratic equations with integral coefficients are represented by infinite periodic continued fractions and *vice versa:* the value of a periodic continued fraction is always the solution of some quadratic equation.

We call an equation in x quadratic if it contains a term Ax^2 with the square x^2 of the unknown x, but no terms of higher powers of x. Thus in general a quadratic equation has three terms and takes the form

$$Ax^2 + Bx + C = 0 \tag{24}$$

where its coefficients A, B, C are given and known numbers. If A, B, C are rational numbers, multiplying the equation (24) by their common denominator reduces it to the case in which all three coefficients are integers. Then both its solutions (since each quadratic equation has two solutions as we will see later) may be represented by periodic continued fractions.

As an example of the fact that each periodic continued fraction represents a solution of some quadratic equation, let us consider the fraction

$$x = 1 + \cfrac{1}{1 + \cfrac{1}{1 + \cfrac{1}{1 + \cfrac{1}{1 + \cdot}}}}$$

with $a_n = b_n = 1$, $n = 1, 2, 3, \ldots$ Writing it as follows

$$x = 1 + \cfrac{1}{\left(1 + \cfrac{1}{1 + \cfrac{1}{1 + \cfrac{1}{1 + \cfrac{1}{1 + \cdot}}}}\right)} \tag{25}$$

we see that its periodicity carries with it the corollary

$$x = 1 + 1/x \tag{26}$$

Thus x is one of the two solutions of the quadratic equation

$$x^2 - x - 1 = 0 \tag{27}$$

obtained by multiplying (26) by x and transposing the terms $x + 1$ from the right to the left.

To solve the equation (27) we note that

$$(x - 1/2)^2 \equiv x^2 + 2(-1/2)\,x + (-1/2)^2 \equiv x^2 - x + 1/4$$

and therefore, transposing $1/4$ to the left member and reading from right to left

$$x^2 - x \equiv (x - 1/2)^2 - 1/4$$

Substituting this value of $x^2 - x$ in the equation (27) we obtain the equivalent equation

$$(x - 1/2)^2 - 5/4 \equiv (x - 1/2)^2 - (\sqrt{5}/2)^2 = 0$$

since $5/4 = (\sqrt{5})^2/2^2 = (\sqrt{5}/2)^2$.

Now the difference of two squares is factorable according to the general identity

$$A^2 - B^2 \equiv (A - B)(A + B)$$

so that taking $A = x - 1/2$, $B = \sqrt{5}/2$, our equation becomes

$$[(x - 1/2) - \sqrt{5}/2][(x - 1/2) + \sqrt{5}/2] = 0$$

A product can be zero only if one of the factors is zero. Therefore we have two different solutions which correspond to the vanishing of the first and of the second factor respectively. If the first factor is zero

$$x - 1/2 - \sqrt{5}/2 = 0$$

then we have, for x, the first solution x_1:

$$x_1 = (\sqrt{5} + 1)/2$$

If it is the second factor which vanishes, then the corresponding condition

$$x - 1/2 + \sqrt{5}/2 = 0$$

gives, for x, the second solution x_2

$$x_2 = -(\sqrt{5} - 1)/2 = 1 - x_1$$

Our infinite periodic continued fraction (25) must have a positive value for all its terms are positive. Hence $x_2 = -(\sqrt{5} - 1)/2$ cannot give its value, because the number x_2 is negative. Therefore it is the first solution $x_1 = (\sqrt{5} + 1)/2$ which is represented by the continued periodic fraction (25):

$$x_1 = \frac{\sqrt{5} + 1}{2} = 1 + \cfrac{1}{1 + \cfrac{1}{1 + \cfrac{1}{1 + \cfrac{1}{1 + \cdot}}}}$$

Subtracting one and changing the signs of both members, we obtain also x_2 in the form of a continued fraction

$$x_2 = 1 - x_1 = -\left(\cfrac{1}{1 + \cfrac{1}{1 + \cfrac{1}{1 + \cfrac{1}{1 + \cdots}}}} \right)$$

Other Representations of Irrational Numbers

Irrational numbers admit of two other representations by infinite expressions, namely: (a) by infinite series (sums of an infinite number of terms) and (b) by infinite products (products with infinite number of factors). In general, an irrational number is always a limit and it cannot be represented by a finite expression. It may be obtained only by a passage to the limit because the concept of irrational number is based on the use of an infinite chain of steps of thought. This is the intrinsic reason why an infinite number of operations is needed to express any irrational number.

The symbol $\sqrt{2}$, for instance, may seem at first glance to symbolize a single operation, the "extraction of the square root of two". However, by a close analysis we always find that an infinite chain of operations is needed to perform the operation indicated in the notation of an irrational number, if we want to know its numerical value.

The same thing happens with π which by definition is the ratio of two lengths: the length of the circumference divided by the length of its diameter. The word "ratio" implies a single operation of division, but we cannot measure the length of the circumference without knowing the value of the number π, and the computation of π needs an infinite number of operations: π also is the limit of a sequence of rational numbers.

Here are two examples of infinite and convergent series representing the irrational numbers π and e. Let us first introduce an abbreviation for the product of the first n natural numbers. Such a product $1 \cdot 2 \cdot 3 \cdot 4 \cdots (n - 1) \cdot n$ of n factors which are the first n consecutive integers from one to n, is called *n-factorial* and is denoted by $n!$ For instance, 5-factorial means $1 \cdot 2 \cdot 3 \cdot 4 \cdot 5$. Its value is 120 and it is denoted by 5!, so that $5! = 120$, while $7! = 5! \cdot 6 \cdot 7 = 5040$. Two consecutive factorials $n!$ and $(n + 1)!$ verify the relation

$$(n + 1)! = n!(n + 1)$$

As will be proved below (Chapter 9), e can be represented as the sum of following infinite series:

$$e = 1 + \frac{1}{1!} + \frac{1}{2!} + \frac{1}{3!} + \frac{1}{4!} + \cdots + \frac{1}{n!} + \cdots \tag{28}$$

while for π we have Leibniz's series

$$\frac{\pi}{4} = 1 - \frac{1}{3} + \frac{1}{5} - \frac{1}{7} + \frac{1}{9} - \frac{1}{11} + \cdots + \frac{(-1)^n}{(2n + 1)} + \cdots \tag{29}$$

The sum of a convergent series, such as (28) or (29) is computed in the same way as the sum $1/(1 - q)$ of the geometric progression $1 + q + q^2 + \cdots + q^n + \cdots$ Take for instance the series (28) for e. It is transformed into an infinite sequence of its partial sums

$$s_0, s_1, s_2, s_3, \ldots, s_n, \ldots$$

where

$$s_0 = 1, s_1 = 1 + \frac{1}{1!} = 2, \quad s_2 = s_1 + \frac{1}{2!} = \frac{5}{2},$$

$$s_3 = s_2 + \frac{1}{3!} = \frac{5}{2} + \frac{1}{6} = \frac{8}{3} \text{ etc.}$$

In general, the symbol s_n represents the sum of the first $n + 1$ terms

$$s_n = 1 + \frac{1}{1!} + \frac{1}{2!} + \cdots + \frac{1}{n!}$$

We will see later that the $\lim_{n=\infty} s_n = e$. The same holds for

$$\frac{\pi}{4} = \lim_{n=\infty} \left[1 - \frac{1}{3} + \frac{1}{5} - \cdots + \frac{(-1)^n}{(2n + 1)} \right]$$

We note that the convergence of the series (29) is due to the alternation of the plus and minus signs of its terms. The absolute values of the terms $1, 1/3, 1/5, 1/7, 1/9, \ldots$ form a decreasing sequence and the so-called general term $(-1)^n/(2n + 1)$ approaches zero for $n \to \infty$, but this fact is not a sufficient reason for convergence: we have seen that the harmonic series $1 + 1/2 + 1/3 + \cdots + 1/n + \cdots$ diverges and its "sum" is infinite. Dividing this "sum" by two we obtain another divergent series:

$$\frac{1}{2} + \frac{1}{4} + \frac{1}{6} + \frac{1}{8} + \cdots$$

whose sum is also infinite. Increasing each term by diminishing all the denominators by one, we obtain the series of positive terms

$$1 + \frac{1}{3} + \frac{1}{5} + \frac{1}{7} + \frac{1}{9} + \cdots \tag{30}$$

which has an infinite sum and is divergent because each term is greater than the corresponding term of the above divergent series. The absolute values of the terms in (29) and (30) are the same. The difference between this divergent series and the convergent series (29) representing $\pi/4$ consists of the fact that the terms of the convergent series (29) are alternatively positive and negative, while in (30) they are all positive. Therefore the convergence in (29) is due to the fact that its terms form a decreasing sequence of *alternatively positive and negative terms.*

The square of π is related to the squares of all integers by a curious convergent infinite series whose terms are reciprocals of squares of integers:

$$\frac{\pi^2}{6} = \frac{1}{1^2} + \frac{1}{2^2} + \frac{1}{3^2} + \frac{1}{4^2} + \cdots \frac{1}{n^2} + \cdots$$

We add the famous representation of $\pi/2$ as an infinite product discovered by John Wallis:

$$\frac{\pi}{2} = \left(\frac{2}{1}\right)\left(\frac{2}{3}\right)\left(\frac{4}{3}\right)\left(\frac{4}{5}\right)\left(\frac{6}{5}\right)\left(\frac{6}{7}\right)\left(\frac{8}{7}\right)\left(\frac{8}{9}\right) \cdots$$

To compute the number represented by this infinite product, we form an infinite sequence of its partial products $P_1, P_2, P_3, \ldots, P_n \ldots,$ where $P_1 = 2/1, P_2 = (2/1)(2/3) = 4/3, P_3 = (2/1)(2/3)(4/3) = 16/9,$ *etc.*, P_n being defined as the product of the first n factors:

$$P_{2n} = \left(\frac{2}{1}\right)\left(\frac{2}{3}\right) \cdots \left[\frac{2n}{(2n-1)}\right]\left[\frac{2n}{(2n+1)}\right]$$

$$P_{2n+1} = \left(\frac{2}{1}\right)\left(\frac{2}{3}\right) \cdots \left[\frac{2n}{(2n-1)}\right]\left[\frac{2n}{(2n+1)}\right]\left[\frac{(2n+2)}{(2n+1)}\right]$$

Kogbetliantz 12

It was proved by Wallis that

$$\pi/2 = \lim_{n=\infty} P_n$$

All these representations of the two most important irrational numbers π and e show clearly that in the last analysis irrational numbers can be expressed only if we apply passage to the limit, that is if we use infinite sequences. All the infinite expressions we met—infinite decimal and continued fractions, infinite series, infinite products—are of course, nothing more than conventional notations for the same fundamental mathematical concept: the limit of an infinite convergent sequence. Irrational numbers are always defined as limits of infinite convergent sequences all the terms of which are rational numbers.

Continuum

Let us now consider the totality of all *real numbers*, rational and irrational, as an entity, or, as mathematicians say, as a *set*. This set of all real numbers is represented by all points of the infinite *continuous* straight line (number-axis) and for this reason it is called in mathematics the *continuum*. Since rational and irrational numbers can be expressed as infinite decimal fractions, the continuum is represented by the totality of all infinite decimal fractions.

We have seen that the set of all rational numbers can be put into one-to-one correspondence with the set of all integers, and we have expressed this fact by saying that the set of all rational numbers is denumerable. If we want to extend the characterization of finite collections by their cardinal numbers, we may introduce, with Georg Cantor, the infinite cardinal number (infinite cardinal numbers are called *transfinite* numbers) aleph-null and say that there are aleph-null rational numbers.

Now, what about the continuum? Is this infinite set denumerable too, or not? If the set of all real numbers could be put into one-to-one correspondence with the set of all integers, then, by definition, it would be denumerable. This however is not probable and we suspect that there are many more irrational numbers than rational, that the continuum is an infinity of different type than aleph-null, than the infinity of all integers.

The reason for our suspicion is the fact that the continuum corresponds to the continuity of the straight line, the irrational points of the number-axis being responsible for the length of its segments. Any denumerable set of points on the number-axis may be treated as we have treated, in Chapter 3, the denumerable set of rational points, and the result will be the same: a denumerable set of points cannot form a length. We suspect then that irrational points must be much more dense on the number-axis than rational points because they are responsible for the fact that a line-segment has a length.

If it is so, we must introduce a special symbol for the totality of all real numbers and, following Georg Cantor, we shall use the symbol C to denote the continuum considered as an entity, namely as the totality of all real numbers. The symbol C is related to the continuum exactly as aleph-null is to the set of all integers. It is the transfinite cardinal number of the continuum.

The question now arises: is the transfinite cardinal number C equal to the aleph-null? or greater? It cannot be smaller since a set which, put into one-to-one correspondence with integers becomes exhausted before all the integers are used, is necessarily a *finite* set and the continuum is infinite.

To clarify this question, let us suppose that the rational points belonging to a straight line are white and the irrational points of the same line are black. What shall be the color of the line?

If C and aleph-null are equal, the line will appear to the eye as a grey line, but if C is greater than aleph-null, then the line will be black, the white rational points being lost among the black irrational points.

We know that the length of a segment is due to the presence of irrational points, and we guess, therefore, that the line will appear to the eye as a black line.

The fact that the continuum is not denumerable, and that consequently C is greater than aleph-null, was proved by Georg Cantor with the aid of decimal representation of numbers. The proof is an indirect one and it starts with the opposite assumption that the totality of all real numbers is denumerable. The contradiction deduced from this assumption shows that the continuum is not comparable to the infinity of rational numbers, that is it non-denumerable and belongs to a higher type of infinity than aleph-null.

Thus the question we now study is that of existence of different types of infinities. They can be classified with the aid of one-to-one correspondence which represents the extension of counting to infinite collections.

Now let us examine Cantor's proof. We suppose that the continuum has actually been enumerated, which means that all rational numbers and all irrational numbers have been ordered in a sequence and have received, each one of them, their ordinal numbers.

This assumption is equivalent to the possibility of writing all infinite decimal fractions in a determined order and therefore, as a necessary result of this assumption, the decimal fractions can be distinguished from each other as first, second, third, ... We write them in their presumed order, limiting ourselves to the numbers between zero and one:

Number	Decimal fraction	
first	$0.a_{11}a_{12}a_{13} \cdots a_{1m} \cdots$	
second	$0.a_{21}a_{22}a_{23} \cdots a_{2m} \cdots$	
third	$0.a_{31}a_{32}a_{33} \cdots a_{3m} \cdots$	(T)
$\cdots$	$\cdots$	
n-th	$0.a_{n1}a_{n2}a_{n3} \cdots a_{nm} \cdots$	
$\cdots$	$\cdots$	

In this table (T) all the decimals are denoted by the same letter a with two subscripts n and m. Thus, a_{nm} denotes the m-th digit of the n-th decimal fraction. The subscripts m and n vary from one to infinity, and each one of the digits a_{nm} has one of ten possible values, 0, 1, 2, 3, 4, ... 9.

Our assumption that the continuum in the interval $(0, 1)$ is denumerable is now explicitly written in the form of an infinite table (T) which extends without limit both to the right and downward. If this assumption is true, all positive decimal fractions not exceeding one are in this table (T) and there can be no others. To prove that our assumption is wrong it will be sufficient to form a single positive decimal fraction less than one, such that it is not contained in the table (T).

This number is easily constructed. Denote by b_n any digit different from the digit a_{nn}, $b_n \neq a_{nn}$, the choice of b_n being restricted to the nine digits different from a_{nn}, and write down the decimal fraction

$$0.b_1b_2b_3b_4 \cdots b_n \cdots \tag{31}$$

In (31) the n-th digit b_n is different from a_{nn} for all values of n, 1, 2, 3, ... The fraction (31) does not belong to the table (T): it has a decimal, b_1, different from the first decimal a_{11} of the first fraction in the table, a second decimal b_2 different from the second decimal a_{22} of the second fraction, and so on, *ad infinitum*, the deviating decimals $b_n \neq a_{nn}$ being located along the principal diagonal of our table (T).

Note that for b_1, as for any b_n, we have 9 choices. For b_1 and b_2, considered as a two digit number $b_1 b_2$, the number of choices is 9^2 because there are nine possible choices of b_2 for each given value of b_1. Likewise, a k-digit number $b_1 b_2 b_3 \cdots b_k$ may be formed in 9^k different ways. Therefore, for the totality of decimals in (31) we have $9^{\text{aleph-null}}$ choices, that is, a power of 9 with exponent aleph-null, because there are aleph-null decimals in (31). The table (T) contains aleph-null decimal fractions and we can form $9^{\text{aleph-null}}$ decimal fractions which do not belong to this table.

We see that the tentative establishment of a one-to-one correspondence (sometimes called *biunique* correspondence) between the set of all integers and the continuum fails because the set of all integers becomes exhausted *before* all the elements of the continuum are taken into consideration.

Therefore the transfinite cardinal number C, attached to continuum as its infinite cardinal number, represents an infinity much richer in elements than aleph-null, the transfinite cardinal number attached to the set of all integers. If we add (or subtract) a finite set of N elements to (or from) a denumerable set, we do not change the cardinal number aleph-null, that is

$$\aleph_0 \pm N = \aleph_0$$

If we add (or subtract) any denumerable set of points to (or from) the set of points of a straight line, we do not change its length because a denumerable set of points does not form a length. But the continuity of the line and the existence if the length find their arithmetic expression in the symbol C of the continuum considered as the totality of all real numbers corresponding to all points of the line. Therefore:

$$C \pm \aleph_0 = C$$

and we see that aleph-null plays the same role with respect to C that a finite number N plays with respect to aleph-null, or zero plays with respect to N

$$\aleph_0 \pm N = \aleph_0; \quad N \pm 0 = N$$

In other words, aleph-null disappears, when compared to C, as a finite number disappears, when compared to aleph-null.

We cannot here continue further the study of different types of infinity, and add only that Georg Cantor succeeded in actually constructing an infinite sequence of infinite sets such that each term in this sequence, being in itself an infinity, disappears when compared with the next term, but makes its predecessor disappear, if this predecessor is compared with it.

The transfinite cardinal numbers attached to the infinities, members of this sequence, are ordered according to their increasing magnitudes as are the natural numbers 1, 2, 3, ...

This classification of infinities however is not yet completely clarified. We know that there is no integer between 1 and 2 or between 2 and 3, but we do not know, whether C can be called aleph-one because the question of whether or not there exists an infinite set whose transfinite cardinal number is greater than aleph-null, but smaller than C still remains open.

Another Geometrical Aspect of Irrationality

In Chapter 2 the rational numbers m/n were represented in a plane XOY, by interpreting m and n as cartesian coordinates $y = m$ and $x = n$ of a point, image of m/n. As a result a straight line through the origin O was associated with each rational fraction reduced to its lowest terms and the value of this associated fraction was seen to be measure of the slope of the line.

The following question was then raised: are there lines through O such they do not pass through any of the point-images of rational numbers? The existence of irrational numbers settles this question: the slope of a line increases continuously when the line rotates around the origin and therefore the numerical value of the slope passes through all rational and irrational numbers. This means that in our geometric picture (see fig. 9 Ch. 3) there are lines which do not pass through any of the dots which mark rational points since their slopes have irrational values. The rational points located around such a line come nearer and nearer to it from below and from above as their distance from the origin O increases, and they picture two rational sequences which approach an irrational number from below and from above.

Operations with irrational numbers follow the same laws as operations with rational numbers since laws can be applied to the rational terms of the infinite sequences defining the irrational numbers. Take as an example the distributive law. Given three irrational numbers α, β, and γ, how can we be sure that

$$\alpha(\beta + \gamma) = \alpha\beta + \alpha\gamma?$$

Let us denote the rational sequences defining α, β, γ, by a_n, b_n, and c_n, respectively, so that

$$\alpha = \lim_{n=\infty} a_n, \quad \beta = \lim_{n=\infty} b_n, \quad \text{and} \quad \gamma = \lim_{n=\infty} c_n$$

for $n = \infty$. We can write

$$a_n(b_n + c_n) = a_n b_n + a_n c_n \tag{32}$$

since a_n, b_n, and c_n are rational numbers for all values of n. Now at the limit, when n reaches aleph-null, the relation (32) is transformed into

$$\alpha(\beta + \gamma) = \alpha\beta + \alpha\gamma$$

and this proves that the distributive law holds for irrational numbers.

To be rigorous, we must eliminate a possible objection, namely: in saying "transformed" we have implicitly used the facts that the limit of a product is the product of the limits of the factors and the limit of a sum is the sum of the limits of the terms. It is easy to complete the proof using the infinitely small differences between a_n, b_n, and c_n and their limits α, β, γ.

The existence of a limit $\lim_{n=\infty} a_n = \alpha$ means that the difference $\varepsilon_n = a_n - \alpha$ between a_n and its limit α approaches zero when n increases, and reaches it for $n = \infty$:

$$\lim_{n=\infty} \varepsilon_n = 0$$

Likewise, if $\lim_{n=\infty} b_n = \beta$ and $\lim_{n=\infty} c_n = \gamma$, then

$$b_n = \beta + g_n, \quad c_n = \gamma + h_n$$

with

$$\lim_{n=\infty} g_n = 0, \quad \lim_{n=\infty} h_n = 0.$$

Noe to prove that

$$\lim_{n=\infty} [a_n(b_n + c_n)] = \alpha(\beta + \gamma)$$

we substitute into $a_n(b_n + c_n)$ the expressions of a_n, b_n, c_n:

$$a_n(b_n + c_n) = (\alpha + \varepsilon_n)(\beta + \gamma + g_n + h_n)$$

$$= \alpha(\beta + \gamma) + \varepsilon_n(\beta + \gamma) + (\alpha + \varepsilon_n)(g_n + h_n)$$

The products $\varepsilon_n(\beta + \gamma)$ and $(\alpha + \varepsilon)(g_n + h_n)$ are infinitely small because in both of them one factor (ε_n and $g_n + h_n$) is infinitely small. Therefore we obtain:

$$a_n(b_n + c_n) = \alpha(\beta + \gamma) + j_n$$

where

$$j_n = \varepsilon_n(\beta + \gamma) + (\alpha + \varepsilon_n)(g_n + h_n)$$

is infinitely small and therefore

$$\lim_{n=\infty} j_n = 0$$

We conclude that

$$\lim_{n=\infty} [a_n(b_n + c_n) = \alpha(\beta + \gamma)$$

In the same way we justify the fact that

$$\lim_{n=\infty} (a_n b_n + a_n c_n) = \alpha\beta + \alpha\gamma$$

Note a general and important conclusion: *the order in which passage to the limit and arithmetic operations (a finite number of them) are performed can be inverted without changing the result.*

In Chapter 1 we mentioned that two segments of definite length AB, CD are not always commensurable: it can happen that no third segment can be found which is contained an integral number of times in both AB and CD. But we have not explained *how* this can happen. Now we can say that to every length AB there corresponds a number, the measure of this length in terms of a given fixed unit of length. This number may be rational or irrational. In the first case the number is obtained by using the common measure of the segment AB and of the unit of length. The segment AB is then said to be commensurable with the unit. If the number measuring AB is irrational that is, if no integer n can be found such that $1/n$ part of the unit is contained an integral number of times in AB, the segment AB is said to be incommensurable with the unit. However, its length can nevertheless be expressed in numbers. To show this we choose a first integer, n_1, divide our unit into n_1 equal parts, and compare AB with segments beginning at A and rational lengths measured by k/n_1, $k = 1, 2, \ldots$

$$AB' = m_1/n_1$$

$$AB'' = (m_1 + 1)/n_1$$

This comparison shows that for some values of k the segment of length k/n_1 is contained in AB, while for others it contains AB. If we denote by m_1 the greatest value of k, for which k/n_1 is less than the length λ of the segment AB, $m_1/n_1 < \lambda$, then for the next value of k, $m_1 + 1$, the length $(m_1 + 1)/n_1$ will exceed λ and $(m_1 + 1)/n_1 > \lambda$.

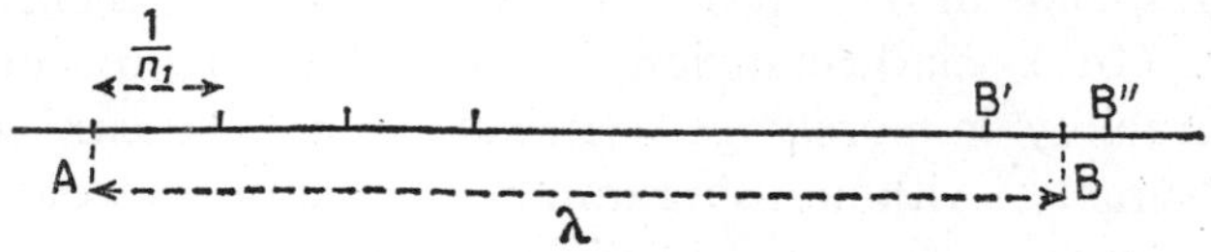

Fig. 5.7

Since AB by hypothesis is incommensurable with the unit the signs of inequality in

$$AB' = m_1/n_1 < \lambda < (m_1 + 1)/n_1 = AB'' \qquad (33)$$

can never be replaced by the sign of equality no matter what value is assigned to n_1. Now we increase n_1, replacing it by $n_2 > n_1$, and repeat the same comparison of AB with the $(1/n_2)$-th parts of our unit of length, obtaining a second inequality

$$m_2/n_2 < \lambda < (m_2 + 1)/n_2 \qquad (34)$$

The same procedure can be repeated an infinite number of times, using the infinite increasing sequence of integers

$$n_1 < n_2 < n_3 < \cdots < n_j < \cdots$$

As final result we obtain an infinite sequence of nested intervals with decreasing lengths

$$\frac{1}{n_1} > \frac{1}{n_2} > \frac{1}{n_3} > \cdots > \frac{1}{n_j} > \cdots$$

shrinking towards the point B, so that the measure λ of the length of AB verifies all the inequalities

$$\frac{m_j}{n_j} < \lambda < \frac{m_j + 1}{n_j}$$

and is the common limit of two rational sequences m_j/n_j and $(m_j + 1)/n_j$

$$\lambda = \lim_{j=\infty} \frac{m_j}{n_j} = \lim_{j=\infty} \frac{m_j + 1}{n_j}$$

This limit λ of rational numbers cannot be a rational number because, by hypothesis, AB is not commensurable with the unit of length. Therefore, λ is an irrational number which expresses the length of a segment incommensurable with the unit of length.

Thus, we see that the incommensurability of two segments in geometry corresponds to the irrationality of the ratio of their lengths in arithmetic. Greek mathematicians studied the phenomenon of incommensurability in purely geometrical form (Eudoxus' theory of incommensurables) without using numbers, because they did not know irrational numbers.

We end this chapter by generalizing the operation of exponentiation and defining powers with irrational exponents. The meaning of a power a^β with the irrational exponent β becomes clear, if we introduce the sequence of rational numbers approaching β

$$b_1, b_2, b_3, \ldots, \to \beta$$

and thus define β as their limit:

$$\beta = \lim_{n=\infty} b_n.$$

We know the meaning of the power a^{b_n} with a rational exponent $b_n = p_n/q_n$:

$$a^{b_n} = a^{p_n/q_n} = \sqrt[q_n]{a^{p_n}}$$

that is, a^{b_n} is such a number that, raised to a power with integral exponent q_n, it gives a^{p_n}. Now the limit of a^{b_n} for $n \to \infty$ does exist:

$$\lim_{n=\infty} (a^{b_n}) = a^{\lim\limits_{n=\infty} b_n}$$

By definition the meaning of the symbol a^β is fixed by

$$a^\beta = \lim_{n=\infty} (a^{b_n}).$$

CHAPTER 6

Complex Numbers

Irrational numbers, introduced and studied in Chapter 5, enable us to extend the extraction of roots to all positive rational numbers, and therefore, by using the passage to the limit, to all positive numbers. But we still cannot say that this operation, the inverse of exponentiation, even now after the introduction of irrational numbers, has become possible for *all numbers.*

Take, for example, the radicals of *negative* numbers, such as $\sqrt{-4}$, $\sqrt[3]{-27}$. Some radicals of negative numbers exist within our field of real numbers. Such is the case with $\sqrt[3]{-27} = -3$, since $(-3)^3 = -27$. Other radicals of negative numbers, however, do not exist for us and the operation indicated by the extraction sign appears as impossible. Consider $\sqrt{-4}$. There is no such positive or negative number as $\sqrt{-4}$, because the square of such a number $(\sqrt{-4})^2$ must by definition equal the negative number -4, while the squares of both positive and negative numbers we know are always *positive.*

Thus the operation symbolized by $\sqrt{-4}$ appears as impossible. Unless we are willing to generalize our number concept even further, we must acknowledge that we are not always able to perform so simple an operation as the extraction of a square root.

If we analyze the problem more closely, we note that $-4 = 4(-1)$ and the rule

$$\sqrt{ab} = (ab)^{1/2} = a^{1/2}b^{1/2} = \sqrt{a}\sqrt{b}$$

when applied to $\sqrt{-4}$, gives

$$\sqrt{-4} = \pm 2\sqrt{-1} = \pm 2(-1)^{1/2}.$$

We now see that it is the apparently meaningless symbol $\sqrt{-1}$ which constitutes an obstacle to the operation symbolized by $\sqrt{-4}$.

Let us study the general case $\sqrt[n]{-1}$, where n is a positive integer. Since, as we saw in Chapter 2, all odd powers of -1 are equal to -1, we can state that $\sqrt[3]{-1}$, $\sqrt[5]{-1}$ and, in general, all radicals $\sqrt[n]{-1}$ of an odd order $n = 2m + 1$, that is $\sqrt[2m+1]{-1}$, do exist, and they all are equal to -1. Thus, radicals of negative numbers exist, provided their order n is odd. On the other hand $\sqrt{-1}, \sqrt[4]{-1}$ and in general radicals $\sqrt[n]{-1}$ of an even order $n = 2m$, that is $\sqrt[2m]{-1}$, are for the time being meaningless, and we find ourselves unable to extract roots of negative numbers, if their irder n is even.

We conclude therefore that our number concept is imperfect. To remedy this situation, we must again generalize our number concept so that we may ascribe a meaning to the radicals $\sqrt{-1}, \sqrt[4]{-1}, \sqrt[6]{-1}$, etc. At first glance this problem seems to consist of an infinity of particular problems: we must assign values to an infinite set of radicals $\sqrt[2m]{-1}$ for $m = 1, 2, 3, \ldots$ creating in the process an infinite set of new numbers.

Astonishingly enough, we can solve this infinite set of problems in one stroke. If we succeed in finding a meaning for the first symbol, $\sqrt{-1}$, all other radicals $\sqrt[2m]{-1}$ of an even order $2m$ take on meaning and our problem is solved.

There is another justification for introducing a number concept more inclusive than our limited one consisting of positive or negative, rational or irrational, numbers. Many important data needed in physics and the applied sciences cannot be expressed in terms of positive and negative numbers alone. Electric or magnetic force, the velocity of the wind or of an airplane, have not only a magnitude (intensity of the force, speed of the airplane) but also a perfectly determined *direction*. They are *vectors*, which means that they are *directed* magnitudes. To measure and express them, to predict their effects, in short to study nature we need *directed* numbers.

We have already seen that displacements (movements) along a line are vectors expressed by positive and negative numbers. But motion is not limited to displacements along a fixed line. They may also take place in a plane, and here again we have two characteristics of such a displacement: *magnitude* (length) and *direction* (angle). Therefore, displacements in a plane, too, are vectors.

Another kind of motion, rotation, plays an important role in all physical phenomena, as well as in all our machines. In electric generators and dynamos, for instance, we have rotating coils (rotating electric currents) or rotating magnetic fields. To compute their design and build such mechanisms, we must have at our disposal numbers which can express rotating quantities. The number field as we have constructed it up to now is not adequate to this problem.

The prodigious development of modern electrical equipment has been made possible by the mathematical theory of electricity and this theory utilizes a number concept more general than that of positive and negative real numbers. These more general numbers, called *complex numbers*, express vectors and rotations.

The introduction of complex numbers was an important event in the evolution of human thinking. It created, and continues to create through the application of complex numbers in physics, a profound repercussion on the material organization of human society and ultimately on the individual lives of human beings.

Vectors

Our frame of reference in a plane is composed of two perpendicular axes, OX and OY, whose intersection point O is called the *origin*. One of the two directions along each axis is considered as positive, and the opposite direction as negative. On the horizontal axis OX, called also the *real axis*, the direction pointing to the right of the origin is defined as positive, while the opposite direction, to the left of the origin, is considered as negative. On the vertical axis OY the direction upwards is defined as positive, and the direction downwards as negative.

Any horizontal vector parallel to the real axis OX is represented by a positive number, if it has a positive direction, that is if it points to the right, as the vector **AB** in the figure 6.1 below.

The length of a vector is measured by the absolute value of the number representing this vector. If, for example, **AB** $= a$, then a is positive ($a > 0$) because **AB** points to the right, and its length AB is equal to a units of length.

A vector such as **CD**, also parallel to OX but pointing to the left, is represented by a negative number b, ($b < 0$), whose absolute value is denoted by $|b|$. The length CD of the vector **CD** is equal to $|b| = -b$ units of length. Since the absolute value of a positive number equals the number itself, it can be said for both kinds of vectors parallel to OX that their length is expressed by the absolute value of the number which represents the vector. Do not confuse the two notations: $b = $ **CD** denotes a vector which has both length and direction, while $|b|$ denotes a length only. In the representation of a vector by the number -5 for example, the minus sign shows that the vector points to the left, and the magnitude of the negative number -5, that is its absolute value $|-5| = 5$, expresses the length of the vector denoted by the number -5.

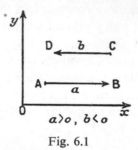

Fig. 6.1

A vector can always be conceived of as a displacement. Given two points, A and B, such that the line **AB** which joins them is parallel to OX, two opposite vectors can be constructed: **AB** and **BA**. These two opposite vectors correspond to two opposite displacements, from A to B, and from B to A. Traveling from A to B, and then back again, we return to the initial point A. The resulting displacement is the sum of two component displacements, **AB** and **BA**, and is equal to zero. The mathematical expression of this addition of two opposite vectors of equal length is **AB** + **BA** = 0 (as well as **CD** + **DC** = 0).

Suppose now that we have to add two mutually perpendicular displacements **AB**//OX and **BC**//OY (the symbol // indicates parallelism of two directions). **AB** has a length of 4 units, and **BC** of 3 units. The resulting displacement, or vector-sum, is **AC**, with a length of 5 units: $5 = (4^2 + 3^2)^{1/2}$, fig. 6.2. This result is written as

$$\textbf{AC} = \textbf{AB} + \textbf{BC}$$

and is called *geometric* addition or addition of two vectors. Observe that the vector-sum **AC** of two perpendicular vectors **AB** and **BC** is represeneted in direction and magnitude by the *diagonal* **AC** of a rectangle of which **AB** and **BC** are adjacent sides.

Now let us consider the general case of geometric addition in which the two component vectors are not at right angle to each other. Their vector-sum is defined by the so-called *parallelogram law*. This famous law has a purely empirical origin. It results from our experience: our observations have shown that the combined effect of two velocities, forces, or, in general, of any two physical actions expressible as vectors, is equivalent to the effect of a single action. This single action is the effect of the vector-sum of the two component causes. The parallelogram law can be stated as follows:

Parallelogram Law

The vector-sum of two given vectors is represented in magnitude and direction by the diagonal of a parallelogram constructed with the two given vectors as sides.

Thus **AB + AD = AB + BC = AC**, as well as **AD + AB = AD + DC = AC**, where **AB** $\underline{\underline{\angle}}$ **DC** and **AD** $\underline{\underline{\angle}}$ **BC** (the symbol $\underline{\underline{\angle}}$ means "is parallel and equal to"). Two vectors having the same magnitude and the same direction, that is two vectors which are parallel and equal, are considered as one and the same vector in two different positions. The vectors are therefore equal, and we can write, using vectorial notation, **AB = DC** and **AD = BC**, (fig. 6.3).

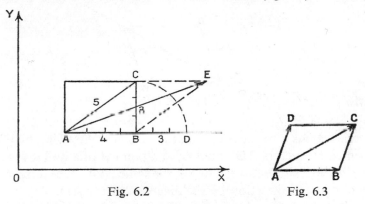

Fig. 6.2   Fig. 6.3

To illustrate the parallelogram law, we consider the addition of two velocities. Suppose that a swimmer, *S*, crosses a river. Represent his velocity in still water by **SA**, and the velocity of the current by **SB**. The true velocity with which the swimmer *S* progresses across the river is his velocity with respect to the bed of the river. This velocity is the sum of velocities **SA** and **SB**, and it is represented by the diagonal **ST** of the parallelogram constructed on sides **SA** and **SB**. It is obvious that, to cross a river in a direction perpendicular to the shore, one must swim obliquely upstream, heading towards such a point *M* on the opposite shore that the diagonal vector **ST** points directly across the river, being perpendicular to the shore, (fig. 6.4).

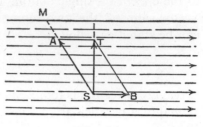

Fig. 6.4

The parallelogram law explains why, in general, an airplane is at an angle to the direction in which it is flying. Here again the still-air velocity **AB** of the airplane is combined with the velocity **AC** of the wind. The resultant velocity of the air plane relative to the ground, **AD**, is the geometric sum **AB** + **AC** of the airplane's and the wind's velocities, (fig. 6.5).

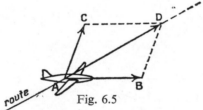

Fig. 6.5

Experience has also taught us that the effect of applying two forces, represented by vectors **AB** and **AC**, at a point *A* of a body is the same as the effect of a single force acting at the same point *A*, and represented in magnitude and direction by the diagonal vector **AD**.

Note that the geometric addition of vectors according to the parallelogram law obeys the commutative and associative laws of addition.

We now are faced with the problem of translating our geometric addition of two perpendicular vectors into the language of algebra. At present, this is impossible for us because we do not yet know how to express by numbers vectors such as **BC** or **AC** in fig. 6.2. If we can find a numerical expression for **BC**, then the addition formula will yield the algebraic expression for the resultant **AC**.

Going back to fig. 6.2, consider a vector **BD** having the same length 3 as **BC**, but parallel to **OX** and pointing to the right. This vector is represented by the positive number 3: **BD** = 3. Our vector **BC** can now be considered as the final position of vector **BD** after a counterclockwise rotation through 90°. Suppose we knew of an algebraic operation which, applied to the numerical expression of a given vector, would rotate the vector counterclockwise through 90°. We could then apply this operation to the number 3 which represents the horizontal vector **BD**. The result will be the algebraic expression of the vector **BC**, perpendicular to the real axis **OX** and pointing upward.

In our search for such an operation, we obtain a clue from Chapter 1. There we saw that the multiplication of a number N by -1 produces a counterclockwise rotation through 180° of the vector represented by N. For this reason, the negative unit -1 was called the *rotation-factor through* 180°. This fact suggests that multiplication in algebra corresponds to rotation in geometry. When we consider that multiplication by -1 always produces the particular rotation through 180°, we conclude that the amount of rotation (rotation angle) is determined by the numerical value of the factor used in the multiplication.

This conclusion suggests the existence of a particular numerical value for the rotation-factor through 90°. Since we do not know what it is, let us call it x. To form the equation verified by the unknown x, we observe that the effect of two successive rotations through 90° is exactly the same as that of a single rotation through 180°. In other words, to rotate a vector represented by the number N through 180°, we can multiply N twice by x (which is the same as multiplying it once by x^2), or else we can multiply it once by -1. The products obtained by either method will be equal: $Nx^2 = N(-1)$. Both members of the relation

$$Nx^2 = N(-1)$$

do, indeed, represent the same vector. Cancelling on both sides of this equality their common factor N, we obtain a new equation

$$x^2 = -1$$

verified by our unknown rotation-factor through 90°, which was denoted by x.

We can replace x in this equation by the symbol $\pm\sqrt{-1}$, since

$$(\pm\sqrt{-1})^2 = (\pm 1)^2 (\sqrt{-1})^2 = 1(-1) = -1.$$

Kogbetliantz 13

Thus we find two possible values for our rotation-factor through $90°$:

and
$$x_1 = +\sqrt{-1} = +(-1)^{1/2}$$
$$x_2 = -\sqrt{-1} = -(-1)^{1/2}$$

The existence of two values for our rotation-factor through $90°$ expresses the fact that two such rotations are possible: clockwise and counterclockwise. Both rotations verify the observation expressed in the equation $x^2 = -1$, which states that two successive rotations through $90°$ are equivalent to a single rotation through $180°$ (see fig. 6.6).

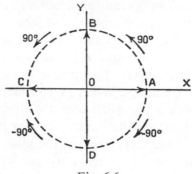

Fig. 6.6

We associate the positive square root of minus one, $(-1)^{1/2}$, with a positive, counterclockwise rotation through $90°$, so that in fig. 6.6 **OB** $= (-1)^{1/2}$ **OA**. The opposite, clockwise, rotation through $90°$, which is in fact a rotation through the negative angle $-90°$, corresponds to the rotation-factor $-(-1)^{1/2}$: **OD** $= -(-1)^{1/2}$ **OA**. These two definitions agree perfectly: fig. 6.6 shows that **OD** $= -$ **OB**, since these two vectors have the same length, but opposite directions. Moreover, the expressions we formed for **OB** and **OD** check this relation

$$\textbf{OB} = \textbf{OA}(-1)^{1/2} = -\ \textbf{OA}[-(-1)^{1/2}] = -\textbf{OD}$$

as it necessarily must.

History of $i = (-1)^{1/2}$.

The square roots of negative numbers were first considered in 1545, when the Italian mathematician Cardano undertook to solve the arithmetic problem: "Find two numbers such that their sum is equal to

10, and their product is equal to 40". Cardano discovered that these two numbers could be represented by $5 + (-15)^{1/2}$ and $5 - (-15)^{1/2}$. We find indeed, applying the identity $(A + B)(A - B) \equiv A^2 - B^2$ with $A = 5$ and $B = (-15)^{1/2}$, that

$$(5 + \sqrt{-15})(5 - \sqrt{-15}) = 5^2 - (\sqrt{-15})^2 = 25 - (-15)$$
$$= 25 + 15 = 40$$

Cardano failed to pursue his discovery further. On the contrary, he declared that, since the squares of all numbers are necessarily positive, numbers such as $\sqrt{-15}$ have no meaning, are impossible and do not exist.

Cardano was also the first *in Europe* to publish a general expression for the solution of a cubic equation of the form $x^3 + ax + b = 0$, where the unknown number is denoted by x, the coefficients a and b being known, given numbers. This general solution expresses x in terms of a and b. It seems that the true author of this solution was Nicolo Fontana, called Tartaglia. Tartaglia revealed his discovery, which was very important at the time, to Cardano, and the latter "neglected" to mention the name of the author in publishing Fontana's work. His stratagem was completely successful: even now the general solution of the cubic equation is referred to as Cardano's solution.

Another Italian mathematician, Bombelli, applying Tartaglia's formula to the numerical equation $x^3 - 15x - 4 = 0$ (Bombelli's work was published in 1572) found for the unknown x the following expression:

$$x = (2 + \sqrt{-121})^{1/3} + (2 - \sqrt{-121})^{1/3} \tag{1}$$

On the other hand the equation $x^3 - 15x - 4 = 0$ admits of the solution $x = 4$, as may be checked by direct substitution:

$$4^3 - 15.4 - 4 = 64 - 64 = 0$$

Bombelli was the first mathematician who dared to consider the symbol $\sqrt{-121}$ as a number. He conceived the possibility that "impossible" expression (1) has a meaning, and is nothing more than a disguised form of the number 4. Bombelli was the first to apply classical algebraic operations to the roots of negative numbers in his computation of expression (1). In order to extract the cube root of the sum $2 + \sqrt{-121}$, he had to prove that this sum is a perfect cube. He succeeded in proving that it is indeed equal to $(2 + \sqrt{-1})^3$. To check his result, we use the fact that the third power of a sum of two terms, $(A + B)^3$, can be computed with the aid of the identity

$$(A + B)^3 \equiv A^3 + 3A^2B + 3AB^2 + B^3 \tag{2}$$

This formula can be deduced by multiplying both members of the identity

$$(A + B)^2 \equiv A^2 + 2AB + B^2$$

by $A + B$:

$$(A + B)^3 \equiv (A + B)^2 (A + B) \equiv (A^2 + 2AB + B^2)(A + B)$$

$$\equiv A^3 + 2A^2B + B^2A + A^2B + 2AB^2 + B^3$$

$$\equiv A^3 + 3A^2B + 3AB^2 + B^3$$

Applying this expansion of $(A + B)^3$ to the particular case of $A = 2$ and $B = \sqrt{-1} = i$, Bombelli found using $i^2 = -1$ that

$$(2 + \sqrt{-1})^3 = 2^3 + 3 \cdot 2^2\sqrt{-1} + 3 \cdot 2(\sqrt{-1})^2 + \sqrt{-1})^3$$

$$= 8 + 12\sqrt{-1} - 6 - \sqrt{-1} = 2 + 11\sqrt{-1}$$

But $121 = 11^2$, and therefore

$$11\sqrt{-1} = \sqrt{121}\sqrt{-1} = \sqrt{121(-1)} = \sqrt{-121}$$

which proves that

$$(2 + \sqrt{-1})^3 = 2 + \sqrt{-121}$$

Extracting the cube root we obtain

$$(2 + \sqrt{-121})^{1/3} = 2 + \sqrt{-1} = 2 + i \tag{3}$$

In the same way Bombelli succeeded in extracting the second cube root in (1); since $(2 - \sqrt{-1})^3 = 2 - 11\sqrt{-1} = 2 - \sqrt{-121}$,

$$(2 - \sqrt{-121})^{1/3} = 2 - \sqrt{-1} \tag{4}$$

When we change the sign of B in the expansion of $(A + B)^3$, we obtain indeed

$$(A - B)^3 \equiv A^3 - 3A^2B + 3AB^2 - B^3$$

Taking $A = 2$, $B = \sqrt{-1}$, this formula yields

$$(2 - \sqrt{-1})^3 = 8 - 12\sqrt{-1} - 6 + \sqrt{-1} = 2 - 11\sqrt{-1}$$

$$= 2 - \sqrt{-121}$$

which proves (4). By adding (3) and (4), Bombelli obtained the value of the expression (1) namely $(2 + i) + (2 - i) = 4$.

Bombelli's work showed first that the square roots of negative numbers are valuable aids in practical computations, and second that in dealing with them we must apply the same laws of operations as we use with ordinary numbers.

Bombelli failed to recognize, however, that this new kind of number represents an important extension of the number concept. That is why he gave to the symbol $\sqrt{-N}$, $N > 0$, the name of "imaginary number", as opposed to positive and negative numbers, which had in his opinion a real existence. Despite Bombelli's reluctance to incorporate this new kind of number into an enlarged number-concept, his computations with imaginary numbers still met with general disapproval and vehement criticism. More than a century was to pass before mathematicians could bring themselves to accept the importance of Bombelli's "imaginary" numbers, and to study and use them according to the principles he had laid down. Even Leibniz said: "Imaginary numbers are... a sort of amphibian being and not being".

Among the first mathematicians, after Bombelli, to use imaginary numbers were De-Moivre (1667–1754) and Euler (1707–1783). It was Euler who introduced the letter i (first letter of the word "imaginary") as an abbreviation for $\sqrt{-1}$, thus creating a new and important mathematical symbol, $i = \sqrt{-1}$. Euler also discovered the famous *Euler's formula*, which involves i and which we study in this chapter. Even Euler, however, had misconceptions about this new kind of number. In his *Algebra*, published in 1770, he says: "All such expressions as $\sqrt{-1}$, $\sqrt{-2}$, etc. are neither nothing nor greater than nothing, nor less than nothing, which necessarily makes them imaginary and impossible".

The number $i = \sqrt{-1}$ is neither mysterious nor imaginary. Every kind of number, natural integers included, is a creation of the human mind and exists only in our imagination. For this reason numbers of all kinds are equally fictitious and imaginary. As a mathematical concept the number $i = \sqrt{-1}$ has the same kind of reality as all other numbers we know.

The words "real" and "imaginary", widely used right up to the present time in speaking about numbers, simply reflect the early feelings of uneasiness aroused by the invention and introduction of complex numbers. Such feelings always accompany the birth of new ideas and concepts. From a purely logical point of view there is no difference between the irrational number $\sqrt{2}$, solution of the equation $x^2 - 2 = 0$, and the "imaginary" unit $\sqrt{-1}$, solution of the similar equation $x^2 + 1 = 0$. Both $\sqrt{2}$ and $i = \sqrt{-1}$ are extensions of the number concept which are necessary to free the extraction of square roots from paralyzing limitations.

Complex Numbers

We can now resume our discussion of the parallelogram law which defines the addition of vectors. We have found the geometric meaning of $\sqrt{-1}$, and know that the number i is the rotation-factor through 90°. We can therefore express the vector **BC**, which is parallel to the vertical axis **OY** in fig. 6.2, as the product of the vector **BD** multiplied by i. Since **BC** may be obtained from **BD** by a rotation through 90°, we see that **BC** = i**BD**; and, since **BD** = 3, we can write **BC** = $3i$. The diagonal vector **AC** = **AB** + **BC** now takes the form

$$\mathbf{AC} = 4 + 3i.$$

DEFINITION.—Such a number, the sum of a real term and an imaginary[1]) term, is called a *complex number*.

Any vector can be represented by a complex number since it can be decomposed into two components, one parallel to the real axis **OX**, and the other parallel to the vertical axis **OY**. The component parallel to **OX** is represented by a real number. The second component, parallel to **OY**, is expressed as an imaginary number, because it can be obtained by a rotation through 90° of a vector parallel to **OX**.

---

[1]) We prefer to retain the customary terminology of "real" and "imaginary" as used in mathematical literature, but with the reservation that these words have only a conventional meaning: "real" refers to any positive or negative number, while numbers of form iN, N being real, are called "imaginary".

The two components of an inclined vector, parallel to OX and to OY, are called its x-component and y-component, respectively. Thus given a vector $a + ib$, its x-component corresponds to the real term a, and its y-component to the imaginary term ib. Vectors parallel to the OY axis are represented by imaginary numbers of the general type ib (b being real) since they lack an x-component.

To break a vector down into its x- and y-components, it is sufficient to draw a rectangle in which the given vector plays the role of diagonal and whose sides are parallel to OX and OY. Thus, for example, if you climb a mountain (an inclined plane), walking a distance of 761 feet and accomplishing a change in elevation of 39 feet, you will progress only 760 feet in a horizontal direction. This is easily checked by the formula $760^2 + 39^2 = 761^2$. Thus, your actual displacement is the geometric sum of a horizontal component (refresented by the real number 760) and a vertical component (expressed by the imaginary number $39i$). You have therefore travelled along a vector expressed by a single complex number, $760 + 39i$.

We are able now to assign an algebraic expression to the geometric addition of two vectors according to the parallelogram law. This important law finds its adequate expression in the algebraical addition of two complex numbers. In figure 6.7 we have vectors

$$\mathbf{AB} = \mathbf{DC} = a + ib \quad \text{and} \quad \mathbf{AD} = \mathbf{BC} = c + id.$$

The x-components of these vectors point to the right, and the y-components point upwards, so that the real numbers a, b, c, d are all positive. We know by the parallelogram law that the vector-sum is $\mathbf{AC}$:

$$\mathbf{AC} = \mathbf{AB} + \mathbf{BC} = (a + ib) + (c + id).$$

If we consider $\mathbf{AC}$ as the vector-sum of its x- and y-components $\mathbf{AE}$ and $\mathbf{EC}$, so that

$$\mathbf{AC} = \mathbf{AE} + \mathbf{EC}$$

we find that

$$\mathbf{AE} = a + c \quad \text{and} \quad \mathbf{EC} = i(b + d)$$

Therefore

$$\mathbf{AC} = (a + c) + i(b + d)$$

We now see that in adding two complex numbers, we must perform separate additions for the real and for imaginary parts:

$$(a + ib) + (c + id) = (a + c) + i(b + d) \tag{5}$$

The addition of complex numbers obeys the commutative law since $a + c = c + a$, and $b + d = d + b$.

There is only one complex number which is zero. This number represents the vector zero, which is to say no vector at all. If a vector vanishes, it can be represented only by $0 + i0$, since both its components vanish. It is possible to deduce this same fact algebraically from the equation $a + ib = 0$. If $a + ib = 0$, then $a = -ib$. Squaring, we get $a^2 = -b^2$, that is $a^2 + b^2 = 0$, which is possible only if both non-negative numbers a^2, b^2 vanish. Therefore, $a + ib = 0$ is possible only when $a = b = 0$.

A complex equation $a + ib = c + id$ is equivalent to two real equations obtained by equating the real and imaginary parts separately: if $a + ib = c + id$, then $a = c$ and $ib = id$, that is $b = d$. Geometrically, this important fact is obvious: two equal vectors having the same length and the same direction must necessarily have the same x- and y-components: $a = c$, $b = d$.

To establish this algebraically, we transpose c to the left and ib to the right:

$$a - c = id - ib = i(d - b)$$

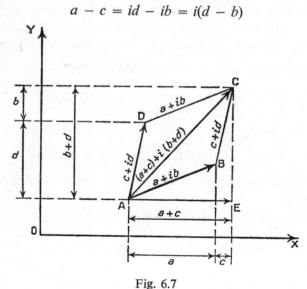

Fig. 6.7

Squaring both sides we obtain

$$(a - c)^2 = [i(d - b)]^2 = -(d - b)^2$$

i^2 being equal to $(\sqrt{-1})^2 = -1$. The equation thus obtained, $(a - c)^2 + (d - b)^2 = 0$ can have a meaning only when both terms in the left-hand member vanish, since the sum of two non-negative terms can vanish only if each term is equal to zero. Therefore, $(a - c)^2 = (b - d)^2 = 0$, and from this it follows that $a = c$ and $b = d$. The result just proved is known as the *principle of separation of real and imaginary*.

The rotation factors i and $-i$ not only represent counterclockwise and clockwise rotations through 90°, but they are also unit vectors parallel to OY, pointing upward in the case of i, and downward in the case of $-i$. In the relations,

$$1i = i \quad \text{and} \quad 1(-i) = -i$$

the righthand members are unit-vectors, while the same symbols i and $-i$ in the lefthand members are not vectors but rotation-factors which rotate the unit vector 1 located on the OX axis. Likewise in the product $i \cdot i = -1$ one of the two symbols i represents the unit-vector located on the OY axis and pointing upwards, while the other i is the rotation-factor through 90° multiplication by which transforms the vector i into the vector -1.

There are four fundamental unit vectors: 1, i, -1 and $-i$. All are derived from the first, 1, by rotations through 90°, and correspond therefore to powers of i:

$$1 = i^0, i = i^1, -1 = i^2 \quad \text{and} \quad -i = i^3.$$

For all positive and negative integers n the integral powers i^n of i can have only these four values 1, i, -1 and $-i$. These four values of i^n are repeated cyclically, as n ascends the scale of integers.

This is a corollary of the fact that $i^4 = 1$, since four successive rotations through 90° bring a vector back to its original position, leaving the vector unchanged. Since there is only one factor, 1, multiplication by which does not change the multiplicand, i^4 must be equal to 1. That $i^4 = 1$ can also be checked algebraically:

$$(\sqrt{-1})^4 = [(\sqrt{-1})^2]^2 = (-1)^2 = 1$$

Raising $i^4 = 1$ to the n-th power, we obtain $i^{4n} = 1$. Using the exponent law, $i^r i^s = i^{r+s}$, we can specify the value for every power of i:

$$i^{4n} = 1; \; i^{4n+1} = i; \; i^{4n+2} = i^2 = -1; \; i^{4n+3} = i^3 = -i.$$

Consider now any power i^N with integral exponent N. Any integer N can be presented in the form $4n + m$, where n and m are integers, m taking only four different values: 0, 1, 2, 3. Indeed, dividing N by 4, we obtain an improper integral quotient n and a remainder m. This remainder must be less than the divisor 4, which leaves a choice of four values 0, 1, 2, 3 only.

Any integral power i^N of i is now represented as $i^{4n+m} = i^{4n}i^m$, where $i^{4n} = (i^4)^n = 1^n = 1$, while m can take only four different values 0, 1, 2, 3. It appears therefore that the value of the remainder m determines the value of i^N, and since i^m takes only the four values 1, i, -1, $-i$, i^N can have also only these same values.

Now x and y being the Cartesian coordinates of a point $P(x, y)$ in the plane OXY, the geometric representation of a complex number $z = x + iy$, as a vector **OP** with its tail at the origin O and its head at the point $P(x, y)$ may be interpreted also as a one-to-one correspondence between the set of all points of the infinite plane OXY and the set of all complex numbers $z = x + iy$, x and y having an infinite range of variations between minus and plus infinity:

$$-\infty < x < \infty, \quad -\infty < y < \infty.$$

This important concept was formulated in 1797 by a Norwegian, C. Wessel, and also, ten years later, independently by Gauss and Argand. It constitutes the foundation of an important branch of mathematics, the theory of analytic functions, which in turn provides the mathematical basis for the electrical industry and aeronautical engineering, as well as for many other practical applications of mathematics.

Polar Coordinates

The location of a point $P(x, y)$ in a plane OXY may be characterized not only by the values, positive or negative, of its Cartesian coordinates x and y, but also by the length and direction of the vector **OP** (often called the *radius-vector* of the point P). The direction of the vector **OP** is fixed by the value θ (theta) of the angle (known as the *azimuth*) XOP formed by **OP** and the OX-axis. The angle $\theta = XOP$ is measured from OX towards **OP**, counterclockwise as positive and clockwise as negative. The length OP of the vector **OP** is denoted by r, which by definition is always positive: $r > 0$. If the angle θ is given, the direction OP is fixed, but the converse is not necessarily true: an infinite number of different angles correspond to a given direction OP. This is because a direction is not changed by any number of positive or negative rotations through 360°. Thus, the angles θ, $\theta \pm 360°$, $\theta \pm 720°$, and in general $\theta + 360°k$ (k being an arbitrary positive or negative integer: $k = 0$, ± 1, ± 2 ...) all correspond to one and the same direction **OP**. We can say that the angle a fixed direction makes with the OX axis has many values which differ from each other by multiplies of 360°.

Given a point P, its distance from the OY-axis is $|x|$, while its distance from OX-axis is $|y|$. The lengths of the coordinates x and y are expressed by absolute values, $|x|$, $|y|$, because a length ($=$ distance) is necessarily positive, while x and y may have negative values. The three segments—distances of point P from the origin O and from the axes OX and OY—r, $|x|$, $|y|$, form a right triangle in which r plays the role of hypotenuse. The Pythagorean theorem gives us $r^2 = x^2 + y^2$ and thus $r = (x^2 + y^2)^{1/2}$. This expression of the length r of a vector **OP** $= x + iy$ is called the *absolute value* of complex number $x + iy$ and is denoted by $|x + iy|$:

$$|x + iy| = (x^2 + y^2)^{1/2} = r$$

EXAMPLE: $|i| = |0 + i \cdot 1| = (0 + 1)^{1/2} = 1$

Also, $|760 + 39i| = 761$, since $(760^2 + 39^2)^{1/2} = 761$

Among the four quantities, x, y, r and θ, which characterize the location of a point P in a plane OXY, only two are independent. If any two

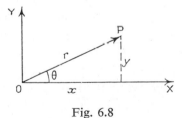

Fig. 6.8

quantities are given, the other two can be computed because they are defined by the values of the two given, known, quantities. Thus, for instance, r and θ are fixed by the choice of x and y, since these two latter determine the position of $P(x, y)$. The formula $r = (x^2 + y^2)^{1/2}$ expresses r in terms of x and y, but it remains to define and fix the value of the azimuth θ.

Sine, Cosine, and Tangent

We know that we can consider the value of the azimuth θ as determined only if we ignore the fact that complete revolutions (rotations through 360°) do not change the straight-line corresponding to the direction of azimuth θ. This is why the concept of slope (Chapter 4) is so useful: the value of a slope, $m = y/x$, does not change when the angle θ, included between the straight line through the origin O and the axis OX increases or decreases by 360°. We can now completely define the concept of azimuth, which is slightly different from that of angle: the angle θ has an infinite range of variation and it can take any value between $-\infty$ and $+\infty$, while the values of the azimuth θ are comprised within a finite range. The azimuth θ varies from $-180°$ to $+180°$ or from 0° to 360°, and this finite range is sufficient to characterize all directions.

The numerical value of the slope of a straight line of azimuth θ is called *tangent of the angle* θ, and is denoted by $\tan \theta$. Later we will study $\tan \theta$ from another point of view, namely as a function of the variable angle θ. Right now it is sufficient to show that to every direction, that is to every azimuth θ, there corresponds a perfectly determined value of $\tan \theta$, and conversely, to every numerical value of slope $\tan \theta$ between $-\infty$ and $+\infty$ there corresponds a perfectly determined line through the origin O. This line, of course, has two opposite directions and, consequently, two values of azimuth θ differing by 180°.

Given a line through O with a known azimuth θ, we mark on it a point P and draw the perpendiculars **PQ** and **PR** through P to axes OX and OY respectively. If the coordinates of P are x and y, then $\mathbf{PQ} = |y|$ and $\mathbf{OQ} = \mathbf{RP} = |x|$. When we consider the four cases that arise when P shifts from the first quadrant to the second, third and fourth quadrants, we observe that to different values of the azimuth θ correspond the following signs of the coordinates x and y and of the slope $\tan \theta = y/x$:

Quadrant	Azimuth θ	Sign of x	Sign of y	Sign of $\tan \theta$	
(I) First	$0° < \theta < 90°$	positive	positive	positive	
(II) Second	$90° < \theta < 180°$	negative	positive	negative	(T)
(III) Third	$-180° < \theta < -90°$	negative	negative	positive	
(IV) Fourth	$-90° < \theta < 0°$	positive	negative	negative	

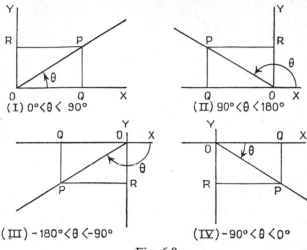

Fig. 6.9

The slope tan θ does not change if the azimuth is increased or decreased by 180°, because the ratio y/x does not depend on the location of point P provided the line remains fixed: if the line passes through the first and third quadrants we can take P in either of these two quadrants, and the same applies to a line passing through the second and fourth quadrants. When the point P moves on the line from the first quadrant to the third, or from the second to the fourth, x and y reverse their signs simultaneously, but the value of the slope does not change. Therefore

$$\tan (\theta \pm 180°) = \tan \theta$$

and it is sufficient to vary θ from $-90°$ to $90°$ to obtain all possible values of the slope tan θ.

To do this we draw (fig. 6.10) a line RQ parallel to OY at a distance $OQ = 1$ so that the point Q on OX has the coordinates $x_Q = 1$, $y_Q = 0$. To compute the value of the slope tan θ of a line OP passing through O and making an angle θ with OX, we choose as point P on this line its intersection-point with the line RQ. By locating the point P on the line RQ, we will always have $x = 1$, and $y = $ QP. Thus the value of the slope tan $\theta = y/x$, will be equal to QP/1 = QP. If point P is above the point Q, QP will be positive, if P is below Q and therefore in the fourth quadrant, QP will be negative. In other words, we have tan $\theta = y$, since $x = 1$. As the angle θ increases from $-90°$ to $90°$ the line OP rotates about O counterclockwise, taking every position between OY'

and OY. Its motion is best compared to that of a clock hand which moves backward from the numeral 6 on the dial through 5, 4, 3, 2, 1 and arrives finally at the numeral 12. The point P moves upward along the line QP, its coordinate y varying from $-\infty$ to $+\infty$, and thus $\tan \theta = y$ increases continuously from $-\infty$ to $+\infty$, running through the set of all real numbers. Here are some of the values of $\tan \theta$, where we take $1/\sqrt{3} \sim 0.577$ and $\sqrt{3} \sim 1.732$ (the symbol $\sim$ means "is approximately equal to"):

θ	$-90°$	$-60°$	$-45°$	$-30°$	$0°$	$30°$	$45°$	$60°$	$90°$
$\tan \theta$ (slope)	$-\infty$	$-\sqrt{3}$	-1	$-1/\sqrt{3}$	0	$1/\sqrt{3}$	1	$\sqrt{3}$	$+\infty$

There exist elaborate tables giving the corresponding value of angle θ for each value of the slope $\tan \theta$. These tables and the formula $\tan \theta$

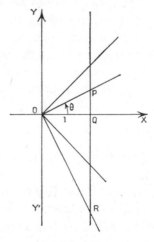

Fig. 6.10

$= y/x$, enable us to compute the value of the azimuth θ onze we know the value of the Cartesian coordinates x and y. But knowing the slope $\tan \theta$ is not enough to distinguish between the two quadrants through which the line OP passes. For this reason we find in the tables two values of θ, differing by 180°, for each value of $\tan \theta$.

We can assign θ to a specific quadrant by taking into consideration the signs of x and y, since, as we have seen in the Table (T), each quadrant is characterized by a particular combination of signs. We can also locate θ in its proper quadrant through the use of two other classical characteristics of a direction θ, called *sine* and *cosine* of the angle θ. They are denoted by symbols $\sin \theta$ and $\cos \theta$, and are defined by the two ratios y/r and x/r:

DEFINITION
$$\sin \theta = y/r = y/(x^2 + y^2)^{1/2}$$
$$\cos \theta = x/r = x/(x^2 + y^2)^{1/2}.$$

Since the length r of the radius-vector is always positive, $\sin \theta$ and $\cos \theta$ have the same sign as y and x, respectively:

	Quadrant			
Angle θ in	I	II	III	IV
Sign of $\sin \theta$	+	+	−	−
Sign of $\cos \theta$	+	−	−	+

Since $|x| \leqslant r$ and $|y| \leqslant r$, all the values of $\sin \theta$ and $\cos \theta$ lie between −1 and 1. Here are some typical values of $\sin \theta$ and $\cos \theta$ where

$$\tfrac{1}{2}\sqrt{2} \sim 0.707, \text{ and } \tfrac{1}{2}\sqrt{3} \sim 0.866:$$

Angle θ	0°	30°	45°	60°	90°	120°	135°	150°	180°
$\sin \theta$	0	0.5	$\tfrac{1}{2}\sqrt{2}$	$\tfrac{1}{2}\sqrt{3}$	1	$\tfrac{1}{2}\sqrt{3}$	$\tfrac{1}{2}\sqrt{2}$	0.5	0
$\cos \theta$	1	$\tfrac{1}{2}\sqrt{3}$	$\tfrac{1}{2}\sqrt{2}$	0.5	0	−0.5	$-\tfrac{1}{2}\sqrt{2}$	$-\tfrac{1}{2}\sqrt{3}$	−1

The values of $\cos \theta$ and $\sin \theta$ for negative azimuths, $-180° < \theta < 0$, are obtained from the values for the corresponding positive azimuths. We observe that when the angle θ changes its sign but retains the same absolute value, the cosine does not change. The sine on the other hand does change its sign along with the angle. Thus, for instance

$$\sin(-45°) = -\sin 45° \quad \text{and} \quad \sin(-30°) = -\sin 30°$$

However,

$$\cos(-60°) = \cos 60° \quad \text{and} \quad \cos(-150°) = \cos 150°$$

In general, $\sin(-\theta) = -\sin \theta; \cos(-\theta) = \cos \theta$ (6)

These rules of sign are deduced geometrically as follows. Given a point $P(x, y)$ in the first quadrant (coordinates x and y positive), we consider the three points Q, R, and S symmetrical to P with respect to the axis OY, origin O and the axis OX (fig. 6.11).

The coordinates of the three symmetrical points can be deduced from those of the point $P(x, y)$ by changing their signs, but not their absolute values. Fig. 6.11 gives us the following coordinates: $Q(-x, y)$,

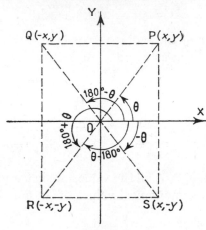

Fig. 6.11

$R(-x, -y)$, and $S(x, -y)$. If the azimuth of **OP** is denoted by θ, the azimuth of **OQ** is equal to $180° - \theta$, that of **OR** to $-(180° - \theta)$ and that of **OS** to $-\theta$. When angle θ changes its sign y also changes its sign, and so does $y/r = \sin \theta$. On the other hand, x is not affected by a change of sign in angle θ, as well as $\cos \theta = x/r$. Rule (6), thus proved, corresponds to the symmetry of points P and S with respect to the OX axis. If we consider point R, symmetrical to P with respect to the origin O, we conclude that both sine and cosine change their signs when the angle θ increases or decreases by $180°$:

$$\sin (\theta \pm 180°) = -\sin \theta; \quad \cos (\theta \pm 180°) = -\cos \theta \qquad (7)$$

Finally, considering the symmetry of P and Q with respect to OY axis, we see that x alone changes sign, if the azimuth θ is replaced by the supplementary azimuth $180° - \theta$. Thus the cosine of the supplementary angle $180° - \theta$ is equal to the cosine of θ with changed sign, while the sine of $180° - \theta$ is the same as the sine of θ:

$$\sin (180° - \theta) = \sin \theta; \quad \cos (180° - \theta) = -\cos \theta \qquad (8)$$

The sine, cosine and tangent of an angle will be treated in greater detail in Chapter 18. At this point we shall limit ourselves to justifying their numerical values assigned in the table above for angles of $0°$, $30°$, $45°$, $60°$, and $90°$.

If $\theta = 0°$, the point P coincides with Q (see fig. 6.10) and its coordinates are $x = 1$, $y = 0$. Therefore,

but
$$\tan 0° = \sin 0° = 0$$

$$\cos 0° = x/r = x/|x| = 1 \quad (\text{if } y = 0, \text{ then } r = |x|).$$

If $\theta = 90°$, point P is on the OY-axis. Its coordinate y is positive, $y > 0$, while x vanishes, $x = 0$. This time,

$$r = |y| \text{ and } \sin 90° = y/r = y/|y| = 1,$$

but
$$\cos 90° = x/r = 0, \text{ because } x = 0.$$

The value of $\tan 90°$ cannot be defined by the ratio y/x, because when $\theta = 90°$, $x = 0$, and division by zero is excluded. But $\tan 90°$ is the value of the slope of OY axis, which by definition is infinite. Therefore,

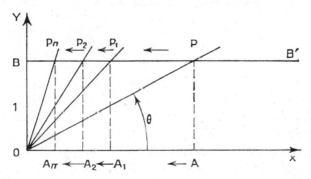

Fig 6.12

$\tan 90°$ is equal to ∞. This is in agreement with the limit of $\tan \theta$, when θ approaches $90°$. To picture what happens as θ approaches $90°$, we draw BB' parallel to OX through point B on OY axis, OB being equal to 1 (fig. 6.12).

As angle θ increases, the line of azimuth θ rotates counterclockwise about O. On each line through O we choose as point P the point of intersection with the line BB'. Thus the coordinate y of P is constantly equal to 1, and $\tan \theta = y/x = 1/x$.

Kogbetliantz 14

As θ approaches 90°, point P (which remains by definition on $\mathbf{BB'}$) approaches point B, and its abcissa $x = \mathbf{BP}_n = \mathbf{OA}_n$ approaches zero, $x \to 0$. Therefore, for $\theta \to 90°$, we obtain

$$\lim_{\theta=90°} \tan \theta = \lim_{x=0} (1/x) = +\infty$$

The reciprocal of x, $1/x$, does indeed increase without limit as x approaches zero.

Consider now the case when $\theta = 30°$. Take a right triangle ABC (fig. 6.13) with its right angle at C and an acute angle of 30° at A. The

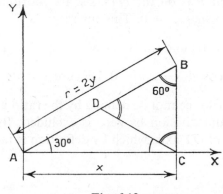

Fig. 6.13

sum of the three angles of a triangle being 180°, the third angle B must be equal to 60°. On the hypotenuse $\mathbf{AB}$ choose a point D such that $\mathbf{BD} = \mathbf{BC}$. Join D to C, and consider the triangle BCD. It is an isosceles triangle, since two sides are equal. Therefore, the angles opposite the equal sides are also equal: angle BCD = angle BDC. The sum of these two angles is 180° − angle B = 180° − 60° = 120°. Since angle BCD = angle BDC, each must be 60°. Therefore, triangle BCD is not only isosceles, but is equilateral, all its angles being equal to 60°. We conclude, that $\mathbf{BD} = \mathbf{CD}$. And since the right angle C is a sum of two angles BCD and ACD,

angle ACD = angle ACB − angle BCD = 90° − 60° = 30°

Now consider the triangle ACD. It has two equal angles CAD = 30° = ACD. Therefore it is isosceles, and

$$\mathbf{AD} = \mathbf{CD} = \mathbf{BD}$$

that is the point D is the midpoint of the hypotenuse AB:

$$\mathsf{AB} = 2\mathsf{BD} = 2\mathsf{BC}$$

($\mathsf{BD} = \mathsf{BC}$ by construction). This important result can be formulated as follows: In a right triangle which has an acute angle of 30°, the side opposite the 30° angle is equal to one half the hypotenuse.

This geometric fact is equivalent to the statement $\sin 30° = 1/2$. To demonstrate this, it is sufficient to consider A as the origin of coordinates and side AC as the OX axis. Then BC, being parallel to OY, is the y coordinate for point B. The distance $r = \mathsf{AB}$ of the point B from the origin A is equal to twice y; $r = 2y$. The angle $CAB = 30°$ is the polar angle θ for point B, and the definition $\sin \theta = y/r$ gives in this case, $\theta = 30°$:

$$\sin 30° = y/r = y/2y = 1/2.$$

To compute $\cos 30°$ and $\tan 30°$ we need to know the value of the third side $\mathsf{AC} = x$. Applying the Pythagorean Theorem to the triangle ABC, we obtain $x^2 + y^2 = r^2 = 4y^2$, since $r = 2y$. Therefore,

as well as
$$x^2 = 3y^2 = 3r^2/4 \text{ and } y^2/x^2 = 1/3$$

$$x^2/r^2 = \tfrac{3}{4}.$$

Extracting the square roots, we find that

$$\tan 30° = y/x = 1/\sqrt{3}, \text{ and } \cos 30° = \tfrac{1}{2}\sqrt{3}.$$

We observe that the definition of the three functions

$$\sin \theta = y/r, \ \cos \theta = x/r \text{ and } \tan \theta = y/x$$

establishes between them the relation

$$\tan \theta = \sin \theta/\cos \theta$$

which is simply a reformulation of the identity $y/x \equiv (y/r)/(x/r)$ with the aid of the functions of an angle. Using this relation we check the numerical values we have obtained for the functions of 30°. Indeed, on the one hand, $\tan 30° = 1/\sqrt{3}$, and on the other hand

$$\sin 30°/\cos 30° = (1/2)/(\sqrt{3}/2) = 1/\sqrt{3}.$$

If $\theta = 60°$, the third angle (see fig. 6.14) opposite side x, must be 30°, since the sum of the triangle's three angles must be 180°. Thus, the hypotenuse $OP = r$ is this time the double of x; $r = 2x$. Again applying the Pythagorean theorem we find that

$$y^2 = r^2 - x^2 = 4x^2 - x^2 = 3x^2$$

so that

$$y = x\sqrt{3} = 2x\,\sqrt{3}/2 = \tfrac{1}{2}r\sqrt{3}.$$

Therefore,

$$\sin 60° = y/r = \tfrac{1}{2}\sqrt{3},\ \cos 60° = 1/2 \text{ and } \tan 60° = \sqrt{3}.$$

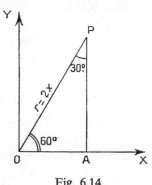

Fig. 6.14

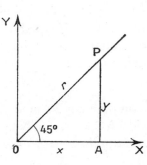

Fig. 6.15

There remains only the case of $\theta = 45°$. Here the triangle OPA (see fig. 6.15) is isosceles, $OA = AP$; that is

$$x = y \text{ and } r^2 = x^2 + y^2,$$

so that

$$\tan 45° = y/x = 1,\ \sin 45° = \cos 45° = x/r = y/r = 1/\sqrt{2} = \tfrac{1}{2}\sqrt{2}$$

since $r^2 = 2x^2$.

The approximate values of the irrational numbers $\sqrt{2}$ and $\sqrt{3}$ correct to the first three exact decimal places are

$$\sqrt{2} \sim 1.414 \text{ and } \sqrt{3} \sim 1.732.$$

We have thus justified our short table for $0° \leqslant \theta \leqslant 90°$. If θ is an obtuse angle, it can be represented as $180 - \varphi$, where φ is an acute angle: $\varphi < 90°$. We can complete the table with the aid of the relation (8).

The numerical values of the sine, cosine and tangent for the five angles $0°$, $30°$, $45°$, $60°$, and $90°$ should be memorized. All these numbers are positive, and it is sufficient to remember their squares. These squares are easy to remember, for they are related to the natural sequence 0, 1, 2, 3, 4. Dividing each of them by four we have the five values of sine squared:

$$0/4, \ 1/4, \ 2/4, \ 3/4, \ 4/4$$

Reversing the order,

$$4/4, \ 3/4, \ 2/4, \ 1/4, \ 0/4,$$

we obtain the values of cosine squared. Finally dividing the values of the sine squared by the values of the cosine squared,

$$0/4, \ 1/3, \ 2/2, \ 3/1, \ 4/0,$$

we get the values of tangent squared for angles 0°, 30°, 45°, 60°, and 90°, respectively (4/0 = ∞ represents a *limit* and is not a quotient). Notice that in the fractions representing the values of tangent squared the numerator and denominator in each case add up to 4. These numerical values may be memorized with the help of the following table:

A	0°	30°	45°	60°	90°
$\sin^2 A$	0/4	1/4	2/4	3/4	4/4
$\cos^2 A$	4/4	3/4	2/4	1/4	0/4
$\tan^2 A$	0/4	1/3	2/2	3/1	4/0

There is one more relation, which expresses the function of the complementary angle $90° - \theta$ in terms of functions of θ:

$$\sin(90° - \theta) = \cos\theta; \ \cos(90° - \theta) = \sin\theta \qquad (9)$$

This relation is based on symmetry with respect to the principal bisector $\mathbf{OT}$ of the right angle XOY (see fig. 6.16). The slope of $\mathbf{OT}$ is equal to 1. When the point $P(x, y)$ is reflected in the line $\mathbf{OT}$, we obtain its symmetrical point $Q(y, x)$. We drop the four perpendiculars $\mathbf{PP_1}, \mathbf{PP_2}, \mathbf{QQ_1},$ and $\mathbf{QQ_2}$. By symmetry,

$$\mathbf{PP_1} = \mathbf{QQ_1}, \text{ and } \mathbf{PP_2} = \mathbf{QQ_2}$$

Therefore the abcissa x_Q of point Q is equal to the ordinate y of P while the ordinate y_Q of Q is equal to the abcissa x of P. In other words, by interchanging the coordinates of a point we replace this point by a point symmetrical with respect to the principal bisector $\mathbf{OT}$.

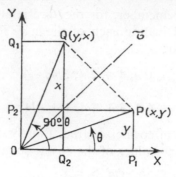

Fig. 6.16

If the azimuth of **OP** is θ = angle XOP, then the azimuth of **OQ** is equal to the complementary angle $90° - \theta$: angle $XOQ \equiv 90°$ − angle QOY, since angle QOY = angle XOP = θ. Therefore, interchanging the coordinates, we replace the azimuth θ by the complementary azimuth $90° - \theta$. Now by definition

$$\sin \theta = y/r, \cos \theta = x/r$$

and

$$\sin (90° - \theta) = x/r, \cos (90° - \theta) = y/r$$

as may be inferred from fig. 6.16.

Comparing these expressions, we obtain the proof of the relations in (9). The term "*co*-sine" means simply "sine of the complementary angle". There is no difference between the two relations in (9) since the angle $\theta = 90° - (90° - \theta)$ may be considered as complementary to $90° - \theta$; thus the second relation (9), $\sin \theta = \cos (90° - \theta)$ is a corollary of the first.

The functions $\sin \theta$, $\cos \theta$, and $\tan \theta$ were introduced by Egyptian, Hindu, and Iranian astronomers more than 2000 years ago. Their purpose was the numerical characterisation of the slopes of lines, that is of angles above the horizon formed by light rays from observed stars with a horizontal line of reference. These functions are generally studied under the heading of trigonometry, but we see that there is no real difference between the trigonometry and metric geometry. The geometric facts pertaining to the measurement of angles can be translated into the language of trigonometry by using sine, cosine and tangent as measures of slope. We shall see in this chapter that the trigonometric functions play an important role in the study of complex numbers: sine and cosine are indeed components of complex rotation-factors.

We have already proved the relation

$$\tan \theta = \sin \theta / \cos \theta \qquad (10)$$

which shows that the numerical value of $\tan \theta$ depends on those of $\sin \theta$ and $\cos \theta$. It remains to prove that sine and cosine are not independent, but related by

$$\sin^2 \theta + \cos^2 \theta = 1 \qquad (11)$$

This formula is nothing more than the Pythagorean theorem $x^2 + y^2 = r^2$ translated into trigonometric language. Dividing both sides of the Pythagorean formula by r^2 we get

$$(x/r)^2 + (x/r)^2 = 1$$

which is precisely the relation (11).

Polar Form of Complex Numbers

Returning to complex numbers, $z = x + iy$, we know that every one of them corresponds to a point $P(x, y)$ in the plane OXY. Instead of Cartesian coordinates x, y, we can use the polar coordinates r, θ to fix the location of the point P. It follows that a complex number $z = x + iy$ must also have a *polar form* in which x and y are replaced by equivalent expressions in terms of r and θ. These expressions are easily obtained from the definitions of sine and cosine,

$$\sin \theta = y/r \text{ and } \cos \theta = x/r$$

by multiplying both sides of each identity by r:

$$x = r \cos \theta; \, y = r \sin \theta \qquad (12)$$

Substituting these values of x and y in the expression $z = x + iy$, and picking out the common factor r, the so-called *polar form* of a complex number z is obtained:

$$z = r \cos \theta + ir \sin \theta = r(\cos \theta + i \sin \theta) \qquad (13)$$

Rotation-Factor

The form (13) has a very important geometric meaning. It expresses a complex number z, that is, a vector **OP**. It is also the product of a real positive number r (the length of vector **OP**) and of a complex factor $\cos \theta + i \sin \theta$, which is related to the vector's azimuth θ. The positive real number, r, may itself be represented by a vector **OA** of length r, located on the OX-axis and pointing to the right (fig. 6.17).

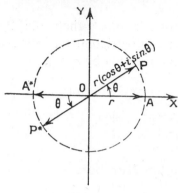

Fig. 6.17

Comparing the vector **OP** $= z = r(\cos \theta + i \sin \theta)$ with the vector **OA** $= r$ we see that **OP** can be obtained from **OA** by a counterclockwise rotation through the angle θ. Furthermore, the algebraic expression of **OP**, $r(\cos \theta + i \sin \theta)$, can be derived from the expression r of the vector **OA** by a multiplication: r times the factor $\cos \theta + i \sin \theta$ yields indeed

$$\mathbf{OA}(\cos \theta + i \sin \theta) = r(\cos \theta + i \sin \theta) = \mathbf{OP}$$

Thus, the multiplication of a vector by the complex factor $\cos \theta + i \sin \theta$ rotates it counterclockwise through the angle θ. We conclude that the expression $\cos \theta + i \sin \theta$ is the rotation factor through θ. But the proof of this important fact is not yet complete since the vector **OA**, which was rotated through θ when multiplied by $\cos \theta + i \sin \theta$, occupied a special position: **OA** was parallel to OX-axis and it was pointing to the right.

To justify our assertion that $\cos \theta + i \sin \theta$ is the rotation factor through θ we set now to prove that any vector $a + ib$ when multiplied by $\cos \theta + i \sin \theta$ is rotated through the angle θ. Since a vector is equivalent to the sum of its two components, if both components a and ib of a vector $a + ib$ are rotated through θ when multiplied by $\cos \theta + i \sin \theta$, the same is true for their sum $a + ib$. Therefore, it will be sufficient to prove that any vector a parallel to OX-axis and any vector ib parallel to OY-axis are rotated through θ when multiplied by $\cos \theta + i \sin \theta$. Here a and b are any two real numbers, positive or negative.

The commutative law of multiplication can be used to prove that the vector $\mathbf{OA^*} = -r$ (fig. 6.17), if multiplied by $\cos \theta + i \sin \theta$, becomes $\mathbf{OP^*} = -\mathbf{OP}$:

$$\mathbf{OA^*}(\cos \theta + i \sin \theta) = (-1)[\mathbf{OA}(\cos \theta + i \sin \theta)] = (-1)\mathbf{OP} = \mathbf{OP^*}$$

which, expressed in geometrical language, means that the effect of two successive rotations, through $180°$ and through θ, does not depend on the order in which they are applied. The factor (-1) is indeed, as we know, the rotation-factor through $180°$.

Therefore, we conclude that any vector a parallel to OX is rotated through θ, if multiplied by $\cos \theta + i \sin \theta$.

Consider now a vector $\mathbf{OB} = ib$ $(b > 0)$ parallel to OY and pointing upwards (fig. 6.18), and denote by $\mathbf{OQ}$ its position after a rotation through θ. Decomposing $\mathbf{OQ}$ into two component vectors $\mathbf{OM}//OX$ and $\mathbf{MQ}//OY$, so that $\mathbf{OQ} = \mathbf{OM} + \mathbf{MQ}$, we obtain a triangle OMQ in which the angle MQO is equal to θ: $MQO = \theta$. The length of the hypotenuse OQ is b, so that the lengths of the sides $\mathbf{OM}$ and $\mathbf{MQ}$ are equal to $b \sin \theta$ and $b \cos \theta$, respectively. The vector $\mathbf{OM}$ is pointing to the *left* and therefore it is expressed by the negative number $-b \sin \theta$, while the vector $\mathbf{MQ}$ is equal to $ib \cos \theta$ since it is directed upwards. Thus, the vector $\mathbf{OQ}$ is represented by the complex number $-b \sin \theta + ib \cos \theta$:

$$\mathbf{OQ} = \mathbf{OM} + \mathbf{MQ} = -b \sin \theta + ib \cos \theta$$

$$= ib \cos \theta + i^2 b \sin \theta = ib(\cos \theta + i \sin \theta)$$

But, $\mathbf{OB} = ib$ and therefore we obtain

$$\mathbf{OQ} = \mathbf{OB}(\cos \theta + i \sin \theta)$$

which proves that the multiplication by $\cos \theta + i \sin \theta$ rotates $\mathbf{OB} = ib$ through the angle θ. Finally, we prove that the same holds for a vector

OB* = −**OB** = −*ib* directed downwards:

$$\textbf{OB*}(\cos \theta + i \sin \theta) = (-ib)(\cos \theta + i \sin \theta)$$

$$= (-1)[ib(\cos \theta + i \sin \theta)] = -\textbf{OQ} = \textbf{OQ*}$$

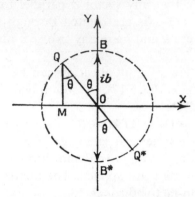

Fig. 6.18

where **OQ*** = −**OQ** is obtained rotating **OB*** counterclockwise through θ.

Thus we state that the complex expression $\cos \theta + i \sin \theta$ used as a factor in multiplication produces a rotation of the second factor through θ, if the second factor is any vector parallel to OX or to OY. Because every vector is a sum of two component vectors parallel to OX and to OY, we conclude that a multiplication by $\cos \theta + i \sin \theta$ rotates *any* vector through θ counterclockwise. This is why the complex expression $\cos \theta + i \sin \theta$ is called *rotation-factor through angle θ*. In many books it is denoted for the sake of brevity by the symbol "cis θ", where c stands for $\cos \theta$, and *is* θ for $+i \sin \theta$.

Here are some examples of rotation-factors for special values of angle θ. We know that -1 and i are rotation-factors through 180° and 90°, respectively. Substituting 180° for θ in $\cos \theta + i \sin \theta$, we do get indeed -1 as a rotation-factor through 180° since

$$\sin 180° = \sin 0° = 0, \text{ and } \cos 180° = -\cos 0° = -1$$

according to (91). Similarly, for $\theta = 90°$, we have

$$\cos 90° + i \sin 90° = 0 + i1 = i$$

since

$$\cos 90° = 0 \text{ and } \sin 90° = 1.$$

The rotation-factor for 45° is equal to:

$$\cos 45° + i \sin 45° = \sqrt{2}/2 + i\sqrt{2}/2 = (1 + i)/\sqrt{2}$$

since

$$\cos 45° = \sin 45° = \tfrac{1}{2}\sqrt{2}.$$

To check this result, we observe that two rotations through 45° are equivalent to a single rotation through 90°. Translating this geometric fact into its algebraic equivalent, we conclude that two multiplications by the factor $(1 + i)/\sqrt{2}$ must have same result as a single multiplication by i. In other words, the complex number $[(1 + i)/\sqrt{2}]^2$ must be equal to i. Computing the square of $(1 + i)/\sqrt{2}$, we find that such is indeed the case:

$$[(1 + i)/\sqrt{2}]^2 = (1 + i)^2/(\sqrt{2})^2 = (1 + 2i + i^2)/2 = 2i/2 = i.$$

This result shows incidentally that

$$i^{1/2} = \sqrt{i} = (1 + i)/\sqrt{2}$$

As another example we consider the rotation-factor through 30°, namely

$$\cos 30 + i \sin 30 = \sqrt{3}/2 + i/2 = (\sqrt{3} + i)/2.$$

The square of the rotation-factor through 30° must be equal to the rotation-factor through 60°, that is to $1/2 + i\sqrt{3}/2$, since

$$\cos 60° = 1/2 \text{ and } \sin 60° = \sqrt{3}/2$$

Squaring $(\sqrt{3} + i)/2$, we obtain

$$[(\sqrt{3} + i)/2]^2 = (\sqrt{3} + i)^2/4 = (3 + 2i\sqrt{3} - 1)/4$$
$$= (1 + i\sqrt{3})/2 = 1/2 + i \cdot \sqrt{3}/2.$$

De-Moivre's Theorem

This brings us to an important relation known as De-Moivre's formula or theorem, which deals with repeated rotations through the same angle θ. Let us assume that n such equal rotations take place. The final result of n rotations through θ is the same as that of a single rotation through $n\theta$, since rotation angles are added, when rotations are applied consecutively.

Algebraically, this means that n successive multiplications by the rotation-factor $\cos \theta + i \sin \theta$ have the same effect as one multiplication by the rotation-factor $\cos (n\theta) + i \sin(n\theta)$. In other words the product of n factors $\cos \theta + i \sin \theta$, that is $(\cos \theta + i \sin \theta)^n$, is equal to the rotation-factor $\cos (n\theta) + i \sin (n\theta)$:

$$(\cos \theta + i \sin \theta)^n = \cos (n\theta) + i \sin (n\theta) \tag{14}$$

De-Moivre's relation is a particular case of Euler's general formula

$$(\cos \theta + i \sin \theta)^a = \cos (a\theta) + i \sin (a\theta) \tag{15}$$

in which the exponent a may be any real or complex, rational or irrational number, while the exponent n in (14) is a positive integer.

Considering equal and successive rotations, we have proved only the particular case (14). We can now generalize our result, extending it to all real exponents a, rational and irrational, positive and negative.

First we extend (14) to positive rational exponents m/n (m and n are integers). The angle θ in (14) being arbitrary, we can replace it by t/n, so that (14) becomes

$$[\cos (t/n) + i \sin (t/n)]^n = \cos t + i \sin t$$

Raising both sides to a power with the rational exponent m/n and reading the result from the right to the left, we have

$$(\cos t + i \sin t)^{m/n} = [\cos (t/n) + i \sin (t/n)]^m \tag{16}$$

On the other hand, replacing in (14) θ by t/n and n by m, we also have

$$[(\cos (t/n) + i \sin (t/n)]^m = \cos (mt/n) + i \sin (mt/n) \tag{17}$$

Comparing (16) and (17), we see that (14) is extended to positive rational exponents m/n since

$$(\cos t + i \sin t)^{m/n} = \cos (mt/n) + i \sin (mt/n) \tag{18}$$

This relation holds for all rational numbers $m/n > 0$. Suppose now that the exponent m/n becomes variable and runs through an infinite convergent sequence of rational numbers whose limit G is an irrational number: $\lim (m/n) = G$. Passing to the limit in (18) we obtain Euler's Formula with positive irrational exponent G:

$$(\cos t + i \sin t)^G = \cos (Gt) + i \sin (Gt).$$

Since every irrational number is the limit of a convergent rational sequence Euler's Formula (15) is proved for all irrational numbers provided they are positive. But what about negative real exponents?

Complex Conjugate Numbers

Here we introduce a new concept, that of complex *conjugate* numbers. The square root of the negative unit has two values $\pm\sqrt{-1} = \pm i$. Therefore, the complex numbers $a + b\cdot\sqrt{-1} = a + ib$ and $a - b\sqrt{-1} = a - ib$ must be related in some way. And indeed, if we plot the two points P and Q represented by numbers $a + ib$ and $a - ib$, we see that they are symmetrical with respect to OX, are at the same distance from the origin O:

$$\mathsf{OP} = \mathsf{OQ} = |a + ib| = |a - ib| = (a^2 + b^2)^{1/2}$$

and have polar angles θ and $-\theta$, equal in absolute value but having opposite signs (see fig. 6.19). Adding $a + ib$ and $a - ib$, we get a *real* sum $2a$. Subtracting the second from the first, we obtain a *purely imaginary* difference $2ib$. Multiplying $a + ib$ by $a - ib$ and applying the formula

$$(A + B)(A - B) \equiv A^2 - B^2,$$

we find that their product is a *real* and *positive* number

$$(a + ib)(a - ib) = a^2 - (ib)^2 = a^2 - i^2b^2 = a^2 + b^2$$

because $i^2 = -1$. All these features are characteristic of two complex numbers which differ from each other only in sign of the imaginary part. Such a pair of complex numbers $a + ib$, $a - ib$ are called *conjugate complex numbers*. Each of them is said to be conjugate to the other. Thus, $\cos\theta + i\sin\theta$ and $\cos\theta - i\sin\theta$ are conjugate complex numbers.

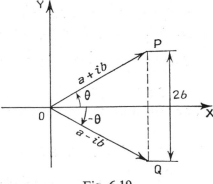

Fig. 6.19

We know that $\cos\theta + i\sin\theta$ is rotation-factor through θ, but what is the geometric meaning of its conjugate number $\cos\theta - i\sin\theta$? Using the relations (6), we can replace $\cos\theta$ by $\cos(-\theta)$ and $\sin\theta$ by $-\sin(-\theta)$. Therefore,

$$\cos\theta - i\sin\theta = \cos(-\theta) + i\sin(-\theta)$$

which shows that the complex number $\cos\theta - i\sin\theta$ is also a rotation-factor, namely the rotation-factor through the *negative* angle $-\theta$. It corresponds to the rotation through θ degrees but *clockwise*. Applying successively to a vector two rotations through angles θ and $-\theta$, we bring it back to its initial position, since two opposite rotations cancel each other. Therefore, the product of corresponding rotation-factors must be equal to one:

$$(\cos\theta + i\sin\theta)(\cos\theta - i\sin\theta) = 1 \qquad (19)$$

Indeed, there is only one factor such that multiplication by it does not change the multiplicand and that factor is the number one.

Moreover, applying the relation

$$(a + ib)(a - ib) = a^2 + b^2$$

to the lefthand member of (19), we deduce from it the fundamental relation $\cos^2\theta + \sin^2\theta = 1$, which is thus obtained, without using the Pythagorean theorem, that is without considering geometrical figures.

Dividing both members of (19) by $\cos\theta + i\sin\theta$, we can write

$$\cos\theta - i\sin\theta = 1/(\cos\theta + i\sin\theta) = (\cos\theta + i\sin\theta)^{-1}$$

where, as we have already seen, $\cos\theta - i\sin\theta$ can also be written as rotation-factor through $-\theta$, namely as $\cos(-\theta) + i\sin(-\theta)$. Thus,

$$(\cos\theta + i\sin\theta)^{-1} = \cos(-\theta) + i\sin(-\theta) \qquad (20)$$

Raising both members of this relation to a power with positive irrational exponent G, we extend Euler's formula to a negative exponent and obtain

$$(\cos\theta + i\sin\theta)^{-G} = [\cos(-\theta) + i\sin(-\theta)]^G$$

$$= \cos(-G\theta) + i\sin(-G\theta)$$

Thus Euler's formula is now justified for all real exponents, the case of complex exponents being postponed to Chapter 9.

Two successive rotations through angles A and B are equivalent to one rotation through an angle $A + B$, sum of A and B. Translated into algebraic language this proposition states that the product of two rotation-factors $\cos A + i \sin A$ and $\cos B + i \sin B$ is again a rotation-factor, namely the rotation-factor through $A + B$, that is $\cos (A + B) + i \sin (A + B)$:

$$(\cos A + i \sin A)(\cos B + i \sin B) = \cos(A + B) + i \sin(A + B) \quad (21)$$

What about the division of a rotation-factor by another? Division is an operation inverse to multiplication and it reduces to the multiplication by the reciprocal of the divisor. Therefore, the effect of the division by a rotation-factor must be opposite to that of multiplication by the same rotation-factor. This means that the effect of division by $\cos \theta + i \sin \theta$ is again a rotation through θ, but in the opposite sense, namely a rotation through the negative angle $-\theta$. This conclusion is confirmed by relation (20) which is nothing more than the algebraical formulation of our reasoning. Using (20) we obtain:

$$(\cos A + i \sin A)/(\cos B + i \sin B) = (\cos A + i \sin A)(\cos B + i \sin B)^{-1}$$

$$= (\cos A + i \sin A)[(\cos(-B) + i \sin(-B)]$$

that is, applying the law (21):

$$(\cos A + i \sin A)/(\cos B + i \sin B) = \cos(A - B) + i \sin(A - B) \quad (22)$$

EXAMPLES:

1°)
$$(\cos 60° + i \sin 60°)(\cos 30° + i \sin 30°) = [(1 + i\sqrt{3})/2][(\sqrt{3} + i)/2]$$
$$= (\sqrt{3} + 3i + i + i^2\sqrt{3})/4$$
$$= 4i/4 = \cos 90° + i \sin 90°$$

because
$$\cos 90° = 0, \ \sin 90° = 1$$

This result agrees with (21), since $60° + 30° = 90°$.

2°)
$$(\cos 60° + i \sin 60°)/(\cos 30° + i \sin 30°) = [(1 + i\sqrt{3})/2]/(\sqrt{3} + i)/2]$$
$$= (1 + i\sqrt{3})/(\sqrt{3} + i)$$

To perform the division by $\sqrt{3} + i$ we must multiply by its reciprocal. Suppose that the reciprocals is $x + iy$. To find the unknowns x and y we express the condition imposed on $x + iy$, namely the fact that the product $(\sqrt{3} + i)(x + iy)$ is equal to one:

$$(\sqrt{3} + i)(x + iy) = (x\sqrt{3} - y) + i(x + y\sqrt{3}) = 1 = 1 + i0$$

Thus we have two equations for our two unknowns x and y:

$$x\sqrt{3} - y = 1; \; x + y\sqrt{3} = 0.$$

Substituting in the first equation instead of x its expression $x = -y\sqrt{3}$ obtained from the second equation, we have $-4y = 1$ and thus $y = -1/4$. For x we get $x = \sqrt{3}/4$, so that the reciprocal to $\sqrt{3} + i$ is equal to the complex number $(\sqrt{3} - i)/4$. We have indeed, checking our result by direct multiplication:

$$(\sqrt{3} + i)(\sqrt{3} - i)/4 = [(\sqrt{3})^2 - i^2]/4 = 4/4 = 1$$

We can now perform our division as follows:

$$(1 + i\sqrt{3})/(\sqrt{3} + i) = (1 + i\sqrt{3})(\sqrt{3} - i)/4$$

$$= (\sqrt{3} + 3i - i + \sqrt{3})/4 = (2i + 2\sqrt{3})/4 = (\sqrt{3} + i)/2$$

This agrees with (22) because

$$(\sqrt{3} + i)/2 = \sqrt{3}/2 + i/2 = \cos 30° + i \sin 30°$$

and

$$60° - 30° = 30°.$$

Operations with Complex Numbers

Geometric pictures are useful in the study of operations with complex numbers as we have seen in the example of addition which corresponds to the parallelogram law. A subtraction, such as $(a + ib) - (c + id)$, can be reduced to an addition of a *symmetric* complex number. Two complex numbers represented by two points symmetrical with respect to the origin 0 are called *symmetric*. Such are $c + id$ and $(-c) + i(-d)$. Two symmetric complex numbers z and z' verify the condition $z + z' = 0$, and thus $z = -z'$. This result means that instead of subtracting z we can add its symmetric number z'. Therefore in general:

$$(a + ib) - (c' + id) = (a + ib) + (-c) + i(-d) = (a - c) + i(b - d) \qquad (23)$$

In the geometric picture of (23) $a + ib =$ **AC** is the diagonal of a parallelogram whose side **AB** $= c + id$ is to be subtracted from this diagonal **AC**. Instead of subtracting **AB**, we can add the opposite vector **CD** which represents the number $(-c) + i(-d)$ symmetric to $c + id$. The result is the other side **AD** of the parallelogram. It is plain that we reach D, if we travel first from A to C (displacement $a + ib$) and then from C to D [displacement

$$\textbf{CD} = -\textbf{AB} = (-c) + i(-d) = -(c + id)].$$

Thus **AC** $-$ **AB** $=$ **AC** $+$ **CD** $=$ **AD** as well as **AC** $-$ **AD** $=$ **AC** $+$ **CB** $=$ **AB**, fig. 6.20.

The example of multiplication of two complex conjugate numbers $a + ib$ and $a - ib$, which was performed with the aid of the identity $(A + B)(A - B) = A^2 - B^2$

$$(a + ib)(a - ib) = a^2 - (ib)^2 = a^2 + b^2$$

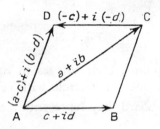

Fig. 6.20

is interesting, when applied to complex integers. A complex number is called a *complex integer* if both its real part a, and the coefficient of the imaginary part b are integers. The product of two complex conjugate integers is a positive integer.

EXAMPLES: $(2 + i)(2 - i) = 5$; $(3 + 2i)(3 - 2i) = 3^2 + 2^2 = 9 + 4 = 13$. These examples prove that the concept of prime integer is a relative one: the numbers 5 and 13 are prime in the domain of *real* integers, but they become composite integers, if considered as belonging to the domain of complex integers. In this larger domain they admit of different decompositions into a product of two conjugate prime factors:

$$(1 + 2i)(1 - 2i) = (-1 + 2i)(-1 - 2i) = 5;$$

$$(2 + i)(2 - i) = (-2 - i)(-2 + i) = 5$$

The absolute value of each of the eight complex integral factors of 5 is the same for all of them and it is equal to $(1^2 + 2^2)^{1/2} = \sqrt{5}$. The

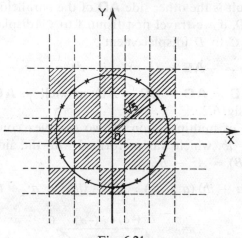

Fig. 6.21

corresponding eight points, their images in the plane XOY, are located on the circumference of a circle with center at the origin and radius $\sqrt{5}$. On a chessboard they represent all eight possible moves of a knight, fig. 6.21.

We study now the multiplication of any two complex numbers $a + ib = r(\cos A + i \sin A)$ and $c + id = p(\cos B + i \sin B)$, where $r = (a^2 + b^2)^{1/2}$ and $p = (c^2 + d^2)^{1/2}$ are their absolute values and A, B their azimuths, so that $\tan A = b/a$ and $\tan B = d/c$. We can apply two methods. The first one, which is purely algebraical, consists of applying the distributive law to the *Cartesian* forms $a + ib$, $c + id$ and of replacing i^2 by minus one. The second method, related to the geometric representation of complex numbers by vectors, uses the *polar* forms $r(\cos A + i \sin A)$, $p(\cos B + i \sin B)$. The algebraical operation gives

$$(a + ib)(c + id) = ac + ibc + iad + i^2bd = (ac - bd) + i(ad + bc)$$

and the expressions $(ac - bd)$ and $(ad + bc)$ give the rules for computing the real part and the coefficient of the imaginary part of our product.

EXAMPLE: $(2 + 3i)(3 - i) = [2 \cdot 3 - 3(-1)] + i[2(-1) + 3 \cdot 3]$
$$= (6 + 3) + i(-2 + 9) = 9 + 7i$$

To multiply the complex numbers $z = a + ib$, $z' = c + id$ we can also use their polar forms:

$$zz' = rp(\cos A + i \sin A)(\cos B + i \sin B)$$

The formula (21) transforms the product of rotation-factors into $\cos (A + B) + i \sin (A + B)$ and, denoting the product of absolute values rp by R:
$$zz' = R[\cos(A + B) + i \sin (A + B)]$$

Thus, the absolute value R of the product of two complex numbers zz' is equal to the product of their absolute values, $R = rp$, while the azimuth of the product zz' is the sum $A + B$ of the azimuths of two factors z and z'. The azimuth of a vector represented by a complex number z is called the *argument* (or *phase*, or *amplitude*) of the complex number z and it is denoted by arg z. Using this notation, we can state the multiplication rule for complex numbers as follows:

$$R = |zz'| = |z| \cdot |z'|; \ \arg (zz') = \arg z + \arg z'. \tag{24}$$

The multiplication of complex numbers can be illustrated by the following construction of the vector product zz' (Fig. 6.22):

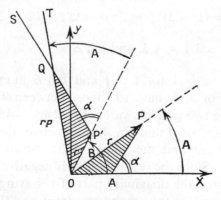

Fig. 6.22

Let **OA** represent a unit of length on the OX-axis, **OA** $= 1$. If $z =$ **OP**, $z' =$ **OP'** are the two factors and the vector **OQ** $= zz'$ represents their product, the triangles OAP and $OP'Q$ are similar. The azimuth XOQ of the vector-product is the sum of azimuths $XOP = A$ and $XOP' = B$ of vectors **OP** and **OP'**. Therefore, the angle $P'OQ$ is equal to the angle XOP: angle $P'OQ =$ angle $XOQ -$ angle XOP' $=$ angle XOP. The sides OQ, OP', OP, OA are proportional since OQ $= R$, OP' $= p$, OP $= r$ and OA $= 1$, and according to (23), we have $R/r = p/1$. Equal angles are included between proportional sides and the triangles are similar. Therefore, to draw the product of two given vectors join the head P of the first to the point A on the OX-axis such that **OA** represents the vector 1 and construct at point P', head of the second vector, an angle equal to the angle $XAP = \alpha$, drawing a line P'S which makes an angle α with the radius-vector **OP'**. Draw finally through the origin O a line making an angle $P'OT = A = AOP$ with the vector **OP'**, so that the angle this line makes with OX will be equal to the sum of azimuths of vectors **OP** and **OP'**. The lines P'S and OT intersect at a point Q, and the vector **OQ** is then the geometric representation of the product **OP** $\cdot$ **OP'** $= z \cdot z'$.

EXAMPLE: Let
$$z = 1 + i\sqrt{3}, \ z' = -\sqrt{2} + i\sqrt{2}$$

To find $z \cdot z'$ we must transform z and z' into polar forms and compute r, p, A, B. The formulas
$$r = (x^2 + y^2)^{1/2} \text{ and } \tan A = y/x$$
give:
$$r = |z| = (1 + 3)^{1/2} = 2; p = |z'| = (2 + 2)^{1/2} = 2$$
$$\tan A = \sqrt{3}/1 = \sqrt{3}, \text{ and } \tan B = -\sqrt{2}/\sqrt{2} = -1$$

The values $\sqrt{3}$ and -1 for $\tan A$ and $\tan B$ alone cannot fix the angles A and B. For A we have to choose between $60°$ and $60° - 180°$ $= -120°$, and the two possible values for B are $-45°$ and $180° - 45°$ $= 135°$. Since both $\cos A$ and $\sin A$ are positive, the angle A belongs to the first quadrant and the value $-120°$ (third quadrant) is eliminated, $A = 60°$. Since the real part of z' is negative, $\cos B$ is negative too, $\sin B$ is positive, the imaginary part of z' having a positive coefficient. Thus B belongs to the second quadrant and the value $-45°$ for it is eliminated: $B = 135°$. Thus we can write:

$$z = \sqrt{3} + i = 2(\cos 60° + i \sin 60°)$$

$$z' = -\sqrt{2} + i\sqrt{2} = 2(\cos 135° + i \sin 135°)$$

Therefore, the azimuth of the product $z \cdot z'$ is equal to $60° + 135° = 195°$ and its absolute value is $rp = 4$, so that

$$z \cdot z' = 4(\cos 195° + i \sin 195°)$$

The tables of values for sine and cosine give the approximate values $\cos 195° = -0.9659\cdots$ and $\sin 195° = -0.2588\cdots$, so that

$$(\sqrt{3} + i)(-\sqrt{2} + i\sqrt{2}) = -3.8636 \cdots -i(1.0352\cdots).$$

The exact expressions for $\cos 195°$ and $\sin 195°$ are:

$$\cos 195° = -(\sqrt{3} + 1)/2\sqrt{2}; \sin 195° = -(\sqrt{3} - 1)/2\sqrt{2}$$

These values can be computed using the relation $195° = 180° + 15°$, which proves according to (7) that

$$\cos 195° = -\cos 15°, \text{ and } \sin 195° = -\sin 15°$$

But $15° = 60° - 45°$, so that by applying (22) we obtain:

$$\cos 15° + i \sin 15° = (\cos 60° + i \sin 60°)/(\cos 45° + i \sin 45°)$$

$$= [(1 + i\sqrt{3})/2]/[(1 + i)/\sqrt{2}] = [(1 + i\sqrt{3})/2] [(1 - i)/\sqrt{2})]$$

$$= [\sqrt{3} + 1 + i(\sqrt{3} - 1)]/2\sqrt{2} \tfrac{1}{2} \left(\sqrt{2 + \sqrt{3}} + i \sqrt{2 - \sqrt{3}}\right)$$

because the reciprocal of

$$\cos 45° + i \sin 45° = (1 + i)/\sqrt{2}$$

is

$$\cos(-45°) + i \sin(-45°) = (1 - i)/\sqrt{2}$$

Thus the equation

$$\cos 15° + i \sin 15° = [\sqrt{3} + 1 + i(\sqrt{3} - 1)]/2\sqrt{2}$$

obtained above proves (25). The approximate values of the sine and cosine of $-195°$ are deduced from their exact value replacing $\sqrt{3}$ and $\sqrt{2}$ by 1.7320 and 1.4142 respectively.

Division

Division by $a + ib$ is equivalent to multiplication by the reciprocal of the divisor $a + ib$. This reciprocal $1/(a + ib)$ can be transformed into the standard form $A + iB$ of a complex number by eliminating i in the denominator. Remembering that the product of two complex conjugate numbers is a real and positive number, we conclude that this elimination of i from the denominator can be achieved by multiplying it by its conjugate.

A fraction must be multiplied both in the numerator and in the denominator by the same number, if we want it to keep its value unchanged. Therefore, we multiply the fraction $1/(a + ib)$ by the conjugate of its denominator, $a - ib$, not only in the denominator, but also in the numerator:

$$1/(a + ib) = (a - ib)/[(a + ib)(a - ib)] = a/(a^2 + b^2) - ib/(a^2 + b^2) \quad (26)$$

because
$$(a + ib)(a - ib) = a^2 + b^2.$$

The identity (26) shows how to compute the reciprocal of a given complex number. The reciprocal of $a + ib$ is equal to the quotient obtained by dividing the conjugate number $a - ib$ by the square $a^2 + b^2$ of its absolute value. Applying this rule to the polar form of a complex number $r(\cos A + i \sin A)$, we see that the quotient $r(\cos A - i \sin A)/r^2$, that is $(\cos A - i \sin A)/r$, is the reciprocal of $r(\cos A + i \sin A)$. The product of these two numbers is indeed equal to one, as can be shown using (19).

Now that we know the expression (26) of the reciprocal of $c + id$, we can perform the division of $a + ib$ by $c + id$. Reducing the division to multiplication by the reciprocal, we have:

$$(a + ib)/(c + id) = (a + ib)(c - id)/(c^2 + d^2)$$

$$= [(ac + bd) + i(bc - ad)]/(c^2 + d^2)$$

Thus, the quotient of two complex numbers is a complex number whose real and imaginary parts are formed according to the rule:

$$(a + ib)/(c + id) = (ac + bd)/(c^2 + d^2) + i(bc - ad)/(c^2 + d^2) \quad (27)$$

In this Cartesian form of the quotient of two complex numbers, the expressions of its absolute value and argument are not immediately evident. They could be computed from the expression (27) of the quotient, but it is much easier to find them, performing the same division in its polar form.

Suppose that the dividend Z and the divisor z are given in polar form

$$Z = R(\cos T + i \sin T); \quad z = r(\cos t + i \sin t)$$

First of all we form the reciprocal $1/z$ of the divisor. Its expression is, as we have seen above,

$$1/z = (\cos t - i \sin t)/r$$

Therefore, reducing the division to multiplication by the reciprocal:

$$Z/z = Z(1/z) = R(\cos T + i \sin T)(\cos t - i \sin t)/r$$

$$= (R/r)[\cos(T - t) + i \sin(T - t)]$$

This result shows clearly that the absolute value of the quotient, $|Z/z|$, is equal to the quotient of absolute values, while the argument, arg (Z/z), is the *difference* $T - t$ of arguments T, t of the dividend and divisor respectively. Thus the rule of division (27) may also be formulated as follows:

$$|Z/z| = |Z|/|z|; \quad \arg(Z/z) = \arg Z - \arg z.$$

EXAMPLE: $(1 + i)/(1 - i) = (1 + i)^2/[(1 + i)(1 - i)] = (1 + 2i$

$+ i^2)/2 = i$. On the other hand

$$1 + i = \sqrt{2}(\cos 45° + i \sin 45°)$$

and

$$1 - i = \sqrt{2}(\cos 45° - i \sin 45°) = \sqrt{2}[\cos(-45°) + i \sin(-45°)]$$

Therefore

$$|(1 + i)/(1 - i)| = \sqrt{2}/\sqrt{2} = 1;$$

$$\arg[(1 + i)/(1 - i)] = 45° - (-45°) = 90°$$

which gives finally

$$(1 + i)/(1 - i) = 1(\cos 90° + i \sin 90°) = 0 + 1(i) = i.$$

The absolute value of the quotient of two conjugate complex numbers $1 + i, 1 - i$ is one and this fact is a general one, since $|a \pm ib| = (a^2 + b^2)^{1/2}$.

Powers and Roots of Complex Numbers

At the beginning of this chapter we stated without proof that the introduction of the imaginary unit $\sqrt{-1} = i$ solves the problem of existence for all radicals of the type $\sqrt[2n]{-1}$, such as for instance

$$\sqrt[4]{-1}, \sqrt[6]{-1}, \sqrt[8]{-1}, \text{etc.}$$

Studying the powers and roots (which are powers with fractional exponents) of complex numbers, we shall prove this fact, as well as the existence for radicals of the type $\sqrt[2n+1]{-1}$ of values other than the real value -1.

Let us study first the powers with a *real* exponent t. To perform the operation $(a + ib)^t$ it is convenient to use the polar form of the base $a + ib$. If r, v denote the absolute value and the argument of $a + ib$, we have, applying (15)

$$(a + ib)^t = [r(\cos v + i \sin v)]^t = r^t[\cos(vt) + i \sin(vt)]$$

Thus the real part and the coefficient of the imaginary part of $(a + ib)$ are equal to $r^t \cos(tv)$ and $r^t \sin(tv)$ respectively. If the exponent t is a positive integer, $t = n$, the functions $\cos(nv)$ and $\sin(nv)$ can be expressed in terms of $\cos v$ and $\sin v$ as polynomials in these variables.

Take for instance $(n = 2)$ $\cos 2v$, $\sin 2v$ which are called in trigonometry the cosine and sine of *double* angle. The formula (14) gives for $n = 2$:

$$\cos 2v + i \sin 2v = (\cos v + i \sin v)^2 = \cos^2 v + 2i \sin v \cos v - \sin^2 v \quad (28)$$

since $i^2 = -1$. The square $(\cos v + i \sin v)^2$ was expanded, using the identity $(A + B)^2 = A^2 + 2AB + B^2$ with $A = \cos v$ and $B = i \sin v$.

Applying the principle of separation of real and imaginary to the identity (28), we split it into two real identities

$$\cos(2v) = \cos^2 v - \sin^2 v; \quad \sin(2v) = 2 \sin v \cos v \quad (29)$$

The expression of cosine of double angle, $\cos(2v)$, combined with the identity $\cos^2 v + \sin^2 v = 1$ gives two important expressions for the squares of $\cos v$ and $\sin v$: adding (29) and the identity $\cos^2 v + \sin^2 v = 1$, we obtain

$$1 + \cos(2v) = 2 \cos^2 v;$$

subtracting (29) from the same identity we find

$$1 - \cos (2v) = 2 \sin^2 v.$$

Replacing in these results the variable v by $u/2$, $v = u/2$ and $2v = u$, we obtain

$$2 \cos^2 (u/2) = 1 + \cos u; \quad 2 \sin^2 (u/2) = 1 - \cos u \qquad (30)$$

These relations are called in trigonometry "half-angle formulas" because they express the functions of a half-angle $u/2$ in terms of cosine of angle u.

EXAMPLE: To illustrate (29) and (30) let us take $v = u/2 = 30°$. One finds

$$\sin 30° = \cos 60° = 1/2 \text{ and } \cos 30° = \sin 60° = \sqrt{3}/2$$

Substituting these numbers, we check easily the relations (29) and (30):

$$1/2 = \cos 60° = \cos^2 30° - \sin^2 30° = 3/4 - 1/4$$

$$\sqrt{3}/2 = \sin 60° = 2 \sin 30° \cos 30° = 2(1/2) \sqrt{3}/2$$

$$2 \cos^2 30° = 2(\sqrt{3}/2)^2 = 2(3/4) = 3/2 = 1 + 1/2 = 1 + \cos 60°$$

$$2 \sin^2 30° = 2(1/2)^2 = 2/4 = 1/2 = 1 - 1/2 = 1 - \cos 60°$$

Likewise we have as above

$$\cos 15° = [(1 + \cos 30°)/2]^{1/2} = (2 + \sqrt{3})^{1/2}/2.$$

$$\sin 15° = [(1 - \cos 30°)/2]^{1/2} = (2 - \sqrt{3})^{1/2}/2$$

The formula (19) for $n = 3$ becomes

$$\cos (3v) + i \sin (3v) = (\cos v + i \sin v)^3$$

and applying the identity (2), it takes the form ($i^3 = -i$):

$$\cos (3v) + i \sin (3v) = \cos^3 v + 3i \cos^2 v \sin v - 3 \cos v \sin^2 v$$
$$- i \sin^3 v.$$

Separating real and imaginary, we obtain

$$\cos (3v) = \cos^3 v - 3 \cos v \sin^2 v;$$

$$\sin (3v) = 3 \sin v \cos^2 v - \sin^3 v.$$

Replacing in these identities $\sin^2 v$ and $\cos^2 v$ by the equivalent expressions $1 - \cos^2 v$ and $1 - \sin^2 v$, their terms $-3 \cos v \sin^2 v$ and $3 \sin v \cos^2 v$ are transformed into $-3 \cos v + 3 \cos^3 v$ and $3 \sin v - 3 \sin^3 v$ respectively. Therefore:

$$\cos (3v) = 4 \cos^3 v - 3 \cos v \qquad (31)$$

$$\sin (3v) = 3 \sin v - 4 \sin^3 v,$$

these identities being the usual form of the expressions of functions of $3v$ (triple angle) as polynomials in cosine and sine of the angle v.

EXAMPLE: Taking again $v = 30°$ with

$$\sin 30° = 1/2, \ \cos 30° = \sqrt{3}/2, \ \sin 3v = \sin 90 = 1,$$

$$\cos 3v = \cos 90° = 0,$$

we easily check (31):

$$0 = 4(\sqrt{3}/2)^3 - 3(\sqrt{3}/2); \ 1 = 3(1/2) - 4(1/2)^3$$

The integral powers z^n of the rotation-factor $z = \cos t + i \sin t$, given by Moivre's formula (14)

$$z_n = z^n = (\cos t + i \sin t)^n = \cos (nt) + i \sin (nt) \ (n = 1, 2, 3, ...)$$

admit of the following geometric interpretation. Since $|z| = \cos t + i \sin t| = (\cos^2 t + \sin^2 t)^{1/2} = 1$, all the powers of z have the same absolute value one. This means that the point-images of all complex numbers

$$z_1 = z, \ z_2 = z^2, \ z_3 = z^3, \ z_4 = z^4 \ etc.$$

are on the circumference of the unit circle, a circle of radius one having its center at the origin 0. These points $z_1, z_2, z_3, z_4, ...$ are equidistant from the origin and are separated by equal arcs of the circle. If the number of degrees contained in the angle t is rational and t therefore is commensurable with $1°$, there are only a finite number of points z_n on the circle. But if the angle t is incommensurable with $1°$, the set of point-images of $z_n = z^n = \cos (nt) + i \sin (nt)$, where $n = 1, 2, ...$ runs through all the integers, is infinite.

Take for instance $t = 22.5°$, (Fig. 6.23). The 16th power z^{16} of

$$z = \cos 22°.5 + i \sin 22°.5$$

is now equal to 1, since $22.5 \times 16 = 360$, and thus

$$z^{16} = \cos 360° + i \sin 360° = 1.$$

The values of sine and cosine of 360° are the same as those of 0°, since the addition to or subtraction from the argument of a multiple of 360° does not change a sine or a cosine.

In general, if t is commensurable with 1°, it is of the form $t = 360°m/n$, where m and n are two integers. Thus $nt = 360°m$ and $z^n = \cos (360°m) + i \sin (360°)m) = 1$. But if $z^n = 1$, then $z_{n+k} = z^{n+k} = z^n z^k = z^k = z_k$ so that there are only n points repeated in a cyclic order, when the integer k increases.

Consider now the case when t is incommensurable with 1°. We shall prove that in such a case there can be no two equal powers of $z = \cos t + i \sin t$ with different integral exponents. To prove this, suppose that $n > m$, but $z^n = z^m$. Dividing both members by z^m, we obtain $z^{n-m} = z^k = 1$, where $k = n - m$ is a positive integer, $k > 0$. The relation

$$z^k = (\cos t + i \sin t)^k = \cos (kt) + i \sin (kt) = 1$$

gives, applying the principle of separation of real and imaginary, $\cos (kt) = 1$ and $\sin (kt) = 0$. Thus, $\cos (kt) = \cos 0°$, and $\sin (kt) = \sin 0°$, which proves that the angle kt is a multiple of 360°: $kt = 360°s$, where s is an integer. We see thus that the hypothesis $z^n = z^m$ entails the conclusion $t = 360°s/k$, which means that t must be commensurable with 1°. But if no two points $z_n = z^n$, $z_m = z^m$ corresponding to different exponents n, m can coincide there will be clearly an infinite set of points z_n, when n runs through all the integers.

The introduction of the radical $\sqrt{-1} = i$ is sufficient to give a full meaning to all the roots of even order of the negative unit -1, $\sqrt[2n]{-1}$, for $n = 2, 3, 4, 5 \cdots$ Generalizing the problem, we consider the n-th root $\sqrt[n]{a + ib}$ (n an integer) of any complex number $a + ib$. To compute this radical we shall use again the polar form

$$r(\cos t + i \sin t) = a + ib$$

of the number $a + ib$. A radical of n-th order being nothing more than a power with the fractional exponent $1/n$ we can write:

$$\sqrt[n]{a + ib} = r^{1/n}(\cos t + i \sin t)^{1/n}$$
$$= \sqrt[n]{r}[\cos (t/n) + i \sin (t/n)] \tag{32}$$

Applying this result to $\sqrt{1}$, for which we know two values, 1 and -1, we choose $n = 2$, $a = 1$, $b = 0$, with $r = 1$ and $t = 0°$. Thus (32) gives for $\sqrt{1}$

$$\sqrt{1} = 1(\cos 0° + i \sin 0°) = 1$$

where the first factor $\sqrt[n]{r} = 1$ is positive because it represents the absolute value of the expression (32).

This result, namely $\sqrt{1} = 1$, is clearly unsatisfactory because it fails to represent the second value -1 of the radical $\sqrt{1}$. We are obliged to conclude that (32) gives only a partial, incomplete answer. To explain the reason for its failure let us observe that $(-1)^2 = 1$ means that the effect of two successive rotations through 180° is equivalent to a single rotation through 360°, and therefore the number 1 in the righthand member appears not only as being equal to $\cos 0° + i \sin 0°$ as we assumed, but also as $\cos 360° + i \sin 360°$. A complete expression for the real number 1 is

$$1 = \cos(360°k) + i \sin(360°k) \qquad\qquad (k = 0, \pm1, \pm2, ...)$$

where the integer k is undetermined, since the vector 1 in general can be obtained as result of any number of rotations, positive or negative,

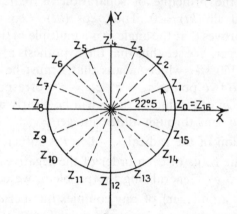

Fig. 6.23

through 360° of the vector $\cos 0° + i \sin 0°$ (any number of revolutions around the origin). In other words, considering a general case of a vector with the *azimuth A*, instead of the azimuth 0° we must take the *polar angle* θ of this vector, related to A by

$$\theta = A + 360°k$$

where k is any integer.

Returning again to $\sqrt{1}$, we take $r = 1$ but $t = 360°k$ and apply (32). Now $t/2 = 180°k$ and

$$\sqrt{1} = \cos(180°k) + i \sin(180°k).$$

We must study this expression for all possible integral values of the integer k. If k is even, $k = 2m$, then $180°k = 360°m$ and the cosine is one, while the sine vanishes. Thus for k even, $\sqrt{1} = 1 + 0i = 1$. But if k is odd, $k = 2m + 1$, then $180°k = 360°m + 180°$ and therefore $\sqrt{1} = -1 + 0i = -1$ because

$$\cos (180°k) = \cos (360°m + 180°) = \cos 180° = -1$$

$$\sin (180°k) = \sin 180° = 0.$$

Thus, for k odd we obtain the second value of $\sqrt{1}$, namely $\sqrt{1} = -1$.

In order to obtain a complete formula for $\sqrt[n]{a + ib}$, giving all its possible values, we must complete our first result (32), introducing in this formula the polar angle $t + 360°k$ instead of the azimuth t. In other words, we must take into consideration the important fact that a vector $a + ib$ with the azimuth t is represented by the same expression $a + ib$ after k full revolutions around the origin which add $360°k$ to its azimuth t.

We have thus, instead of

$$a + ib = r(\cos t + i \sin t)$$

the more exact expression

$$a + ib = r[\cos (t + 360°k) + i \sin (t + 360°k)], \qquad (33)$$

where t may be considered as the *azimuth* of the vector $a + ib$, k being *any* integer. Using (33) we find now a complete set of values of the radical $\sqrt[n]{a + ib}$. They are given by

$$\sqrt[n]{a + ib} = \sqrt[n]{r}\, [\cos \{(360°k + t)/n\} + i \sin \{(360°k + t)/n\}] \quad (34)$$

Before studying the formula (34) in its general case, where n is any fixed integer, let us consider, as an example, $\sqrt[3]{-1}$. In this case $n = 3$, $a = -1$, and $b = 0$. Plotting the point with coordinates $x = -1$, $y = 0$, we find that its distance r from origin 0 is 1 and its azimuth t is equal to $180°$. Applying (34), we obtain

$$\sqrt[3]{-1} = \sqrt[3]{1}\, [\cos (120°k + t/3) + i \sin (120°k + t/3)]$$

$$= \cos (120°k + 60°) + i \sin (120°k + 60°) = u_k$$

denoting by u_k the value of $\sqrt[3]{-1}$ corresponding to some choice of k.

To $k = 0$, for instance, corresponds

$$u_0 = \cos 60° + i \sin 60° = 1/2 + i\sqrt{3}/2$$

We find therefore, instead of our familiar $\sqrt[3]{-1} = -1$, a *complex* value $1/2 + i\sqrt{3}/2$ for the same $\sqrt[3]{-1}$ whose real value is -1. If we choose $k = 1$, the corresponding, second value of the radical $\sqrt[3]{-1}$ is obtained

$$u_1 = \cos 180° + i \sin 180° = -1$$

Choosing $k = 2$, we obtain a third value

$$u_2 = \cos 300° + i \sin 300°$$

$$= \cos(-60°) + i \sin(-60°) = \cos 60° - i \sin 60°$$

and finally

$$u_2 = 1/2 - i\sqrt{3}/2$$

We have thus three different values of $\sqrt[3]{-1}$, (Fig. 6.24):

$$u_0 = 1/2 + i\sqrt{3}/2; \quad u_1 = -1; \quad u_2 = 1/2 - i\sqrt{3}/2 \qquad (35)$$

With the aid of the identity (2) we can check the fact that the cubes of u_0 and u_2 are indeed equal to -1:

$$(1/2 \pm i\sqrt{3}/2)^3 = (1 \pm i\sqrt{3})^3/2^3$$

$$= (1 \pm 3i\sqrt{3} - 9 \mp 3i\sqrt{3})/8 = -1$$

The three numbers (35) are the only values of $\sqrt[3]{-1}$; all other values of k give u_0, u_1, or u_2. Increasing or decreasing k by a multiple $3m$ of 3, we do not change the value of the radical $\sqrt[3]{-1}$, given by $\cos(120°k + 60°) + i \sin(120°k + 60°)$ because then the angle $120°k + 60°$ increases or decreases by a multiple of $360°$:

$$120°(k + 3m) + 60° = (120°k + 60°) + 360°m$$

In other words, the equation of third order $u^3 + 1 = 0$, which is solved by $u = \sqrt[3]{-1}$, has three and only three roots given by (35). The third root, $u_2 = 1/2 - i\sqrt{3}/2$, could be obtained also by choosing $k = -1$. All three roots are rotation-factors: u_0—through $60°$, u_1—through $180°$, and u_2—through $(-60°)$. This readily agrees with the fact that the vector -1 can be obtained from the vector 1 by three successive rotations either through $\pm 60°$ or through $180°$.

The introduction of complex numbers brings a harmony into algebra. If we limit the number-field to real numbers only, we are obliged to state that the quadratic equation $x^2 = -1$ has no roots at all, while a similar cubic equation $x^3 = -1$ has a root $x = -1$. An equation of fourth order and of the same type $x^n = -1$, namely $x^4 = -1$, would have no roots again, as well as all the equations of this type with even exponents $x^{2m} = -1$. The equations with odd exponents, $x^{2m+1} = -1$ would have one root each, namely $x = -1$. The general result in the field of real numbers would be then formulated in an awkward statement: if the order n of the equation $x^n = -1$ is even, then this equation has no roots at all, but if this order is odd, then there is one root namely $x = -1$.

If we change the sign of the righthand member and consider the type $x^n = 1$, the statement just formulated would not be true and we would be obliged to replace it by another, equally awkward statement: if n is even, there are *two* roots, ± 1, for each equation of the type $x^n = 1$, but if n is odd, there can be only *one* root, namely $x = 1$. There would be as many particular and complicated statements about the number of roots as there would be different types of equation we could form, that is an infinite number.

All these complications are caused by artificial limitations imposed on the number-field. In the larger field of complex numbers, which includes real numbers, we have a very simple and elegant theorem:

THEOREM: *Any equation of n-th order has n solutions, called its roots.*

In particular the equation $z^n = -1$ has n roots, that is, there are n different values of the radical $\sqrt[n]{-1}$. We have seen this for $n = 3$. Let us study the case $n = 4$. The radical $\sqrt[4]{-1}$ as expressed with the aid of (34), where now $t = 180°$, $n = 4$, is represented by a vector v_k:

$$\sqrt[4]{-1} = \cos (90°k + 45°) = i \sin (90°k + 45°) = v_k$$

For $k = 0$ we obtain

$$v_0 = \cos 45° + i \sin 45° = (\sqrt{2} + i\sqrt{2})/2 = (1 + i)/\sqrt{2}$$

Increasing k by one we add $90°$ to the argument of v_k, that is, we rotate the vector v_k through $90°$. Therefore, the four vectors v_0, v_1, v_2, v_3 point from the origin O to four vertices of a square, forming two diagonals of this square (see fig. 6.24). The sides of this square are parallel to the coordinate axes since the vector v_0 makes with OX axis an angle of 45°. Note that the three values of the radical $\sqrt[3]{-1}$, given by (35), have as their point-images the vertices of a regular triangle inscribed in a circle of radius one (see fig. 6.24). We expect that the n values $z_1, z_2, z_3, ..., z_{n-1}, z_n$ of the radical $z = \sqrt[n]{1}$, roots of the equation $z^n = 1$, are located at the n vertices of a regular inscribed polygon with n sides, the point $A(1, 0)$ being one of the vertices.

This generalization is valid. The formula (34) gives $z = \sqrt[n]{1}$ for $a = r = 1, b = t = 0$:

$$\sqrt[n]{1} = z_k = \cos(360°k/n) + i\sin(360°k/n) \tag{36}$$

If n is added or subtracted from k, the argument $360°k/n$ of the cosine and sine is increased or decreased by 360°, and the value of $z_k = \sqrt[n]{1}$ does not change. Note that

$$z_k = z_1^k = [\cos(360°/n) + i\sin(360°/n)]^k$$

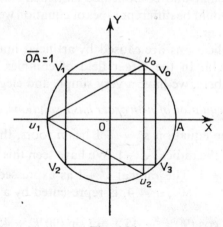

Fig. 6.24

Therefore, the radical $\sqrt[n]{1}$ can have only n different values which are obtained by giving to k any n successive integral values, for instance $k = 0, 1, 2, ..., n - 2, n - 1$. The n vectors $z_1, z_2, z_3, ... z_n$ given by (36) join the origin to n vertices of a regular polygon with a vertex at the point A (1, 0) and are separated by equal angles whose common value $360°/n$ is the n-th part of 360°.

The formula (34) may also be written, using (21), as follows:

$$\sqrt[n]{a + ib} = \sqrt[n]{r}\,[\cos(t/n) + i\sin(t/n)] \times$$

$$\times [\cos(360°k/n) + i\sin(360°k/n)]$$

Denoting the radical $\sqrt[n]{a + ib}$ by U and its first value, given by (32) for $k = 0$, by U_0:

$$U_0 = \sqrt[n]{r}\,[\cos(t/n) + i\sin(t/n)]$$

we can express all n values of U given by (34) with the aid of U_0 and z_k as follows:

$$U_k = U_0 z_k = U_0 \cdot z_1^k \quad (k = 0, 1, ..., n - 1)$$

But z_k is a rotation-factor through $360°k/n$ degrees which is equal to z_1^k since k rotations through $360°/n$ are equal to a single rotation through $360°k/n$ degrees. Therefore, we have the relation

$$U_{k+1} = z_1 U_k$$

which proves that the n values $U_1, U_2, ..., U_n$ of the radical $U = \sqrt[n]{a + ib}$ form a regular polygon with vertices U_k beginning at the point $U_0 = U_n$, instead of the point 1 for $\sqrt[n]{1}$.

In particular, the inscribed regular polygon representing by its vertices the n values of $\sqrt{-1}$ has as one of its vertices the point $\cos(180°/n) + i\sin(180°/n)$ since the azimuth t of the number -1 is equal to $180°$. Thus, all the radicals of the type $\sqrt[n]{-1}$ are simply complex numbers and have, therefore, perfectly determined meanings, if only one among them, namely $i = \sqrt{-1}$, is defined.

The explanation of the fundamental fact that the n-th root of 1 has n different values is simple, if we turn to the geometric interpretation and study the rotations. The number 1 as a rotation factor represents the rotation through $360°$ and through all the multiples $360°k$ of $360°$, k being any integer. The radical $\sqrt[n]{1}$ is also a rotation-factor but such one that, if the rotation it represents is repeated n times, the global effect is a rotation through any multiple of $360°$. If the polar angle of $\sqrt[n]{1}$ is represented by w, we must have $nw = 360k$. Thus, $w = 360°k/n$ has—as we have seen it above—n different values as k runs through all the integers.

EXAMPLE: 1°) Three values of $\sqrt[3]{8}$ given by (34) are:

$$\sqrt[3]{8} = 2[\cos (120°k) + i \sin (120°k)]$$

since $360°/3 = 120°$. Giving k the values 0, 1, 2 we obtain

$$2; -1 + i\sqrt{3}; -1 - i\sqrt{3} = -(1 + i\sqrt{3})$$

Using the identity

$$(a + b)^3 \equiv a^3 + 3a^2b + 3ab^2 + b^3$$

with $a = -1$, $b = \pm i\sqrt{3}$, it is easy to check that $(-1 \pm i\sqrt{3})^3 = 8$.

2°) To compute $\sqrt{5 + 12i} = \sqrt{a + ib}$ with $a = 5$, $b = 12$, we observe that $r = (a^2 + b^2)^{1/2} = 13$, while

$$\sin t = b/r = 12/13, \ \cos t = a/r = 5/13,$$

$$\tan t = b/a = 12/5 = 2.4.$$

Therefore:

$$\sqrt{5 + 12i} = \sqrt{13} \, [\cos (180°k + t/2) + i \sin (180°k + t/2)]$$

$$= \sqrt{13} \, [\cos (t/2) + i \sin (t/2)] \, [\cos (180°k) + i \sin (180°k)]$$

where the second rotation-factor, $\cos (180°k) + i \sin (180°k)$, is equal to 1 and -1 for $k = 0$ and $k = 1$ respectively, so that

$$\sqrt{5 + 12i} = \pm[\sqrt{13} \cos (t/2) + i\sqrt{13} \sin (t/2)]$$

The relations (30) with $u = t$ allow to compute $\sin (t/2)$ and $\cos (t/2)$:

$$2 \cos^2 (t/2) = 1 + \cos t = 1 + 5/13 = 18/13$$

$$\text{so that } 13 \cos^2 (t/2) = 9$$

as well as

$$2 \sin^2 (t/2) = 1 - \cos t = 1 - 5/13, \text{ so that } 13 \sin^2 (t/2) = 4.$$

Before extracting square roots we must fix the choice of their signs. Now the angle t belongs to the first quadrant, $0 < t < 90°$, since both its sine and cosine are positive. Hence $t/2$ is also in the first quadrant, namely $0 < t/2 < 45°$ and therefore $\sin (t/2)$ and $\cos (t/2)$ must be positive. Consequently:

$$\sqrt{13} \cos (t/2) = 3; \ \sqrt{13} \sin (t/2) = 2$$

and finally (see fig. 6.25):

$$\sqrt{5 + 12i} = \pm(3 + 2i)$$

From a purely formal algebraical point of view, with the creation of complex numbers the evolution of the number-concept reaches its final phase. The result of any operation applied to complex numbers is again a complex number, so that in the field of complex numbers all the inverse operations being always possible, they cease to be a source of new kinds of number. We have seen this for all operations except for powers with complex exponents and logarithms for which the proof will be given in Chapter 9.

Thus, the field of complex numbers is closed in the sense that no operation can lead us out of it. In this sense the complex numbers are self-sufficient. However, this does not mean that mathematics uses only complex numbers.

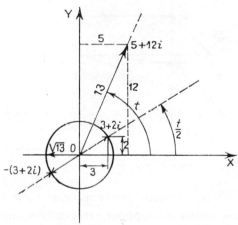

Fig. 6.25

A great variety of other useful generalizations of the number-concept were created and are used in pure and applied mathematics. One of them is the important generalization of the planar vector concept. Physical quantities which may be represented by vectors occur in our experience not only in a plane but much more often in a three-dimensional space, and this more general condition demands a more general form of number, if numbers are to be applied to the study of our environment.

We cannot study here all the generalizations of complex numbers and can only try to give and idea of what kind of numbers represent vectors in space and how quaternions express rotations in three-dimensional space.

Unit-vectors in Space

To locate a point in space three coordinates x, y, z and three coordinate-axes OX, OY, OZ are needed. The axes form at the origin O a so-called trirectangular trihedral angle (see Chapter 19), which might be thought of as an idefinitely extended corner of an ordinary rectangular

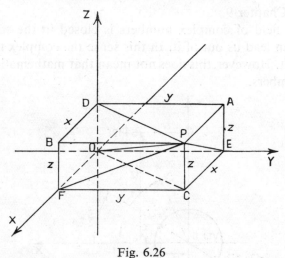

Fig. 6.26

box or room. Its three mutually perpendicular faces (two walls and floor or ceiling for a room) are supposed to extend without limit so that they become three mutually perpendicular infinite planes XOY, YOZ, ZOX through the origin O (see fig. 6.26). The three coordinate-axes appear as mutually perpendicular intersection lines of three coordinate planes.

The whole space is divided by each infinite coordinate plane into two separate regions which lie on different sides of the plane. The plane XOY, for instance, defines two half-spaces one of which is above the plane, and the other below it.

The vertical plane ZOX divides each one of these two regions (half-spaces above and below XOY) into two again: one lying to the right of ZOX and the other to the left of it. Thus the two coordinate planes

XOY and ZOX together divide the space into *four* regions. Add now to the picture the third coordinate plane YOZ (in fig. 6.26 this plane YOZ coincides with the plane of the page itself). This third plane subdivides again every one of four regions into two parts: one lying behind the plane YOZ and the other before it.

In all we have *eight* contiguous trirectangular trihedral angles around the common vertex O. They are called *octants* since, being identical, each of them is one-eighth part of the whole space. Each face belongs to two adjacent octants, and around each edge we have four octants. The space appears to us as subdivided by three coordinate planes into eight *octants*, as a plane is subdivided by two coordinate-axes OX, OY into four *quadrants*.

The eight octants are characterized by different combinations of signs of the three Cartesian coordinates x, y, z which fix the location of a point P in space. The coordinates x, y, z are defined as follows: Given a point P in one of the eight octants (fig. 6.26), drop three perpendiculars from P to the coordinate-planes: $AP \perp YOZ$, $BP \perp ZOX$ and $CP \perp XOY$, the sign $\perp$ meaning "perpendicular to". These perpendiculars are parallel to the coordinate-axes, namely $AP \| OX$, $BP \| OY$ and $CP \| OZ$. These three perpendiculars determine three planes parallel to three coordinate-planes and which pass through the point P. They are defined by groups of three points each: $APB \| XOY$, $BPC \| YOZ$ and $CPA \| ZOX$. These planes cut the coordinate-axes in points D, F, and E. Thus a rectangular parallelepiped is built with OP as its principal diagonal. The coordinates of its vertices are denoted in the order x, y, z and marked in this order in the parentheses. So, for instance, the point P has the coordinates x, y, z and this fact is denoted simply by writing $P(x, y, z)$. Thus, we find with the aid of fig. 6.26: $A(o, y, z)$; $B(x, o, z)$; $C(x, y, o)$; $D(o, o, z)$; $E(o, y, o)$; $F(x, o, o)$; and $O(o, o, o)$, the origin of coordinates O having all its three coordinates equal to zero.

We define the three coordinates of the point P by the three vectors **AP**, **BP**, **CP** directed towards the point P: $x = $ **AP**, $y = $ **BP**, $z = $ **CP**. Therefore, a coordinate is negative, if the direction of the vector defining it is opposite to the positive direction of the corresponding axis to which this vector is parallel, and it is positive, if the vector points in the same direction as the axis. On fig. 6.26 the point P is to the right of the plane XOZ, before the plane YOZ and above the plane XOY. Therefore, all three coordinates of this point are by definition positive numbers. The octant to which belongs P is called the *first* octant and it is characterized by the fact that for all its points the three coordinates x, y, z are positive. This rule of signs for the eight octants is formulated as follows:

Octant	Sign of x	Sign of y	Sign of z
First	plus	plus	plus
Second	minus	plus	plus
Third	minus	minus	plus
Fourth	plus	minus	plus
Fifth	minus	minus	minus
Sixth	plus	minus	minus
Seventh	plus	plus	minus
Eighth	minus	plus	minus

The $(m + 4)$-th octant is symmetrical and opposite to the m-th octant with respect to the origin O, $m = 1, 2, 3, 4$.

To every point P corresponds a vector **OP** (principal diagonal on fig. 6.26) with its tail at the origin O and head at $P(x, y, z)$. The coordinates of P are projections of **OP** on axes and are called the x-, y-, and z-*components* of the vector **OP**. Any vector **MN** parallel to **OP**, having the same direction and length and thus located somewhere on a line parallel to **OP**, is by definition *equal* to **OP**, as having the same three components as **OP**. The three components of a vector are by definition its three projections on the axes OX, OY and OZ. So, for instance, drawing on fig. 6.26. the diagonals PF, PE, PD of the faces $PBFC$, $PCEA$, $PADB$ we see that OF $=$ **AP** $= x$ is the projection of the vector **OP** on the axis OX. Likewise **OE** $=$ **BP** $= y$ and **OD** $=$ **CP** $= z$ are projections of **OP** on OY and OZ respectively. This property of components of a vector, namely to be its projections on coordinate-axes, explains why the components of two equal vectors are equal.

Any vector is the geometric sum of three vectors which are its three projections on the coordinate-axes. To show this it is sufficient to twice apply the parallelogram law. First we have (see fig. 6.26)

$$\mathbf{DP} = \mathbf{DB} + \mathbf{DA}$$

and then

$$\mathbf{P} = \mathbf{OC} + \mathbf{CP} = \mathbf{DP} + \mathbf{CP} = \mathbf{DB} + \mathbf{DA} + \mathbf{CP}$$

But

$$\mathbf{DB} = \mathbf{AP} \qquad \mathbf{DA} = \mathbf{BP}$$

and therefore the diagonal vector **OP** appears as a sum of three vectors **AP**, **BP**, **CP** which are its components:

$$\mathbf{OP} = \mathbf{AP} + \mathbf{BP} + \mathbf{CP}$$

Any vector parallel to the OX axis can be represented by a number, if we know how to represent a unit-vector parallel to this axis, and the same is true for vectors parallel to OY or OZ. Therefore we need three different numerical units to represent three fundamental unit-vectors on the axes OX, OY and OZ respectively. These fundamental unit-vectors are denoted by the three symbols i[1]), j, k which are considered as numbers of absolute value one

$$|i| = 1 \qquad |j| = 1 \qquad |k| = 1.$$

These unit-vectors are pointing in positive directions, so that $-i$, $-j$ and $-k$ represent vectors of length one pointing in negative directions that is to the left on OX, for instance, or downwards on OZ.

The length and direction of a vector parallel to OX are represented both of them, by the number ix, that is by the x-component of this vector multiplied by the unit-vector i, two other components being zero since it is parallel to OX: $y = z = 0$. The vector is well represented by ix since the fact that it is parallel to OX is expressed by the first factor i, the direction in which it is pointing is fixed by the *sign* of the real number x and the length is equal to the absolute value $|x|$ of the number x. Thus we can write **AP** $= ix$ and, likewise **BP** $= jy$, **CP** $= kz$. We can also say that multiplying the vector i by x we stretch it x times and reverse its direction, if x is a negative number.

We have built up the numerical representation of any space vector with given three vector-components ix, jy, kz: **OP** $-$ **AP** $+$ **BP** $+$ **CP** $= ix + jy + kz$. At the same time a generalization of complex number is obtained.

The vectors in a plane with components x and y are represented by complex numbers $x + iy$, because in a plane the unit-vectors on OX and OY axes were associated by definition with unit-numbers 1 and i respectively. In the three-dimensional space we have as fundamental frame of reference three mutually perpendicular axes (three components of a space vector correspond to them) and therefore we need three unit-numbers to represent three unit-vectors. Thus, we see that the funda-

[1]) The symbol i this lime is not related to $\sqrt{-1}$.

mental units i, j, k in the space correspond exactly to the units 1, i of complex numbers in a plane. The compound number $ix + jy + kz$ generalizes the complex number $x + iy$ in the sense that it has three heterogeneous parts ix, jy, kz instead of two heterogeneous parts, real x and imaginary iy, of a complex number. Note, in passing, the different meanings of the symbol i in dealing with complex numbers (*two*-dimensional vectors) and with compound numbers of the type $ix + jy + kz$ (*three*-dimensional space and vectors).

Operations with Numbers of the Type $ix + jy + kz$

Addition and subtraction of compound numbers which represent vectors in three-dimensional space follow the law of parallelogram and this is expressed in the algebraical language as follows:

$$(ia + jb + kc) \pm (ir + js + kt)$$

$$= i(a \pm r) + j(b \pm s) + k(c \pm t)$$

where a, b, c and r, s, t are real numbers. This formula expresses for example the resultant velocity in a motion which is caused by two simultaneous motions with velocities $ia + jb + kc$ and $ir + js + kt$.

The multiplication of compound numbers we are studying is defined in accordance with our experience, as it is reflected in our perceptions of physical environment. Without specifying physical magnitudes and phenomena concerned, it is sufficient to state that given two vectors $\mathbf{U}(a, b, c)$ and $\mathbf{V}(r, s, t)$, two combinations of their components have important physical meaning. They are of entirely different mathematical character: the first one, namely $ar + bs + ct$, is a real number and, as such, has no other proprieties, while the second one is a vector and has not only a magnitude but also a direction. Therefore, the combination $ar + bs + ct$ is called a *scalar*, which means that it represents only a magnitude, while the second combination, as a vector, has three components A, B, C with respect to OX, OY, OZ respectively:

$$A = bt - cs; \quad B = cr - at; \quad C = as - br$$

Both of these two combinations are called products of two vectors $\mathbf{U}$ and $\mathbf{V}$. To distinguish them the first one is considered as the result of a *scalar multiplication* and called *scalar product* (or also *inner product*), while the second is a *vector product* (also *cross product*) and it is considered as the result of a *vectorial multiplication*. For compound numbers $ix + jy + kz$ there are therefore two different kinds of operation of multiplication. They are denoted by symbols $\mathbf{UV}$ or $(\mathbf{U}, \mathbf{V})$ and $[\mathbf{U}, \mathbf{V}]$ or $[\mathbf{U} \times \mathbf{V}]$ respectively:

$$\mathbf{UV} = (\mathbf{U}, \mathbf{V}) = ar + bs + ct$$

$$\mathbf{U} \times \mathbf{V} = [\mathbf{U}, \mathbf{V}] = i(bt - cs) + j(cr - at) + k(as - br)$$

Scalar Multiplication

The word "scalar" means purely numerical magnitude as opposed to "vector" which is a directed magnitude. Thus the work done by a force $F = iX + jY + kZ$ along a displacement $D = ia + jb + kc$ of its application point is expressed by the scalar product

$$(\mathbf{D}, \mathbf{F}) = aX + bY + cZ$$

and it is a pure number having no direction. The square $\mathbf{U}^2 = (\mathbf{U}, \mathbf{U})$, that is the *scalar* square, of a vector $\mathbf{U} = ia + jb + kc$ is, by definition of scalar multiplication, equal to

$$\mathbf{U}^2 = (\mathbf{U}, \mathbf{U}) = a^2 + b^2 + c^2$$

and by Pythagorean Theorem it expresses the square of the vector's length. This length is also represented by the absolute value of the vector denoted by $|\mathbf{U}|$, and we have therefore

$$|\mathbf{U}|^2 = (\mathbf{U}, \mathbf{U}) = a^2 + b^2 + c^2$$

Table of scalar multiplication

	i	j	k
i	1	0	0
j	0	1	0
k	0	0	1

The scalar multiplication obeys the fundamental arithmetical laws and it is performed as every algebraical multiplication of two sums, using the scalar multiplication table of fundamental units i, j, k. In this table we read $(i, i) = (j, j) = (k, k) = 1$, but all other products of fundamental units vanish: $(i, j) = (j, k) = (k, i) = 0$. The scalar multiplication obeys the commutative law and the table is commutative. We have indeed

$$(i, j) = (j, i) = 0; \ (j, k) = (k, j) = 0; \ (k, i) = (i, k) = 0$$

The geometric interpretation of scalar multiplication shows that the scalar product is related to the angle of two vectors, factors in a scalar product. It is equal to the product of lengths of two factors times the cosine of the angle they form. Thus, for instance, the work done by a force $F = iX + jY + kZ$ of magnitude $|F| = (X^2 + Y^2 + Z^2)^{1/2}$ along a displacement $D = ia + jb + kc$ of length $|D| = (a^2 + b^2 + c^2)^{1/2}$ is equal to $aX + bY + cZ$ and at the same time it is equal to $|F| \cdot |D| \cdot \cos t$, where t is the angle of two vectors F and D:

$$(\mathbf{F}, \mathbf{D}) = aX + bY + cZ = |\mathbf{F}| \cdot |\mathbf{D}| \cos t \tag{37}$$

We postpone the proof which can be found in the Chapter 19.

Vectorial Multiplication

As its name implies, the vector product of **U** and **V** is a third vector [**U**, **V**]. A table of vectoral multiplication corresponds to the definition of this kind of multiplication, which can be formulated as follows:

$$[ia + jb + kc, \ ir + js + kt]$$
$$= i(bt - cs) + j(cr - at) + k(as - br) \tag{38}$$

This definition shows that the vectorial squares of fundamental units vanish

$$[i, i] = [j, j] = [k, k] = 0$$

since the products ar, bs and ct are absent in the righthand member of (38). On the other hand the vectorial product of two unit-vectors is the third unit vector perpendicular to both factors:

$$[i, j] = -[j, i] = k; \ [j, k] = -[k, j] = i; \ [k, i] = -[i, k] = j$$

There are two different unit-vectors perpendicular to i and j for example. One of them is k, the other $-k$, and both are represented as vectorial products of i and j: $k = [i, j]$ and $-k = [j, i]$. Therefore, the vectorial multiplication *does not obey the commutative law*, and the value of a vectorial product depends on the *order* of its two factors: the vectorial product of two unit vectors changes its sign if the order of its factors is inverted.

Thus, the table of vectorial products for fundamental units is as follows:

		Right factor		
		i	j	k
	i	0	k	$-j$
Left factor	j	$-k$	0	i
	k	j	$-i$	0

The vectorial squares of fundamental units must vanish, since being symmetrical they do not change with the reversal of order of their two factors and at the same time they must change their sign: $(i, i) = -(i, i)$ gives $2(i, i) = 0$ and thus $(i, i) = 0$.

Applying the definition (38) to vectorial product $[\mathbf{V}, \mathbf{U}] = [ir + js + kt, \ ia + jb + kc]$, we conclude that in general a vectorial product of any two vectors changes its sign when the order of its factors is inverted:

$$[\mathbf{V}, \mathbf{U}] = -[\mathbf{U}, \mathbf{V}] \tag{39}$$

Therefore, the vectorial square of any vector vanishes necessarily:

$$[\mathbf{U}, \mathbf{U}] = [\mathbf{U}]^2 = 0$$

as it follows also from (38), if $\mathbf{U} = \mathbf{V}$, that is if $a = r$, $b = s$ and $c = t$.

The vectorial product of two fundamental unit vectors is perpendicular to the plane defined by two factors. To prove now that the vector $[\mathbf{U}, \mathbf{V}]$ is perpendicular to both factors $\mathbf{U}$ and $\mathbf{V}$ it is sufficient to verify that the angles it forms with $\mathbf{U}$ and $\mathbf{V}$ are right angles. On the other hand, an angle is equal to $90°$ if its cosine vanishes. Therefore, our problem reduces to the following one: show that a vectorial product $\mathbf{W} = [\mathbf{U}, \mathbf{V}]$ forms with its factor $\mathbf{U}$ (or $\mathbf{V}$, which is the same) an angle the cosine of which vanishes.

The general relation (37) shows that the scalar product of two vectors vanishes, if and only if the cosine of the angle formed by these two vectors is zero. Therefore, it will be sufficient to prove that the scalar products $(\mathbf{W}, \mathbf{U})$ *and* $(\mathbf{W}, \mathbf{V})$ vanish to conclude that the vector. $\mathbf{W}$ is perpendicular to the plane defined by vectors two $\mathbf{U}$ and $\mathbf{V}$.

Three components of $\mathbf{W} = [\mathbf{U}, \mathbf{V}]$ being given by (38) and those of $\mathbf{U}$ being a, b, c we have to verify that the expression $(\mathbf{W}, \mathbf{U})$ vanishes. We have indeed

$$(\mathbf{W}, \mathbf{U}) = ([\mathbf{U}, \mathbf{V}], \mathbf{U}) = (bt - cs)\,a + (cr - at)\,b + (as - br)\,c = 0$$

and the result holds for $(\mathbf{W}, \mathbf{V})$. Thus, it is proved that the vectorial product $[\mathbf{U}, \mathbf{V}]$ is a vector parallel to the normal of the plane of two vectors $\mathbf{U}$ and $\mathbf{V}$.

To become fully determined this direction must be identified with one of two possible directions on the normal to a plane. It is well fixed in the product $[i, j] = k$ and since we can transform the vectors i and j continuously into any two arbitrary vectors $\mathbf{U}$ and $\mathbf{V}$, stretching and rotating them, the same rule applies to all vector products. Stretching and rotating the two vectors $\mathbf{U}$ and $\mathbf{V}$ continuously, we stretch and rotate continuously their vector-product and therefore its direction remains always on the same side of the normal to the plane of $\mathbf{U}$ and $\mathbf{V}$ without jumping suddenly through $180°$.

The choice between two possible directions, both normal to the plane of $\mathbf{U}$ and $\mathbf{V}$, is to be made as follows: the left factor $\mathbf{U}$ and the right factor $\mathbf{V}$ of a vectorial product $[\mathbf{U}, \mathbf{V}]$ being identified with OX and OY axes respectively, the direction of the vectorial product itself will coincide with the positive direction of the OZ axis. Applying the rule to the product $[j, i]$ we find $-k$: the vector $[j, i]$ is pointing downward.

Another way of memorizing this rule is based on an important interpretation of three fundamental unit vectors i, j, k as rotation-factors through $90°$ *counterclockwise around their respective axes*, when the rotation appears as counterclockwise to an observer standing along the rotation-axis with his feet at the origin 0 and his head somewhere on the *positive* half of the rotation-axis.

Our customary reading of a product from the right to the left, as for instance $4 \cdot 3$ which is read "three multiplied by four", is a reminiscence of the oriental origin of multiplication.

Therefore, distinguishing between the multiplicand and multiplier, we state that the *right* factor denotes the multiplicand, while the multiplier is denoted by the *left* factor. Considering now the vectorial product $[i, j]$ we observe that in this operation a *unit vector j* located on the

OY-axis (multiplicand) is multiplied by the *rotation factor i* which plays the role of multiplier. The result is a rotation of the multiplicand j through 90° around OX-axis counterclockwise (see fig. 6.27) which brings the multiplicand on the OZ-axis, transforming j into k: $[i, j] = k$.

A similar interpretation of the product $[j, i]$ states that this time the unit *vector i* multiplied by the rotation factor j must be rotated through 90° around the OY axis counterclockwise. The result of such a rotation

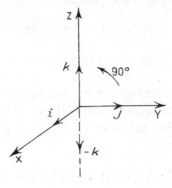

Fig. 6.27

is manifestly $-k$ and thus the non-commutativity of the vectorial multiplication is the algebraical expression of geometric properties of rotations in the three-dimensional space.

The rule of choice between two directions normal to the same plane and opposite to each other, applied in our definition of a vectorial product, is known in physics under the name of "the lefthand rule". Take, for instance, the effect of a magnetic field on an electric current flowing in a wire whose direction is perpendicular to that of the magnetic field. The wire carrying the current is acted upon by a force which tends to move the wire in a direction perpendicular to both the magnetic field and the wire. The rule for determining the direction of this force (the lefthand rule) can be formulated as follows: if the thumb, fore-finger, and middle finger of the left hand are outstretched at right angles to one another, the forefinger pointing in the direction of the magnetic field while the middle finger points in the direction of the current in the wire, then the thumb will indicate the direction of the force acting upon the wire.

The length of the vector $[\mathbf{U}, \mathbf{V}]$, that is its absolute value $|[\mathbf{U}, \mathbf{V}]|$, can be found computing its square which is equal to the sum of squares of three components $bt - cs, cr - at, as - br$:

$$|[U, V]|^2 = (bt - cs)^2 + (cr - at)^2 + (as - br)^2$$

$$= (a^2 + b^2 + c^2)(r^2 + s^2 + t^2) - (ar + bs + ct)^2 \quad (40)$$

On the other hand, the relation (37) gives, writing it for the scalar product (U, V) and squaring both sides:

$$(U, V)^2 = (ar + bs + ct)^2 = |U|^2 \cdot |V|^2 \cdot \cos^2 t$$

$$= (a^2 + b^2 + c^2)(r^2 + s^2 + t^2) \cdot \cos^2 t$$

where t denotes the angle formed by two vectors U and V.

Substituting in the expression (40) of $|[U,V]|^2$ instead of $(ar + bs + ct)^2$ the equivalent expression $(a^2 + b^2 + c^2)(r^2 + s^2 + t^2) \cos^2 t$, we find the value of $|[U, V]|^2$:

$$|[U, V]|^2 = |U|^2 \cdot |V|^2 - |U|^2 \cdot |V|^2 \cdot \cos^2 t$$

$$= |U|^2 \cdot |V|^2(1 - \cos^2 t) = |U|^2 \cdot |V|^2 \cdot \sin^2 t$$

because $1 - \cos^2 t = \sin^2 t$. Extracting the square root we obtain finally

$$|[U, V]| = |U| \cdot |V| \cdot |\sin t| \quad (41)$$

Therefore, the absolute value of the vectorial product $[U, V]$, that is the length of this vector, is equal to the area of a parallelogram with the sides $|U|$ and $|V|$. We can also say that the sum of squares of (U, V) and of $|[U, V]|$ is equal to the square of $|U| \cdot |V|$:

$$(U, V)^2 + |[U, V]|^2 = |U|^2 \cdot |V|^2$$

We add that both kinds of multiplication, scalar and vectorial, do not allow inverse operations, so that there is no division in the number field of the type $ia + jb + kc$. To re-establish the possibility of division one must add a fourth term to the sum $ia + jb + kc$, this fourth term being a *scalar*, a real number d. Such a number $d + ia + jb + kc$ which has four heterogeneous parts is called *quaternion*. Quaternions were introduced into mathematics by the famous Irish scientist Hamilton, in 1843. We have only a few words to say about this kind of numbers.

Quaternions

Multiplication of quaternions is non-commutative and the great discovery of Hamilton consisted precisely in the negation of the law of commutativity, this negation permitting the extension of number concept. The non-commutative algebra of quaternions revealed itself as a source of knowledge. It obeys the associative and distributive laws. Here is the table of multiplication for its four fundamental units $1, i, j, k$

		Right factor			
		1	i	j	k
	1	1	i	j	k
	i	i	-1	k	$-j$
Left factor	j	j	$-k$	-1	i
	k	k	j	$-i$	-1

The quaternion reciprocal to a given quaternion $d + ia + jb + kc$ is unique and it is the solution of the quaternionic equation

$$(S + iX + jY + kZ)(d + ia + jb + kc) = 1$$

which involves four unknowns S, X, Y, and Z. Two quaternions $d + ia + jb + kc$ and $d - ia - jb - kc$ are called *conjugate* and their product is a positive scalar:

$$(d + ia + jb + kc)(d - ia - jb - kc) = d^2 + a^2 + b^2 + c^2$$

This identity gives the reciprocal to $d + ia + jb + kc$:

$$1/(d + ia + jb + kc) = (d + ia + jb + kc)^{-1}$$
$$= (d - ia - jb - kc)/(a^2 + b^2 + c^2 + d^2)$$

There is only one reciprocal to $d + ia + jb + kc$, since changing the signs of a, b, c we have also the identity

$$(d - ia - jb - kc)(d + ia + jb + kc) = d^2 + a^2 + b^2 + c^2$$

so that the multiplication of two *conjugate* quaternions is *commutative*.

The existence of a unique reciprocal entails the possibility of division: to divide by a quaternion $d + ia + jb + kc$ it is sufficient to multiply by the quaternion $d - ia - jb - kc$ and divide by the positive scalar $d^2 + a^2 + b^2 + c^2$, because the quaternion $(d - ia - jb - kc)/(d^2 + a^2 + b^2 + c^2)$ is the reciprocal of the divisor $d + ia + jb + kc$.

The multiplication being non-commutative, there are two different products of two given quaternions Q_1 and Q_2. These two products $Q_1 Q_2$ and $Q_2 Q_1$ are different quaternions and their difference is a compound number of the type $ix + jy + kz$. The same holds for the division. One can divide a quaternion Q by another quaternion F from the right or from the left and the quotients are different quaternions. In the first case the quotient is $Q \cdot (1/F)$ while in the second case it is $(1/F) Q$ and these two products are different.

The most general rotation and stretching of a vector in the four-dimensional space can be performed by a quaternion multiplication. Therefore the general rotation and stretching in our familiar three-dimensional space are also represented with the aid of quaternion multiplication. Since a stretching of a vector $ia + jb + kc$ is achieved by multiplying the vector by a scalar (pure number) we mention here

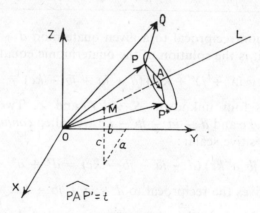

Fig. 6.28

only the use of quaternion multiplication to represent and perform an arbitrary rotation in our space. Suppose that the rotation-axis **OL** passes through the origin O, being defined by one of its points M, (fig. 6.28) whose distance from O is equal to 1, **OM** $= 1$, so that the coordinates of M are given and known numbers a, b and c. Having defined the rotation-axis **OL**, we complete the definition of a rotation around **OL** by prescribing the value t of the rotation-angle PAP*.

If now a given vector $ix + jy + kz$ is rotated around **OL** through the angle t, we denote its final position by $iX + jY + kZ$. The problem consists in finding a representation of $iX + jY + kZ$ in terms of the initial vector $ix + jy + kz$ and of the elements a, b, c, t of the rotation around OL which brings the initial vector $OP = ix + jy + kz$ in the terminal position $OP^* = iX + jY + kZ$. The solution is as follows:

$$iX + jY + kZ = [\cos (t/2) + (ia + jb + kc) \sin (t/2)] \times$$

$$\times (ix + jy + kz) [\cos (t/2) - (ia + jb + kc) \sin (t/2)] \qquad (42)$$

The coordinates X, Y, Z of the point P^* are computed performing the indicated quaternion multiplications and equating the coefficients of unit vectors i, j, k in both members. The last operation is a generalization of the principle of separation of real and imaginary since it separates the heterogeneous parts of a compound equation.

EXAMPLE: Consider the rotation of the unit vector i on OX axis through $t = 120°$ around the line OL which is equally inclined to all three coordinate axes. Any point on OL has its three coordinates equal and we take a point M on OL with coordinates $a = b = c = 1/\sqrt{3}$. Here $\sin (t/2) = \sqrt{3}/2$ and $\cos (t/2) = 1/2$, so that (42) becomes

$$iX + jY + kZ = (1 + i + j + k) i(1 - i - j - k)/4 = j$$

Thus, $X = 0$, $Y = 1$ and $Z = 0$: the rotation brings unit vector i on the OY axis and after the rotation it becomes j.

CHAPTER 7

Solution of Linear and Quadratic Equations

In Chapters 1–6 we have explored the evolution of the number concept from integer to complex number. In this chapter we will apply this concept to the study of numerical and algebraic equations with the purpose of solving them.

But first of all, what is an equation, and how is it obtained and formed? An equation is a particular kind of equality. It consists always of two members, that is of two expressions, separated by a sign of equality, $=$, and called lefthand and righthand members. For example

$$3(x - 3) = 7 - x; \quad x^2 + a^2 = 2a(2x - a) \tag{1}$$

An equation always involves two kinds of symbols: *known quantities* and the *unknown x*. The known quantities may be given in an explicit numerical form, as in the first equation, or they may be represented by letters other than the unknown's symbol x, as in the second equation.

The letters are used for known quantities when one needs to write down in a single general form and study a whole class of innumerable numerical equations having all the same structure and therefore solvable by the same process. Thus in $x^2 + a^2 = 2a(2x - a)$ the letter a represents any given, fixed and known quantity. Its particular numerical value can be chosen arbitrarily and therefore this *algebraic* equation is in fact an infinite set of *numerical* equations obtainable for different numerical values of the algebraic quantity a. For instance, if we choose $a = 1$, one equation of this set is $x^2 + 1 = 2(2x - 1)$. For $a = 5$ we obtain another equation of the same class $x^2 + 25 = 10(2x - 5)$, *etc.*

The letter x symbolizes a *variable quantity*: it must be considered as variable in every equation, given and known quantities involved in the equation being chosen once for all and fixed. When x varies, both members of the equation also vary, since they involve x, and in general they are not equal, so that the sign of equality does not hold. The problem of solving the equation consists in the choice, that is in the determination,

258

of such special, *exceptional* value—or values—of the variable x for which the equalization of both members is attained, both members receiving equal values. The sign of equality then holds and the equation becomes true.

These special values of x which satisfy the equation are called its *roots* or *solutions*. Thus the value $x = 4$ is the only root of the equation $3(x - 3) = 7 - x$ since, substituting in it the number 4 for x, we obtain an equality $3 = 3$, while for all other numerical values of x different from 4, $x \neq 4$, the two members of this equation have different values, and the equation is not justified.

Every equation becomes an equality if and only if one of its roots is substituted for the unknown x; but for the variable x, that is, in the general case of *any* x, an equation is not a symbol of equality of its two, in general unequal members.

Identities

There exist in algebra, however, permanent equalities which are true for any values of letters involved, the letter x included if it is used. Such are the equalities:

$$(x + a)^2 - 2ax \equiv x^2 + a^2 \tag{2}$$

$$x^3 - b^3 \equiv (x^2 + bx + b^2)(x - b) \tag{3}$$

These are not equations, and in them the symbol x has the same meaning as the letters a or b. In this case x does not denote an unknown. There is no unknown in an equality which is not an equation.

Such permanent equalities are called *identities*. An identity cannot be solved because in it the sign of equality remains true for all values of x and no special values of x can be singled out as "unknown".

An equation can be reduced to the form $0 = 0$ only if it is already solved and the solution, its root, is substituted in the equation for x. An identity can be transformed into the special equality $0 \equiv 0$ without ascribing particular values to the letters involved, the letter x included. Take for instance (2). Squaring out $(x + a)^2$, and substituting for it its expansion $x^2 + 2ax + a^2$, we have

$$x^2 + 2ax + a^2 - 2ax \equiv x^2 + a^2$$

Transporting $x^2 + a^2$ into the left member and grouping the six terms as follows

$$(x^2 - x^2) + (2ax - 2ax) + (a^2 - a^2) \equiv 0$$

we reduce (2) to the form $0 \equiv 0$, the reduction being valid for all possible values of quantities denoted by the letters x and a. The same is true for (3) since $x^2 + bx + b^2$ is a proper quotient in the division of $x^3 - b^3$ by $x - b$.

Here are some other useful algebraic identities:

$$x^n - a^n \equiv (x - a)(x^{n-1} + ax^{n-2} + a^2 x^{n-3} + \cdots + a^{n-2}x + a^{n-1})$$

$$x^{2n+1} + a^{2n+1} \equiv (x + a)(x^{2n} - ax^{2n-1} + a^2 x^{2n-2} \cdots - a^{2n-1}x + a^{2n})$$

$$(x + a)^3 \equiv x^3 + 3ax^2 + 3a^2 x + a^3$$

$$(x + a)^4 \equiv x^4 + 4ax^3 + 6a^2 x^2 + 4a^3 x + a^4$$

$$4xy \equiv (x + y)^2 - (x - y)^2.$$

In an identity there is no difference between the meanings of various letters involved: they all denote *arbitrary* numbers.

The sign of equality has in algebra a double meaning, when used between expressions involving letters. Its meaning in an identity is entirely different from the meaning it has in an equation. For this reason two different signs of equality are often used: the usual one, $=$, for equations and a special one, $\equiv$, for identities.

Linear Equations

Returning to the type of equality known as an equation and considering the equations of first order which involve the unknown x only in the first degree, let us begin with the geometrical facts which correspond to the solution of an equation of this type $mx + b = 0$, where the quantities m and b are considered as given and known.

We observe that the equation $mx + b = 0$ corresponds to the vanishing of y in the linear expression

$$y = mx + b \tag{4}$$

To solve the equation $mx + b = 0$ we transpose b to the right and divide both members of the new equation $mx = -b$ by m. Thus, a special value x_1 of x obtained, $x_1 = -b/m$, such that if substituted in $mx + b$ for x it makes the expression $mx + b$ vanish. We have indeed

$$mx_1 + b = m(-b/m) + b = -b + b = 0.$$

It is plain that $y = mx + b$ vanishes together with $mx + b$, if $x = x_1 = -b/m$, but if x is different from the special value $x_1 = -b/m$, y cannot vanish.

The equality (4) is an equation defining y in terms of m, b, and x. The quantities m and b are considered as fixed, while x is variable. A variation of x causes corresponding variation of y, and both x and y appear as variable numbers. Their values are not independent from each other and are related by a one-to-one correspondence, so that they can be grouped in pairs (x, y); if x is given and known, there can be one and only value of y, expressed by (4), which corresponds to it, and *vice versa*.

Suppose, indeed, that now it is y which is given and known. We can solve the relation (4) for x, since, if y is a known number, it becomes an equation for the unknown x. Writing (4) in such a case as $mx = y - b$ and dividing both members by m, we obtain the solution

$$x = (y - b)/m \qquad (5)$$

This result proves that x is determined, if y is given and known. Therefore, the variation of y carries with it the variation of x and *vice versa*.

A variable number such as x or y in our example (4) is called simply a *variable* which is an abbreviation for *variable quantity*. Mutual dependence such as (4) established between the two variables x and y, is called in mathematics a *functional relationship*. Each one of the two variables tied together by a functional relationship can be considered as determined by the other and, if considered as dependent upon the other, is called a *function* of the other. Thus the functional relationship expressed by (4) implies that y is a function of x as well as, conversely, that x is a function of y. The explicit expression of y as a function of x is given by (4), while the explicit expression (5) of x as a function of y was deduced from (4) by solving it with respect to the unknown x.

If one of two variables is considered as a function of the other, this other variable is called the *independent variable*. Thus in (4) y is a function of the independent variable x, while in (5) the independent variable is y and x is a function of y.

The functional dependence between two variables x and y can be expressed in two different ways. If x is chosen as the independent variable and y is considered as a function of x, the functional relationship is denoted by the symbol $y = F(x)$, where the letter F stands for the word function and the parentheses replace the word "of". The notation

$y = F(x)$ is read "y is a function of x". If, on the contrary, x is considered as a function of the independent variable y, we write $x = f(y)$, which is read "x is a function of y". If both notations correspond to the same functional relationship and $y = F(x)$, then also $x = f(y)$. We use different letters F and f to stress the fact that formulas [such as (4) and (5)] expressing x in terms of y and y in terms of x are different.

The idea of functional relationship stems from experience: the function concept represents the generalization of the concept of causal relation. In $y = F(x)$ the value of the independent variable x plays the role of cause, while the value of the function y appears as the effect of this cause, the choice of x fixing the value of y. Our mathematical concept however is a generalization of our experience because the causal relation is not reversible: the cause C of an effect E can never be considered inversely as the effect of the cause E. In other words, the causal relation $C \to E$ precludes the inverse relation $E \to C$ and in it the cause C and the effect E do not play symmetrical roles. Consider, for instance, two different phenomena: phenomenon A which consists in the rotation of the globe around its polar axis and phenomenon B—regular cyclic sequence of days and nights. It is true that A causes B but it would be wrong to say that the globe rotates *because* days and nights follow each other in their cyclic repetitions.

We have seen in the example (4) that in mathematics the functional relationship, which is a generalization of the causal relation in nature, is reversible since x is a function of y, if y is a function of x. Thus the mathematical expression of causal relation, being reversible, is much more flexible.

The geometric picture of a functional relationship is a *graph*, that is a curve such that the coordinates x and y of every one of its points satisfy the relation which establishes the functional relationship between x and y.

Let us study the graph of the function $y = mx + b$ (see fig. 1). Each pair (x, y) of corresponding values of two mutually dependent variables x and y is represented by a point $P(x, y)$ in the plane XOY in which x and y are Cartesian coordinates. If x and y were independent from each other (no algebraic relation binding their values), we would need all the points of the plane XOY to represent all the pairs (x, y) and no curve could be isolated. But the relation (4), $y = mx + b$, by the very fact of its existence, establishes a mutual dependence between the coordinates x and y of the point $P(x, y)$. Giving x different numerical values such as

$x_1 = 0$, $x_2 = 1$, *etc.* we find with the aid of (4) the corresponding values $y_1 = b$, $y_2 = m + b$ of y and therefore we can plot the points $P_1(O, b)$ and $P_2(1, m + b)$ with $OP_1 = b$, $OA = 1$. The segment OP_1 of the OY axis cut off by the straight line is called the *y-intercept*. Drawing a straight line P_1P_2 through the points P_1 and P_2, we choose any point $P(x, y)$ on this line and drop the perpendiculars $P_2A = y_2 = m + b$ and $PB = y$ to the OX axis from the points P_2 and P.

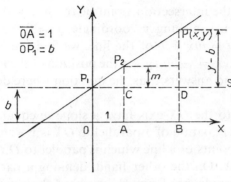

Fig. 7.1

A parallel P_1S to the OX axis through the point P_1 intersects AP_2 at C and BP at D. We compare now the two triangles P_1CP_2 and P_1DP. Since AP_2 and BP are parallel these triangles P_1CP_2 and P_1DP have equal angles. Therefore, they are similar and their corresponding sides are proportional:

$$P_1D/P_1C = DP/CP_2. \qquad (*)$$

On the other hand we have $P_1D = OB = x$, $P_1C = OA = 1$ as well as $DP = BP - BD = y - b$ and $CP_2 = AP_2 - AC = (m + b) - b = m$. Therefore, the proportion (*) can be written as a relation involving the fixed quantities m, b and the coordinates x, y of an arbitrary point $P(x, y)$ on the line P_1P_2: $x/1 = (y - b)/m$, which is another form of the equation (4) since the proportion gives $mx = y - b$ and thus $y = mx + b$.

The coordinates of points on the line P_1P_2 satisfy the equation $y = mx + b$ and this straight line is the graph of the function $y = mx + b$. The slope of this line is equal to $CP_2/P_1C = m$ and its y-intercept $OP_1 = b$. Thus, we have found the geometric meaning of the coefficients m, b in the equation $y = mx + b$ of a straight line.

Conversely, given a straight line we can measure its slope and its y-intercept which give the coefficients m and b. Knowing m and b, we can write the equation $y = mx + b$ of this line. Thus each straight line is characterized by an equation of the type $y = mx + b$. The coordinate axes OX and OY have the equations $y = 0$ and $x = 0$ respectively.

The problem of solving the linear equation $mx + b = 0$ may be interpreted as the following geometric problem: where does the straight line $y = mx + b$ meet the OX axis? Since the OX axis is characterized by the equation $y = 0$, the intersection point of the line $y = mx + b$ and of the OX axis has a vanishing y coordinate, $y = 0$. Substituting $y = 0$ in the equation $y = mx + b$ of the line, we find the equation $mx + b = 0$. The solution $x = -b/m$ gives the position of the intersection point on the OX axis and answers thus the question where does the line meet the OX axis.

Lines parallel to the OX axis have a slope m equal to zero, $m = 0$, and therefore the equation of a parallel to OX is $y = b$. It expresses the fact that all the points of a line which is parallel to OX are at the same distance from OX. On the other hand, defining a parallel to OX as a locus of points equidistant from OX we have the condition $|y| = $ constant, since by definition the distance from OX is equal to the absolute value of y. The condition $|y| = $ constant can be written in this case also as $y = $ constant, since a parallel does not cross the line to which it is parallel. All the points of a parallel to OX are on the same side of OX and therefore their coordinates y are all of the same sign. Denoting in $y = $ constant this constant by b we obtain finally $y = b$ as the equation of a parallel to OX. The same reasoning shows that the equation of a parallel to OY is $x = a$.

We saw that in geometry the solution of the equation $mx + b = 0$ corresponds to the location of the intersection point of the line $y = mx + b$ with the OX axis. But this holds only for the linear equations with *real* coefficients. If b or m or both are complex numbers, no straight line can correspond to the equation $y = mx + b$ as its graph. The y-intercept b and the slope m of a straight line must necessarily be *real* quantities. The equation with complex coefficients $m = m_1 + im_2$, $b = b_1 + ib_2$ admits of the same solution $x = -b/m$ as in the case of real coefficients, but this time to the complex root $x = -(b_1 + ib_2)/(m_1 + im_2)$ no point corresponds on the OX axis.

System of two Equations with two Unknowns

A linear equation with two unknown x and y involves three terms: a term with x, another with y, and a third term c which represents a given and known quantity. The terms x and y are products of two factors, the first of which is a known quantity called the *coefficient*, while the second is the unknown x or y. Denoting the coefficients of x and y by a and b respectively, we have the terms ax and by, so that the general form of a linear equation with two unknowns is as follows: $ax + by = c$.

The form $ax + by = c$ does not differ essentially from $y = mx + n$ and it can be reduced to this form. Dividing both terms of $ax + by = c$ by b, we write first $(a/b)x + y = c/b$. Denoting now the quotients (a/b) and (c/b) by $(-m)$ and n respectively, we have $-mx + y = n$, so that, transposing the term $-mx$ into the righthand member, we obtain finally $y = mx + n$, where $n = c/b$ is the y intercept and $m = a/b$ is the slope of the straight line represented by the equation $ax + by = c$.

Therefore, the general linear equation $ax + by = c$ in two variables x, y represents a straight line which can be plotted computing with the aid of coefficients a, b and constant term c of this equation the slope $m = -a/b$ and the y intercept $n = c/b$ of our straight line.

EXAMPLE: Draw two straight lines represented by the equations $x + 2y = 3$ and $4x - 3y = 5$. Dividing the first one by 2 and the second by -3, we write them as follows: $x/2 + y = 3/2$ and $(-4/3)x + y = -5/3$. Solving for y, we obtain the same equations in standard form: $y = (-1/2)x + 3/2$ and $y = (4/3)x - 5/3$. We can now plot our two straight lines since we know their slopes and y-intercepts: for the first line we have $m = -1/2$, $n = 3/2$, while for the second $m = 4/3$ and $n = 5/3$.

Denoting the slope and the intercept of the first line by m_1 and n_1, where the subscript 1 means "of the first line", and those of the second by m_2, n_2, we mark on the OY axis (fig. 2) the intercepts $OA_1 = n_1 = 3/2$ and $OA_2 = n_2 = -5/3$. To draw the lines it is sufficient to mark for each of them a second point. The second point is chosen on the parallel to OY whose equation is $x = 1$, which gives $y = y_1 = -1/2 + 3/2 = 1$ for the first and $y = y_2 = 4/3 - 5/3 = -1/3$ for the second line. Plotting now the points $B_1(1, 1)$ and $B_2(1, -1/3)$ and drawing A_1B_1, A_2B_2, we have our lines.

If only one equation with two unknowns x, y is given, we cannot uniquely determine the values of both x and y. A unique solution would mean that two fixed values $x = x_0$, $y = y_0$ exist, which satisfy the equation $ax + by = c$ and which are uniquely determined, that is, they are such that *no other* pair of two numbers (x, y) except the pair (x_0, y_0) justifies the sign of equality in our equation $ax + by = c$. But, to a pair (x_0, y_0) corresponds on the graph of our line one and only point P_0 whose coordinates are precisely these two numbers x_0, y_0. And we know that the equation $ax + by = c$ is satisfied by the co-ordinates x, y of *all* points on our line since this line is the graph of the equation. Therefore, one equation with two unknowns cannot have a unique solution.

To find a unique solution for two unknowns x and y, that is to find a *fixed determined* point $P(x_0, y_0)$ on our line $ax + by = c$ we must introduce another straight line which intersects the first in one deter-mined point only. In other words, and using the language of algebra,

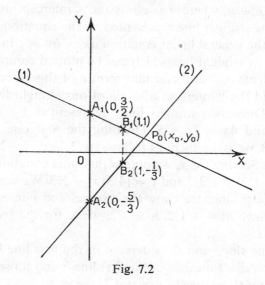

Fig. 7.2

we must consider *two* linear equations with *two* unknowns to have the right to speak about and look for a *unique* solution.

To distinguish our two linear equations we will use subscripts 1 and 2. Thus, instead of speaking about the coefficients of the first and second equations we shall denote the coefficients a, b and the constant term c of the first equation by a_1, b_1, c_1, and those of the second equation by a_2, b_2, c_2.

We study now how to solve a given system (S) of two linear equations with two unknowns x, y

$$a_1 x + b_1 y = c_1; \qquad a_2 x + b_2 y = c_2 \qquad \text{(S)}$$

Transforming these into the standard form $y = mx + n$, we obtain, as we know already, the equivalent system

$$y = (-a_1/b_1)\, x + c_1/b_1; \qquad y = (-a_2/b_2)\, x + c_2/b_2 \qquad \text{(S*)}$$

The solution of the system (S*) must ascribe to the variable y the same value $y = y_0$ in both equations (S*). Therefore to find it we can equalize the two expressions of y given by the two equations (S*) which gives a single equation with only one unknown x, the unknown y being eliminated:

$$(-a_1/b_1)\, x + c_1/b_1 = (-a_2/b_2)\, x + c_2/b_2$$

We can now solve this equation, for it contains only one unknown, and its solution will yield us the value of the unknown x. To do this we get rid of the denominators b_1, b_2 by multiplying all the terms by the product $b_1 b_2$. Thus, we obtain first

and finally
$$(-a_1 b_2)\, x + c_1 b_2 = (-a_2 b_1)\, x + c_2 b_1$$
$$x = x_0 = (c_1 b_2 - c_2 b_1)/(a_1 b_2 - a_2 b_1).$$

We have therefore obtained the explicit expression of the value x_0 of the unknown x in terms of six quantities $a_1, a_2, b_1, b_2, c_1, c_2$ which are given as data in our system (S). It remains to find the similar expression for y. This can be done by substituting x_0 for x in the first or the second of our equations in (S) or (S*). Using, for instance, the first equation in (S*), we prepare for this substitution by multiplying the equation $y = (-a_1/b_1)\, x + c_1/b_1$ by the denominator $(a_1 b_2 - a_2/b_1)$ of the expression of x_0. This will facilitate the substitution, since the product $x_0(a_1 b_2 - a_2 b_1)$ is equal to the difference $c_1 b_2 - c_2 b_1$:

$$y(a_1 b_2 - a_2 b_1) = (-a_1/b_1)\, x_0(a_1 b_2 - a_2 b_1) + c_1(a_1 b_2 - a_2 b_1)/b_1$$

Multiplying by b_1 to get rid of the denominator and substituting for x_0, we get

$$b_1 y(a_1 b_2 - a_2 b_1) = (-a_1)(c_1 b_2 - c_2 b_1) + c_1(a_1 b_2 - a_2 b_1)$$

Computing the righthand member, we obtain

$$b_1 y(a_1 b_2 - a_2 b_1) = -a_1 c_1 b_2 + a_1 c_2 b_1 + c_1 a_1 b_2 - c_1 a_2 b_1$$
$$= b_1(a_1 c_2 - a_2 c_1)$$

Dividing both members by their common factor b_1, we obtain for the value y_0 of y the equation

$$y(a_1b_2 - a_2b_1) = a_1c_2 - a_2c_1.$$

Dividing this last relation by the coefficient $(a_1b_2 - a_2b_1)$ of y we have y_0, so that the solution of the system (S) is as follows:

$$x = x_0 = (c_1b_2 - c_2b_1)/(a_1b_2 - a_2b_1);$$
$$y = y_0 = (a_1c_2 - a_2c_1)/(a_1b_2 - a_2b_1).$$

This solution of the system (S) has a simple geometric interpretation: the two straight lines represented by the equations (S) intersect each other in a single point P_0 (see fig. 2), whose coordinates are precisely x_0, y_0.

The numbers x_0, y_0 satisfy indeed both equations (S), that is, the signs of equality in (S) hold only when $x = x_0$ and $y = y_0$:

$$a_1x_0 + b_1y_0 = c_1; \quad a_2x_0 + b_2y_0 = c_2.$$

Therefore the point $P(x_0, y_0)$ belongs at the same time to both straight lines and is their intersection point.

EXAMPLE: Find the intersection point of two straight lines defined by the equations $4x - 3y = 5$ and $x + 2y = 3$. In this example $a_1 = 4$, $b_1 = -3$, $c_1 = 5$, $a_2 = 1$, $b_2 = 2$ and $c_2 = 3$. Therefore, $a_1b_2 - a_2b_1 = 8 - (-3) = 11$, $c_1b_2 - c_2b_1 = 10 - (-9) = 19$, and $a_1c_2 - a_2c_1 = 12 - 5 = 7$. Applying (6), we obtain the coordinates x_0, y_0 of the intersection point: $x_0 = 19/11$ and $y_0 = 7/11$. To check this solution of the system $4x - 3y = 5$, $x + 2y = 3$ we substitute it in the equations and as result find that the signs of equality are satisfied:

$$(4 \cdot 19 - 3 \cdot 7)/11 = 55/11 = 5; \quad (19 + 2 \cdot 7)/11 = 33/11 = 3.$$

The solution (6) presupposes that the denominator $a_1b_2 - a_2b_1$ does not vanish since the division by zero has no meaning. But what can be said about the system (S) in the exceptional case when $a_1b_2 - a_2b_1 = 0$?

In this case the four constants a_1, a_2, b_1, b_2 satisfy the proportion $a_2/a_1 = b_2/b_1$ and, denoting the common value of these two ratios by r, we can express a_2, b_2 as follows: $a_2 = a_1r$, $b_2 = b_1r$. Therefore, in the case when the formulae (6) do not hold, the second equation becomes $(a_1x + b_1y) r = c_2$ and the system (S) is equivalent to the following system:

$$a_1x + b_1y = c_1; \quad a_1x + b_1y = c_2/r \qquad (r \neq 0) \text{ (S')}$$

We state that in this system, the slope of two lines represented by the equations of this system is *the same*, namely $-a_1/b_1$, so that the lines are parallel unless they coincide. In general two numbers c_1 and c_2/r are unequal and therefore the lines do not coincide, but if $c_1 = c_2/r$ they do and we have then in fact only one equation with two unknowns, instead of a system of two equation. It is plain that in such a case the unique solution $x = x_0$, $y = y_0$ does not exist since *all* the points of an infinite straight line satisfy the equation $a_1 x + b_1 y = c_1$.

Eliminating this singular case, we assume that c_2/r is not equal to c_1 so that in (S′) we have a system of two distinct equations represented by two parallel lines. The question of existence of a unique solution depends on the definition of what is to be considered as a solution. If, by definition, only *finite* values x_0, y_0 of x and y can form a solution (x_0, y_0) of the system (S′), then evidently we must state that this system has no solution at all, since the expression $a_1 x_0 + b_1 y_0$ for no pair of finite numbers x_0, y_0 can have two different values c_1 and $c_2/r \neq c_1$. In other words, the two equations of the system (S′) appear to us as incompatible and contradictory. In geometrical language the same fact is stated as follows: two parallel lines do not meet and have no point in common. Euclid's definition of two parallel lines states indeed that two lines which do not meet are said to be parallel.

On the other hand, modern geometry introduces a new element, the so-called "point at infinity", and in it two parallel lines *do have* a point in common but it is relegated to infinity. Thus, two parallel lines meet as do two intersecting lines, the difference between these two cases being in the *location* of the common point *with respect to the observer*: if the common point of two lines is at a *finite* distance from the observer the lines appear to him as intersecting each other, if the common point is at an *infinite* distance from the observer it becomes for him a "point at infinity" and the two lines appear to the observer as parallel to each other.

Translating this modern geometric point of view into the algebraic language we assume by definition that a pair of infinite values x_∞ and y_∞ for our two unknowns x, y can also be considered as forming a solution of the system (S′). The infinite values x_∞ and y_∞ cannot be independent from each other since they are coordinates of the point at infinity in a perfectly determined direction.

This point at infinity, common to both lines $a_1 x + b_1 y = c_1$ and

$a_2x + b_2y = c_2$, where $a_2/a_1 = b_2/b_1 \neq c_2/c_1$, lies in the direction to which these lines are parallel, so that it belongs also to the straight line $a_1x + b_1y = 0$ passing through the origin and having the same slope $m = -a_1/b_1$ as our two lines in the system (S'). The equation of this third parallel can be written also as follows: $y/x = -a_1/b_1$ and thus, at the limit when both x and y become infinite, $\lim_{x=\infty} (y/x) = m = -a_1/b_1$.

This explains the compatibility of two equations in the system (S') for infinite values x_∞ and y_∞ of x and y: dividing both equations by x and passing to the limit for x equal infinity, we obtain first

$$a_1 + b_1(y/x) = c_1/x; \quad a_1 + b_1(y/x) = c_2/rx$$

which at the limit gives the same result, namely $a_1 + b_1m = 0$.

In other words, when both x and y become infinite both terms, a_1x and b_1y, of the lefthand member are also infinite in magnitude. Therefore, the finite righthand terms c_1 and c_2/r, when compared to the infinite terms in the lefthand members, are actually completely negligible. They are equivalent to zero in this new scale of magnitude to which belong the terms a_1x_∞ and b_1y_∞, so that the finite difference between them vanishes and both equations of the system are satisfied at the same time.

We observe that the assumption of the existence of a point at infinity common to all straight lines parallel to a given direction is one of examples of the use of the concept of absolute infinity in mathematics. Both concepts, point at infinity and unique solution of the system (S'), are thus based on the concept of absolute infinity and have no meaning if the existence of absolute infinity is denied.

We consider now a system of three linear equations with two unknowns x and y where the number of equations (three) exceeds the number (two) of unknowns:

$$a_1x + b_1y = c_1; \quad a_2x + b_2y = c_2; \quad a_3x + b_3y = c_3. \tag{7}$$

In general such a system has no solution: if it had one, $x = x_0$ and $y = y_0$, its substitution in the equations (7) would satisfy the three equations and this would mean that the point $P(x_0, y_0)$ belongs to each of the three lines (7) which is a very particular case. The nine coefficients and constant terms $a_1, \ldots c_3$, are in general any numbers, that is, the three lines (7) are arbitrary straight lines. But three lines in general are not concurrent. They intersect in *three* points and form a triangle (see fig. 3).

The intersection point A of two lines L_1 and L_2, represented by the first and the second of equations (7), does not belong to the third line L_3 and therefore the solution (6) of these two equations does not satisfy the third equation: substituting the expressions x_0, y_0 given by (6) for x and y in the equation $a_3x + b_3y = c_3$, we find that $a_3x_0 + b_3y_0$ is not equal to c_3. In the same way the solution of the second and third equations in (7) cannot satisfy the first equation because the point B, intersection point of the lines L_2 and L_3, is not on the line L_1. Finally, point C being outside of the line L_2, the solution of the first and third equations does not justify the sign of equality in the second equation. We express these facts in the following statement: in general, a system of three linear equations with two unknown is incompatible.

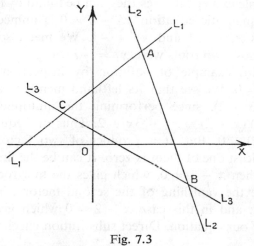

Fig. 7.3

There are special and exceptional systems (7), which correspond to three *concurrent* straight lines, that is, lines passing through the same point. Such exceptional systems have a solution $x = x_0$, $y = y_0$, where x_0, y_0 are the coordinates of the common point. In such a case the nine given and known quantities a_m, b_m, c_m with $m = 1, 2, 3$ cannot be chosen freely: the must verify the condition

$$(a_1b_2 - a_2b_1) c_3 + (a_2b_3 - a_3b_2) c_1 + (a_3b_1 - a_1b_3) c_2 = 0$$

which expresses precisely the fact that the three lines (7) are concurrent.

Quadratic Equations

We recall that a quadratic equation involves three terms. The first term ax^2 which determines that the equation is quadratic is a product of the square x^2 of the unknown x and of the coefficient a which in general is a complex number. The second and the third terms bx and c contain two more coefficients b, c which in general are also complex numbers. The general form of a quadratic equation

$$ax^2 + bx + c = 0 \qquad (8)$$

becomes an equality and is satisfied only when x takes two special numerical values $x = x_1$ and $x = x_2$ which are called *roots* or solutions of (8). The problem of solution consists in the computation of these two numbers x_1, x_2.

In some simple numerical cases they can be found by inspection. For example, the quadratic equation $x^2 - 1 = 0$ is immediately seen to have the roots $x_1 = +1$ and $x_2 = -1$. We met also the equation $x^2 + 1 = 0$ whose two roots were $x_1 = +i$ and $x_2 = -i$. Let us consider as a third example of solution by inspection the equation $x^2 - 3x + 2 = 0$. We see that its lefthand member can be factored into $(x - 1)(x - 2)$, since performing the multiplication we find indeed $(x - 1)(x - 2) \equiv x^2 - 3x + 2$. Thus our equation becomes $(x - 1)(x - 2) = 0$. But, if a product of two factors vanishes, it means that at least one of them is zero. It can be the first factor which vanishes and then $x - 1 = 0$, which gives the first root $x_1 = 1$. But it may also be the vanishing of the second factor which makes the product vanish and in this case $x - 2 = 0$ which gives the second root $x_2 = 2$ of our equation. Direct substitution checks our result:

$$x_1^2 - 3x_1 + 2 = 1 - 3 \cdot 1 + 2 = 0, \text{ as well as}$$

$$x_2^2 - 3x_2 + 2 = 2^2 - 3 \cdot 2 + 2 = 0$$

In this last example we have a hint: if a quadratic equation can be written in the form of a product of two linear factors involving x in the first power only, its solution becomes very easy, since it is reduced to the solution of two linear equations obtained by equating to zero each of the linear factors separately. It is the factoring of the lefthand member $ax^2 + bx + c$ of the quadratic equation which is difficult. Factoring by inspection is possible only in exceptional cases.

Instead of studying the factoring of every particular quadratic equation with given numerical coefficients, we can perform the factoring of the general equation (8) once for all. The purpose of this factoring is to find general expressions for the two roots x_1, x_2 of the equation (8) in terms of the three coefficients a, b, and c without specifying their numerical values. The general expressions thus obtained will give the numerical values of x_1, x_2 in each particular case when, a particular equation being given, the three coefficients a, b, and c are known numbers. Before describing the algebraic process leading to the solution of (8), we shall study the geometric facts related to the quadratic equation and its solution. In the quadratic polynomial $ax^2 + bx + c$, considered in itself, without any relation to the equation (8), the variable x can take any value from $-\infty$ to $+\infty$. We denote the value of the polynomial by y:

$$y = ax^2 + bx + c \tag{9}$$

It is plain that y depends on the choice of the coefficients a, b, c. But if we fix their value, choosing once for all a particular polynomial $ax^2 + bx + c$, then the number y depends only upon the value of the independent variable x: y varies when x changes its value and therefore y is a function of x. The relation (9) establishes between the two variables x and y a functional relationship.

Although in the general case a, b, c, and x can take complex values, so that y can also be a complex number, we begin by studying the so-called *real case* where the coefficients a, b, and c are given *real* numbers. Giving to the variable x in (9) real values too, we obtain real values for y, and thus we are able to represent in this particular case the quadratic function y of the real variable x by a graph, using the system of coordinates x, y in the plane XOY.

The graph of the linear function $y = mx + b$ is a straight line and, as such, it has only one intersection point with the OX axis $y = 0$. We have seen that to this geometric fact corresponds in algebra the uniqueness of the solution of a linear equation $mx + b = 0$.

The graph of the quadratic function $y = ax^2 + bx + c$ is a curve called a *parabola*. We study the shape of this curve and its intersection points with OX axis, since, the equation of the OX axis being $y = 0$, these intersection points corresponds to the vanishing of the variable y. Therefore, the solutions of a quadratic equation $ax^2 + bx + c = 0$ determine the intersection points of the parabola (9) with the OX axis $y = 0$.

Kogbetliantz 18

We cannot plot a curve point-by-point without knowing the numerical values of both coordinates of its points. For the independent variable x we can arbitrarily choose different numerical values but the computation of the corresponding values of y as defined by (9) is possible only when we have a particular numerical case with known numerical values of a, b, and c.

Let us therefore consider first three particular quadratic polynomials:

$$y = x^2 - 4x + c \qquad\qquad (c = 3, 4, 5)$$

with $a = 1$, $b = -4$, and $c = 3$ or 4 or 5. Since $x^2 - 4x \equiv x^2 - 4x + 4 - 4 \equiv (x - 2)^2 - 4$, we can rewrite this polynomial as

$$y = (x - 2)^2 + c - 4.$$

Its first term $(x - 2)^2$ is positive or zero. It is variable since it involves the variable x and, being positive, it reaches its minimum value when it vanishes. Using as usual the abbreviation "minimum" instead of "minimum value", we can say that the minimum of the first term $(x - 2)^2$ is zero. This minimum is reached when $x - 2 = 0$, that is for $x = 2$. The second term, $c - 4$, is a constant and therefore the whole polynomial y reaches its minimum for $x = 2$. The minimum of y equals $c - 4$ so that the inequality

$$y = x^2 - 4x + c \geqslant c - 4$$

holds for any x.

Case $c = 3$: We give now to c the value $c = 3$, so that $c - 4 = -1$ and the inequality becomes: $y \geqslant -1$ with min $y = -1$. Geometrically speaking this inequality $y \geqslant -1$ says that all the points of the parabola $y = x^2 - 4x + 3$ are *above* the straight line $y = -1$ which is parallel to the OX axis and lies below it at a distance of one unit (see fig. 4), except the point which corresponds to the minimum of y since min $y = -1$. This minimum being reached for $x = 2$, the lowest point of the parabola called its *vertex* is the point $P(2, -1)$ with coordinates $x = 2$, $y = -1$.

The vertex is thus seen to be below the OX axis. On the other hand, when x takes very large values, positive or negative ones, the square $(x - 2)^2$ of the large number $|x - 2|$ is also very large and always positive. Thus, the y coordinate of a point $P(x, y)$ of the parabola which is far to the right (positive and large x) or to the left of the origin (large in absolute value and negative x) is positive and very large: when the absolute value of x, $|x|$, increases, y increases and tends towards $+\infty$. In other words, our curve has two infinite branches in the right and left upper corners of the plane XOY. This geometric structure of

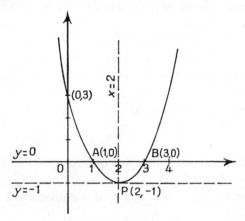

Fig. 7.4

the parabola proves that it crosses the OX axis in two points one of which is to the right and the other to the left of the vertex. To plot the curve we can tabulate the values of the function y, giving to the independent variable x for instance integral values symmetrical with respect to the value $x = 2$:

Table of values of the polynomial

$$y = x^2 - 4x + 3 = (x - 2)^2 - 1$$

Lefthand branch		Righthand branch	
x	y	x	y
2	−1	2	−1
1	0	3	0
0	3	4	3
−1	8	5	8
−2	15	6	15
−3	24	7	24
−4	35	8	35
−5	48	9	48

It becomes clear that the function y tends to $+\infty$ when x approaches $+\infty$ or $-\infty$. This occurs because the variable and positive term $(x - 2)^2$ becomes infinite, if $|x| \to \infty$. The curve is symmetrical with respect to the vertical line $x = 2$. The graph of y crosses the OX axis $(y = 0)$ at the two points $A(1, 0)$ and $B(3, 0)$ for

$$x = x_1 = 1 \text{ and } x = x_2 = 3.$$

The two values of x corresponding to the intersection points A, B of the graph with the OX axis are roots of the quadratic equation $x^2 - 4x + 3 = 0$. They can be found algebraically as follows: we write the equation as a difference of two squares:

$$x^2 - 4x + 3 = (x - 2)^2 - 1^2 = [(x - 2) + 1] \, [(x - 2) - 1] = 0,$$

where we have factored the difference of two squares using the formula $A^2 - B^2 \equiv (A + B)(A - B)$.

Thus, the equation $x^2 - 4x + 3 = 0$ is equivalent to

$$(x - 1)(x - 3) = 0.$$

Equating to zero each of the factors, we obtain the two roots.

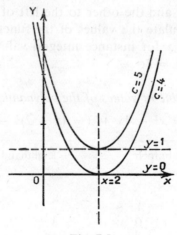

Fig. 7.5

Case $c = 4$: If $c = 4$, we have the equation $x^2 - 4x + 4 = (x - 2)^2 = 0$ which can be verified only when $x = 2$. The graph of the function $y = (x - 2)^2$ is the same parabola as in the case $c = 3$, but it is shifted upwards one unit since increasing c by one we also increase, for any given value of x, the coordinate y by one. This time (see fig. 5) the vertex of the parabola is on the OX axis, the parabola being tangent to the OX axis at this point $x = 2$, $y = 0$, so that all its points other than the vertex are above OX axis. Again, the point $P(2, 0)$ common to the OX axis and the graph of the equation corresponds to the root $x = 2$ of this equation.

In this special case when the vertex of the parabola is on the OX axis, the root $x = 2$ is called *double* root. From the geometrical point of view this terminology is justified if we consider the position occupied by the parabola for $c = 4$ as reached by moving the same parabola for $c = 3$ one unit upwards. We saw that if $c = 3$ two intersection points $A(1, 0)$ and $B(3, 0)$ exist on the OX axis. As the vertex of this parabola moves up along the line $x = 2$ from the point $(x = 2, y = -1)$ to the point $(x = 2, y = 0)$, c increasing from 3 to 4, these two points on OX come closer and closer together until finally they coalesce in the point $P(x = 2, y = 0)$, this point thus becoming a limit point of the two intersection points of the parabola and the OX axis.

From the algebraic point of view, the root $x = 2$ may be seen to be a double root since the equation $(x - 2)^2 = 0$ can be factored into the product $(x - 2)(x - 2) = 0$. If it is the first factor which equals zero, then $x - 2 = 0$ and $x_1 = 2$. If the second factor equals zero, then $x - 2 = 0$ again and $x_2 = 2$, so that both roots x_1 and x_2 are equal. Two equal roots of an equation are said to form a *double* root of this equation if no other root is equal to them.

A double real root corresponds to the point on the OX axis where the graph of the function y represented by the righthand member of the equation is tangent to the axis.

Case $c = 5$: The most interesting is the third case $c = 5$. Let us solve the corresponding equation $x^2 - 4x + 5 = 0$. Replacing again $x^2 - 4x + 4$ by the square $(x - 2)^2$, we rewrite it as follows:

$$x^2 - 4x + 5 = (x - 2)^2 + 1^2 = [(x - 2) + i][(x - 2) - i] = 0,$$

factoring the sum of two squares.

If the first factor vanishes, we obtain the first root $x_1 = 2 - i$ of the equation $x^2 - 4x + 5 = 0$. If it is the second factor which is zero, the second root $x_2 = 2 + i$ is obtained. Two complex roots are obtained because the lefthand member of the quadratic equation is represented by a *sum* of two squares rather than a difference of two squares as the case was for $c = 3$, when we obtained two real and distinct roots.

A complex value of x cannot be interpreted as a coordinate of a point in the plane XOY. Therefore we conclude that in the case $c = 5$ there are no points on the graph of the function $y = x^2 - 4x + 5$ which correspond to two roots of the equation $x^2 - 4x + 5 = 0$. We know that in general such points must lie on the OX axis since this equation is obtained from $y = x^2 - 4x + 5$ for $y = 0$. Thus, from the fact that the roots are complex numbers we conclude that the graph does not intersect the OX axis for $c = 5$.

This conslusion checks with the geometrical picture: the graph of the function $y = x^2 - 4x + 5$ is obtained from the graph of the function $y = x^2 - 4x + 4$ by moving it upwards one unit (see fig. 5). Therefore, its vertex is above the OX axis and the graph cannot intersect the axis and cannot have points in common with it.

This example shows that if we are trying to determine the existence of real roots of an equation, we need only to plot its graph. Thus, first plotting the graph of $x^2 - 4x + 5$ we could say immediately that the equation cannot have a *real* root because its graph does not intersect the OX axis.

Thus, the solutions of $x^2 - 4x + c = 0$ obtained in the three cases $c = 3, 4, 5$ belong to three different kinds: if $c = 3$, there are two real and distinct roots; if $c = 4$, the two real roots are equal and they form a double root; if $c = 5$, there are no real roots, but two conjugate complex roots are obtained.

We see now that the introduction of complex numbers allows us to formulate a very simple and general conclusion: *a quadratic equation always has two roots*. This is justified in our example of the equation $x^2 - 4x + c = 0$ for all values of c, since increasing c we move the parabola upwards and therefore, for $c > 5$ the parabola is entirely above OX and the roots remain complex, while for $c < 3$ its vertex is below OX and two real roots always correspond to the two intersection points with OX. The geometric figure indicates that these inequalities $c > 5$ and $c < 3$ can be replaced by $c > 4$, $c < 4$ without modifying the conclusions about the relative location of the parabola with respect to OX.

Let us now deduce the same conclusions about the nature of the roots of the equation $x^2 - 4x + c = 0$ by solving it for any c that is without specifying the numerical value of the coefficient c. The expressions of the two roots will necessarily involve the symbol c. We obtain again by factoring the lefthand member:

$$x^2 - 4x + c = (x^2 - 4x + 4) - (4 - c) = (x - 2)^2 - [(4 - c)^{1/2}]^2$$

$$= [x - 2 + \sqrt{4 - c}][x - 2 - \sqrt{4 - c}].$$

Therefore, the equation $x^2 - 4x + c = 0$ is equivalent to

$$[x - 2 + \sqrt{4 - c}][x - 2 - \sqrt{4 - c}] = 0$$

and its two roots may be obtained by splitting the product which is equal to zero into two linear equations:

$$x - 2 + \sqrt{4 - c} = 0; \quad x - 2 - \sqrt{4 - c} = 0.$$

The roots we obtain are: $x_1 = 2 - \sqrt{4 - c}$ and $x_2 = 2 + \sqrt{4 - c}$ The square root $\sqrt{4 - c}$ involved in these expressions has a value that is real only when the radicand, that is the expression $4 - c$ under the radical sign, is positive. Thus for $4 - c > 0$, that is if $c < 4$, the roots are real and distinct, since the square root does not vanish. If it vanishes, which happens for $c = 4$, both roots become equal to the same number 2 and we have the case of a double root. Finally, when c increasing further becomes greater than 4, the square root acquires a purely imaginary value since

$$\sqrt{4 - c} = \sqrt{-(c - 4)} = i\sqrt{c - 4} \quad (c > 4)$$

and for $c > 4$ the equation has two conjugate complex roots.

We have seen that a vertical displacement of the graph corresponds to a variation of the coefficient c. When c increases the parabola moves upwards and the two real intersection points, located on the OX axis symmetrically with respect to the point $x = 2$ (image of the double root) approach the point $x = 2$ when c approaches 4. This character of symmetry of the two real roots with respect to the double root persists also for c greater than 4 and is expressed in the fact that the two complex roots are *conjugate* complex numbers.

Here we meet with a general feature characterizing all algebraic equations of any order with *real* coefficients: if a complex value of x, $x = u + iv$, verifies an algebraic equation of any order with real coefficients $a_0, a_1, a_2, \ldots, a_n$

$$a_0x^n + a_1x^{n-1} + \cdots + a_{n-1}x + a_n = 0 \qquad (10)$$

then the conjugate complex number $u - iv$ verifies it, too.

To prove this statement we observe that by hypothesis the substitution of $u + iv$ for x in the lefthand member of (10) gives zero. Let us denote the result of this substitution, which is also a complex number, by $U + iV$:

$$a_0(u + iv)^n + a_1(u + iv)^{n-1} + \cdots + a_{n-1}(u + iv) + a_n = U + iV$$

Changing in this relation the sign of i, that is, replacing i by $-i$, we obtain

$$a_0(u - iv)^n + a_1(u - iv)^{n-1} + \cdots + a_{-n1}(u - iv) + a_n = U - iV$$

and this change of sign dies not destroy the equality sign because the fact that two complex numbers $M + iN$ and $P + iQ$ are equal, $M + iN = P + iQ$ implies the equality of their conjugates $M - iN$ and $P - iQ$. We have indeed $M = N$, $P = Q$ as a result of the equality $M + iN = P + iQ$, so that $M - iN = P - iQ$ necessarily.

But, $U + iV = 0$ and this is equivalent to $U = 0$ and $V = 0$, so that $U - iV = 0$ too. Therefore the result of substituting $u - iv$ for x in (10) is zero since its value is $U - iV$ and $U - iV = 0$. Thus if $u + iv$ is a root of the equation (10) then $u - iv$ must also be a root, and our assertion is proved.

This proof fails if the coefficients $a_0, a_1, \ldots, a_n$ are not real but complex numbers because in this general case the sign of the symbol i in the expressions of the coefficients does not change when we replace $u + iv$ by $u - iv$ and the results of the two substitutions no longer give two conjugate complex numbers.

The complex roots of equations with *real* coefficients always occur in pairs of conjugate complex numbers and their number is therefore always even. For instance, a cubic equation whose coefficients are real can have two complex roots and a real root or no complex roots at all, the three roots being real numbers. A quantic equation (equation of fourth degree involving terms with powers of x not exceeding the fourth power x^4) can have four or two or no complex roots.

Here are some examples which illustrate that nothing can be said about the number of complex roots, if the coefficients of an equation are complex numbers. The linear equation $x - 1 + i = 0$ has one complex root $x = 1 - i$ and no other root. The conjugate number $1 + i$ does not verify this equation because the result of the substitution of this number, $1 + i - 1 + i = 2i$, is not zero. The quadratic equation $x^2 + x + 1 - i = 0$ has two complex roots $x_1 = i$ and $x_2 = -i - 1$, but they are not a pair of conjugate complex numbers. Another quadratic equation $x^2 - (2 + i)x + 1 + i = 0$ has only one complex root $x_1 = 1 + i$, the other root $x_2 = 1$ being real.

We have studied the quadratic equation $ax^2 + bx + c = 0$ with $a = 1$ and $b = -4$, the minus sign before the term $-4x$ being included in the coefficient b because in the general form $ax^2 + bx = 0$ a *sum* of the three terms is considered and thus $x^2 - 4x + c = 0$ must be read as $1x^2 + (-4)x + c = 0$. If the first coefficient a were minus one instead of plus one, the parabolic graph of the function $y = ax^2 + bx + c$ would turn its concavity downward, and this is true for any negative a.

The reason for this fact is the predominance of the first term ax^2 for large values of x. Dividing and multiplying each term of the quadratic polynomial y by ax^2, we rewrite its expression as follows:

$$y = ax^2 + bx + c \equiv ax^2 + ax^2(bx/ax^2) + ax^2(c/ax^2)$$

$$\equiv ax^2[1 + b/(ax) + c/(ax^2)].$$

Increasing now the absolute value of x we decrease the values of the two terms $b/(ax)$ and $c/(ax)^2$ since their denominators increase with x. Both fractions approach zero when $|x|$ increases without limit, and therefore their values can be made as small as we want by choosing sufficiently large values for $|x|$. Thus the value of the second factor in the expression of y, namely the value of $1 + b/(ax) + c/(ax^2)$ becomes and remains positive for large positive or negative values of x, because the sum of the last two terms becomes less than one in absolute value. Therefore the sign of $y = ax^2[1 + b/(ax) + c/(ax^2)]$ for large values of $|x|$ is that of the first coefficient a, because x^2 and the expressions in the brackets are positive numbers, so that y approaches $+\infty$ with $|x| \to \infty$, if a is positive, but y approaches $-\infty$ with $|x| \to \infty$, if a is negative. In geometric language this means that the infinite branches of parabola are directed upward, if $a > 0$, while they are directed downward, if $a < 0$. The sense of concavity being the same as the direction of the two infinite branches of parabola, our assertion is justified. In other words, the vertex of the parabola which opens upward corresponds to a *minimum* of $y = ax^2 + bx + c$ with $a > 0$, while it corresponds to a *maximum* of y when $a < 0$ and the parabola opens downward (see fig. 6).

To take an example let us consider the equation $-x^2 + 4x - c = 0$ and the graph of the corresponding function $y = -x^2 + 4x - c$ for three different values $c = 3, 4, 5$. Comparing the function y with the function $Y = x^2 - 4x + c$ whose graphs are represented on figs. 4

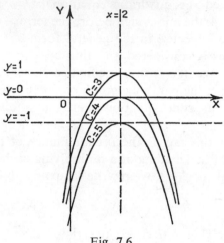

Fig. 7.6

and 5 we state that $y = -Y$, so that is sufficient to change the sign of y in those figures to obtain the graphs of our function $y = -x^2 + 4x - c$. But a change of sign of the coordinate y, when the sign of x does not change, is a reflection of the figure in the OX axis, so that the new figure is symmetrical to the original figure with respect to OX. The parabolas in fig. 6 thus obtained show clearly that their vertices correspond to maxima of y, the concavity being directed downward.

General Equation

Having studied a few particular cases, we pass now to the general quadratic equation $ax^2 + bx + c = 0$, where, to consider the most general case, the three coefficients are any fixed complex numbers a, b, c. The solution of

$$ax^2 + bx + c = 0 \qquad (11)$$

is also based on the factoring of the difference of two squares. To rewrite (11) in the form $A^2 - B^2 = 0$, where the expression A involves the unknown x and B does not, we first multiply (11) by $4a$:

$$4a^2x^2 + 4abx + 4ac = 0$$

and replace $4a^2x^2$ and $4abx$ by $(2ax)^2$ and $2b(2ax)$ respectively:

$$(2ax)^2 + 2(2ax)\,b + 4ac = 0.$$

The sum $(2ax)^2 + 2(2ax)\,b$ represents the first two terms in the expansion of the square $(2ax + b)^2$:

$$(2ax + b)^2 \equiv (2ax)^2 + 2(2ax)\,b + b^2.$$

Transposing b^2 and reading from the right to the left we obtain

$$(2ax)^2 + 2(2ax)\,b \equiv (2ax + b)^2 - b^2.$$

By substitution the equation (11) now takes the form

$$(2ax + b)^2 - b^2 + 4ac = 0.$$

The constant term $-b^2 + 4ac$ can be written as follows:

$$-b^2 + 4ac = -(b^2 - 4ac) = -[(b^2 - 4ac)^{1/2}]^2,$$

so that equation (11) becomes a difference of two squares

$$(2ax + b)^2 - [(b^2 - 4ac)^{1/2}]^2 = 0. \tag{12}$$

Applying the identity $A^2 - B^2 \equiv (A - B)(A + B)$ with $A = 2ax + b$, $B = (b^2 - 4ac)^{1/2}$, we can factor (12)

$$[2ax + b - (b^2 - 4ac)^{1/2}]\,[2ax + b + (b^2 - 4ac)^{1/2}] = 0$$

and the product must vanish if the value of x verifies the equation (11).

Two cases are now possible: the product is zero because its first factor vanishes or it is zero because the second factor vanishes. In the first case x is found by solving the linear equation

$$2ax + b - (b^2 - 4ac)^{1/2} = 0 \tag{13}$$

while in the second by solving another linear equation

$$2ax + b + (b^2 - 4ac)^{1/2} = 0. \tag{14}$$

Thus, the equation (11) is reduced to two independent linear equations (13) and (14) which are mutually exclusive and incompatible unless $b^2 - 4ac = 0$. Indeed, if the three coefficients a, b, c of the general quadratic equation (11) verify the important condition

$$b^2 - 4ac = 0 \qquad (15)$$

then the radical $(b^2 - 4ac)^{1/2}$ vanishes and both equations (13) and (14) are reduced to the same equation $2ax + b = 0$ the solution $x = -b/(2a)$ of which gives the *double root* of the general equation since $x_1 = x_2 = -b/(2a)$, if (15) holds.

This is why the condition (15) is called the *condition of double root*. In the general case when the coefficients a, b, c are any complex numbers, the double root $-b/(2a)$ can be a complex number. The equation (11) has a double root only when the condition (15) is satisfied.

Suppose now that the condition (15) does not hold, the expression $b^2 - 4ac$ being different from zero. Solving the linear equations (13) and (14) we obtain general expressions of the two roots x_1, x_2 of the equation (11) in terms of its three coefficients a, b, c

$$x_1 = [-b + (b^2 - 4ac)^{1/2}]/(2a); \quad x_2 = [-b - (b_2 - 4ac)^{1/2}]/(2a). \qquad (16)$$

This general solution is often written down in the form

$$x_1, x_2 = [-b \pm (b^2 - 4ac)^{1/2}]/(2a).$$

This same result can be deduced also from (12) replacing the operation of factoring by the extraction of a square root. Transposing the term $-[(b^2 - 4ac)^{1/2}]^2$ to the righthand member, we can write (12) as $(2ax + b)^2 = [(b^2 - 4ac)^{1/2}]^2$. Extracting the square root on both sides, we obtain

$$\pm(2ax + b) = \pm(b^2 - 4ac)^{1/2},$$

where the double signs $\pm$ in both members are independent of each other.

If the signs are the same on both sides we obtain

$$2ax + b = (b^2 - 4ac)^{1/2}.$$

If they are different we have

$$2ax + b = -(b^2 - 4ac)^{1/2}.$$

Transposing b to the right and dividing by $2a$, we obtain the roots (16).

Besides reducing the equation (11) to the difference of squares (12) there is another way of solving the equation (11). It is based on the substitution of a new variable $z = x + b/(2a)$ for x. If the value of z is found then x can be computed, since $x = z - b/(2a)$. Substituting for x its expression in terms of z, $x = z - b/(2a)$, in the equation (11), we transform it into an equation for the new unknown z. To perform this substitution we compute the square x^2:

$$x^2 = [z - b/(2a)]^2 = z^2 - bz/a + b^2/(4a^2)$$

which gives us the following expression of the first term ax^2 in (11):

$$ax^2 = az^2 - bz + b^2/(4a).$$

We also have $bx = bz - b^2/(2a)$ so that with the aid of the substitution $x = z - b/(2a)$, the equation (11) for x becomes an equation for z

$$az^2 - bz + b^2/(4a) + bz - b^2/(2a) + c = 0.$$

The reason why the substitution $x = z - b/(2a)$ is useful becomes now evident: its effect consists in the elimination of the linear term which involves the first power of the unknown. The equation for z indeed is an incomplete equation and contains only a quadratic term az^2 and the constant term, the term with z at the first power being absent. The constant term can be written as

$$b^2/(4a) - b^2/(2a) + c = (b^2 - 2b^2 + 4ac)/(4a)$$
$$= -(b^2 - 4ac)/(4a)$$

and the final form of the equation for z becomes:

$$az^2 - (b^2 - 4ac)/(4a) = 0.$$

Transposing the constant term to the right and dividing both sides by a, we obtain
$$z^2 = (b^2 - 4ac)/(4a).$$

Extracting the square root two possible values for z are obtained:

$$z = \pm (b^2 - 4ac)^{1/2}/(2a).$$

Using these values of z in the relation $x = -b/(2a) + z$, we obtain the two roots (16) of the equation (11) which is thus solved with the aid of the substitution $x = z - b/(2a)$.

The Sum and the Product of the Two Roots

The two roots x_1, x_2 and the three coefficients a, b, c of the general quadratic equation (11) form a set of five quantities related to each other by the relations (16). Therefore, any three of them can be considered as independent and then two other will be expressed in terms of these three independent quantities. In the relations (16) the coefficients a, b, c of the equation (11) are chosen as independent and the two roots x_1, x_2 are expressed in terms of a, b, c, but we can deduce from these relations (16) the expressions of any two among the five quantities in terms of the other three. For example if a_1, x_1, x_2 are known, we can compute b and c, thus constructing the quadratic equation having two prescribed roots. Indeed we will find that the expressions of b and c can be formed by computing the sum and the product of the two roots, that is by computing $x_1 + x_2$ and $x_1 x_2$. The expressions of the roots (16) give upon addition a very simple result, namely $-b/a:x_1 + x_2$ $= (-b + \sqrt{b^2 - 4ac} - b - \sqrt{b^2 - 4ac})/(2a) = (-2b)/(2a) = -b/a$. The two radicals are canceled by the addition since their signs are opposite. The quantity under the radical, $b^2 - 4ac$, which—as we will see later—plays an important role in the theory of quadratic equations, is called the *discriminant*. We will use an abbreviation for it and denoting the discriminant by the first letter of this word: $b^2 - 4ac = D$. Using this notation, we rewrite (16) as follows:

$$x_1 = (-b + \sqrt{D})/(2a); \quad x_2 = (-b - \sqrt{D})/(2a).$$

Multiplying the two roots we obtain

$$x_1 x_2 = -(b + \sqrt{D})(-b + \sqrt{D})/(2a)^2 = -(D - b^2)/(4a^2)$$

$$= -(-4ac)/(4a^2) = c/a$$

since $D - b^2 = b^2 - 4ac - b^2 = -4ac$. The product $(b + \sqrt{D})$ $\times (-b + \sqrt{D})$ was transformed into the difference of two squares $D - b^2$, using the identity $(A + B)(A - B) \equiv A^2 - B^2$.

The results, $x_1 + x_2 = -b/a$ and $x_1 x_2 = c/a$, are very important. They prove that the sum and the product of two roots of a quadratic equation can be found without solving the equation. It is sufficient to apply the rules:

$$x_1 + x_2 = -b/a; \quad x_1 x_2 = c/a. \tag{17}$$

EXAMPLE: The sum and the product of two roots of the equation $3x^2 - 5x + 7 = 0$ are $-b/a = 5/3$ and $c/a = 7/3$, respectively, since for this equation we have $a = 3$, $b = -5$ and $c = 7$. To compute its roots we must apply (16) and we begin by forming and computing the discriminant D. We obtain $D = b^2 - 4ac = 25 - 4 \cdot 3 \cdot 7 = 25 - 84 = -59$, so that the roots are: $x_1 = (5 + \sqrt{-59})/6$ and $x_2 = (5 - \sqrt{-59})/6$. They are complex conjugate numbers, and the fact that they are conjugate explains why their sum and product are real numbers.

The roots of the equation $3x^2 - 5x + 7 = 0$ the coefficients of which are real numbers are complex because the value of its discriminant $D = -59$ is negative. This fact is general for all quadratic equations with real coefficients. If a, b, c are three real numbers the complex or real character of the roots given by (16) is determined uniquely by the sign of the quantity $b^2 - 4ac$ under the radical, since $-b$ and $2a$ are by hypothesis real numbers. If the sign of the discriminant $D = b^2 - 4ac$ is plus, $D > 0$, then the value of the radical $\sqrt{D}$ is a real number and both roots are real. If, on the contrary, the discriminant D of a quadratic equation is negative, the radical $\sqrt{D}$ is imaginary and the roots are complex conjugate numbers:

$$\sqrt{D} = (b^2 - 4ac)^{1/2} = [-(4ac - b^2)]^{1/2} = (-1)^{1/2} (-D)^{1/2}$$
$$= i(-D)^{1/2} = i(4ac - b^2)^{1/2},$$

where the number $-D = 4ac - b^2$ under the radical is positive when $D < 0$.

The case $D = 0$ [see (15)], corresponds to a double root. The name *discriminant* was chosen for the expression $D = b^2 - 4ac$ precisely because its sign plus or minus, as well as its vanishing value, determine immediately and without solving the equation to which of the three cases belongs a particular equation with *real* coefficients a, b, c:

Character of the roots	*Value of discriminant*	*Graph*
Real and unequal	Positive	Cuts OX in 2 points
Real and equal	Vanishing	Tangent to OX
Complex and conjugate	Negative	No common points with OX

The relations (17) can be written also as follows:

$$b = -a(x_1 + x_2); \quad c = ax_1x_2 \tag{18}$$

and these expressions of b and c can be used to form a quadratic equation with two prescribed roots. If the roots x_1 and x_2 are prescribed and therefore known numbers and it is proposed to form the equation which has these two roots, we can choose for the first coefficient a any value we want, and then the corresponding values of b and c are given by (18).

EXAMPLE: To find the quadratic equation with roots 5 and -7 we observe that the sum and the product of these roots are equal to -2 and -35 respectively. Choosing $a = 1$ and applying (18), we find that $b = 2$ and $c = -35$, so that the equation is

$$x^2 + 2x - 35 = 0.$$

To check this answer we apply the general solution formulas (16): $D = 4 + 4 \cdot 35 = 4 + 140 = 144$ and therefore $\sqrt{D} = 12$; $-b = -2$ and $2a = 2$. Thus

$$x_1 = (-2 + 12)/2 = 5; \quad x_2 = (-2 - 12)/2 = -7.$$

The relations (18) can also be used to prove that a general polynomial of second order $ax^2 + bx + c$ can be factored into a product of two linear factors times the first coefficient a. Replacing in it b and c by their expressions (18), we obtain:

$$ax^2 + bx + c \equiv ax^2 - ax_1x - ax_2x + ax_1x_2$$

$$\equiv a(x^2 - x_1x - x_2x + x_1x_2).$$

Now the expression in parentheses is the expansion of the product of the two linear factors $(x - x_1)(x - x_2)$ which is obtained when the multiplication is performed and the parentheses are opened. Therefore the final result is the identity

$$ax^2 + bx + c \equiv a(x - x_1)(x - x_2) \qquad (19)$$

This proves that every quadratic polynomial is factorable in the field of complex numbers. The two factors of a polynomial of second order are of the general type $x - u$, where u is a root of the equation obtained by equating this polynomial to zero. This fact suggests that in the field of complex numbers polynomials of any order are factorable into products of linear factors of the same type $x - u$, the number of such factors being equal to the order of the polynomial that is to the greatest exponent of the variable x in the expression of the polynomial.

But in the field of *real* numbers the polynomials fall into two different classes. Not all polynomials are factorable into products of real linear factors and therefore there are two classes of polynomials: factorable and non-factorable polynomials. The latter ones are called irreducible and they are analogous to prime integers. A few examples of irreducible polynomials which we have already met are $x^2 + 1$, $x^2 + x + 1$, and $(x + p)^2 + q^2$ for any real p and q.

The factoring (19) of a quadratic polynomial allows us to write down a quadratic equation as soon as its roots are given. To take an example, let us form, using (19), the quadratic equation with roots $x_1 = (1 + i)/\sqrt{2}$ and $x_2 = \sqrt{3}/\sqrt{2}$. Choosing $a = 2$, the polynomial $a(x - x_1)(x - x_2)$ becomes

$$2[x - (1 + i)/\sqrt{2}][x - \sqrt{3}/\sqrt{2}]$$

$$= 2x^2 - (1 + \sqrt{3} + i) x\sqrt{2} + (1 + i)\sqrt{3}$$

and therefore the quadratic equation obtained by equating it to zero, namely

$$2x^2 - (1 + i + \sqrt{3}) x\sqrt{2} + (1 + i)\sqrt{3} = 0$$

has the roots $x_1 = (1 + i)/\sqrt{2}$; $x_2 = \sqrt{3}/\sqrt{2}$. To check this we apply (16). Computing first the discriminant $D = b^2 - 4ac$, where $a = 2$, $b = -(1 + i + \sqrt{3})\sqrt{2}$ and $c = (1 + i)\sqrt{3}$, we find

$$D = 2[(1 + \sqrt{3})^2 + 2i(1 + \sqrt{3}) - 1] - (4)(2)(1 + i)\sqrt{3}$$

$$= 2[3 + 2i - 2(1 + i)\sqrt{3}] = 2[(\sqrt{3})^2 - 2(1 + i)\sqrt{3} + (1 + i)^2]$$

$$= 2[\sqrt{3} - (1 + i)]^2.$$

Thus, extracting the square root and applying (16), we find indeed

$$x_1 = [(1 + i + \sqrt{3})\sqrt{2} - (\sqrt{3} - 1 - i)\sqrt{2}]/4 = (1 + i)/\sqrt{2}$$

$$x_2 = [(1 + i + \sqrt{3})\sqrt{2} + (\sqrt{3} - 1 - i)\sqrt{2}]/4 = \sqrt{3}/\sqrt{2}.$$

The case when the first coefficient a is equal to one is often considered as general because in a polynomial of second order $ax^2 + bx + c$ the first coefficient cannot vanish, $a \neq 0$, otherwise we would have a linear expression $bx + c$ which does not involve x^2. Since $a \neq 0$ we can divide by a and thus we obtain a polynomial of the form $x^2 + bx + c$ with $a = 1$. An equation of the form $x^2 + bx + c = 0$ has its two coefficients b and c equal to $-(x_1 + x_2)$ and x_1x_2, respectively, and, if the sum and the product of two roots are denoted by s and p, it can be written as

$$x^2 - sx + p = 0. \tag{20}$$

For the equation (20) the general solution (16) takes a simplified form:

$$x_1, x_2 = s/2 \pm (s^2/4 - p)^{1/2}. \tag{21}$$

Its discriminant is $s^2 - 4p$ and the condition for real roots becomes $s^2 \geqslant 4p$, if the particular case of *real* coefficients s and p is considered.

This particular case is important and the limitation $s^2 \geqslant 4p$ imposed on the real data s and p insures the existence of such two real numbers that their sum and product are equal to s and p respectively.

EXAMPLE: If we ask what are two numbers such that their sum is 30 and their product is -216, we have $s = 30, p = -216$ and the equation which gives these two numbers is

$$x^2 - 30x - 216 = 0.$$

Here $s^2 = 30^2 = 900$, while $4p = -864$, so that the condition of real roots is verified. Computing first the radical $[s^2/(4 - p)]^{1/2} = (225 + 216)^{1/2} = 441^{1/2} = 21$, we obtain according to (21) $x_1 = 15 + 21 = 36$, and $x_2 = 15 - 21 = -6$.

Let us now change the sign of the product and ask for two numbers such that their sum and product are equal to 30 and 216 respectively. Again the condition of real roots is satisfied since $s^2 = 900$ exceeds $4p = 864$. Using (21) we find that $(s^2/4 - p)^{1/2} = (225 - 216)^{1/2} = 9^{1/2} = 3$ and thus $x_1 = 15 + 3 = 18, x_2 = 15 - 3 = 12$. We have indeed $18 + 12 = 30$ and $18 \cdot 12 = 216$.

Finally, we ask what are two numbers such that their sum s and product p are equal to 10 and 34 respectively? Now $s^2 = 100$ and $4p = 136$ is greater than s^2. Therefore the condition of real roots does not hold and there are no two real numbers with the sum 10 and the product 34. Solving the equation $x^2 - 10x + 34 = 0$ which gives the answer, we find indeed complex conjugate roots

$$x_1, x_2 = 10/2 \pm (100/4 - 34)^{1/2} = 5 \pm (-9)^{1/2} = 5 \pm 3i$$

These two complex numbers satisfy the conditions $s = 10$, $p = 34$ because

$$(5 + 3i) + (5 - 3i) = 10;$$

$$(5 + 3i)(5 - 3i) = 5^2 + 3^2 = 25 + 9 = 34.$$

Quartic Equation

Equations of fourth order involving powers of the unknown up to but not exceeding the fourth power are called quartic equations. The symbol x in $ax^2 + bx + c = 0$ may denote the unknown numerical value of an algebraic expression involving another unknown. This circumstance is used in the solutions of some quartic equations with the aid of a chain of two quadratic equations.

Not all quartic equations of general type

$$a_0t^4 + a_1t^3 + a_2t^2 + a_3t + a_4 = 0 \tag{22}$$

can be solved by reducing them to a chain of two quadratic equations but some of them can. Here is an example. Suppose that we are given the quartic equation

$$t^4 - 6t^3 - 5t^2 + 42t + 40 = 0 \tag{23}$$

Our problem consists of finding the special values of t for which the left member in (23) is equal to zero. Let us try to represent (23) as a quadratic polynomial $ax^2 + bx + c$, where the symbol x denotes itself a quadratic polynomial in another variable t, so that $x = t^2 + mt + n$. In all we must introduce five real coefficients to be chosen in such a way that the following identity be true:

$$a(t^2 + mt + n)^2 + b(t^2 + mt + n) + c$$

$$\equiv t^4 - 6t^3 - 5t^2 + 42t + 40 \tag{24}$$

This identity can be valid only if the polynomials of fourth order in t standing in both members are identical, that is, if they have the same coefficients for like powers of t. The term $a(t^2 + mt + n)^2$ expanded becomes:

$$at^4 + 2at^2(mt + n) + a(mt + n)^2$$

$$\equiv at^4 + 2amt^3 + a(2n + m^2)t^2 + 2amnt + an^2$$

and comparing the coefficients of t^4 in both members we conclude that a must be equal to one, $a = 1$. The coefficient of t^3 in the lefthand member, $2am$, becomes now $2m$ since $a = 1$ and it must be equal to the coefficient -6 of t^3 in the righthand member. Thus, $2m = -6$ and $m = -3$.

Substituting in (24) $a = 1$ and $m = -3$ and dropping the identical terms in t^4 and t^3, we have

$$(2n + 9 + b) t^2 + (-6n - 3b) t + (n^2 + bn + c)$$
$$\equiv -5t^2 + 42t + 40$$

Therefore the remaining three coefficients n, b, c must satisfy three conditions

$$2n + 9 + b = -5; \quad -6n - 3b = 42;$$

$$n^2 + bn + c = 40 \tag{25}$$

The first two are identical, and both of them can be reduced to the condition $b + 2n = -14$. Therefore, (25) is a system of two equations with three unknowns

$$b + 2n = -14; \quad n^2 + bn = 40 - c \tag{26}$$

We saw that if the number of equations exceeds the number of unknowns the solution of the system is in general impossible. In our case the system (26) to the contrary has *less* equations than unknowns and in such case we can choose as we want the value of one or many unknowns reducing thus the number of unknowns to be equal to the number of equations. In our case let us consider c as a known quantity since we can ascribe to it any numerical value we choose. Then the system (26) becomes a system of two equations with two unknowns b and n. Solving the first one with respect to the unknown b we express it in terms of the second unknown n: $b = -2n - 14$. Substituting this value of b in the second equation, we obtain

$$n^2 + (-2n - 14) n = n^2 - 2n^2 - 14n = -n^2 - 14n = 40 - c$$

Therefore the unknown n satisfies the quadratic equation $n^2 + 14n + 40 - c = 0$. Applying (21), we obtain two values for n: $s = -14$, $p = 40 - c$ and

$$n_1 = -7 + (9 + c)^{1/2}; \quad n_2 = -7 - (9 + c)^{1/2}$$

We could choose any value for c, and this fact proves that there are an infinite number of substitutions each of which enables us to form a chain of quadratic polynomials identically equal to the lefthand member of the quartic euation (23). Any value of c will serve our purpose and if we take, for instance, $c = -9$ the corresponding value of n is $n = -7$.

The final result of this discussion is as follows: if we define x by $x = t^2 - 3t - 7$, the quadratic polynomial $x^2 - 9$ will be identical with our quartic polynomial in t which stands in the lefthand member of (23). Indeed, replacing n by -7 in the expression of $b = -2n - 14$, we find $b = 0$ and the values $a = 1$, $c = -9$ give $ax^2 + bx + c \equiv x^2 - 9$. It is easy to check that in fact $(t^2 - 3t - 7)^2 - 9 = 0$ is the same equation as the equation (23).

Therefore the equation (23) can be written also as $x^2 - 9 = 0$, where x denotes the numerical value of the polynomial $t^2 - 3t - 7$. Solving this equation $x^2 - 9 = 0$ we find two values for x, namely $x_1 = 3$ and $x_2 = -3$. Thus the quartic equation (23) is verified by the special values of t for which the quadratic polynominal $t^2 - 3t - 7$ takes the value 3 or the value -3. This means that the roots of (23) are also those of two quadratic equations.

$$t^2 - 3t - 7 = 3; \quad t^2 - 3t - 7 = -3 \qquad (27)$$

Both of them are of the type (20) with $s = 3$, $\mathrm{p} = -10$ for the first and $s = 3$, $p = -4$ for the second. Applying (21) we obtain the solutions $t_1 = 5$, $t_2 = -2$ for the first and $t_3 = 4$, $t_4 = -1$ for the second equation (27).

Thus the quartic equation (23) has four roots $t_1 = 5$, $t_2 = -2$, $t_3 = 4$ and $t_4 = -1$. The number of roots is equal to the order of the equation. We could use other numerical values of c instead of -9, but the result would be the same because the roots of (23) do not depend on the choice of the chain of two quadratic polynomials used to represent the quartic polynomial.

To decide if a given quartic equation can be solved by the process just described, we must know the characteristic property of a quartic polynomial which can be represented by a chain of quadratic polynomials. A quartic polynomial can always be reduced, by dividing it by a_0, to the form $t^4 + a_1 t^3 + a_2 t^2 + a_3 t + a_4$, and if it is obtainable by substituting $t^2 + mt + n = x$ into a quadratic polynomial $x^2 + bx + c$, we must have the identity

$$t^4 + a_1 t^3 + a_2 t^2 + a_3 t + a_4 \equiv (t^2 + mt + n)^2 + b(t^2 + mt + n) + c$$

This identity implies the relations

$$a_1 = 2m; \quad a_2 = m^2 + 2n + b;$$

$$a_3 = m(2n + b); \quad a_4 = n^2 + bn + c$$

Forming now the two expressions $a_1^3 + 8a_3$ and $4a_1a_2$ we find that they are equal both to $8m(m^2 + 2n + b)$. Thus,

$$a_1^3 + 8a_3 = 4a_1a_2$$

and this relation between the three coefficients a_1, a_2, a_3 is characteristic of quartic polynomials which are reducible to a chain of two quadratic polynomials.

We have studied polynomials with $a_0 = 1$. If the general polynomial of fourth order $a_0t^4 + a_1t^3 + a_2t^2 + a_3t + a_4$ is considered, the coefficients a_1, a_2, a_3 in the characteristic relation must be replaced by the quotients $a_1/a_0, a_2/a_0, a_3/a_0$ which gives

$$(a_1/a_0)^3 + 8(a_3/a_0) = 4(a_1/a_0)(a_2/a_0)$$

Multiplying by a_0^3 we obtain

$$a_1^3 - 4a_0a_1a_2 + 8a_0^2a_3 = 0 \tag{28}$$

We reach the conclusion that among all quartic equations (22)

$$a_0t^4 + a_1t^3 + a_2t^2 + a_3t + a_4 = 0$$

only those whose coefficients a_0, a_1, a_2, a_3 satisfy the relation (28) can be solved by reducing them to a chain of two quadratic equations. The equation (23) we just solved by this process belongs to this class. Its coefficients $a_0 = 1$, $a_1 = -6$, $a_2 = -5$, $a_3 = 42$ do satisfy the condition (28):

$$(-6)^3 - 4 \cdot 1(-6)(-5) + 8 \cdot 1^2 \cdot 42 = -216 - 120 + 336 = 0.$$

Principle of Extremum

Given a quadratic equation $Ax^2 + Bx + C = 0$, with real coefficients, A, B, C the condition of real roots

$$B^2 - 4AC \geqslant 0 \tag{29}$$

is satisfied if the coefficient A of x^2 and the constant term C have opposite signs because in this case the product $4AC$ is a negative number and the second term of the lefthand member in (29), namely $-4AC$, is positive. The first term B^2 is always positive since by hypothesis B is a real number. Thus, in the left member of (29) we have the sum of two positive terms and (29) holds.

Let us study the case in which the coefficients A and C have the same sign. If A and C are both positive or both negative, the condition of real roots (29) becomes a limitation imposed on the data A, B, C which establishes a minimum admissible value for $|B|$ or a maximum admissible value for either $|A|$ or $|C|$.

Thus, transposing the term $4AC$ to the right, we obtain the inequality $B^2 \geqslant 4AC$ which proves that the absolute value of B is at least equal to $2\sqrt{AC}$, so that, if (29) is to hold, then min $|B| = 2\sqrt{AC}$ or, in other words, $B \geqslant 2\sqrt{AC}$, if B is positive, and $B \leqslant -2\sqrt{AC}$, if B is negative. But the same inequality $B^2 \geqslant 4AC$ solved for A gives $A \leqslant B^2/4C$, if A and C (they are of the same sign by hypothesis) are positive, or max $A = B^2/4C$. If A and C are negative, we obtain $|A| \leqslant B^2/4|C|$ or max $|A| = B^2/4|C|$. In other words, the admissible values of $|A|$ must lie in the interval $(0, B^2/4|C|)$. Solving for $|C|$, we obtain a similar limitation imposed on the absolute value of C: $0 < |C| \leqslant B^2/4|A|$.

This extremum property (*extremum* means extreme value, that is, a maximum or a minimum) of quadratic equations with real coefficients and roots, whose coefficients A and C have the same sign, has important applications. The natural laws governing physical phenomena such as motion and propagation of light are in most cases nothing more than a formulation of conditions under which a certain physical quantity the value of which depends on the course of the phenomenon, reaches its extreme value (maximum or minimum). The actual course of the phenomenon corresponds to the realization of this extreme value.

Thus, optical phenomena are governed by Fermat's Principle of least time: the actual path of light ray travelling in a heterogeneous medium (variable velocity of light) is a curve whose shape is such that the time necessary to travel between any two points of this curve is a minimum.

Stable equilibrium of a mechanical system corresponds to the minimum of its potential energy. The motion of a mechanical system too, is perfectly determined by Hamilton's principle of least action (formulated in 1834 by the famous Irish mathematician W. R. Hamilton, 1805–1865): a mechanical system always moves in such a way that the total action corresponding to the actual motion is a minimum. In other words, nature is always economical with respect to some physical quantity such as time, energy, action *etc.*

Furthermore, in translating a physical problem into mathematical language we always denote by x an unknown physical quantity which can have only real values. If a quadratic equation $Ax^2 + Bx + C = 0$ is obtained for this unknown quantity x, its coefficients are expressed in terms of known physical data, which of necessity are real quantities and these coefficients A, B, C then must also be real. If the roots of the equation $Ax^2 + Bx + C = 0$ are complex, it can only mean that the physical problem, as it is formulated, has no solution at all and is impossible. Thus, the condition (29) of real roots becomes a condition of the problem's solvability in general.

Interpreted in terms of physical data this condition imposes a limitation on the numerical values of these physical data, a limitation without which the problem cannot be solved since there is no answer if the condition of real roots does not hold. The extreme case of this condition, $B^2 - 4AC = 0$ (condition of double root), is especially important. It corresponds always to a maximum or minimum of some physical quantity and therefore expresses a physical law.

Reflection Law

Let us study the physical meaning of the condition $D = B^2 - 4AC = 0$ on the example of reflection of light in a plane mirror. Suppose that a ray of light AP emanating from a point A at a given distance $AC = H$ from the mirror CD and reflected at some point P of the mirror, passes after the reflection through another fixed point B at a distance $BD = h$ from the mirror, the distance $CD = a$ being also fixed (see fig. 7).

We suppose that the position of the point P is unknown (the reflection law fixes the position of the point P, but we suppose that the law itself is not known and must be found) and it must be deduced from the data $CD = a$, $CA = H$, $DB = h$.

The unknown position of P can be characterized by its distance $CP = x$ from the point C, the distance PD then being equal to $a - x$. Let y denote the distance travelled by the light from A to B: $y = AP + PB$. This distance obviously depends on the position of the point P.

In other words $AP + PB = y$ is a variable quantity and its value depends on the value of the variable $x = CP$. Thus the length $y = AP + PB$ is a function of x.

We ask now what is the actual path of a ray of light emanating from A and passing after the reflection through the point B? Where between C and D is the point P actually located? What is the value of our variable x which corresponds to the reflection law?

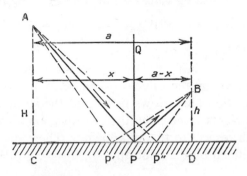

Fig. 7.7

From physics we know that the actual position of the point P is such that the incident ray of light AP and the reflected ray PB are equally inclined to the mirror CPD, that is they form with the perpendicular PQ to the mirror two equal angles: $APQ = QPB$. This reflection law was discovered and known long ago, long before the Greek scientist Heron of Alexandria (first century A.D.) pointed out that a *minimum* of the total length $AP + PB$ of the path of light between A and B corresponds to the actual position of P. If P in fig. 7 represents the true position of the reflection point and if P' and P'' are any two points to the left and to the right of P respectively, we will have $AP' + P'B > AP + PB$, as well as $AP'' + P''B > AP + PB$. The velocity of light in a homogeneous medium being constant, a path of minimum length requires a minimum of travel time and therefore, according to Fermat's principle, the reflection law realizes the shortest possible length $AP + PB = y$, that is, the minimum of the function $y = AP + PB$ with P considered as a variable point (variable x).

We now have to show how the principle of minimum of time is translated into the reflection law $APQ = QPB$. Applying the Pythagorean theorem to the right triangles ACP and BDP, we express the function $y = AP + PB$ for any value of the variable x, that is for any position of the variable point P. But P is between C and D, so that the range of variation of x is defined by the inequality $0 < x < a$. In these two triangles AP and BP play the role of hypotenuses and therefore

$$AP = (AC^2 + CP^2)^{1/2} = (H^2 + x^2)^{1/2}$$

$$PB = (PD^2 + DB^2)^{1/2} = [(a - x)^2 + h^2)^{1/2}$$

which gives the following expression of the total length y of the path:

$$y = (H^2 + x^2)^{1/2} + [(a - x)^2 + h^2]^{1/2} \tag{30}$$

The formula (30) expresses y in terms of three fixed and given quantities H, h, a and a variable x. It establishes a functional relationship between x and y, so that the value of y can be computed, if x is known. But the same relation (30) allows us to find the value of x, when y is known. It is sufficient to consider (30) as an equation with the unknown x and solve it with respect to this unknown x. Therefore x appears as a function of y defined by the relation (30), if we consider y as a fourth physical datum.

We know that in a functional relationship between two variables x and y either of them can be considered as the independent variable and then the other appears as its function. We may choose the independent variable at our will and in what follows we consider x as a function of y.

The equation in x (30) which defines this function can be simplified, if we eliminate the radicals it contains by squaring. We can foresee that as result of this elimination a quadratic equation in x will be obtained. We know indeed that the actual reflection of light at the point P corresponds to the minimum of y and y increases when the point P is shifted to either of the two positions P' and P'', to the left and to the right of its true position. Therefore, to a value of y which exceeds its minimum value there correspond two positions of P, that is two different values of x. We conclude that our equation (30) is a disguised form of a quadratic equation, because it must yield two different values of x for each prescribed value of y and we know that a quadratic equation always has two roots.

To write this equation in its explicit form $Ax^2 + Bx + C = 0$ we now get rid of the radicals. Transposing the radical $(H^2 + x^2)^{1/2}$ to the righthand member

$$[(a - x)^2 + h^2]^{1/2} = y - (H^2 + x^2)^{1/2}$$

and squaring both members of the relation thus obtained, we have

$$(a - x)^2 + h^2 = y^2 - 2y(H^2 + x^2)^{1/2} + H^2 + x^2$$

Expanding $(a - x)^2 = a^2 - 2ax + x^2$ and transposing all four terms of the lefthand member to the right, while the term with the radical, namely $2y(H^2 + x^2)^{1/2}$ is transposed to the left, we obtain

$$2y(H^2 + x^2)^{1/2} = H^2 - a^2 - h^2 + y^2 + 2ax$$

the two terms x^2 and $-x^2$ cancelling out.

To get rid of the radical in the lefthand member we must square again and the result of this second operation of squaring is a quadratic equation in x:

$$4y^2H^2 + 4y^2x^2 = (H^2 - a^2 - h^2 + y^2)^2$$
$$+ 4ax(H^2 - a^2 - h^2 + y^2) + 4a^2x^2$$

Transposing all the terms of the righthand member to the left, we give to this quadratic equation the usual form $Ax^2 + Bx + C = 0$.

$$4(y^2 - a^2)\, x^2 - 4a(H^2 - a^2 - h^2 + y^2)\, x + 4H^2y^2$$
$$- (H^2 - a^2 - h^2 + y^2)^2 = 0 \tag{31}$$

Thus, the coefficients A, B, and C are expressed in terms of the four physical data H, h, a, y as follows:

$$A = 4(y^2 - a^2)$$
$$B = -4a(H^2 - a^2 - h^2 + y^2) \tag{32}$$
$$C = 4H^2y^2 - (H^2 - a^2 - h^2 + y^2)^2$$

Now we can apply the principle of extremum. We observe that the value of the unknown x must be a real number because its physical meaning is distance. Therefore, complex roots of (31) have no sense and the condition of real roots must be imposed on the values of the four physical data H, h, a, y.

Forming this condition $D = B^2 - 4AC \geqslant 0$, we find

$$16y^2[(H^2 - a^2 - h^2 + y^2)^2 - 4H^2y^2 + 4H^2a^2] \geqslant 0$$

The first factor $16y^2$ is positive. Omitting it we obtain

$$[(H^2 - a^2 - h^2) + y^2]^2 - 4H^2y^2 + 4H^2a^2 \geqslant 0 \tag{33}$$

Expanding the square in the lefthand member

$$(H^2 - a^2 - h^2)^2 + 2y^2(H^2 - a^2 - h^2)$$
$$+ y^4 - 4H^2y^2 + 4H^2a^2 \geqslant 0$$

we rewrite this condition as follows:

$$y^4 - 2y^2(H^2 + a^2 + h^2) + (H^2 + a^2 + h^2)^2 - 4H^2h^2 \geqslant 0$$

since $(H^2 - a^2 - h^2)^2 + 4H^2a^2 = (H^2 + a^2 + h^2)^2 - 4H^2h^2$ as can be easily checked by transposing $(H^2 - a^2 - h^2)^2$ to the right and $4H^2h^2$ to the left.

But the last form of our condition can be written simply as

$$[y^2 - (H^2 + a^2 + h^2)]^2 - (2Hh)^2 \geqslant 0$$

Factoring this difference of two squares

$$[y^2 - (H^2 + a^2 + h^2) + 2Hh]\,[y^2 - (H^2 + a^2 + h^2) - 2Hh] \geqslant 0$$

and observing that $H^2 \pm 2Hh + h^2 = (H \pm h)^2$, we discover finally that the condition of real roots can be expressed in terms of the physical data H, h, a, y as follows:

$$\{y^2 - [(H + h)^2 + a^2]\}\,\{y^2 - [(H - h)^2 + a^2]\} \geqslant 0 \qquad (34)$$

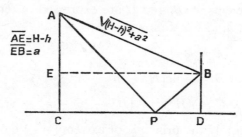

Fig. 7.8

We now prove that the second factor $y^2 - [(H - h)^2 + a^2]$ is positive and cannot vanish. In the triangle APB in fig. 8 the sum of two sides $AP + PB = y$ is always greater than the third side AB: $y > AB$. Considering now the right triangle AEB in which AB is the hypotenuse, we express AB with the aid of Pythagorean theorem:

$$AB = (AE^2 + EB^2)^{1/2} = [(H - h)^2 + a^2]^{1/2}$$

Therefore, $y > [(H - h)^2 + a^2]^{1/2}$ and squaring, $y^2 > (H - h)^2 + a^2$

so that $y^2 - [(H - h)^2 + a^2] > 0$. Hence we see that in the inequality (34) the second factor is a positive number. Dividing both members of (34) by it, we give to our condition $B^2 - 4AC$ the form

$$y^2 - [(H + h)^2 + a^2] \geqslant 0.$$

Representing $(H + h)^2 + a^2$ as the square of its square root $[\sqrt{(H + h)^2 + a^2}]^2$ and factoring the difference of two squares $y^2 - [\sqrt{(H + h)^2 + a^2}]^2$, we have

$$[y - \sqrt{(H + h)^2 + a^2}] [y + \sqrt{(H + h)^2 + a^2}] \geqslant 0$$

where again the second factor is always a positive number and cannot vanish. Dividing both members by it, we obtain the final form of the condition of real roots:

$$y \geqslant [(H + h)^2 + a^2]^{1/2} \tag{35}$$

This is the physical meaning of the condition of real roots in our problem. The total length y of the light's path cannot be less than $[(H + h)^2 + a^2]^{1/2}$: the minimum of y is equal to the square root $[(H + h)^2 + a^2]^{1/2}$.

Applying now Fermat's principle of least time we say that the actual length of y *is* precisely represented by $[(H + h)^2 + a^2)^{1/2}$ because the reflection law must realize the minimum of travel time between the points A and B, that is, the minimum of the length y. But if the inequality (35), which is the same as the inequality $D \geqslant 0$, reduces to the equality $y = \min y = [(H + h)^2 + a^2]^{1/2}$, then the discriminant D of our equation $Ax^2 + Bx + C = 0$ is equal to zero. The vanishing of the discriminant D proves that there is only one root x, namely the double root $x = -B/(2A)$ of the equation $Ax^2 + Bx + C = 0$ and this unique root fixes the actual position of the point P, where the reflection takes place between the points C and D.

The double root is equal to the quotient $-B/(2A)$, but now when we know that the actual value of y is $[(H + h)^2 + a^2]^{1/2}$ we can simplify the expression (32) of the coefficients A and B, replacing in them y^2 by $H^2 + h^2 + a^2 + 2Hh$. We obtain

$$A = 4(H + h)^2$$

and

$$B = -4a(H^2 - a^2 - h^2 + H^2 + h^2 + a^2 + 2Hh) = -8Ha(H + h)$$

Dividing the value of $-B$ by $2A = 8(H + h)^2$ we find the double root x:

$$x = aH/(H + h) \qquad (36)$$

Forming $a - x$, we have also $a - x = ah/(H + h)$. Thus the two products hx and $H(a - x)$ are equal:

$$hx = H(a - x) = aHh/(H + h)$$

But the relation $hx = H(a - x)$ gives the proportion

$$H/x = h/(a - x) \qquad (37)$$

as can be shown by dividing both members of the equality $H(a - x) = hx$ by the product $x(a - x)$.

It remains to show that the proportion (37) expresses the reflection law as it is formulated in physics. Consider two triangles ACP and BPD (fig. 9). Computing the tangents of acute angles APC, BPD we have by definition of tangent of an angle.

$$\tan APC = \mathsf{AC/CP} = H/x; \quad \tan BPD = \mathsf{BD/PD} = h/(a - x).$$

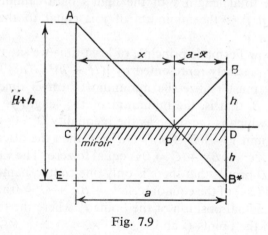

Fig. 7.9

Therefore the two tangents are equal, which proves that the two acute angles themselves are equal: $APC = BPD$. This is the reflection law. We add that the solution (36) suggests a simple geometric construction of the point P: join the image B^* of the point B, obtained by reflecting B in the mirror CD, to the point A. The line $\mathsf{AB^*}$ intersects CD at the point P (see fig. 9).

To justify this construction we observe that the triangles ACP and

PDB^* have equal angles. Therefore, they are similar triangles and their sides are proportional

$$AC/CP = DB^*/PD$$

But $AC = H$, $CP = x$, $DB^* = h$ and $PD = a - x$, so that this proportion is nothing else than the proportion (37) and the construction is justified. We add that AEB^* is a right triangle and thus $y = AP + PB = AB^* = [(H + h)^2 + a^2]^{1/2}$ which agrees with our previous statements.

Farmer's Problem

Our next example of the extremum principle is a problem familiar to all farmers. It is a well known economic fact that the price per unit weight of any crop decreases with time when more and more products come to the market. On the other hand, the total yield in units weights increases with time. Denoting the total yield in units weights by w and the market price of a unit weight by p, we find that the value of the crop is equal to the product wp. Both factors of this product are variable because they change with time, and therefore so is the value $V = wp$ of the crop.

The farmer's problem is to realize the maximum value of V that is to choose such a moment t that the function of time V reaches its maximum. To fix our ideas let us suppose that the farmer wants to choose the best moment t for digging out his potatoes. He knows the four elements involved in his problem. They are: the yield w_0 he could obtain, if he digs out his potatoes today, the present price p_0, the daily rate of increase u of the yield and the daily rate of decrease q of the marked price of a unit weight. Choosing today as origin of time intervals, he can express the yield w and the price p at any moment t, that is t days after today, if he neglects possible variations with time of the daily rates u and q. In pratical computations these two elements are always considered as two fixed numbers. In t days from now the yield will increase by ut and will become equal to $w_0 + ut$. The price will decrease by qt and will be equal to $p_0 - qt$. Thus, the total value of the potatoes crop t days from now, as expressed by the product $V = wp$, where $w = w_0 + ut$ and $p = p_0 - qt$, is represented by a polynomial of second order with respect to the variable t.

$$V = (w_0 + ut)(p_0 - qt)$$

The four other quantities w_0, u, p_0, q involved in this expression of V are four *constants* which are known to our farmer.

The unknown of the farmer's problem is the time t because what the farmer wants to know is the number t such that t days from now the function V reaches its maximum value. In practice the farmers solve this problem by trial: they compute the future values of V separately for each day and compare them. This trial method corresponds to the plotting point by point of the parabola which is the graph of the function V of time t. The expression we found for V proves indeed that V is a quadratic function of t because performing the multiplication we have

$$V = -uqt^2 + (up_0 - qw_0)\, t + w_0 p_0 \tag{38}$$

and we know that the variation of a quadratic function $At^2 + Bt + C$ is represented by a parabola. Moreover we know that if the first coefficient A is positive the parabola opens upward and its vertex is the lowest point of the curve which corresponds to a minimum of the function represented by the parabola. But in our case the coefficient A

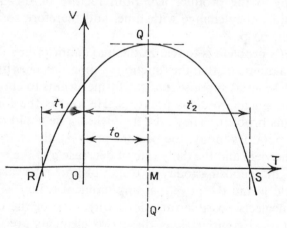

Fig. 7.10

cannot be a positive number. Its expression $A = -uq$ proves that it is necessarily a negative number because the daily rates u and q are both positive by definition. Thus, as we have seen above, the parabola (38) representing the total value V of the crop turns its concavity downwards and the function V has a maximum which corresponds to the uppermost point Q of the graph (see fig. 10).

Before solving the quadratic equation (38) for the unknown t algebraically, we will find its solution with the aid of the graph sketched in
fig. 10. The parabola RQS is symmetrical with respect to the vertical
line $Q'Q$ which runs parallel to the axis $\mathbf{OV}$ of the dependent variable V,
passing through the vertex Q of the parabola. Therefore the intersection
point M of the line $\mathbf{Q'Q}$ with the time axis $\mathbf{OT}$ is the midpoint of the
interval $\mathbf{RS}$ between the two points R and S where the parabola intersects the time axis $\mathbf{OT}$.

The graphic representation of the function V by points of the parabola is based on the conventional assumption that at each point of the
curve the corresponding value of V is the measure of the distance from
this point to the time axis $\mathbf{OT}$. Therefore, at the points R and S, whose
distances to $\mathbf{OT}$ are zero, the function V vanishes and the corresponding
coordinates t for these two points can be found with the aid of the equation $V = 0$. But we have seen that $V = (w_0 + ut)(p_0 - qt)$ so that the
equation $V = 0$ is simply

$$(w_0 + ut)(p_0 - qt) = 0.$$

Solving this equation we have $w_0 + ut = 0$ or $p_0 - qt = 0$ which
gives us the two roots $t_1 = -w_0/u$ and $t_2 = p_0/q$ of the equation $V = 0$.
We have in fact found the two distances

$$\mathbf{OR} = t_1 = -w_0/u \quad \text{and} \quad \mathbf{OS} = t_2 = p_0/q$$

of points R, S from the origin O. The negative sign of the first root t_1
corresponds to the fact that the point R is to the left of the origin O.

The maximum of V corresponds to the vertex Q and the coordinate t_0
of the vertex is precisely the unknown value of the independent
variable t for which V reaches its maximum. This coordinate of Q is
represented on fig. 10 by the segment $\mathbf{OM}$ of the time axis and to find
it we can use the vectorial relation $\mathbf{RM} = \mathbf{MS}$. Denoting the unknown
$\mathbf{OM}$ by t_0 and recalling that $\mathbf{OR} = t_1$, $\mathbf{OS} = t_2$, we have $\mathbf{RM} = \mathbf{RO}$
$+ \mathbf{OM} = \mathbf{OM} - \mathbf{OR} = t_0 - t_1$, as well as $\mathbf{MS} = \mathbf{OS} - \mathbf{OM}$
$= t_2 - t_0$. Thus the relation $\mathbf{RM} = \mathbf{MS}$ can be written also as follows

$$t_0 - t_1 = t_2 - t_0.$$

Solving this equation with respect to the unknown t_0, we obtain

$$2\mathbf{OM} = 2t_0 = t_1 + t_2 = p_0/q - w_0/u = (up_0 - qw_0)/uq.$$

Kogbetliantz 20

The solution t_0 is explicitly expressed in terms of the four data of our problem by the following algebraic fraction

$$t_0 = (up_0 - qw_0)/(2uq). \qquad (39)$$

We proceed now to the algebraic discussion of the same problem which will give us again the solution (39). Considering the value V of the crop as one of our data, we rewrite the equation (38) as a quadratic equation with unknown t:

$$uqt^2 - (up_0 - qw_0)\, t + (V - p_0w_0) = 0 \qquad (40)$$

The roots t_1, t_2 of this equation must be real because the complex values of time t have no meaning. Therefore, the condition of real roots

$$D = (up_0 - qw_0)^2 - 4uq(V - p_0w_0) \geqslant 0$$

must be satisfied by the five numbers p_0, w_0, q, u, V because otherwise the problem has no solution at all. The four numbers p_0, q_0, w, u being fixed once for all, the condition of real roots imposes a limitation on the value of V.

Opening the parentheses, adding like terms and transposing the term with V to the right, we obtain successively

$$(up_0)^2 - 2(up_0)\,(qw_0) + (qw_0)^2 + 4(up_0)\,(qw_0) - 4uqV \geqslant 0$$

$$(up_0)^2 + 2(up_0)\,(qw_0) + (qw_0)^2 = (up_0 + qw_0)^2 \geqslant 4uqV$$

Thus, the limitation imposed on V is as follows:

$$V \leqslant (up_0 + qw_0)^2/(4uq).$$

The maximum of the farmer's benefit is attained when V reaches its maximum value, namely when

$$V = \max V = (up_0 + qw_0)^2/(4uq).$$

But this maximum value of V corresponds to the sign of equality in the condition of real roots $D \geqslant 0$. Thus, the farmer's problem is solved when $D = 0$, which means that the equation (40) in t has a double root. The double root of a general quadratic equation is expressed by the quotient $-B/(2A)$ and because in our case (40) $B = -(up_0 - qw_0)$, and $A = uq$ we find for the double root t_0 the same expression (39) which was found with the aid of the graph of V:

$$t_0 = -B/(2A) = (up_0 - qw_0)/(2uq)$$

The algebraic discussion based on the principle of extremum is very concise and it gives not only the value t_0 of the unknown t but also the maximum value of the function V which is equal to $(up_0 + qw_0)^2/(4uq)$.

We add a numerical example of the farmer's problem. Suppose that a farmer estimates that if he digs his potatoes now he will have 600 bushels worth 80 cents a bushel, while for each *week* he waits the crop will increase 50 bushels and the price will drop five cents.

With our notation we must use $w_0 = 600$, $p_0 = 80$, $u = 50/7$ and $q = 5/7$. The answer to the question how long should he wait, if he wants to realize the maximum benefit is given by

$$t_0 = (up_0 - qw_0)/(2uq) = (4000/7 - 3000/7)/(500/49) = 14 \text{ days}$$

and the maximum of the crop's value in cents is

$$\max V = (up_0 + qw_0)^2/(4uq) = (4000 + 3000)^2/1000 = 49\,000$$

This is easily checked: in 14 days the yield is 700 bushels and the price 70 cents.

There are many geometric problems on maxima and minima which lead to quadratic equations. The area of a rectangle, for example is expressed (in units of area) by the product of the length of the base times the length of the altitude. Its perimeter, by definition of this term as the total length of the area's boundary, is the *double* of the sum of the base and the altitude. Let us consider now all possible rectangles having the same fixed, perimeter $4p$. For all of them the sum of the base plus the altitude will have the same value, namely $2p$. If the length of the base of a rectangle is denoted by x, then its altitude will be $2p - x$, because the sum of the base plus the altitude must be $2p$. But different rectangles of the same perimeter $4p$ may have different bases. Thus the length x can vary and its range of variation extends from zero to $2p$, $0 < x < 2p$.

The different rectangles of the family we are considering have also different areas because in the expression of a rectangle's area A by the product of the base times the altitude, that is $A = x(2p - x)$, a variable quantity x is involved. Fixing x so that the condition $0 < x < 2p$ is satisfied, we in fact choose a rectangle in the family of all rectangles with the perimeter $4p$.

We ask now what is the shape of the rectangle which belongs to this family and has maximum possible area? In other words, what is the value of the variable x for which the function $A = x(2p - x)$ reaches its maximum?

This question again is solved with the aid of the principle of extremum. The value of x satisfies the quadratic equation $A = 2px - x^2$ or

$$x^2 - 2px + A = 0 \qquad (41)$$

which therefore must have real roots. The corresponding condition $D \geqslant 0$ which can be written $D = 4p^2 - 4A = 4(p^2 - A) \geqslant 0$ shows that the problem has a sense and admits of a real solution only if the area A is less or at most equal to the square p^2 of a quarter of the perimeter, namely if $A \leqslant p^2$.

Therefore the rectangle of maximum area with perimeter $4p$ will have an area equal to p^2 and this greatest possible value of area is obtained when the discriminant D of the equation (41) vanishes. A quadratic equation with a vanishing discriminant has a double root and therefore the corresponding length x of the base is equal to $-B/(2A) = 2p/2 = p$. But if the base is p the altitude is also p because its length is given by $2p - x = 2p - p = p$.

We come to the conclusion therefore, that among all the rectangles of same perimeter the square possesses the greatest area.

Here is another proof of the same fact based on the identity

$$4xy \equiv (x + y)^2 - (x - y)^2.$$

Let x and y denote the base and altitude of a rectangle with perimeter $4p$ and area A. Thus, the sum $x + y$ and the product xy are equal to $2p$ and A respectively. Replacing in the identity $4xy$ by $4A$ and $(x + y)^2$ by $4p^2$, we have $4A = 4p^2 - (x - y)^2$, and therefore, dividing by 4

$$A = p^2 - [(x - y)/2]^2.$$

Since the square $[(x - y)/2]^2$ is a positive number, unless $x = y$, it is plain that for all rectangles the area A remains less than p^2, except the particular rectangle for which $x = y$ and $A = \max A = p^2$. This rectangle is a square because its base x and altitude y are equal.

Now we invert the question and ask what rectangle of given area A has the least perimeter? This question is solved with the aid of the same identity $A = p^2 - [(x - y)/2]^2$ which we write now as follows

$$p^2 = A + [(x - y)/2]^2$$

We see that for all rectangles having the same area A the quarter p of their perimeter verifies the inequality $p^2 > A$, except the special rectangle for which the term $[(x - y)/2]^2$ vanishes. Therefore, the rectangle with minimum perimeter is characterized by the condition $x = y$ which proves that it is again a square of side $x = y = p = A^{1/2}$. Thus, among all rectangles of equal area the square has the least perimeter. This characteristic property of having the maximum area for a given perimeter or the minimum perimeter for a given area can be taken as the definition of the square.

The problem we just considered admits of interesting generalizations. We could replace rectangles by quadrilaterals and again we would find that among all quadrilaterals of same area the square has the least perimeter, as well as greatest area for a given perimeter. If triangles instead of quadrilaterals are considered, the same conditions are fulfilled by regular triangle, that is by equilateral triangle. In this problem the number of sides of polygons considered does not matter and the general result is as follows: among all polygons with N sides the regular polygon (equilateral and equiangular) has the greatest area for a given perimeter and the least perimeter for a given area. For $N = 4$ we had the square, for $N = 3$ the regular triangle.

Increasing the number N of sides of a polygon without limit in such a way that at the limit for $N = \infty$ all its sides vanish, we transform in general this polygon into a closed curve. Applying this passage to the limit to a *regular* polygon with N equal sides, we obtain at the limit for $N = \infty$ a *circle*. At every step of the process the extremum properties hold and quite naturally the following guess is suggested to our mind: in the family of all closed curves with finite area and finite length the circle has the largest area for a given total length and the least total length for a given area. This conjecture is true and it has been proved. Recalling that the area A and the length of the circumference L of the circle of radius R are expressed by $A = \pi R^2$ and $L = 2\pi R$, we form $4A = 4\pi R^2$ and $L^2 = 4\pi^2 R^2$. Comparing them we find a characteristic property of circles:

$$4\pi A = L^2$$

Applying now their extremum property, namely maximum possible value A of area for a given length L, we conclude that for all closed curves with area A and total length L, except the circles, we have the inequality

$$4\pi A < L^2$$

which also can be written as $A < L^2/4\pi$ or as $L > 2(\pi A)^{1/2}$. This fact itself is not at all surprising because a closed curve of given length cannot include too large an area as well as a given area cannot have too short a boundary curve. Therefore, we must have some relation between A and L which establishes the least value L can have for a given area A and, at the same time, the largest value of area A which can be bounded by a closed curve of given length L. What is interesting in the result is the shape of the curve, namely a circle, which realizes the extrema of A and of L, and also the numerical factors $1/4\pi$ and $s\pi^{1/2}$ which are involved in the inequalities $A < L^2/4\pi$ and $L > 2(\pi A)^{1/2}$ satisfied for all closed curves except the circle.

There is a further generalization in the line of thought we are studying. It is obtained by increasing the number of dimensions from two (plane closed curves) to three, that is, considering the same problem in the three-dimensional space instead of two-dimensional plane. Instead of the class of closed plane curves let us consider the class of all closed surfaces. A closed surface has a total surface area S and it encloses a volume V. In the space S plays the role of L, the length of a closed curve, and the volume V replaces the area A enclosed inside the curve.

We now ask what is the shape of the particular surface which among all closed surfaces of the same volume V has the least surface area S? Or, what is the shape of the particular surface which among all closed surfaces of the same surface area S has the largest volume V?

The answer to both questions is the *sphere* which is quite natural because a sphere plays the same role in space a circle plays in the plane. The extremum property of the sphere explains why the soap bubbles blown by children are perfect spheres: the surface tension of soap film tends to reduce as much as possible the exterior surface of the film, but the volume of air inside the soap bubble is fixed and therefore the surface tension gives to the film a spherical shape which realizes the minimum surface area for a given interior volume.

Method of Least Squares

Among innumerable applications of the theory of quadratic equations one of the most important is perhaps the method of least squares which is one of the basic tools of applied sciences. This method solves the following question. It is a well known experimental fact that repeating the measurements of the same physical quantity one does not obtain the same number: the result of a series of measurements, say of a series on n measurements, are n different numbers $s_1, s_2, s_3, ...,$ s_{n-1}, s_n. Therefore each measurement is affected by an error and the exact value s of the measured quantity remains unknown.

Nevertheless this unknown quantity is represented in some way by the set of n numbers s_k, $k = 1, 2, 3, ... , n$, which are n approximate values of s. We cannot use all of them because what we need is a single approximate value of s and we want the best approximate value possible. This best approximate value is to be deduced from the set of n known approximations $s_1, s_2, s_3, ... , s_n$.

A very important practical question arises: how can we deduce a best approximate value x of an unknown quantity s from the sequence of n known and different approximations $s_1, s_2, s_3, ... , s_n$? In other words, what is the algebraical expression of the best approximation x in terms of known approximations s_k?

The answer is given by the method of least squares which states that the arithmetic mean of all n measurements

$$M_n = (s_1 + s_2 + s_3 + \cdots + s_{n-1} + s_n)/n \qquad (42)$$

represents the unknown quantity s with the least error and is therefore the best approximation to s which can be deduced from n measurements performed.

EXAMPLE: If four measurements yield $s_1 = 4.75$, $s_2 = 5.15$, $s_3 = 4.8$ and $s_4 = 5.0$, the best approximation which could be obtained from these four measurements is

$$M_4 = (4.75 + 5.15 + 4.8 + 5.0)/4 = 4.925$$

In the assertion that the arithmetic mean (42) represents s with *least* error we have not yet defined the meaning of the term "least error". This meaning is a relative one: the error made in replacing the n different approximations s_k, $1 \leqslant k \leqslant n$, by the arithmetic mean M_n is the least relative to the sequence of these n approximations which were observed in the measurements. In other words, this number M_n represents the *set* of n numbers s_k with a least error possible. But in fact we have not yet defined what we call "error" when we replace a set of n numbers s_k by a single number x. We only know the deviations $x - s_1, x - s_2$, etc. which can be considered as errors made in replacing s_1 by x, s_2 by x, etc. What we call error in replacing all the numbers s_k by x is a kind of a total error resulting from all partial errors $x - s_k$ for $k = 1, 2, 3, \ldots, n$.

The simple algebraic sum of all the deviations

$$x - s_1, x - s_2, x - s_3, \ldots, x - s_{n-1}, x - s_n \qquad (43)$$

cannot be used as a representation of the total error we are looking for, because this sum can vanish or be negligibly small although the partial deviations (43) are very large. These deviations (43) in general are positive and negative so that a compensation of large positive and large negative terms in the sum of all deviations may be responsible for the smallness of the sum notwithstanding the large values of partial deviations (43).

To avoid this compensation of deviations of opposite sign the sum of *squares* of deviations (43) is introduced as a measure of total deviation of a number x from the *set* of n numbers s_k. Thus, so called *quadratic errors* $(x - s_1)^2$, $(x - s_2)^2$, *etc.* are considered and their arithmetic mean E^2 is introduced as the measure of total error made in replacing n approximations s_k by a single approximation x. Therefore the arithmetic means E^2 is defined as follows

$$nE^2 = (x - s_1)^2 + (x - s_2)^2 + \cdots + (x - s_n)^2 \qquad (44)$$

The square root of E^2 is called *mean quadratic error* and the relation (44) establishes a functional relationship between the mean quadratic error E and x. The best approximation x is defined as the number for which the error E is the least possible. The righthand member of (44) is a sum of squares which reaches its least value when x is the best approximation and our problem is to find this best approximation, namely to prove that the minimum of the mean quadratic error E corresponds to $x = M_n$, that is to the arithmetic mean of observed quantities s_k defined by (42).

Expanding the squares in the righthand member of (44) according to the formula
$$(x - s_k)^2 = x^2 - 2xs_k + s_k^2$$

we write (44) as follows:

$$nE^2 = nx^2 - 2(s_1 + s_2 + s_3 + \cdots + s_n) x + s_1^2 + s_2^2 + s_3^2 + \cdots + s_n^2 \qquad (45)$$

Multiplying both members of (42) by n, we obtain

$$s_1 + s_2 + s_3 + \cdots + s_n = nM_n$$

where M_n is the arithmetic mean of n observations s_k. Transposing nE^2 to the right, replacing the sum $s_1 + s_2 + \cdots + s_n$ by its value nM_n and dividing both sides by n, we rewrite (45) as follows:

$$x^2 - 2M_n x + [(s_1^2 + s_2^2 + s_3^2 + \cdots + s_n^2)/n - E^2] = 0 \qquad (46)$$

The quadratic equation (46) shows that to each value of the mean quadratic error E correspond different approximations x which can be computed by solving the quadratic equation (46). The case of complex roots is excluded because a complex approximate value of a physical quantity has no sense. Thus, the condition of real roots

$$D = 4M_n^2 - 4[s_1^2 + s_2^2 + \cdots + s_n^2)/n - E^2] \geqslant 0$$

must be satisfied. Dividing by 4 and solving this inequality for E^2, we find the least possible value of E^2:

$$E^2 \geqslant (s_1^2 + s_2^2 + s_3^2 + \cdots + s_n^2)/n - M_n^2 \qquad (47)$$

Thus, the minimum of the mean quadratic error E is attained when $D = 0$, that is when the quadratic equation (46) has a double root $x = M_n$ which justifies the choice of the arithmetic mean M_n as the best approximation in the sense of the method of least squares. The minimum of E^2 is equal to

$$\min E^2 = (s_1^2 + s_2^2 + \cdots + s_n^2)/n - M_n^2$$

and if we replace E^2 in (46) by the value of its minimum, the equation (46) reduces indeed to

$$x^2 - 2M_n x + M_n^2 = 0, \text{ or to } (x - M_n)^2 = 0.$$

Radicals $\sqrt[n]{1}$

The quadratic equation is useful in the study of complex n-th roots of one. We begin with the cube root $\sqrt[3]{1} = z$ which satisfies the cubic equation $z^3 = 1$. We have not yet studied the solution of cubic equations but this one can be reduced to a quadratic equation because one of its three roots, namely the root 1, is known. If a product of linear factors is known to vanish for $z = a$ it must contain the particular factor $z - a$ because otherwise it could not take the value zero when a is substituted for z. Therefore, factoring the equation $z^3 - 1 = 0$, we must have the linear factor $z - 1$, the second factor being a quadratic polynomial. To find this second quadratic factor we divide $z^3 - 1$ by $z - 1$, applying the usual operation of long division:

$$
\begin{array}{r}
z^2 + z + 1 \\
z - 1\,\overline{\big|\,z^3 \qquad\qquad - 1} \\
\underline{z^3 - z^2\qquad\qquad} \\
z^2 \\
\underline{z^2 - z\qquad} \\
z - 1 \\
\underline{z - 1}
\end{array}
$$

The quotient is $z^2 + z + 1$, so that we obtain:

$$z^3 - 1 \equiv (z - 1)(z^2 + z + 1) = 0$$

The vanishing of the first factor $z - 1$ corresponds to the known root $\sqrt[3]{1} = 1$, and to find the two other, complex, roots $\sqrt[3]{1}$ it is sufficient to solve the quadratic equation obtained by equating to zero the second factor. This equation:

$$z^2 + z + 1 = 0$$

has, according to the general formula (16), the solutions:

$$z_1 = (-1 + i\sqrt{3})/2; \quad z_2 = (-1 - i\sqrt{3})/2$$

which proves, as we have seen above, that the radical $\sqrt[3]{1}$ has three values $1, z_1, z_2$.

The cubic equation $z^3 = 1$ can also be solved by substituting for the complex unknown z two real unknowns x and y such that $z = x + iy$, and therefore $(x + iy)^3 = 1$. The cube of the sum $x + iy$ can be expanded according to the formula

$$(A + B)^3 \equiv A^3 + 3A^2B + 3AB^2 + B^3 \tag{48}$$

We have already deduced this formula. It can be justified geometrically, if we interpret $(A + B)^3$ as the volume of a cube whose edges have the length $A + B$. Dissecting this cube by three planes parallel to its faces, and which divide the edges into two segments of lengths A and B respectively (fig. 11), we split the cube of volume $(A + B)^3$ into eight parts: two cubes with edges A and B and volumes A^3 and B^3, three equal parallelepipeds with volume A^2B and finally three other equal parallelepipeds with volume AB^2. Thus (48) is seen to be valid.

Using now in (48) $A = x$, $B = iy$ we transform the equation

into

$$(x + iy)^3 = 1$$

$$x^2 + 3ix^2y - 3xy^2 - iy^3 = 1$$

The principle of separation of real and imaginary splits this equation into two real equations with two real unknowns x and y:

$$x^3 - 3xy^2 = 1; \quad 3x^2y - y^3 = y(3x^2 - y^2) = 0$$

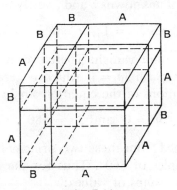

Fig. 7.11

The second equation, a vanishing product of two factors, is satisfied in either of the two cases $y = 0$, or $y^2 = 3x^2$. If $y = 0$, then the first equation reduced to $x^3 = 1$ and, the unknown x being a real number, $x = 1$. Thus, a real value $z = 1 + i \cdot 0 = 1$ of the radical $\sqrt[3]{1}$ is obtained.

If $y^2 = 3x^2$, then substituting $3x^2$ for y^2 in the first equation, we transform it into

$$x^3 - 3x \cdot 3x^2 = 1, \text{ that is, } -8x^3 = 1$$

The number x is found by extracting cubic roots on both sides. Since x must be real by definition, the cube root of 1 is one, so that

$$\sqrt[3]{-8x^3} = -2x = 1$$

and thus to $y^2 = 3x^2$ corresponds $x = -1/2$. Knowing the value $-1/2$ of x, we can compute y: $y^2 = 3x^2 = 3/4$ and therefore $y = \pm\sqrt{3}/2$ which gives the two complex values of $\sqrt[3]{1}$, namely $(-1 \pm i\sqrt{3})/2$.

Let us consider finally the complex polar form of the same radical $\sqrt[3]{1} = z$, namely $z = r(\cos v + i \sin v)$. The equation

$$z^3 = r^3(\cos v + i \sin v)^3 = 1$$

involves two unknowns v and r. The unknown r represents the length of the vector $z = \sqrt[3]{1}$ and therefore it cannot vanish and must have a positive value. Applying (14), Chapter 6, we write our equation as

$$r^3(\cos 3v + i \sin 3v) = r^3 \cos 3v + ir^3 \sin 3v = 1$$

Therefore, our two real unknowns v and r verify the two real equations:

$$r^3 \cos 3v = 1; \quad r^3 \sin 3v = 0.$$

We know that r^3 cannot vanish. Therefore, it is the second factor $\sin 3v$ of the product $r^3 \sin 3v = 0$ which is zero, $\sin 3v = 0$. There are two principal solutions of the equation $\sin 3v = 0$, namely

$$3v = 0° \text{ and } 3v = 180°.$$

The others are obtained from these two principal solutions by adding or substracting multiples of 360°. Thus for the angle $3v$ whose sine vanishes we have two groups of values:

$$3v = 0° + 360° n; \quad 3v = 180° + 360° n.$$

But the second group is inadmissible because it contradicts the first equation. Indeed, if

$$3v = 180° + 360° n, \quad \text{then } \cos 3v = \cos 180° = -1$$

which is incompatible with $r^3 \cos 3v = 1$, because r^3 is a positive number. Therefore, $3v = 360° n$, which gives $\cos 3v = 1$ and therefore, using the first equation, $r^3 = 1$.

Thus the two unknowns are found:

$$r = 1 \text{ and } v = 120° n$$

where n is an integer, positive, negative or zero. We are interested in the values of $\cos v$ and $\sin v$, and these values do not change when the argument v increases or decreases by 360°. Therefore, it is sufficient to consider only three consecutive values of the integer n, for instance $n = 0, 1, 2$ because $v = 120° n$ increases or decreases by 360° when we add or subtract three from n. In other words, we obtain only three different values of $\sqrt[3]{1}$ and they correspond to

$$v = 0°, \quad v = 120°, \quad v = 240°$$

These three values of the radical $\sqrt[3]{1}$ agree with those obtained by other methods.

Radical $\sqrt[4]{1}$

These values of $\sqrt[4]{1}$ are roots of the quartic equation $z^4 - 1 = 0$ which is easy to solve by factoring:

$$z^4 - 1 \equiv (z^2)^2 - 1^2 \equiv (z^2 - 1)(z^2 + 1)$$
$$\equiv (z - 1)(z + 1)(z - i)(z + i) = 0$$

A product of four factors vanishes, if one of them is zero. Therefore, there are four possible cases and our equation of fourth order is equivalent to a set of four linear equations

$$z - 1 = 0, \quad z + 1 = 0, \quad z - i = 0, \quad z + i = 0$$

which must be considered separately. Thus the radical $\sqrt[4]{1}$ has four different values

$$z_1 = 1, \quad z_2 = -1, \quad z_3 = i, \quad z_4 = -i.$$

The two complex roots z_3, z_4 are conjugate complex numbers as it must be since the coefficients of our equation are real numbers.

In the solution of the equation $z^4 - 1 = 0$ just discussed the quadratic equation does not play a role, but if we solve the equation $(x + iy)^4 - 1 = 0$, separating real and imaginary, an incomplete quartic equation, which can be solved as a quadratic equation, gives the solution of our problem. To apply this second method we need an algebraical identity which gives the expansion of the fourth power $(A + B)^4$ of a sum of two terms $A + B$:

$$(A + B)^4 \equiv A^4 + 4A^3B + 6A^2B^2 + 4AB^3 + B^4 \qquad (49)$$

The identity (49) can be deduced from the expansion (48) of the cube $(A + B)^3$ of the sum $A + B$, multiplying both sides by $A + B$. Substituting in (49) x for A and iy for B, we obtain the identity:

$$(x + iy)^4 \equiv x^3 + 4ix^3y - 6x^2y^2 - 4ixy^3 + y^4$$

which allows us to split the equation $(x + iy)^4 = 1$ into two real equations with two real unknowns x and y:

$$x^4 - 6x^2y^2 + y^4 = 1; \quad 4xy(x^2 - y^2) = 0$$

The second equation, after the elimination of the numerical factor 4, can be factored as follows:

$$xy(x + y)(x - y) = 0$$

We have therefore four cases to consider: $x = 0$, $y = 0$, $x = -y$, $x = y$. If $x = 0$, the expression of y^2 in terms of x^2 gives $y^4 = 1$ and thus $y^2 = 1$ and $y = \pm 1$. The first case $x = 0$ gives therefore two values i and $-i$ of the radical $x + iy = \sqrt[4]{1}$. The second case, $y = 0$, gives likewise $x^2 = 1$, and two other values 1 and -1 of $\sqrt[4]{1}$ are obtained. The third and fourth cases which arise from $x^2 = y^2$ are incompatible with the first equation, because if $x^2 = y^2$ the first equation becomes $-4x^4 = -4y^4 = 1$ and the negative values of $x^4 = y^4 = -1/4$ contradict the fact that both x and y are real numbers.

Radical $\sqrt[5]{1}$

The fives values of the radical $\sqrt[5]{1}$ can be found with the aid of a quadratic equation applying the separation of real and imaginary to the complex equation $z^5 = 1$ satisfied by the values $z = x + iy$ of the radical $z = \sqrt[5]{1}$.

To perform the separation of real and imaginary in $(x + iy)^5 = 1$ we need the expansion of the fifth power $(A + B)^5$ of a sum of two numbers $A + B$:

$$(A + B)^5 \equiv A^5 + 5A^4B + 10A^3B^2 + 10A^2B^3 + 5AB^4 + B^5 \qquad (50)$$

The identity (50) can be deduced from that of (49), multiplying both members of (49) by the sum $A + B$, exactly as (49) was deduced from (48).

Substituting in (50) x and iy for A and B respectively, and using the expansion of the fifth power $(x + iy)^5$ thus obtained in the left-hand member of the equation $(x + iy)^5 = 1$, we transform this equation into the system:

$$x^5 - 10x^3y^2 + 5xy^4 = 1; \quad 5x^4y - 10x^2y^3 + y^5 = 0$$

The second equation of this system of two equations with two real unknowns x and y can also be written as follows:

$$x^4 y[(y/x)^4 - 10(y/x)^2 + 5] = 0$$

The first factor x^4 cannot vanish because if $x = 0$, then the first equation would become a contradiction $0 = 1$. Since $x^4 \neq 0$, only two cases are to be considered in solving the second equation of the system:

$$y = 0 \text{ or } (y/x)^4 - 10(y/x)^2 + 5 = 0.$$

In the first case, when $y = 0$, the first equation reduces to $x^5 = 1$ and its solution $x = 1$ must be associated with $y = 0$, which gives the real value of our radical namely $\sqrt[5]{1} = 1 + 0 \cdot i = 1$.

The four complex values of $\sqrt[5]{1}$ are obtained by solving the system

$$x^5 - 10x^3y^2 + 5xy^4 = 1, \quad t^2 - 10t + 5 = 0$$

where we use an auxiliary unknown t such that $(y/x)^2 = t$. Substituting this auxiliary unknown t for $(y/x)^2$ in the equation $(y/x)^4 - 10(y/x)^2 + 5 = 0$ we obtain indeed $t^2 - 10t + 5 = 0$.

Thus, the quadratic equation $t^2 - 10t + 5 = 0$ is the tool with which can be found the four complex values of $\sqrt[5]{1}$. Solving it, we obtain two values for the square $(y/x)^2$ of the ratio (y/x):

$$(y/x)^2 = t_1 = 5 + 2\sqrt{5}; \quad (y/x)^2 = t_2 = 5 - 2\sqrt{5}$$

We turn now to the first equation of the system. Since $y^2/x^2 = t$, we can replace y^2 and y^4 by tx^2 and t^2x^4 respectively and write the first equation as follows:

$$x^5 - 10x^5 t + 5x^5 t^2 = 1$$

Picking out the common factor x^5, we have also

$$x^5(1 - 10t + 5t^2) = 1$$

This form of the first equation gives us the value of x when t is known. Substituting in it the value $t_1 = 5 + 2\sqrt{5}$ for t we find for the corresponding value x_1 of x the equation

$$x_1^5[1 - 10(5 + 2\sqrt{5}) + 5(5 + 2\sqrt{5})^2]$$

$$= x_1^5(176 + 80\sqrt{5}) = x_1^5(1 + \sqrt{5})^5 = 1$$

because, as it is easy to verify with the aid of (50),

$$(1 + \sqrt{5})^5 = 176 + 80\sqrt{5}$$

Extracting the fifth root on both sides of the equation $x_1^5(1 + \sqrt{5})^5 = 1$, we find for x_1 the equation $x_1(1 + \sqrt{5}) = 1$, so that to t_1 corresponds the value x_1 of x where

$$x_1 = 1/(\sqrt{5} + 1) = (\sqrt{5} - 1)/[(\sqrt{5} + 1)(\sqrt{5} - 1)] = (\sqrt{5} - 1)/4$$

Squaring x_1 we have

$$x_1^2 = (\sqrt{5} - 1)^2/16 = (6 - 2\sqrt{5})/16 = (3 - \sqrt{5})/8$$

and we can now find the value of $y^2 = tx^2$. Since we are dealing with the first value t_1 of t, we denote the corresponding value of y^2 by y_1^2 and thus

$$y_1^2 = t_1 x_1^2 = (5 + 2\sqrt{5})(3 - \sqrt{5})/8 = (5 + \sqrt{5})/8 = (10 + 2\sqrt{5})/16$$

Extracting the square root, two symmetrical values for y_1 are obtained and thus, for $t = t_1$, we find two conjugate complex values of $\sqrt[4]{1}$:

$$z_2 = [\sqrt{5} - 1 + i(10 + 2\sqrt{5})^{1/2}]/4 \quad \text{and}$$

$$z_3 = [\sqrt{5} - 1 - i(10 + 2\sqrt{5})^{1/2}]/4$$

because to $t = t_1$, $x = x_1 = (\sqrt{5} - 1)/4$ correspond two values of

$$y_1 = \pm(10 + 2\sqrt{5})^{1/2}/4$$

We have used the equation

$$x^5(1 - 10t + 5t^2) = 1 \text{ with } t = t_1,$$

but it can and must also be used with $t = t_2 = 5 - 2\sqrt{5}$. The computation is the same as with $t = t_1$ with the only difference that the sign before the square root $\sqrt{5}$ must be replaced by the opposite sign. Thus we obtain

$$x = x_2 = (-\sqrt{5} - 1)/4 = -(\sqrt{5} + 1)/4$$

as well as

$$y_2 = \pm(10 - 2\sqrt{5})^{1/2}/4$$

Therefore, to $t = t_2$ correspond also two complex conjugate values of the radical $\sqrt[5]{1}$, namely

$$z_4 = [-\sqrt{5} - 1 + i(10 - 2\sqrt{5})^{1/2}]/4 \text{ and}$$

$$z_5 = [-\sqrt{5} - 1 - i(10 - 2\sqrt{5})^{1/2}]/4$$

Together with the real value $z_1 = 1$ we have now all five values of $\sqrt[5]{1}$.

It is possible to compute the four complex values z_2, z_3, z_4, z_5 solving the quartic equation $z^4 + z^3 + z^2 + z + 1 = 0$ which has them as its roots and it is interesting to observe that again this equation of fourth order is reducible to a quadratic equation. First we have to prove that the four complex values of $\sqrt[5]{1}$ are roots of the equation $z^4 + z^3 + z^2 + z + 1 = 0$. The five values of the radical $\sqrt[5]{1}$ are roots of the equation $z^5 - 1 = 0$ and one of these five roots is known: it is $z_1 = 1$. Therefore, the linear expression $z - 1$ is a factor of the product obtained by factoring the difference $z^5 - 1$. The simplest way of proving that the second factor will be $z^4 + z^3 + z^2 + z + 1$ is to check by direct multiplication and show that

$$(z - 1)(z^4 + z^3 + z^2 + z + 1) \equiv z^5 - 1.$$

But this operation presupposes the result to be proved: it is only a justification of a fact we already know. On the other hand, dividing $z^5 - 1$ by $z - 1$ we find the second factor without assuming its knowledge:

$$
\begin{array}{r}
z^4 + z^3 + z^2 + z + 1 \\
\hline
z - 1\,)\,z^5 \qquad\qquad\qquad\qquad - 1 \\
\underline{z^5 - z^4} \\
z^4 \\
\underline{z^4 - z^3} \\
z^3 \\
\underline{z^3 - z^2} \\
z^2 \\
\underline{z^2 - z} \\
z - 1 \\
\underline{z - 1}
\end{array}
$$

After the elimination of the factor $z - 1$ corresponding to the known root $z_1 = 1$, remains the quartic equation

$$z^4 + z^3 + z^2 + z + 1 = 0 \tag{51}$$

To solve it we first divide (51) by z^2 transforming it by this division into

$$z^2 + z + 1 + 1/z + 1/z^2 = 0 \tag{52}$$

The equation (52) can be reduced to a quadratic equation with the aid of the substitution $z + 1/z = t$. If this relation $z + 1/z = t$ is squared,

$$z^2 + 2 + 1/z^2 = t^2$$

is obtained and therefore the sum $z^2 + 1/z^2$ is equal to $t^2 - 2$.

Replacing in (52) $z + 1/z$ and $z^2 + 1/z^2$ by t and $t^2 - 2$ respectively, we obtain instead of a quartic equation in z a quadratic equation in t:

$$t^2 + t - 1 = 0$$

The two roots of the equation in t are

$$t_1 = (-1 + \sqrt{5})/2 \text{ and } t_2 = (-1 - \sqrt{5})/2$$

If the value of t is known, the relation $z + 1/z = t$ becomes an equation for the unknown z. Multiplying it by z and transposing the term tz to the left, we obtain for z a quadratic equation

$$z^2 - tz + 1 = 0$$

Since we know two different values of t we obtain in fact two different quadratic equations for z namely:

$$z^2 - (-1 + \sqrt{5})\, z/2 + 1 = 0 \text{ and } z^2 + (1 + \sqrt{5})\, z/2 + 1 = 0$$

Computing their roots with the aid of the general formula (16), we find again the four complex values of $\sqrt[5]{1}$ obtained above. We omit the details of numerical computations and mention here only that the value of the discriminant for the first equation is

$$(-1 + \sqrt{5})^2/4 - 4 = (6 - 2\sqrt{5})/4 - 16/4 = -(10 + 2\sqrt{5})/4$$

so that the square root of it is equal to

$$\pm i(10 + 2\sqrt{5})^{1/2}/2$$

For the second equation the discriminant has the value $-(10 - 2\sqrt{5})/4$ and its root is equal to

$$\pm i(10 - 2\sqrt{5})^{1/2}/2$$

The method just used to solve the equation (51) can be applied with success to all quartic equations which belong to the special type

$$Az^4 + Bz^3 + Cz^2 \pm Bz + A = 0$$

In such quartic equations the coefficient of z^4 and the constant term are equal, while the coefficients of z^3 and z have equal absolute values.

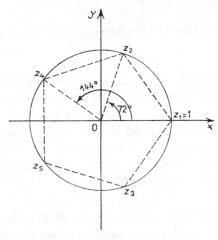

Fig. 7.12

If their signs are the same, as was the case with the equation (51), the substitution $z + 1/z = t$ is used, but if their signs are different, $z - 1/z = t$ must be used.

The values of $\sqrt[5]{1}$ can be used to find the sine and cosine of 18°, 36°, 54°, and 72°. As we know the five values of $\sqrt[5]{1}$ are represented in the plane of the complex numbers $z = x + iy$ by five vertices of a regular pentagon inscribed in the circle of radius one and having one of its vertices at the point $z_1 = 1$ (see fig. 12). For all of them $|\sqrt[5]{1}| = 1$. Therefore

$$z_2 = \cos 72° + i \sin 72°; \qquad z_4 = \cos 144° + i \sin 144°$$

Comparing these trigonometrical expressions of z_2 and z_4 with their numerical expressions

$$z_2 = [\sqrt{5} - 1 + i(10 + 2\sqrt{5})^{1/2}]/4$$

$$z_4 = [-\sqrt{5} - 1 + i(10 - 2\sqrt{5})^{1/2}]/4$$

we find the following values of sine and cosine of 72° and 144°:

$$\cos\ 72° = \sin 18° = (\sqrt{5} - 1)/4 = 1.236 \ldots /4 = 0.309 \ldots$$

$$\sin\ 72° = \cos 18° = (10 + 2\sqrt{5})^{1/2}/4 = \sqrt{14.472} \ldots /4 = 0.976 \ldots$$

$$\cos 144° = \cos 36° = -\sin 54° = -(\sqrt{5} + 1)/4 = -3.236 \ldots /4$$
$$= -0.809 \ldots$$

$$\sin 144° = \sin 36° = \cos 54° = (10 - 2\sqrt{5})^{1/2}/4 = \sqrt{5.527} \ldots /4$$
$$= 0.587 \ldots$$

Case $a = 0$: The study of quadratic equations would be incomplete if we failed to discuss what happens to the roots of $ax^2 + bx + c = 0$ when the first coefficient a tends to zero. We do not say that a is zero, because in such a case we would have a linear equation $bx + c = 0$. What we want to study is the behaviour of the two roots x_1 and x_2 given by (16) when a approaches zero. At the limit, when a reaches zero, the quadratic equation $ax^2 + bx + c = 0$ is transformed into a linear equation $bx + c = 0$ which has the root $x = -c/b$. Therefore, it is plain that *one* of the two roots x_1, x_2 must at the limit, for $a = 0$, take the value $-c/b$. But it is necessary to prove this fact and moreover it is interesting to know what happens to the root, whose limit is not equal to $-c/b$.

To answer this question we cannot use the general solution (16) because the denominator of x_1 and x_2 is precisely the coefficient a. But the expression of two roots given by (16) can be transformed in such a way that the coefficient a in the denominator will cancel out. Let us first consider the root x_1 whose expression is

$$x_1 = [-b + (b^2 - 4ac)^{1/2}]/(2a)$$

Multiplying the numerator and the denominator of this fraction by the same number $b + (b^2 - 4ac)^{1/2}$, we do not change its value and therefore a new expression for x_1 is obtained:

$$x_1 = [-b + (b^2 - 4ac)^{1/2}]\,[b + (b^2 - 4ac)^{1/2}]/2a[b + (b^2 - 4ac)^{1/2}]$$
$$= (b^2 - 4ac - b^2)/2a[b + (b^2 - 4ac)^{1/2}]$$
$$= -4ac/2a[b + (b^2 - 4ac)^{1/2}] = -2c/[b + (b^2 - 4ac)^{1/2}]$$

This form of x_1
$$x_1 = -2c/[b + (b^2 - 4ac)^{1/2}]$$

is well adapted to our purpose. When the coefficient a vanishes, the denominator takes the value $2b$, so that x_1 at the limit for $a = 0$ becomes equal to $-c/b$.

We formulate this result in writing

$$\lim_{a=0} x_1 = -c/b.$$

This allows us to find out what happens to the second root x_2 because the product of two roots $x_1 x_2$ is equal to c/a. This relation

$$x_1 x_2 = c/a$$

solved for x_2 gives

$$\lim_{a=0} x_2 = \lim_{a=0} (c/ax_1) = -\lim_{a=0} (b/a) = \infty$$

Thus, when the first coefficient a of a quadratic equation vanishes, one of its roots becomes infinite, while the other approaches $-c/b$.

This conclusion has a practical importance because it can happen that a quadratic equation has its first coefficient a exceedingly small in comparison with the two other coefficients b and c. In such a case one of the two roots is extremely large, while the other is very near to $-c/b$. Thus, if the solution of the problem which corresponds to such a quadratic equation does not admit of an extremely large answer, the quadratic equation $ax^2 + bx + c = 0$ with a very small coefficient a can be replaced by the approximate linear equation $bx + c = 0$ and the solution $-c/b$ of this linear equation is a good approximation to the solution of the problem.

To take an example let us consider the equation

$$0.00001x^2 - 5x + 1 = 0$$

If we are not interested in an answer which is extremely large, we replace this equation by $-5x + 1 = 0$ and consider the solution of this linear equation 0.2 as an approximate value of the root x_1 of the quadratic equation. The second root x_2 is very large and its approximate value can be deduced with the aid of the relation

$$x_1 x_2 = c/a = 1/0.00001 = 100000$$

Substituting in it 0.2 for x_1, we obtain for x_2 the approximate value

$$x_2 \sim 100000/0.2 = 500000$$

Thus we avoid the exact computation of x_1 which is long and tedious.

Quadratic Equations and Continued Fractions

In Chapter 4 it was mentioned without proof that a solution of a quadratic equation can be represented by a convergent infinite periodic continued fraction, if this solution is a real number. We do not intend to develop here the proof which is given in Appendix IV. Our aim is to describe this representation of a real root of the quadratic equation by a continued fraction.

Given an equation $ax^2 + bx + c = 0$, with $a \neq 0$, we divide it by a and denote the quotients b/a and c/a by p and $-q$ respectively, so that the equation is now:

$$x^2 + px - q = 0.$$

It is still a general quadratic equation with the discriminant

$$D = p^2 + 4q.$$

We suppose that its roots are not complex and therefore we consider the case when $p^2 + 4q$ is not negative:

$$p^2 + 4q \geqslant 0.$$

To solve our equation we transpose the constant term $-q$ to the right and pick out the common factor x in the first two terms:

$$x(p + x) = q.$$

Dividing both sides by the sum $p + x$, we obtain the recurrent relation

$$x = q/(p + x).$$

It is recurrent in the sense that one can insert for x which stands in the denominator $p + x$ of the righthand member its value $q/(p + x)$ given by this relation. A finite continued fraction with two links is thus obtained

$$x = \cfrac{q}{p + \cfrac{q}{p + x}}$$

It still involves x in the righthand member and therefore cannot be considered as a solution of the quadratic equation $x^2 + px - q = 0$. But the operation can be repeated and the number of links of the continued fraction can be increased *without limit*. The final result is an infinite periodic continued fraction

$$x = \cfrac{q}{p + \cfrac{q}{p + \cfrac{q}{p + \cfrac{q}{p + \cfrac{q}{p + \cdots}}}}}$$

which has no last link and therefore no longer involves the unknown x.

This infinite continued fraction represents a solution of the quadratic equation $x^2 + px - q = 0$. Its numerators a_n are all equal to q, $a_n = q$, while the denominators b_n are all equal to p, $b_n = p$. It cannot represent a complex number because all its elements are real numbers and therefore it must diverge, if $p^2 + 4q < 0$. If $p^2 + 4q \geqslant 0$, this periodic continued fraction converges (Appendix IV) and represents the root of least absolute value. If we denote the roots as usual, that is

$$x_1 = [-p + (p^2 + 4q)^{1/2}]/2; \quad x_2 = [-p - (p^2 + 4q)^{1/2}]/2$$

the root of least absolute value represented by the continued fraction is x_1, if the coefficient p is positive, and x_2 if p is negative.

EXAMPLE: The equation $x^2 + 5x - 6 = 0$ has two, real roots $x_1 = 1$, and $x_2 = -6$. The root represented by the continued fraction is here $x_1 = 1$ and we have

$$1 = \cfrac{6}{5 + \cfrac{6}{5 + \cfrac{6}{5 + \cfrac{6}{5 + \cfrac{6}{5 + \cdots}}}}}$$

We end our study of quadratic equations by observing that some special quadratic equations were already solved by the Greek mathematician Diophantus *circa* 250 A.D. Hindu mathematicians used square roots and Iranians completely solved the general equation $ax^2 + bx + c = 0$ in the ninth century A.D. Al. Khowarizmi used the method of factoring the difference of two squares, as we did in this chapter.

CHAPTER 8

Cubic and Quartic Equations

In Chapter 7 we have studied the solutions of a linear equation

$$bx + c = 0$$

and of a quadratic equation

$$ax^2 + bx + c = 0.$$

While the solution of the linear equation, $x = -c/b$, is obtained as result of a division, the solution of the quadratic equation as given by formula (16) in Chapter 7 necessitates the extraction of a square root which is more complicated operation than a division. When we introduce now a term with the third power x^3 of the unknown x, forming a equation of third order, so called *cubic equation,*

$$Ax^3 + Bx^2 + Cx + D = 0 \qquad (1)$$

its solution is performed with the aid of extraction of a cube root.

The necessity of using the cube root is exemplified already in the simplest case of the equation $z^3 - 1 = 0$, whose three solutions are values of the cube root $\sqrt[3]{1}$, namely

$$z_1 = 1, z_2 = \left(-1 + i\sqrt{3}\right)/2, \text{ and } z_3 = \left(-1 - i\sqrt{3}\right)/2$$

They play an important role in the solution of the general equation (1) because the expressions of three roots of (1) in terms of four coefficients A, B, C, D involve also z_2 and z_3. A special notation is used for the complex number z_2 in the theory of cubic equation. We will denote it by the last letter of the Greek alphabet, namely ω (omega):

$$z_2 = \omega = \left(-1 + i\sqrt{3}\right)/2.$$

The square of ω is equal to z_3 because z_2 and z_3 are rotation factors through 120° and 240°, respectively, so that

$$z_3 = z_2^2 = \omega^2.$$

Thus, we will use the three values of the radical $\sqrt[3]{1}$ denoting them by 1, ω, ω^2. In Chapter 7 we have obtained z_2 and z_3 as two roots of the quadratic equation $z^2 + z + 1 = 0$. Therefore, the symbol ω verifies the equation

$$\omega^2 + \omega + 1 = 0, \quad \text{as well as} \quad \omega^3 = 1.$$

The fact that the solutions of equations of second and third orders are performed with the aid of extractions of square and cube roots respectively, may suggest that the equation of fourth order, which involves powers of the unknown x not exceeding the fourth power x^4, is solved with the aid of radicals of fourth order, but this guess is wrong: the general equation of fourth order

$$Ax^4 + Bx^3 + Cx^2 + Dx + E = 0 \qquad (2)$$

—as we will see in this chapter—has four roots and the expressions of these four roots in terms of five coefficients A, B, C, D, E involve radicals of second and third order only, that is equation (2) is solved with the aid of operations which include four rational operations of addition, subtraction, multiplication, division, and also square and cube roots. In this respect there is no difference between equations (1) and (2).

It is important to mention that only quadratic, cubic, and quartic equations can be solved exactly with the aid of extractions of roots. Equations of higher order, beginning with the equation of fifth order cannot be solved in the sense in which a quadratic equations is solved by general expressions of its roots (equation (16) of Chapter 7) in terms of its coefficients: no algebraical formula involving four rational operations and radicals of any order can express the roots of equations of orders exceeding fourth order. After the formulas giving general solutions of cubic and quartic equations were found, mathematicians of ten generations have spent enormous efforts trying in vain to find the similar solutions for equations of fifth and higher orders. The profound reason of their failure was found only at the beginning of the nineteenth century when the French mathematician Galois discovered and proved that such solutions are simply impossible.

In this chapter we will study the solution of general equations (1) and (2) and deduce algebraical formulas expressing the three roots of (1) and the four roots of (2) in terms of their respective coefficients.

Cubic Equations

We know that a cubic equation has three roots. Suppose that they are prescribed, that is, a cubic equation is known to possess three *given* roots, x_1, x_2, and x_3. The question arises what are the coefficients of this equation? In other words, what is the cubic equation having these known roots?

It is easy to write down a linear equation whose root is x_1: it is plain that the equation $x - x_1 = 0$ has the solution $x = x_1$. Likewise the linear equations $x - x_2 = 0$ and $x - x_3 = 0$ have the roots x_2 and x_3, respectively. These equations

$$x - x_1 = 0; \quad x - x_2 = 0; \quad x - x_3 = 0$$

have together three prescribed roots x_1, x_2, x_3, but we want a single equation of third order having the same three roots. It is formed by multiplying out the three linear equations. The equation thus obtained

$$(x - x_1)(x - x_2)(x - x_3) = 0$$

is indeed a cubic equation because, performing the multiplication of three linear factors, a polynomial of third order in x is formed:

$$x^3 - (x_1 + x_2 + x_3) x^2 + (x_2 x_3 + x_3 x_1 + x_1 x_3) x - x_1 x_2 x_3 = 0 \quad (3)$$

The cubic equation (3) has prescribed roots x_1, x_2, x_3 because it can also be written as a vanishing product of three linear factors $(x - x_1)(x - x_2)(x - x_3)$ and this product vanishes in there cases when each one of its three factors is zero. Therefore, the equation (3) is satisfied if $x - x_1 = 0$ or if $x - x_2 = 0$ or, finally, if $x - x_3 = 0$.

Comparing (3) with the general form (1) of a cubic equation, we must first of all transform (1) in such a way that its principal term with x^3 be simply x^3 otherwise we cannot identify (3) and (1). This is done by dividing (1) by the coefficient A. This division is certainly possible because the coefficient A cannot be zero. Should A vanish we would not have a cubic equation. Therefore, the equation (1) can be written as follows:

$$x^3 + (B/A) x^2 + (C/A) x + (D/A) = 0 \qquad (4)$$

Identifying now the equations (3) and (4), which both represent general cubic equation and expressing the fact that their coefficients are equal, we find three relations between the roots and the coefficients of a general cubic equation. These three relations are:

$$-(x_1 + x_2 + x_3) = B/A; \quad x_1x_2 + x_2x_3 + x_3x_1 = C/A;$$

$$-x_1x_2x_3 = D/A \tag{5}$$

The relations (5) are analogous in the theory of cubic equations to relations (17) in Chapter 7, namely to

$$-(x_1 + x_2) = b/a \text{ and } x_1x_2 = c/a$$

for the quadratic equation. They can be rewritten also as follows

$$B = -A(x_1 + x_2 + x_3); \quad C = A(x_1x_2 + x_2x_3 + x_3x_1)$$

$$D = -A(x_1x_2x_3) \tag{5*}$$

where the coefficient A can be chosen independently of three roots. But, if the roots are prescribed and the coefficient A is already chosen, the three other coefficients are to be computed according to (5*) and thus the formation of a cubic equation having prescribed roots is governed by the rule (5*).

EXAMPLE: Let us suppose that a certain cubic equation has as its three roots the numbers 1, 2, 3. To write it down we must first of all fix our choice of the first coefficient A. The simplest choice is $A = 1$ and we compute now the three other coefficients B, C, D in the hypothesis that $A = 1$. The rule (5) gives now, with $A = 1$, $x_1 = 1$, $x_2 = 2$, and $x_3 = 3$:

$$B = -(1 + 2 + 3) = -6; \quad C = 1 \cdot 2 + 2 \cdot 3 + 3 \cdot 1 = 11$$

$$D = -1 \cdot 2 \cdot 3 = -6$$

and the cubic equation having the roots 1, 2, 3 is formed:

$$x^3 - 6x^2 + 11x - 6 = 0. \tag{6}$$

We observe that the sum of its four coefficients $1 - 6 + 11 - 6$ is equal to zero. The lefthand member of (6) reduces to the sum of coefficients if the value of x is one. Therefore, substituting one for x, we see that the equation is satisfied because the sum of coefficients is zero. The vanishing of the sum of all coefficients is thus explained by the fact that this particular equation has one of its roots equal to one and it is a general rule which holds for all algebraical equations of any order: if the sum of coefficients in an equation is zero, $x = 1$ is a root of the equation. *Vice versa*, if $x = 1$ is a root of an equation, the sum of all coefficients of this equation vanishes.

As another example of important relations (5) we consider the case of a very simple cubic equation $x^3 - 1 = 0$, whose three roots are, as we know,

$$x_1 = 1, \ x_2 = \omega, \quad \text{and} \quad x_3 = \omega^2$$

where the symbol ω denotes the complex number $(-1 + i\sqrt{3})/2$. The coefficients of the equation $x^3 - 1 = 0$ are $A = 1$, $B = 0$, $C = 0$, and $D = -1$. Therefore, the relations (5) give for it

$$1 + \omega + \omega^2 = 0, \quad \omega + \omega^3 + \omega^2 = 0, \quad \text{and} \quad 1 \cdot \omega \cdot \omega^2 = 1$$

The second relation follows from the first because it can be written, picking out the common factor ω, as follows $\omega(1 + \omega_1 + \omega^2) = 0$.

Before discussing the solution of the general equation (1), we will show on the example of the equation (6) how a cubic equation can be reduced to a simplified form in which the quadratic term containing x^2 is missing.

The first two terms of the complete equation (6), namely $x^3 - 6x^2$, may be interpreted as first two terms in the expansion of the cube $(A + B)^3$ of a sum of two numbers A, B. The identity (48) in Chapter 7 shows that these two first terms are $A^3 + 3A^2B$ so that $A = x$ and $-6 = 3B$. We find that the cube of the difference $x - 2$ has the same first two terms as our equation (6), namely

$$(x - 2)^3 = x^3 - 6x^2 + 12x - 8$$

Therefore, we can rewrite the equation (6) replacing $x^3 - 6x^2$ by its value obtained from the expansion of $(x - 2)^3$, namely $x^3 - 6x^2 = (x - 2)^3 - 12x + 8$:

$$(x - 2)^3 - 12x + 8 + 11x - 6 = (x - 2)^3 - (x - 2) = 0$$

We see that this new form of the equation (6) can be written very simply, if we use, instead of the variable x, the difference $x - 2$ as our unknown. Introducing an auxiliary variable t related to our original unknown x by the substitution $x - 2 = t$, we have indeed the equation $t^3 - t = 0$. This cubic equation has no term with t^2 and this fact is a corollary of our substitution of $t = x - 2$ for x. That it has no constant term either is an accidental peculiarity of the equation (6) and it does not happen in general. This peculiar circumstance allows us to solve rapidly the incomplete cubic equation in t: picking out the common factor t and factoring $t^2 - 1$ which remains, after the common factor t was removed, we obtain

$$t^3 - t = t(t^2 - 1) = t(t + 1)(t - 1) = 0$$

and the three roots of the simplified equation are

$$t_1 = -1, t_2 = 0, \text{ and } t_3 = 1$$

Now, knowing the values of the auxiliary variable t, we deduce from them the corresponding values of the principal unknown $x = t + 2$:

$$x_1 = -1 + 2 = 1, x_2 = 0 + 2 = 2, \text{ and } x_3 = 1 + 2 = 3$$

which agrees well with the definition of this equation (6).

Simplified Form of Cubic Equation

The reduction of a complete cubic equation to its simplified form in which the quadratic term with the square of the unknown is missing is always the first step of its solution. This reduction is performed with the aid of a substitution for x of an auxiliary variable t related to x by a linear relation $t = x + m$. The constant term m must be chosen in such a way that the new equation in t will have no term with t^2.

Denoting the simplified form of the general equation (1) by

$$t^3 + pt + q = 0$$

we will now deduce the expressions of two coefficients p, q of the equation in t in terms of the four coefficients of the original equation (1).

To compute their expressions we observe that $x = t - m$ gives following expressions of x^2 and x^3 in terms of t and m:

$$x^2 = t^2 - 2mt + m^2; \quad x^3 = t^3 - 3mt^2 + 3m^2t - m^3.$$

Substituting the expressions of x, x^2, x^3 in terms of t and m in the equation (1) and adding the terms which contain the same power of t, we transform (1) into a cubic equation in t:

$$At^3 + (-3Am + B)t^2 + (3m^2A - 2mB + C)t$$

$$+ [-m^3A + m^2B - mC + D] = 0 \tag{7}$$

In this equation the number m is not yet chosen and its value is at our disposal. We want to cancel the term with t^2 and this can be done by annihilating its coefficient $B - 3mA$. In this coefficient the undetermined element m can be fixed in such a way that the coefficient vanishes: $B - 3mA = 0$. This condition, imposed on the coefficient, becomes for m an equation which will yield the value of m to be used in the substitution $t = x + m$. If $B - 3mA = 0$, then $m = B/(3A)$ and the final form of the substitution is

$$t = x + B/(3A) \text{ or } x = t - B/(3A)$$

Using this value of m in the expressions of the coefficient p of t and of the constant term q in the equation

$$t^3 + pt + q = 0$$

obtained by dividing (7) by A,

$$p = (3m^2A - 2mB + C)/A, \quad q = (-m^3A + m^2B - mC + D)/A$$

we deduce the following rule for writing down the simplified form in t for any complete cubic equation with known coefficients A, B, C, D:

$$p = C/A - (B/A)^2/3; \quad q = D/A - BC/(3A^2) + 2(B/A)^3/27 \quad (8)$$

We formulate now the rule which we have just deduced: Given a complete cubic equation with known coefficients A, B, C, D form the expressions p and q given in terms of A, B, C, D by (8) and write down the equation in t, namely

$$t^3 + pt + q = 0$$

The roots of the complete equation (1) and of this equation in t are related by

$$x = t - B/(3A)$$

so that the roots of (1) are deduced from those of the equation $t^3 + pt + q = 0$.

It is sufficient therefore to solve the reduced equation $t^3 + pt + q = 0$. In general the four coefficients of the complete equation (1) are any complex numbers and the coefficients p, q of the reduced equation, given by (8), are also complex numbers. Nothing can be said about the nature of three roots of a cubic equation in this general case. But, if the coefficients A, B, C, D of (1) are real numbers then the expressions (8) of p and q prove that the coefficients of the reduced equation are real numbers too. In this particular case the reduced cubic equation

$$t^3 + pt + q = 0 \tag{9}$$

can have complex roots but, as it was proved in the preceding chapter, its eventual complex roots go by conjugate pairs and there may be also two cases only: two conjugate complex roots and a third real root or no complex roots at all, all three roots being real. To these two funda- mental cases we add the intermediary case, when there is a double root.

To justify the assertion that the case of a double root is intermediary between two other cases we shall study the graph of the cubic poly- nomial

$$y = t^3 + pt + q.$$

We can use the graph only because the coefficients p and q are *real* by hypothesis. This important particular case may be called real cubic equation and our study begins with it.

Real Cubic Equation

Interpreting t and y as two coordinates of a point in the plane TOY (see fig. 1), we plot first the auxiliary curve $y_1 = t^3$. This curve passes through the origin O and also through the points

$$y = t = -1 \text{ and } y = t = 1.$$

When t increases so does y too. Therefore, the branch of the curve situated in the first quadrant, where both y and t are positive, rises continuously. To each point (a, b) on this branch corresponds a point $(-a, -b)$ in the third quadrant symmetrical to (a, b) with respect to the origin. To prove it we observe that $b = a^3$, since the point (a, b) is chosen on the curve $y = t^3$, and b is a particular value of y, as a is a corresponding particular value of t. The relation $b = a^3$ entails $-b = -a^3$, but $-a^3$ is the cube of $-a$ and therefore

$$b = a^3 \text{ entails also } -b = (-a)^3$$

which proves that the point $(-a, -b)$ belongs to our curve, if the point (a, b) is one of its points.

Thus, the curve $y = t^3$ is symmetrical with respect to the origin O. To justify completely its graph as represented on fig. 1 we study the variation of the slope y/t of the chord $\mathbf{OP}$ when the point $P(t, y)$

describes the curve, moving upwards that is with increasing t. The slope of the chord OP is equal to the ratio y/t where $y = t^3$. Thus, the slope is t^2: it approaches zero when t decreases and tends to zero, which means that the curve is tangent to the **OT** axis at the origin O, but when t increases the slope t^2 increases too, and the curve is rising continuously.

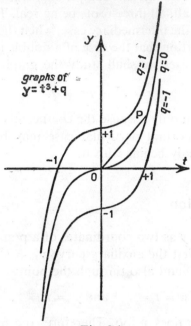

Fig. 8.1

The graph of our cubic polynomial $y = t^3 + pt + q$ is obtained if we add the linear function $y_2 = pt + q$ to the first auxiliary function $y_1 = t^3$ because

$$y = t^3 + (pt + q) = y_1 + y_2$$

The graph of this linear function $y_2 = pt + q$ is a straight line whose slope is equal to p and whose y-intercept is q. The variation of the constant term q does not change the shape of the curve $y = t^3 + pt + q$: it corresponds to a translation of the curve as a whole in vertical direction. If q increases the curve $y = t^3 + pt + q$ moves upwards, if q decreases it moves downwards. Let us first study the general shape of the curve. Since the value of q has no relation to the shape we assume for a moment that $q = 0$, so that $y = t^3 + pt$.

The linear function $y_2 = pt$ is represented now by a straight line through the origin O and we distinguish three cases: the coefficient p (value of the slope) is positive, zero, or negative. Figure 1 corresponds to the case $p = 0$, while the cases $p > 0$ and $p < 0$ are represented on figs. 2 and 3.

If p is positive (fig. 2), adding the term pt to the term t^3 we only increase the slope of the chord **OP** so that, for $q = 0$, the graph of the function $y = t^3 + pt$ is the curve through the origin O traced continuously while $y_1 = t^3$ and $y_2 = pt$ are represented by dotted curve and straight line. On a vertical $t = t_0$ we have the points P, Q, R of three graphs and these graphs are related by the condition **AR = AP + AQ** because **AP** $= t_0^3$ and **AQ** $= pt_0$.

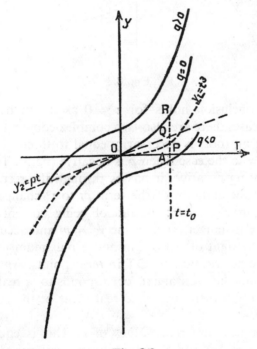

Fig. 8.2

Considering now different values of the constant term q, we have different positions of the same graph shifted upward or downward. An important conclusion is thus reached: if p is positive there is only one real root of the equation $t^3 + pt + q = 0$ because its graph intersects the horizontal axis **OT** in one point only.

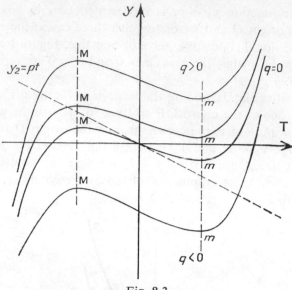

Fig. 8.3

The same conclusion holds for $p = 0$ as it can be inferred from fig. 1. In both cases there are also two complex conjugate roots because the number of all roots is necessarily equal to three.

We pass now to the case when p is negative (fig. 3). The slope of the line $y_2 = pt$ being negative, it passes through the second and fourth quadrants and the addition of the term pt to t^3 changes radically the shape of the curve $y_1 = t^3$: instead of being tangent to OT at the origin O, it is now tangent to the line $y_2 = pt$ and accuses therefore a minimum to the right of the origin and a maximum to the left of it, intersecting the horizontal axis OT in *three* points. An intersection of the graph with the horizontal axis corresponds to a real root and thus if $q = 0$ and $p < 0$ there are three real roots of the equation $y = t^3 + pt + q = 0$.

We consider now different values of q. This is equivalent to the shifting our graph up and down vertically without alteration of its shape. If the vertical translation is not too important there remain always three intersection points, that is using the algebraical language, there are three *real* roots of cubic equation $t^3 + pt + q = 0$, if, p being negative, q is not large in absolute value.

But if the translation upwards shifts the graph too much its minimum point m occupies a position which is above the horizontal axis and there remains only one intersection point, only one real root. The same happens if the translation downwards shifts the graph too much down: its maximum point M is then below the horizontal axis and again there is only one intersection point, only one real root. In other words, if, p being negative, the constant term q is sufficiently large in absolute value, the cubic equation $t^3 + pt + q = 0$ has two complex roots and only one real root.

This geometrical approach to the real cubic equation suggests an important question: what are the two critical values of the constant term q, one positive and the other negative, such that when q exceeds the positive critical value or is less than the negative critical value, the equation $t^3 + pt + q = 0$ with negative coefficient p has only one real root (and two complex conjugate roots), while it has three real roots if the value of q is comprised between these two critical values?

We observe that the positions of minimum and maximum points m, M with respect to the horizontal axis OT depend not only on the importance of vertical displacement of the original graph, but also on the slope of the straight line which fixes the shape of the graph. In other words, the two critical values of q depend on the value of the negative coefficient p.

The question formulated above can be answered in observing that during the continuous translation of the graph upwards or downwards (continuous increase or decrease of q) the minimum and maximum points m, M cannot go from one side of the horizontal axis OT to the other without coinciding for an instant with one of its points. At this very instant the graph becomes *tangent* to the horizontal axis OT at its minimum point m or its maximum point M. We have seen in the preceding chapter that in algebraical language this means that the equation $t^3 + pt + q = 0$ has a double root.

Therefore, it is proved that the case of double root is intermediary one between the cases of three real roots and of two complex conjugate and one real root. Moreover, if the critical values of q for which the graph becomes tangent to the horizontal axis are denoted by Q_1 and Q_2, where $q = Q_1 < 0$ corresponds to the position of the maximum point M on the OT axis, while $q = Q_2 > 0$ brings the minimum point m on the OT axis, we can state that there are three real roots, when the value of q verifies the double inequality

$$Q_1 < q < Q_2.$$

If q is less than Q_1 or greater than Q_2 then the graph of the function

$$y = t^3 + pt + q$$

intersects the OT axis in one point only and the equation

$$t^3 + pt + q = 0$$

has two complex and one real root.

To compute the critical values Q_1, Q_2 of q it is sufficient to express that the equation $t^3 + pt + q = 0$ has a double root when q is equal to a critical value: $q = Q_1$ or $q = Q_2$. The incomplete equation $t^3 + pt + q = 0$ belongs to the general case (1) in which

$$A = 1, B = 0, C = p \text{ and } D = q$$

Denoting its three roots by t_1, t_2, t_3 and applying the fundamental relations (5*) to our incomplete equation, we obtain

$$t_1 + t_2 + t_3 = 0; \quad p = t_1 t_2 + t_2 t_3 + t_3 t_1; \quad q = -t_1 t_2 t_3 \quad (10)$$

We suppose now that the equation

$$t^3 + pt + q = 0$$

has a double root a and a third simple root b, so that

$$t_1 = t_2 = a \text{ and } t_3 = b$$

The relations (10) become in this case

$$2a + b = 0; \quad a^2 + 2ab = p; \quad -a^2 b = q \quad (11)$$

These three relations involve four quantities $a, b, p,$ and q. The first two

$$2a + b = 0 \text{ and } a^2 + 2ab = p$$

may be considered as a system of two equations with two unknowns a and b. Solving this system, we can obtain the explicit expressions of a and b in terms of p. Suppose that it was done. Substituting the expressions of a and b in the third relation, we will have a relation between p and q and this relation characterizes the case of double root, because we have postulated that $t_1 = t_2 = a$. Therefore, the critical values of q will be obtained in terms of p, solving the relation between p and q with respect to q.

The first step consists in the elimination of a and b from the three relations (11). We eliminate first b which is equal, according to the first relation, to $-2a$: $b = -2a$. Substituting this value of b into two other relations, we transform them into

$$-3a^2 = p; \quad 2a^3 = q$$

The elimination of a from these two relations may be performed by comparing two values of the sixth power a^6 of a obtained by raising these relations to the third and second power respectively:

$$-27a^6 = p^3; \quad 4a^6 = q^2$$

Thus, a^6 is equal to $p^3/(-27)$ and also equal to $q^2/4$. Therefore, these two expressions of a^6 being equal, $-p^3/27 = q^2/4$ which can be written as

$$p^3/27 + q^2/4 = 0 \tag{12}$$

The relation (12) was deduced from the hypothesis that the cubic equation $t^3 + pt + q = 0$ has a double root. Therefore (12) is the *condition of the existence of a double root* whose value a is then equal to $-3q/(2p)$ because dividing $a^3 = q/2$ by $a^2 = -p/3$ we obtain precisely

$$a = -3q/(2p)$$

The condition (12) proves that there can be a double root if and only if the coefficient p is negative: if p is positive or zero the lefthand member of (12) cannot vanish and the condition of double root is not satisfied.

When p is negative, $-p^3$ is positive and two critical values of q for which the equation $t^3 + pt + q = 0$ has a double root are obtained solving (12) with respect to q. First we have $q^2 = -4p^3/27$ and then, extracting the square root,

$$Q_1 = -2(-p^3/27)^{1/2}; \quad Q_2 = 2(-p^3/27)^{1/2}$$

These two critical values define an interval (Q_1, Q_2) symmetrical with respect to the origin.

Now we can state the condition of three real roots as follows: The real cubic equation $t^3 + pt + q = 0$ with a negative coefficient p has all its three roots real, if the constant term q verifies the double inequality

$$Q_1 = -2(-p^3/27)^{1/2} < q < 2(-p^3/27)^{1/2} = Q_2 \tag{13}$$

This condition (13) of three real roots expresses that the absolute value of q is less than $2(-p^3/27)^{1/2}$, so that q^2 is less than $-4p^3/27$ and $q^2/4$ is less then $-p^3/27$. In other words, the sum $q^2/4 + p^3/27$ is a negative number:

$$q^2/4 + p^3/27 < 0 \qquad (13^*)$$

which is another form of the condition of real roots.

If

$$q^2/4 + p^3/27 = 0 \qquad (13^{**})$$

then the cubic equation $t^3 + pt + q = 0$ has a double root. But, if the absolute value of q is greater than $2(-p^3/27)^{1/2}$, that is, if q is less than Q_1 or greater than Q_2, then

$$q^2/4 + p^3/27 > 0$$

and, we saw it by studying the graph of the function $y = t^3 + pt + q$, the cubic equation has one real root and two complex conjugate roots.

Summing up, we can say that the expression $q^2/4 + p^3/27$ may be called *discriminant* of the cubic equation $t^3 + pt + q = 0$ because its sign fixes the nature of roots: when the discriminant is positive the equation has two complex and one real root, when it is negative all its three roots are real and, finally, when the discriminant vanishes the equation has a double root.

In the last case, namely when

$$q^2/4 + p^3/27 = 0$$

the double root is equal to $-3q/(2p)$ and $3q/p$ is the third root.

EXAMPLE: Let us solve the following problem: find for what value of k the cubic equation

$$3x^3 - 4x + k = 0$$

has a double root. Dividing the equation by 3, we write it as follows:

$$x^3 - (4/3)x + k/3 = 0$$

so that for it

$$p = -4/3 \quad \text{and} \quad q = k/3$$

The condition of double root (13^{**}) becomes

$$3k^2 - 256/27 = 0$$

and, solving it for k, we find the answer:

$$|k| = (256/81)^{1/2} = 16/9$$

Therefore, the equations

$$3x^3 - 4x + 16/9 = 0 \quad \text{and} \quad 3x^3 - 4x - 16/9 = 0$$

both have a double root. Considering first the equation

$$3x^3 - 4x + 16/9 = 0$$

for which

$$p = -4/3 \quad \text{and} \quad q = 16/27$$

we have for the value of the double root

$$-3q/(2p) = -(16/9)/(-8/3) = 2/3$$

while the other, simple, root is $-4/3$. The second equation

$$3x^3 - 4x - 16/9 = 0$$

may be obtained from the first equation changing the sign of q and its double root is $-2/3$, the simple root being equal to $4/3$. The critical values of k namely $-16/9$ and $16/9$, show that the equation

$$3x^3 - 4x + k = 0$$

has three real roots, if k is comprised between $-16/9$ and $16/9$. If k is less than $-16/9$ or if it exceeds $16/9$, this equation has two complex roots and only one real. Having studied the three possible cases when the discriminant is positive, negative or zero, we have only to add that for the incomplete equation $t^3 + pt + q = 0$ a triple root $t_1 = t_2 = t_3 = c$ is possible only when it is equal to zero. Indeed the equations (10) give immediately $c = 0$, as well as $p = 0$ and $q = 0$.

It is not difficult to express the conditions of three real roots, of two complex and one real, of double and of triple root in terms of the four coefficients A, B, C, D of the complete equation (1). It would be sufficient to replace p and q in these conditions by their expressions (8), but it has no sense: the complicated expressions thus obtained are never used in practical applications because a complete equation is always transformed into the incomplete form $t^3 + pt + q = 0$ with the aid of the substitution $x = t - B/(3A)$. Therefore, they are omitted.

It is important to emphasize that all the foregoing about the discriminant and the nature of roots does not apply to the general case, when p and q are any two complex numbers, but only to a so-called real equation whose coefficients are real numbers. When A, B, C, D and therefore also p, q are any complex numbers, all four possible cases of three, two, one or none complex roots may be realized. The fundamental relations (5*) prove that in the last case, when all three roots are real, the rations B/A, C/A, and D/A must be real, too. Since the equation (1) can be divided by A and written in the form

$$x^3 + (B/A)\, x^2 + (C/A)\, x + (D/A) = 0$$

it can be said that the case of three real roots characterizes real cubic equations because a cubic equation having three real roots is reducible to the cubic equation with real coefficients.

Solution of a General Cubic Equation

There are many different algebraical algorithms which can be used to solve a cubic equation. All of them are applied to the incomplete form $t^3 + pt + q = 0$ and reduce its solution to the solution of an auxiliary quadratic equation. In what follows we consider only two algorithms which both quite naturally lead to Tartaglia's expressions of three roots in terms of two coefficients p and q.

Given an incomplete equation

$$t^3 + pt + q = 0, \qquad\qquad (14)$$

we replace in it the unknown t by two auxiliary unknowns u and v related to t by substitution $t = u + v$. The reason for increasing the number of unknowns is the following one. To find two unknowns one must have two equations, while the direct substitution of the sum $u + v$ instead of t into the equation (14) yields only one equation between u and v. Therefore, a second equation between u and v can be chosen as we want. This freedom of choice of second equation will be used in such a way that the two auxiliary unknowns u and v will be easy to find.

Performing first the direct substitution, we write (14) as follows

$$(u + v)^3 + p(u + v) + q = 0$$

We have

$$(u + v)^3 = u^3 + 3u^2v + 3uv^2 + v^3$$

so that our equation becomes

$$u^3 + 3uv(u + v) + v^3 + p(u + v) + q = 0$$

Two of its five terms have a common factor $(u + v)$. Picking it out, we obtain

$$(3uv + p)(u + v) + u^3 + v^3 + q = 0 \qquad (15)$$

To this first equation (15) between u and v, we must now add a second one whose choice is at our disposal. Studying the structure of the left member in (15), we observe that this equation can be greatly simplified and reduced to the form

$$u^3 + v^3 + q = 0$$

if its first term $(3uv + p)(u + v)$ vanishes. The second factor of this term, namely the sum $u + v$, represents t and therefore is different from zero, but the first factor $3uv + p$ will vanish, if we choose, as a second equation between u and v, the equation

$$3uv + p = 0$$

With such a choice of the second equation the two unknowns u, v satisfy the system of two equations

$$3uv + p = 0; \quad u^3 + v^3 + q = 0 \qquad (16)$$

and the values of u and v will be obtained by solving this system. If they are found, then t is known also because $t = u + v$.

From (16) we deduce that the product uv is equal to $-p/3$, while the sum of cubes $u^3 + v^3$ is $-q$:

$$uv = -p/3, \quad u^3 + v^3 = -q$$

We remember that two unknown numbers whose product and sum are known may be found by solving a quadratic equation which has these two numbers as its roots. It is easy to write it down because its constant term is equal to the product of two unknowns, the coefficient of the linear term with changed sign is their sum and the first coefficient, that of quadratic term, is one.

But, here we have the sum of *cubes* of our unknowns, while $-p/3$ is the product of their *first* powers. A sum of cubes of two numbers $u^3 + v^3$ cannot be transformed into the sum of their first powers $u + v$, but forming the cube of the product uv, we obtain the product of cubes because

$$(uv)^3 = u^3 v^3$$

This suggests the replacement of the relation $uv = -p/3$ by an equivalent relation obtained by cubing $uv = -p/3$. Therefore, we form $u^3v^3 = -p^3/27$ and consider instead of the system (16) the equivalent system

$$u^3 + v^3 = -q; \quad u^3v^3 = -p^3/27 \qquad (17)$$

In these two equations the veritable unknowns are the two cubes u^3 and v^3. Denoting them by $X_1 = u^3$ and $X_2 = v^3$, we transcribe the equations (17) as follows

$$X_1 + X_2 = -q; \quad X_1X_2 = -p^3/27 \qquad (18)$$

Now the fundamental relations (17), Chapter 7, prove that the numbers X_1, X_2 are the two roots of the quadratic equation

$$X^2 + qX - p^3/27 = 0 \qquad (19)$$

and, therefore, the solution of the cubic equation (14) is reduced to that of the quadratic equation (19). Once (19) is solved, the two auxiliary unknowns u and v can be found, extracting cube roots:

$$u = \sqrt[3]{X_1} \quad \text{and} \quad v = \sqrt[3]{X_2}$$

Solving (19), we find

$$u^3 = X_1 = -q/2 + (q^2/4 + p^3/27)^{1/2};$$
$$v^3 = X_2 = -[q/2 + (q^2/4 + p^3/27)^{1/2}]$$

To simplify the notation we introduce two symbols P and Q which denote the values of $u^3 = X_1$ and $-v^3 = -X_2$ as they were found solving (19):

$$P = -q/2 + (q^2/4 + p^3/27)^{1/2}; \quad Q = q/2 + (q^2/4 + p^3/27)^{1/2} \qquad (20)$$

Using these notations P, Q we have

$$u = \sqrt[3]{P} \quad \text{and} \quad v = -\sqrt[3]{Q},$$

so that each of the two auxiliary unknowns u, v can have three different values. We know, indeed, that the three values of a radical $\sqrt[3]{N}$ may be deduced from any one of them by multiplying it by ω and ω^2 which are complex values of the radical $\sqrt[3]{1}$. It is easy, indeed, to check that $(\sqrt[3]{N})^3 = N$ entails also

$$(\omega\sqrt[3]{N})^3 = (\omega^2\sqrt[3]{N})^3 = N$$

because $\omega^3 = \omega^6 = 1$ by definition of the symbol $\omega = (-1 + i\sqrt{3})/2$.

Thus, having formed by the rule (20) the numbers P and Q and chosen the values of two radicals $\sqrt[3]{P}$ and $\sqrt[3]{Q}$, we find three values for each one of two auxiliary unknowns u, v:

$$u_1 = \sqrt[3]{P}, \quad u_2 = \omega\sqrt[3]{P}, \quad u_3 = \omega^2\sqrt[3]{P} \qquad (21)$$
$$v_1 = -\sqrt[3]{Q}, \quad v_2 = -\omega\sqrt[3]{Q}, \quad v_3 = -\omega^2\sqrt[3]{Q}$$

The values of u and v associated in $t = u + v$ cannot be chosen arbitrarily among three values of u and as many values of v. They must satisfy the first of two equations (16) we imposed on u and v, namely

$$3uv + p = 0 \quad \text{or} \quad uv = -p/3$$

If a value of $\sqrt[3]{P}$ is chosen as u_1, then $v_1 = -\sqrt[3]{Q}$ must be chosen in such a way that the product $u_1 v_1$ be equal to $-p/3$. Therefore, we have already a first value of t: $t_1 = u_1 + v_1$.

To find the two other roots t_2, t_3 of the equation (14) we have to study all other eight possible associations of u_m and v_n, where

$$u_m = \omega^m u_1 \quad \text{and} \quad v_n = \omega^n v_1$$

give, for $m, n = 0, 1, 2$, all values (21) of u and v. Now the nine possible products of one among three values of u times one among three values of v are all given by

$$u_m v_n = \omega^{m+n} u_1 v_1 = -\omega^{m+n} p/3$$

Among them are admissible only products equal to $-p/3$ and therefore the subscript m, n must be chosen so that the power of ω with exponent $m + n$ be equal to one. It can happen only, if $m + n = 0$ or 3 and therefore only three associations are admissible: 1) $m = n = 0$ which was already mentioned and which governs the choice of values u_1, v_1; 2) $m = 1$ and $n = 2$ which associates u_2 with v_3; 3) $m = 2, n = 1$ which associates u_3 with v_2. In other words, studying all possible products of the type uv we find only three of them, namely $u_1 v_1$, $u_2 v_3$, and $u_3 v_2$, which are equal to $-p/3$. All six others do not satisfy the condition $uv = -p/3$ and therefore are discarded.

This important condition eliminates six sums of the type $u + v$ among nine possible and gives thus exactly three roots of the equation (14):

$$t_1 = u_1 + v_1; \quad t_2 = u_2 + v_3; \quad t_3 = u_3 + v_2 \qquad (22)$$

Using (21), we can write the solution (22) of (14) as follows:

$$t_1 = \sqrt[3]{P} - \sqrt[3]{Q}; \quad t_2 = \omega\sqrt[3]{P} - \omega^2\sqrt[3]{Q}; \quad t_3 = \omega^2\sqrt[3]{P} - \omega\sqrt[3]{Q}$$
$$(22^*)$$

EXAMPLE: Let us study this first method on the example of a very simple cubic equation

$$x^3 - x^2 + x - 1 = 0$$

whose three roots can be found easily by factoring the lefthand member:

$$x^3 - x^2 + x - 1 = (x^2 + 1)(x - 1) = (x + i)(x - i)(x - 1) = 0$$

It is plain that $x_1 = -i$, $x_2 = i$, and $x_3 = 1$. These three roots are obtained by equating to zero every one of three factors of the lefthand member.

Our problem is now to find the same roots by applying the general method. The first step consists in the reduction to the incomplete form. This reduction is to be performed by using instead of x a new unknown t related to it by the formula

$$x = t - B/(3A)$$

In our case the coefficients are: $A = C = 1$ and $B = D = -1$, as the comparison with (1) shows. Thus $-B/(3A) = 1/3$ and we must use the substitution $x = t + 1/3$, which entails

$$x^3 = (t + 1/3)^3 = t^3 + t^2 + t/3 + 1/27$$
$$x^2 = (t + 1/3)^2 = t^2 + 2t/3 + 1/9$$

The substitution $x = t + 1/3$ transforms the equation

$$x^3 - x^2 + x - 1 = 0$$

into

$$t^3 + 2t/3 - 20/27 = 0$$

so that in our case

$$p = 2/3 \quad \text{and} \quad q = -20/27$$

The second step consists in the computation of P and Q given by (20). We begin by computing the quantity under the square root, namely the discriminant

$$q^2/4 + p^3/27 = (27q^2 + 4p^3)/108 = (400/27 + 32/27)/108 = 4/27$$

Extracting the square root from 4/27, we find that in our case

$$(q^2/4 + p^3/27)^{1/2} = (12/81)^{1/2} = (2\sqrt{3})/9$$

so that for P and Q we obtain

$$P = (2\sqrt{3})/9 + 10/27; \quad Q = (2\sqrt{3})/9 - 10/27$$

Both P and Q are positive and the radicals $\sqrt[3]{P}, \sqrt[3]{Q}$ have, both of them, one real and two complex values. Let us try first as u_1 and v_1 the real values, so that

$$\sqrt[3]{P} = u_1 = [(6\sqrt{3} + 10)/27]^{1/3}, \quad -\sqrt[3]{Q} = v_1 = -[(6\sqrt{3} - 10)/27]^{1/3}$$

Now the operations $(6\sqrt{3} + 10)^{1/3}$ and $(6\sqrt{3} - 10)^{1/3}$ can be performed exactly: the sum $6\sqrt{3} + 10$ can be written also as follows:

$$6\sqrt{3} + 10 = 1^3 + 3 \cdot 1^2 \sqrt{3} + 3 \cdot 1 \cdot (\sqrt{3})^2 + (\sqrt{3})^3 = (3^{1/2} + 1)^3$$

and the same holds for the difference $6\sqrt{3} - 10$:

$$6\sqrt{3} - 10 = (\sqrt{3})^3 - 3 \cdot (\sqrt{3})^2 \cdot 1 + 3(\sqrt{3}) \cdot 1^2 - 1^3 = (3^{1/2} - 1)^3$$

Therefore, extracting the cube root, we obtain real values

$$(6\sqrt{3} + 10)^{1/2} = 3^{1/2} + 1; \quad (6\sqrt{3} - 10)^{1/2} = 3^{1/2} - 1$$

and for u_1 and v_1 we have the following values

$$u_1 = (3^{1/2} + 1)/3; \quad v_1 = -(3^{1/2} - 1)/3 \tag{23}$$

We must check that these values satisfy the condition

$$uv = -p/3 = -2/9$$

Forming the product $u_1 v_1$, we have indeed

$$u_1 v_1 = -(3^{1/2} + 1)(3^{1/2} - 1)/9 = -(3 - 1)/9 = -2/9$$

so that the values (23) are well chosen. They give already the first root

$$t_1 = u_1 + v_1 = (3^{1/2} + 1 - 3^{1/2} + 1)/3 = 2/3$$

of the equation

$$t^3 + 2t/3 - 20/27 = 0$$

The formulas (22*) yield the two other roots:

$$t_2 = [\omega(3^{1/2} + 1) - \omega^2(3^{1/2} - 1)]/3 = [\omega + \omega^2 + 3^{1/2}(\omega - \omega^2)]/3$$

$$t_3 = [\omega^2(3^{1/2} + 1) - \omega(3^{1/2} - 1)]/3 = [\omega + \omega^2 - 3^{1/2}(\omega - \omega^2)]/3$$

Replacing ω and ω^2 by their values $(-1 + i\sqrt{3})/2$ and $-(1 + i\sqrt{3})/2$, we easily deduce that

$$t_2 = -1/3 + i \quad \text{and} \quad t_3 = -1/3 - i$$

The substitution we used

$$x = t + 1/3$$

associates a value of x to each value of t and thus the three roots of the equation

$$x^3 - x^2 + x - 1 = 0$$

are obtained:

$$x_1 = t_1 + 1/3 = 2/3 + 1/3 = 1;$$

$$x_2 = t_2 + 1/3 = i; \quad x_3 = t_3 + 1/3 = -i$$

Second Method

The same general solution (22*) can be obtained with the aid of the substitution

$$t = z - p/(3z)$$

The incomplete cubic equation (14) is transformed by this substitution into a quadratic equation. We have indeed, using (48) in Chapter 7:

$$t^3 + pt + q = (z - p/3z)^3 + p(z - p/3z) + q$$

$$= z^3 - p^3/(27z^3) + q = 0$$

because

$$(z - p/3z)^3 = z^3 - pz + p^2/3z - p^3/(27z^3)$$

In fact there is no difference between the first and the second method because if u of the first method is denoted by z then

$$v = -p/(3u) = -p/(3z)$$

so that

$$t = u + v = z - p/(3z)$$

The equation for z, namely

$$z^3 + q - p^3/(27z^3) = 0$$

after the multiplication by z^3 becomes

$$(z^3)^2 + qz^3 - p^3/27 = 0$$

and for the unknown z^3 it is the same quadratic equation (19) which was obtained in the first method. Solving it we get two values P and $-Q$ for the cube z^3 of z. Extracting cube roots, we obtain for z six values which are simply all the values of u and v considered in the first method. Any of these six values of z can be used in computing the corresponding value of $t = z - p/(3z)$, but we obtain only three different values for t because, if we choose for z a value of u, the second term $-p/(3z)$ $= -p/(3u)$ will give the *associated* value of v and if z is equal to some value of v, then the second term reproduces the associated value of u. Thus, only the three combinations $u_1 + v_1, u_2 + v_3, u_3 + v_2$ are again obtained, each one twice.

Discussion

The general solution (22*) holds for any complex p and q. But, if p and q are two real numbers, it is interesting to observe that this general solution (22*) represents the three real roots in a disguised form of sums of two complex *conjugate* numbers. We know that the condition of three real roots is the negative discriminant:

$$q^2/4 + p^3/27 < 0$$

Denoting the discriminant by D, we state that the radical $D^{1/2}$, which is involved in the expressions of u_1 and v_1, is a purely imaginary number. Let us denote it by iN, where N is a real number: $D^{1/2} = iN$. Thus, the numbers P and Q can be written as follows:

$$P = -q/2 + iN \quad \text{and} \quad Q = q/2 + iN$$

which gives for u_1 and v_1 the following expressions

$$u_1 = P^{1/3} = (-q/2 + iN)^{1/3}; \quad v_1 = (-Q)^{1/3} = (-q/2 - iN)^{1/3}$$

The two quantities u_1 and v_1 are in this case complex conjugate numbers and if the first one, u_1, is denoted by $r + is$ the second, v_1, is equal to $r - is$:

$$u_1 = r + is; \quad v_1 = r - is$$

The three roots

$$t_1 = u_1 + v_1, \ t_2 = u_2 + v_3, \ t_3 = u_3 + v_2$$

given by (22*) can also be expressed in terms of u_1, v_1, ω only because

$$u_2 = \omega u_1, \quad u_3 = \omega^2 u_1$$

as well as

$$v_2 = \omega v_1 \quad \text{and} \quad v_3 = \omega^2 v_1$$

Therefore, we have also

$$t_2 = \omega u_1 + \omega^2 v_1 \quad \text{and} \quad t_3 = \omega^2 u_1 + \omega v_1$$

In the case of a negative discriminant the three roots are represented as follows:

$$t_1 = (r + is) + (r - is) = 2r$$

$$t_2 = \omega(r + is) + \omega^2(r - is)$$
$$= (\omega + \omega^2) r + (\omega - \omega^2) is = -r - s\sqrt{3}$$

$$t_3 = \omega^2(r + is) + \omega(r - is)$$
$$= (\omega + \omega^2) r - (\omega - \omega^2) is = -r + s\sqrt{3}$$

because, as we have already seen in the example, replacing ω and ω^2 by their values, we obtain

$$\omega + \omega^2 = -1 \quad \text{and} \quad \omega - \omega^2 = i\sqrt{3}$$

The expressions just obtained for t_1, t_2, t_3 prove that all three roots are real, when the discriminant is negative.

Suppose now that the discriminant vanishes. If $D = 0$, then

$$P = -Q = -q/2$$

so that

$$u_1 = v_1 = (-q/2)^{1/3} = -(q/2)^{1/3}$$

and the roots become:

$$t_1 = -2(q/2)^{1/3}$$

$$t_2 = (\omega + \omega^2) u_1 = -u_1 = (q/2)^{1/3}$$

$$t_3 = (\omega^2 + \omega) u_1 = (q/2)^{1/3}$$

Thus, the double root is found:

$$t_2 = t_3 = (q/2)^{1/3}$$

This value of the double root is equal to $-3q/(2p)$ because the discriminant vanishes and thus

$$(q/2)^2 = (-p/3)^3$$

Extracting the cube root both sides of this equality, we have

$$(q/2)^{2/3} = -p/3$$

so that

$$-3q/(2p) = (q/2)/(-p/3) = (q/2)/(q/2)^{2/3}$$
$$= (q/2)^{2/3} = (-p/3)^{1/2}$$

where in the last value of the double root the sign of square root must be chosen accordingly to that of $(q/2)^{1/3}$.

If the discriminant is positive the numbers P and Q are real and so are u_1 and v_1. Therefore, the root $t_1 = u_1 + v_1$ is real. Two other roots are:

$$t_2 = -(u_1 + v_1)/2 + i(u_1 - v_1)\sqrt{3}/2$$
$$t_3 = -(u_1 + v_1)/2 - i(u_1 - v_1)\sqrt{3}/2$$

These two complex roots are conjugate complex numbers.

Quartic Equation

As a cubic equation is solved with the aid of an auxiliary unknown which satisfies a quadratic equation, so the quartic equation is reduced to a cubic equation in an auxiliary unknown, the solution of which yields the roots of the quartic equation.

Again the first step consists in the reduction of a complete equation

$$Ax^4 + Bx^3 + Cx^2 + Dx + E = 0 \tag{2}$$

to an incomplete equation of fourth order in which the cubic term with the cube of the unknown is missing. This reduction is performed with the aid of a linear substitution $x = t + m$, where the constant term m is chosen in such a way that the coefficient of t^3 vanishes.

To perform the substitution of $t + m$ instead of x in the equation (2) it is necessary to form the expansions of x^4, x^3, x^2. They are given by equations (49) and (48) in Chapter 7, respectively:

$$x^4 = t^4 + 4mt^3 + 6m^2t^2 + 4m^3t + m^4$$

$$x^3 = t^3 + 3mt^2 + 3m^2t + m^3$$

$$x^2 = t^2 + 2mt + m^2$$

Inserted in (2) they transform this equation into a quartic equation in the unknown t

$$At^4 + B^*t^3 + C^*t^2 + D^*t + E^* = 0 \qquad (24)$$

where the coefficients B^*, C^*, D^*, E^* are expressed in terms of A, B, C, D, E and m by the following formulas:

$$B^* = B + 4mA$$

$$C^* = C + 3mB + 6m^2A$$

$$D^* = D + 2mC + 3m^2B + 4m^3A$$

$$E^* = E + mD + m^2C + m^3B + m^4A$$

Choosing m so that $B^* = 0$, we find for m the linear equation

$$B + 4mA = 0$$

and therefore $m = -B/(4A)$ gives an incomplete equation in t. Using this value of $m = -B/(4A)$, we find the corresponding values of other three coefficients

$$C^* = C - 3B^2/(4A) + 6B^2/(16A) = C - 3B^2/(8A)$$

$$D^* = D - BC/(2A) + B^3/(8A^2) \qquad (25)$$

$$E^* = E - BD/(4A) + B^2C/(16A^2) - 3B^4/(256A^3)$$

Denoting the ratios C^*/A, D^*/A, E^*/A by p, q, r, respectively, and dividing the equation (24) by its first coefficient A, we obtain for the incomplete quartic equation in t the following form

$$t^4 + pt^2 + qt + r = 0 \qquad (26)$$

The coefficients $p = C^*/A$, $q = D^*/A$, and $r = E^*/A$ are computed with the aid of expressions (25) of C^*, D^*, E^* in terms of A, B, C, D and E.

The four roots of the complete equation (2) are related to the roots of the incomplete equation (26) by the substitution

$$x = t - B/(4A)$$

To compute them it is sufficient to solve the equation (26). We consider first the case of a quartic equation with *real* coefficients p, q, r, which can be called real quartic equation.

Real Quartic Equation

The second step of the solution is the most important. It is the reduction of the incomplete equation (26) to the cubic equation

$$u^3 + 2pu^2 + (p^2 - 4r)u - q^2 = 0 \tag{27}$$

whose real and positive root u is involved in the following explicit expressions of four roots of (26):

$$
\begin{aligned}
t_1 &= -u^{1/2}/2 + (2qu^{-1/2} - 2p - u)^{1/2}/2 \\
t_2 &= -u^{1/2}/2 - (2qu^{-1/2} - 2p - u)^{1/2}/2 \\
t_3 &= u^{1/2}/2 + (-2qu^{-1/2} - 2p - u)^{1/2}/2 \\
t_4 &= u^{1/2}/2 - (-2qu^{-1/2} - 2p - u)^{1/2}/2
\end{aligned}
\tag{28}
$$

The expressions (28) give the general solution of the equation (26) based on the knowledge of the *real positive* root u of the auxiliary cubic equation (27). We must now first deduce the cubic equation (27) and then prove that it has always a real and positive root.

Given an incomplete quartic equation (26), we transpose the linear part of it, namely $qt + r$, to the right and add both sides the same expression, sum of two terms, $ut^2 + (p + u)^2/4$ where the symbol u denotes any *positive* number to be chosen afterwards. These two operations give us the equation

$$t^4 + pt^2 + ut^2 + (p + u)^2/4 = ut^2 - qt + (p + u)^2/4 - r \tag{29}$$

The lefthand member is a perfect square because the quadratic term $(p + u)t^2$ is equal to the doubled product of $(p + u)/2$ and t^2 whose squares are also terms of the lefthand member. Therefore, this member can be written as a square of the sum $t^2 + (p + u)/2$:

$$t^4 + pt^2 + ut^2 + (p + u)^2/4 = (t^2 + p/2 + u/2)^2$$

The righthand member is a quadratic polynomial in t of the classical type $at^2 + bt + c$ with

$$a = u, \ b = -q \ \text{ and } \ c = (p + u)^2/4 - r$$

In general a quadratic polynomial is not a perfect square, but our polynomial depends on the undetermined positive number u and this number u can be chosen in such a way that also the righthand member will be a perfect square. The advantage of having both members perfect squares is evident: if our quartic equation can be written as a difference of two squares $X^2 - Y^2 = 0$, then its factoring is easy. The equation becomes a product

$$(X + Y)(X - Y) = 0$$

and it can be replaced by two quadratic equations

$$X + Y = 0, \quad X - Y = 0$$

where X is a quadratic polynomial in t, namely

$$X = t^2 + p/2 + u/2$$

while Y is a linear expression involving t in the first power.

Therefore, our next step consists in the choice of such a value of u for which the righthand member in (29) becomes a perfect square. A quadratic polynomial $at^2 + bt + c$ is a perfect square, if the corresponding quadratic equation

$$at^2 + bt + c = 0$$

has a double root. Therefore, $at^2 + bt + c$ is a perfect square if and only if the discriminant $b^2 - 4ac$ vanishes. In our case we have

$$a = u, \ b = -q, \ \text{ and } \ c = (p + u)^2/4 - r$$

so that the discriminant of the quadratic polynomial in the righthand member is given by the expression $q^2 - u(p + u)^2 + 4ru$.

Because we want a perfect square in the righthand member of (29) we must choose the positive number u so that the discriminant be zero. In other words, the number u must satisfy the condition

$$q^2 - u(p^2 + 2pu + u^2) + 4ru = 0$$

Changing the sign, we write this condition as an equation with the unknown u

$$u^3 + 2pu^2 + (p^2 - 4r)u - q^2 = 0 \qquad (27)$$

Having explained the origin and the meaning of the cubic equation (27), we must now prove that it has always a real and positive root which will serve as the number u defined above. A cubic equation has always at least one real root which in general may be negative, but the equation (27) is a particular cubic equation since its constant term $-q^2$ is a negative number.

We will prove that a general cubic equation (1) with the first coefficient A equal to *one*, $A = 1$, and the negative constant term D, $D < 0$, has at least one real positive root. This proof is based on the shape of the graph of the function

$$y = x^3 + Bx^2 + Cx + D \quad (D < 0) \qquad (30)$$

whose constant term D is negative.

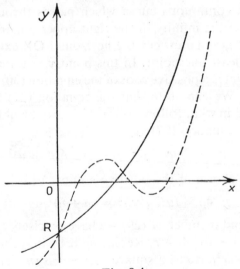

Fig. 8.4

It is sufficient to study that part of the graph which corresponds to positive values of the abcissa x. We observe that the point on the OY axis, where the graph crosses this axis and for which $x = 0$, lies below the horizontal OX axis because, for $x = 0$, we have $y = D$ and D by hypothesis is a negative number. Thus, the intersection point R where the graph cuts the OY is below the origin (see fig. 4).

On the other hand, when x becomes infinitely large and positive the terms $Bx^2 + Cx + D$ are negligible with respect to the first cubic term x^3. We can, indeed, pick x^3 as common factor out and write y as follows:

$$y = x^3 + x^3(B/x) + x^3(C/x^2) + x^3(D/x^3)$$
$$= x^3(1 + B/x + C/x^2 + D/x^3)$$

It is evident that the three fractions B/x, C/x^2, D/x^3 tend to zero when their denominators increase with x without limit, so that the second factor in the expression of y, namely

$$1 + B/x + C/x^2 + D/x^3$$

approaches one and remains positive. But, the first factor x^3 tends towards positive infinity, so that y tends to positive infinity when x does. In geometrical language this simultaneous growth of x and y by positive values towards plus infinity means that our graph climbs up in the right upper quadrant of the plane XOY, having there an infinite branch. The graph itself is a continuous curve which passes through the point R and disappears at the infinity in the right upper quadrant.

Therefore, the graph must cut the horizontal OX axis at the right of the origin in at least one point. In this point $y = 0$ that is the coordinate x of this point is a positive root of the equation (30) whose existence is thus proved. We can state that the equation (27) has at least one positive root and in what follows this positive root will be denoted by u.

Rewriting the equation (27) as

$$q^2 = u(u^2 + 2pu + p^2 - 4r) = u[(p + u)^2 - 4r]$$

we have for our choice of the positive number u

$$q^2/4u = (q/2u^{1/2})^2 = (p + u)^2/4 - r$$

In the righthand member of (29) we have precisely as constant term the expression $(p + u)^2/4 - r$. Replacing it by its value $(q/2u^{1/2})^2$ and writing the term ut^2 also as a square, namely as $(u^{1/2}t)^2$ we give to the righthand member of (29) the form of a perfect square

$$ut^2 - qt + (p + u)^2/4 - r = (u^{1/2}t)^2 - 2(u^{1/2}t)(q/2u^{1/2})$$
$$+ (q/2u^{1/2})^2,$$

namely the square of the difference $u^{1/2}t - q/(2u^{1/2})$.

The equation (29) takes now the following aspect

$$(t^2 + p/2 + u/2)^2 - (u^{1/2}t - qu^{-1/2}/2)^2 = 0$$

and it is easy to factor this difference of two squares:

$$[t^2 + u^{1/2}t + (p + u - qu^{-1/2})/2] \times$$

$$\times [t^2 - u^{1/2}t + (p + u + qu^{-1/2})/2] = 0 \qquad (31)$$

The equation (31) is a quartic equation, but of a peculiar kind. Its lefthand member is a product of two quadratic factors with real coefficients. Thus, an incomplete real polynomial of fourth order can always be represented as a product of two real quadratic polynomials, this factoring being based on the preliminary solution of a cubic equation deduced from the given incomplete quartic polynomial.

The quartic equation (31) is equivalent to two independent quadratic equations obtained by equating to zero either one of its two quadratic factors:

$$t^2 + u^{1/2}t + (p + u - qu^{-1/2})/2 = 0 \qquad (32a)$$

$$t^2 - u^{1/2}t + (p + u + qu^{-1/2})/2 = 0 \qquad (32b)$$

The four roots of (31) which are the same as four roots of the equivalent equation (26) are now split in two groups of two roots, namely the two roots of the quadratic equation (32a) and the two roots of (32b).

Therefore, the solution of the incomplete equation (26) is reduced to the solution of two quadratic equations (32). Solving them, we obtain precisely the four roots (28) of the equation (26): t_1, t_2 are the two roots of (32a) while t_3, t_4 are the roots of (32b).

The formulas (28) involve the extraction of square root, but to find u that is to solve the auxiliary cubic equation (27) we must also use the extraction of cube roots. Therefore, the general solution (28) of a quartic equation necessitates the extraction of square and cube roots.

Factoring the two quadratic polynomials in (31), we obtain

$$t^2 + u^{1/2}t + (p + u - qu^{-1/2})/2 = (t - t_1)(t - t_2)$$

$$t^2 - u^{1/2}t + (p + u + qu^{-1/2})/2 = (t - t_3)(t - t_4)$$

because their roots are respectively t_1, t_2 and t_3, t_4.

Therefore, the equation (26) can be written as a product of four linear factors each of which corresponds to a root of this equation

$$(t - t_1)(t - t_2)(t - t_3)(t - t_4) = 0$$

Fundamental Relations

The roots x_1, x_2, x_3, x_4 of the complete equation (2) are related to those t_1, t_2, t_3, t_4 of the incomplete equation (26) by the same formula

$$x_k = t_k - B/(4A)$$

where $k = 1, 2, 3, 4$, as the formula $x = t - B/(4A)$ which holds for any two corresponding values of variables x and t. Therefore, forming the differences $x - x_1$, $x - x_2$, etc., we find that they are *equal* to the corresponding differences $t - t_1$, etc.:

$$x - x_1 = t - t_1, \; x - x_2 = t - t_2,$$

$$x - x_3 = t - t_3, \; x - x_4 = t - t_4.$$

Therefore, the equation (26) is equivalent to

$$(x - x_1)(x - x_2)(x - x_3)(x - x_4) = 0$$

whose roots are the four roots of the general equation (2). Multiplying it by the first coefficient A of (2)

$$A(x - x_1)(x - x_2)(x - x_3)(x - x_4) = 0 \tag{2*}$$

we obtain the factoring of (2).

Performing the multiplications (2*) can be written as follows

$$Ax^4 - A(x_1 + x_2 + x_3 + x_4)x^3 + A(x_1x_2 + x_1x_3 + x_1x_4 + x_2x_3$$
$$+ x_2x_4 + x_3x_4)x^2 - A(x_1x_2x_3 + x_2x_3x_4 + x_3x_4x_1 + x_4x_1x_2)x$$
$$+ Ax_1x_2x_3x_4 = 0 \tag{2**}$$

Comparing the two different forms (2) and (2**) of the same general equation of fourth order, we deduce four fundamental relations between the roots and the coefficients of a general quartic equation:

$$\left.\begin{aligned} -B &= A(x_1 + x_2 + x_3 + x_4) \\ C &= A(x_1x_2 + x_1x_3 + x_1x_4 + x_2x_3 + x_2x_4 + x_3x_4) \\ -D &= A(x_1x_2x_3 + x_2x_3x_4 + x_3x_4x_1 + x_4x_1x_2) \\ E &= Ax_1x_2x_3x_4 \end{aligned}\right\} \tag{33}$$

EXAMPLE: All this will now be illustrated on the example of the quartic real equation

$$x^4 - 12x^3 + 48x^2 - 192x + 512 = 0 \tag{34}$$

with coefficients:

$$A = 1, \ B = -12, \ C = 48, \ D = -192, \ \text{and} \ E = 512$$

The substitution $x = t - B/(4A)$, transforming the given complete equation into the corresponding incomplete equation, is here

$$x = t - (-3) = t + 3$$

The incomplete equation can be computed directly, performing all the necessary operations in

$$(t + 3)^4 - 12(t + 3)^3 + 48(t + 3)^2 - 192(t + 3) + 512 = 0$$

or its coefficients may be found with the aid of (25) which give in this case

$$p = C^*, \ q = D^*, \ \text{and} \ r = E^*$$

because in (34) the coefficient A is equal to one.

Both methods yield the same incomplete equation

$$t^4 - 6t^2 - 120t + 125 = 0 \tag{35}$$

so that in our case

$$p = -6, \ q = -120, \ \text{and} \ r = 125$$

The next step is the determination of the positive number u, root of the auxiliary cubic equation (27). Because now

$$2p = -12, \ p^2 - 4r = 36 - 500 = -464,$$

$$\text{and} \ q^2 = 120^2 = 14400,$$

this cubic equation is

$$u^3 - 12u^2 - 464u - 14400 = 0 \tag{36}$$

The substitution $u = z - (-12)/3 = z + 4$ transforms it into the corresponding incomplete cubic equation

$$(z + 4)^3 - 12(z + 4)^2 - 464(z + 4) - 14400 = 0$$

that is into

$$z^3 - 512z - 16384 = 0 \tag{37}$$

with

$$p = -512 \ \text{and} \ q = -16384$$

The direct computation of the solution does not present other difficulty than the manipulations of very large numbers. It can be avoided if we take into consideration the structure of two coefficients. We have, indeed,

$$512 = 2^9 \quad \text{as well as} \quad 16384 = 2^{14}$$

so that the equation (37) can be written also as follows

$$z^3 - 2^9 z - 2^{14} = 2^9[(2^{-3}z)^3 - z - 2^5] = 0$$

Cancelling the non-vanishing factor 2^9 and introducing an auxiliary unknown v related to z by $z = 8v$, we obtain a simpler cubic equation, namely

$$v^3 - 8v - 32 = 0 \qquad (38)$$

Its discriminant

$$D = (p/3)^3 + (q/2)^2$$

is computed easily:

$$D = (-8/3)^3 + (-32/2)^2 = -512/27 + 256$$

$$= (16/3)^2 \cdot 25/3 = (80/9)^2 \cdot 3 > 0$$

The discriminant is positive and there is only one real root. To find it we observe that the square root of the discriminant is

$$D^{1/2} = 80\sqrt{3}/9 \quad \text{and} \quad q/2 = -16$$

Therefore, the unique real root is given by the formula

$$v = (80\sqrt{3}/9 + 16)^{1/3} - (80\sqrt{3}/9 - 16)^{1/3}$$

In this numerical expression the difference $80\sqrt{3}/9 - 16$ is negative since $80\sqrt{3}/9 < 9\sqrt{3} < 16$. Thus, extracting the cube root from -1, we write

$$v = (16 + 80\sqrt{3}/9)^{1/3} + (16 - 80\sqrt{3}/9)^{1/3}$$

But

$$16 \pm 80\sqrt{3}/9 = (8/27)(54 \pm 30\sqrt{3})$$

and thus, extracting the cube root from the common factor $8/27$, we obtain

$$v = (2/3)\,[(54 + 30\sqrt{3})^{1/3} + (54 - 30\sqrt{3})^{1/3}]$$

The two cube roots can be extracted exactly: the unique irrationality involved is the radical $\sqrt{3}$. Therefore, if $54 \pm 30\sqrt{3}$ is an exact cube it must be the third power of an expression of the type $m \pm n\sqrt{3}$, where m and n are two unknown integers. To find them we write that the cube of $m \pm n\sqrt{3}$ is equal to $54 \pm 30\sqrt{3}$

$$(m \pm n\sqrt{3})^3 = m^3 \pm 3m^2n\sqrt{3} + 9mn^2 \pm 3n^3\sqrt{3} = 54 \pm 30\sqrt{3}$$

But the principle of separation of rational and irrational states that the rational terms of both members on the one hand and the irrational terms on the other are equal separately. Thus, we can obtain two equations for m and n:

$$m^3 + 9mn^2 = 54 \qquad 3m^2n + 3n^3 = 30$$

These equations are easy to solve because the unknowns m and n are integers. The second equation may be written

$$n(m^2 + n^2) = 10$$

and only two values of the integer n are possible: $n = 1$ and $n = 2$ because already $n = 3$ makes the lefthand member greater than 27. Using these two values of n in the same second equation we find that $m = 3$, if $n = 1$, and also $m = 1$, if $n = 2$. Substituting the first solution $m = 3$, $n = 1$ into the first equation

$$m(m^2 + 9n^2) = 54$$

we see that it works because $3(9 + 9) = 54$. Substituting the second solution $m = 1$, $n = 2$, we find a contradiction because $1^2 + 9 \cdot 4 = 37$ instead of 54. Therefore, it is proved that

$$(3 \pm 3^{1/2})^3 = 54 \pm 30 \cdot 3^{1/2}$$

and the extraction of cube root gives the two results we were looking for, namely

$$(54 + 30 \cdot 3^{1/2})^{1/3} = 3 + 3^{1/2}; \quad (54 - 30 \cdot 3^{1/2})^{1/3} = 3 - 3^{1/2}$$

These numerical relations allow us to find the value of v:

$$v = (2/3)(3 + 3^{1/2} + 3 - 3^{1/2}) = (2/3)6 = 4.$$

Knowing $v = 4$, we have immediately

$$z = 8v = 8 \cdot 4 = 32$$

and this value of z yields finally the number u:

$$u = z + 4 = 32 + 4 = 36$$

The four roots of the incomplete equation (35) in t can now be computed with the aid of formulas (28) in which we must substitute

$$u = 36, \ u^{1/2} = 6, \ p = -6, \ \text{and} \ q = -120$$

Computing the two expressions under the square root, we have

$$2qu^{-1/2} - 2p - u = -240/6 + 12 - 36 = -64$$

$$(2qu^{-1/2} - 2p - u)^{1/2} = 8i$$

$$-2qu^{-1/2} - 2p - u = 240/6 + 12 - 36 = 16$$

$$(-2qu^{-1/2} - 2p - u)^{1/2} = 4$$

and therefore

$$t_1 = -3 + 8i/2 = -3 + 4i; \ t_2 = -3 - 4i$$

$$t_3 = 3 + 4/2 = 5; \qquad\qquad t_4 = 3 - 4/2 = 1$$

Adding to the roots t_k of the incomplete equation (35) the number 3, we obtain the roots x_k of the complete equation (34). They are:

$$x_1 = 4i, \ x_2 = -4i, \ x_3 = 8, \ x_4 = 4$$

It is easy to check, using the values of these four roots, the fundamental relations (33) on the example of the equation (34). Assuming $A = 1$, we find indeed, applying (33):

$$-B = 4i - 4i + 8 + 4 = 12$$

$$C = 4i(-4i) + 32i + 16i - 32i - 16i + 32 = 48$$

$$-D = 4i(-4i)8 - 128i + 128i + 4(4i)(-4i) = 192$$

$$E = 4i(-4i)32 = 512$$

The equation (34) can be simplified, dividing all its terms by $4^4 = 256$:

$$(x/4)^4 - 3(x/4)^3 + 3(x/4)^2 - 3(x/4) + 2 = 0$$

and using an auxiliary unknown $x/4 = y$. The equation in y

$$y^4 - 3y^3 + 3y^2 - 3y + 2 = 0$$

has a vanishing sum of all its coefficients and therefore it possesses a root equal to one. This root $y = 1$ corresponds to the root $x_4 = 4$.

To the root $y = 1$ corresponds the linear factor $y - 1$ and the left-hand member of the equation in y must be exactly divisible by $y - 1$

because this equation has a root $y = 1$. Dividing it by $y - 1$, we find as quotient the polynomial of third order $y^3 - 2y^2 + y - 2$, so that the equation in y becomes

$$(y - 1)(y^3 + y - 2y^2 - 2) = 0$$

The factoring can be continued and the second factor can be written as follows:

$$y(y^2 + 1) - 2(y^2 + 1) = (y - 2)(y + i)(y - i)$$

The final result of the factoring is the equation

$$(y - 1)(y - 2)(y + i)(y - i) = 0$$

and therefore the roots of the equation in y are: $1, 2, -i$ and i. Multiplying them by 4, we obtain again the roots of the equation (34).

Both of two quadratic equations (32) can have either two complex or two real and distinct roots or a double root. Therefore, the quartic equation (26) may have four, two, or no complex roots. If it has two complex conjugate roots it can have a double root or two real and distinct roots. If all four roots are real many cases may be distinguished: a quadruple root, a triple and one simple root, two double roots, one double and two real distinct simple roots, and, finally, four real distinct roots.

It is not difficult to form the discriminants of two quadratic equations (32) in terms of p, q, and u. They are equal to

$$2qu^{-1/2} - 2p - u \quad \text{and} \quad -2qu^{-1/2} - 2p - u$$

where $u^{-1/2}$ is positive. Using these expressions, we can formulate the conditions of all cases enumerated above in terms of p, q, and u. So, for instance, the quartic equation (26) has two double roots if both discriminants vanish, that is if $u = -2p$ and $q = 0$. But, the use of the number u deprives these conditions of pratical utility. Such conditions must be expressed in terms of coefficients p, q, and r of the equation (26) because then one can judge the nature of roots by inspection, without solving the equation. The chief difficulty of the solution consists precisely in finding the number u and therefore conditions involving this number are not useful.

Sometimes a condition expressed in terms of p, q, u can be transformed easily into an expression involving p, q, r. Such is the case of the condition of two double roots; substituting the value $u = -2p$ of u

into the equation (27) we find that $u = -2p$ is equivalent to

$$2p(p^2 - 4r) + q^2 = 0$$

which together with $q = 0$ gives

$$2p(p^2 - 4r) = 0$$

The coefficient p cannot vanish because if both p and q vanish the remaining equation $t^4 + r = 0$ will have four distinct roots. Thus, the condition of two double roots is $p^2 = 4r$ and $q = 0$. But, most of conditions become so complicated, if expressed in terms of p, q, r, that we omit their formulation.

General Case

In the general case, when the coefficients A, B, C, D and E of the quartic equation (2) are any complex numbers, nothing can be said about the nature of its roots. The multiple (double, triple or quadruple) roots may be complex numbers. The complex simple roots do not form conjugate pairs. The number of complex roots may be odd and can vary from zero to four.

The function
$$y = Ax^4 + Bx^3 + Cx^2 + Dx + E$$

has complex values even for real values of its argument x and therefore it cannot be represented by a curve in the plane XOY, as it was in the particular case of real coefficients.

But the algorithm of solution described for the real equation can be applied with success to general quartic equation with complex coefficients with the difference that the number u is no more real and *any root* of the auxiliary cubic equation (27) with complex coefficients p, q, r can play the role of u. The two quadratic equations (32) have complex coefficients in general, but the four roots of (26) are represented by (28) also in the general case of complex coefficients.

Equations of Higher Order

Some particular equations of orders higher than fourth can be solved reducing them to cubic or quartic equation. We do not intend here to study such equations and will limit ourselves to examples of equations of sixth and eight order

$$Ax^6 + Bx^5 + Cx^4 + Dx^3 + Ex^2 + Fx + G = 0 \qquad (39)$$

$$Hx^8 + Kx^7 + Lx^6 + Mx^5 + Nx^4 + Px^3 + Qx^2 + Rx + S = 0 \qquad (40)$$

whose coefficients satisfy the special conditions $A \neq 0$, $H \neq 0$ and

$$(E/C)^3 = (F/B)^{3/2} = G/A = a^3 \qquad (39^*)$$

$$(P/M)^4 = (Q/L)^2 = (R/K)^{4/3} = S/H = b^4 \qquad (40^*)$$

a^3 and b^4 being known values of ratios G/A and S/H respectively. Replacing in (39) the last three coefficients by their values

$$G = Aa^3, \ F = Ba^2, \ E = Ca$$

and dividing by x^3, we transform (39) into

$$A(x^3 + a^3 x^{-3}) + B(x^2 + a^2 x^{-2}) + C(x + ax^{-1}) + D = 0 \qquad (41)$$

and the substitution $x + a/x = t$ reduces (41) to the following *cubic* equation in t:

$$A(t^3 - 3at) + B(t^2 - 2a) + Ct + D = 0$$

The last four coefficients in (40) have the values

$$S = Hb^4, \ R = Kb^3, \ Q = Lb^2, \text{ and } P = Mb$$

Using these values and dividing (40) by x^4, we can write it as

$$H(x^4 + b^4 x^{-4}) + K(x^3 + b^3 x^{-3}) + L(x^2 + b^2 x^{-2})$$
$$+ M(x + bx^{-1}) + N = 0 \qquad (42)$$

and the substitution $x + b/x = t$ transforms (42) into a *quartic* equation:

$$H(t^4 - 4bt^2 + 2b^2) + K(t^3 - 3bt) + L(t^2 - 2b) + Mt + N = 0$$

Thus, equations (39), (40) whose coefficients satisfy (39*), (40*) are reducible to cubic and quartic equations, respectively, and admit of general solutions. With these examples of use of cubic and quartic equations in the solution of particular equations of higher order we end this chapter.

CHAPTER 9

Binomial Theorem; Exponential e^z.

We have seen the importance of identities which arise when integral powers $(A + B)^n$ of a sum $A + B$, such as $(A + B)^2$, $(A + B)^3$, $(A + B)^4$ and $(A + B)^5$, are expanded into a sum of terms of the general type $A^m B^p$ with numerical coefficients. Thus, we met the identities

$$(A + B)^2 \equiv A^2 + 2AB + B^2$$

$$(A + B)^3 \equiv A^3 + 3A^2B + 3AB^2 + B^4$$

$$(A + B)^4 \equiv A^4 + 4A^3B + 6A^2B^2 + 4AB^3 + B^3$$

$$(A + B)^5 \equiv A^5 + 5A^4B + 10A^3B^2 + 10A^2B^3 + 5AB^4 + B^5$$

These four identities have many common properties which come from the fact that the four powers of $A + B$ with exponents 2, 3, 4, and 5 are particular cases of the n-th power $(A + B)^n$ for $n = 2, 3, 4$ and 5. Among their common features, we note the following ones:

(1) The number of terms exceeds the exponent of $A + B$ by one.

(2) The expansions begin by a power of A with same exponent as that of $A + B$ and end by the same power of B.

(3) Reading the expansion from the left to the right, the exponents of A decrease by one and the exponents of B increase by one when we pass from one term to the next one; their sum remains equal to the exponent of $A + B$.

(4) Numerical coefficients of two terms equidistant from two ends of the expansion are equal.

(5) The sum of numerical coefficients is a power of two with the same exponent as that of $A + B$.

To check the last assertion, observe that

$$1 + 2 + 1 = 4 = 2^2, \, 1 + 3 + 3 + 1 = 8 = 2^3$$

$$1 + 4 + 6 + 4 + 1 = 16 = 2^4 \quad \text{and} \quad 1 + 5 + 10 + 10 + 5 + 1 = 32 = 2^5$$

In this chapter, we shall study the general expansion of $(A + B)^n$ known in algebra as the Binomial Theorem.

Considering the expansions of power $(A + B)^n$ for $n = 2, 3, 4, 5$, together with the cases

$$(A + B)^0 = 1 \text{ and } (A + B)^1 = A + B$$

we rewrite them as follows:

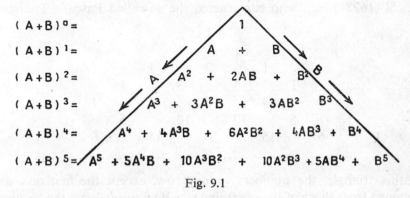

$(A + B)^0 =$

$(A + B)^1 =$

$(A + B)^2 =$

$(A + B)^3 =$

$(A + B)^4 =$

$(A + B)^5 =$

$$1$$
$$A + B$$
$$A^2 + 2AB + B^2$$
$$A^3 + 3A^2B + 3AB^2 \quad B^3$$
$$A^4 + 4A^3B + 6A^2B^2 + 4AB^3 + B^4$$
$$A^5 + 5A^4B + 10A^3B^2 + 10A^2B^3 + 5AB^4 + B^5$$

Fig. 9.1

This triangular table exhibits the common features, already formulated, governing the structure of each row. But there is more. Observing the formation of terms of two adjacent rows, we find a law which allows to deduce any term of a row from two terms located *above it* in the preceding row: the numerical coefficient is the sum of two coefficients above it; the exponent of A increases by one along any line parallel to the side of the triangle marked $\rightarrow A \rightarrow$ while that of B does not change. Likewise the exponent of B increases by one along any line parallel to the other side $\rightarrow B \rightarrow$, that of A remaining unchanged.

For instance, the term $10A^2B^3$ of the last row is below the terms $6A^2B^2$ and $4AB^3$ of the preceding row. And, indeed, its coefficient 10 is equal to $6 + 4$ the exponent of A is 2, while in $4AB^3$ it is one and the exponent of B is 3, while in $6A^2B^2$ it is 2.

In the expansion of a power of the sum $A + B$, each term is a product of three factors, viz. the numerical coefficient, the power of A, and the power of B. The sum of exponents of A and B is constant, and it is equal to the exponent of the sum $A + B$. Thus, $(A + B)^4$ is expanded in a sum of terms such that the sum of exponents of A and B in each of them is 4. In the first term, $A^4 = A^4B^0$ the exponent of B

is zero ($B^0 = 1$), and the exponent of A is four. In the second term, we have $A^3B = A^3B^1$, so that the exponent of B increases by one and that of A decreases by one, when we pass from the first to the second term. The same rule applies when we pass from any term to the next one, so that the last term is $A^0B^4 = B^4$ and there are $4 + 1 = 5$ terms in the expansion of $(A + B)^4$. The law of formation of coefficients was formulated for the first time by the French mathematician Blaise Pascal (1623–1662), who constructed the so-called Pascal's Triangle:

$$
\begin{array}{ccccccccccccc}
&&&&&& 1 &&&&&& \\
&&&&& 1 && 1 &&&&& \\
&&&& 1 && 2 && 1 &&&& \\
&&& 1 && 3 && 3 && 1 &&& \\
&& 1 && 4 && 6 && 4 && 1 && \\
& 1 && 5 && 10 && 10 && 5 && 1 & \\
1 && 6 && 15 && 20 && 15 && 6 && 1 \\
\end{array}
$$

In this triangle, the numbers in any row, except the first one, are obtained from those of the preceding row by writing down the terminal units and adding together the successive pairs of numbers in a row to form the numbers of the next row. But Pascal's Triangle can be extended downwards without limit, and it gives the numerical coefficients of all the expansions $(A + B)^n$ with any integral and positive exponent n, no matter how large we choose it.

The French philosopher and mathematician Blaise Pascal was a most extraordinary man. Before the age of sixteen, he discovered and proved one of the most important and beautiful geometrical theorem known as Pascal's theorem. His *Essai sur les Coniques* deals with projective geometry, which was entirely new and unknown at his time. In 1641 at the age of eighteen, he invented and built the first digital calculating machine based on the same principles as our modern electronic computers. In his correspondence with Fermat (1654) he founded the mathematical theory of probability. It was in connection with the study of probabilities that he discovered the famous Pascal's triangle and formulated the law of binomial expansion.

There are vague indications that the finite sequences of integers of Pascal's triangle were known already to the famous Iranian writer, mathematician, and philosopher of the twelfth century, Omar Khayyám, author of the *Rubáiyát*.

Returning to binomial expansions, we denote the coefficients of the expansion of $(A + B)^n$ by $C_m^{(n)}$, where the subscript m is related to the ordinal number r of the r-th term by the rule $m = r - 1$. Thus, the coefficient of the first term is denoted by $C_0^{(n)}$, of the second by $C_1^{(n)}$, of the third by $C_2^{(n)}$, and so on until the last $(n + 1)$-th term, whose coefficient is $C_n^{(n)}$. In all, we have $n + 1$ terms in the expansion of $(A + B)^n$, and their coefficients are

$$C_0^{(n)} = 1, C_1^{(n)}, C_2^{(n)}, \ldots, C_{n-1}^{(n)}, C_n^{(n)} = 1$$

ther terminal ones, $C_0^{(n)}$ and $C_n^{(n)}$, being equal to *one*.

Therefore, generalizing the expansions of $(A + B)^2$, $(A + B)^3$, $(A + B)^4$, $(A + B)^5$, etc., we form a general expansion of the n-th power $(A + B)^n$ for any integral and positive exponent n:

$$(A + B)^n = A^n + C_1^{(n)}A^{n-1}B + C_2^{(n)}A^{n-2}B^2 + \cdots \tag{1}$$

$$+ C_m^{(n)}A^{n-m}B^m + \cdots + C_{n-1}^{(n)}AB^{n-1} + B^n.$$

The structure of a binomial expansion is characterized by the fact that in each term of the general expansion the sum of exponents of A and B is constant and equal to the exponent n of the power of the sum $A + B$. The subscript m in the coefficient $C_m^{(n)}$ and the exponent of B are equal, and the order of the term exceeds them by one unit. The second term is, for instance, $C_1^{(n)}A^{n-1}B$, the exponent of B being one, and the first term A^n could be written $C_0^{(n)}A^nB^0$ since $C_0^{(n)} = B^0 = 1$. The total number of terms is $n + 1$ because there are as many terms as powers of B with exponents $0, 1, 2, 3, 4, \ldots, n - 1, n$; that is, in all $n + 1$ terms.

The term denoted by $C_m^{(n)}A^{n-m}B^m$ is called the general term. It expresses the law of structure and represents all $n + 1$ terms, since the symbol m represents any integer between zero and n, $0 \leqslant m \leqslant n$. Therefore, if m varies, running through all the integers from zero until n, we obtain, one after another, all the terms of the general binomial expansion (1), the r-th term being obtained for $m = r - 1$.

Now we will prove (1) by mathematical induction. We know that, for $n = 2$, we have

$$(A + B)^2 = A^2 + 2AB + B^2$$

and in it $C_1^{(2)} = 2$. Similarly,

$$(A + B)^3 = A^3 + 3A^2B + 3AB^2 + B^3$$

gives $C_1^{(3)} = C_2^{(3)} = 3$, and, for these first values of n, we have the rule

$$C_m^{(n+1)} = C_{m-1}^{(n)} + C_m^{(n)} \qquad (m \leqslant n) \quad (2)$$

which expresses the fundamental feature of the Pascal's triangle.

Let us now prove that the coefficients of the expansion (1) satisfy the rule (2) for any n. First of all, we must justify the form (1) which we know only for $n = 2, 3, 4, 5$. We suppose that for $n = k$ the expansion (1) is true, and we want to prove that it obeys the same law (1) for $n = k + 1$, if this law is true for $n = k$ (hereditary property). Therefore, we consider the expansion

$$(A + B)^k = A^k + C_1^{(k)} A^{k-1} B + \cdots + C_{m-1}^{(k)} A^{k-m+1} B^{m-1}$$
$$+ C_m^{(k)} A^{k-m} B^m + \cdots + B^k$$

as granted. Multiplying both members of it by $A + B$, we find an expansion of

$$(A + B)^{k+1} = A^{k+1} + C_1^{(k)} A^k B + \cdots + C_{m-1}^{(k)} A^{k-m+2} B^{m-1}$$
$$+ C_m^{(k)} A^{k-m+1} B^m + \cdots + AB^k + A^k B + \cdots$$
$$+ C_{m-1}^{(k)} A^{k-m+1} B^m + \cdots + C_{k-1}^{(k)} AB^k + B^{k+1},$$

where the first $k + 1$ terms represent the partial product resulting from the multiplication by A, while the last $k + 1$ terms are obtained multiplying the expansion of $(A + B)^k$ by B. Adding the like terms, we find that the expansion of $(A + B)^{k+1}$ follows the law (1): the number of terms is $k + 2$, and the exponents of A and B in each term obey this law. Applying mathematical induction, we justify the *form* of the expansion (1) for all values of n.

To prove that the coefficients of (1) satisfy the rule (2) it is sufficient to check the structure of the coefficient $C_m^{(k+1)}$ of the general term with $A^{k-m+1} B^m$. This term is a sum of two terms:

$$C_m^{(k)} A^{k-m+1} B^m + C_{m-1}^{(k)} A^{k-m+1} B^m = [C_{m-1}^{(k)} + C_m^{(k)}] A^{k-m+1} B^m$$

and, thus, the rule (2) is justified: the coefficient $C_m^{(k+1)}$ of the general term in the expansion of $(A + B)^{k+1}$ is obtained by adding $C_{m-1}^{(k)}$ and $C_m^{(k)}$.

Since $(A + B)^n = (B + A)^n$, the binomial expansion of $(A + B)^n$ can also be written as follows:

$$(A + B)^n = B^n + C_1^{(n)} AB^{n-1} + \cdots + C_m^{(n)} A^m B^{n-m} + \cdots + A^n \qquad (1^*)$$

Comparing the expansions (1) and (1*), we find that the general term with $A^m B^{n-m}$, whose coefficient in (1*) is $C_m^{(n)}$, has in (1) the coefficient $C_{n-m}^{(n)}$, because in (1) the subscript of the coefficient is equal to the exponent of B. Therefore, *the binomial coefficients equidistant from both ends of the expansion are equal:*

$$C_m^{(n)} = C_{n-m}^{(n)} \qquad (2^*)$$

This important relation is exemplified in Pascal's triangle.

We will now form the explicit expression of the binomial coefficient $C_m^{(n)}$ in terms of two integers n (exponent of the expanded power) and m (ordinal number of the term diminished by one), where m can take any of $n + 1$ values: $m = 0, 1, 2, 3, \dots, n - 1, n$. This expression involves products of the type $1 \cdot 2 \cdot 3 \cdot 4 \cdots (k - 2)(k - 1)k$, whose factors are successive integers from 1 to k. They are called *factorials*, and, more specifically, *k-factorial* is a product of the first k integers. Thus, five-factorial is equal to 120, since $1 \cdot 2 \cdot 3 \cdot 4 \cdot 5 = 120$. A special symbol is used to denote factorials: if k denotes an integer, k followed by an exclamation mark indicates the k-factorial:

$$k! = 1 \cdot 2 \cdot 3 \cdot 4 \cdots (k - 1)k.$$

EXAMPLE:

$1! = 1, 2! = 2, 3! = 6, 5! \cdot 6 = 6!$, as well as $8! \cdot 9 \cdot 10 = 10!$

Note the important property of the symbol $n!$:

$$n!(n + 1) = (n + 1)! \qquad (3)$$

Substituting in this relation zero for n, we find $0! \cdot 1 = 1$, so that the symbol $0!$ is equal by definition to *one*: $0! = 1$.

To form the expression of $C_m^{(n)}$ for any m and n with $0 \leqslant m \leqslant n$ we must use the relation (2). Substituting $k - 1$ for n in (2), we transcribe it as follows:

$$C_m^{(k)} - C_m^{(k-1)} = C_{m-1}^{(k-1)}$$

Giving now to k a sequence of decreasing integral values $n, n - 1, n - 2, \dots, m + 1$ and adding the resulting $n - m$ relations

$$C_m^{(n)} - C_m^{(n-1)} = C_{m-1}^{(n-1)}$$
$$C_m^{(n-1)} - C_m^{(n-2)} = C_{m-1}^{(n-2)}$$
$$\dots\dots\dots\dots\dots\dots\dots\dots$$
$$C_m^{(m+1)} - C_m^{(m)} = C_{m-1}^{(m)} \qquad (C_m^{(m)} = 1)$$

we obtain the expression of a coefficient $C_m^{(n)}$ of binomial expansion with exponent n in terms of coefficients $C_{m-1}^{(i)}$ of expansions with exponents $i = m, m + 1, \ldots, n - 1$:

$$C_m^{(n)} = 1 + C_{m-1}^{(m)} + C_{m-1}^{(m+1)} + \cdots + C_{m-1}^{(n-2)} + C_{m-1}^{(n-1)} \quad (1 = C_{m-1}^{(m-1)})$$

This relation is clearly recognizable in Pascal's triangle: the sum of elements belonging to a parallel to the left side of the triangle obtained summing downwards, is always equal to the element in the line below the last term of the sum, standing adjacent to and to the right of this last term.

Thus
$$1 + 3 + 6 + 10 = 20.$$

We apply this relation first to the case $m = 1$ because we know that $C_0^{(i)} = 1$ for all i. Thus, $C_1^{(n)}$ is a sum of n terms, all of them equal to one, so that $C_1^{(n)}$ is equal to n. In the binomial expansion of $(A + B)^n$, the coefficient of the second term is always equal to the exponent n: $C_1^{(n)} = n$.

Applying now the same relation to the case $m = 2$, we have

$$C_2^{(n)} = 1 + C_1^{(2)} + C_1^{(3)} + \cdots + C_1^{(n-1)} = 1 + 2 + 3 + 4 + \cdots + (n - 1)$$

$$= n(n - 1)/2$$

as it was proved in the Chapter 1. Having found that

$$C_2^{(n)} = n(n - 1)/2,$$

we can now compute the expression of $C_3^{(n)}$: $n(n - 1)/2 = n^2/2 - n/2$, so that

$$C_3^{(n)} = 1 + C_2^{(3)} + C_2^{(4)} + \cdots + C_2^{(n-1)}$$

$$= 1 + [3^2 - 3 + 4^2 - 4 + 5^2 - 5 + \cdots + (n - 1)^2 - (n - 1)]/2$$

$$= [1^2 + 2^2 + 3^2 + \cdots + (n - 1)^2]/2 - [1 + 2 + 3 + \cdots + (n - 1)]/2$$

$$= (n - 1) n(2n - 1)/2 - (n - 1) n/4$$

$$= (n - 1) n(2n - 1 - 3)/12 = n(n - 1) (n - 2)/6$$

A comparison of these three expressions

$$C_1^{(n)} = n/1, \; C_2^{(n)} = n(n - 1)/2, \; C_3^{(n)} = n(n - 1) (n - 2)/6$$

suggests (simple induction) the following law of structure for $C_m^{(n)}$:

A binomial coefficient $C_m^{(n)}$ is a fraction with m factors in the numerator and as many factors in the denominator. The factors of the numerator form a decreasing sequence of successive integers beginning with the factor n. The factors of the denominator form an increasing sequence of successive integers beginning with the factor 1, so that the denominator is m!

Expressing this law of structure by an algebraical formula, we obtain

$$C_m^{(n)} = n(n - 1)(n - 2) \cdots (n - m + 1)/m! \tag{4}$$

It is easy to check the validity of this formula for $n = 2, 3, 4$. Take, for instance, $n = 4$. From Pasal's triangle, we know the values of five binomial coefficients in the expansion of $(A + B)^4$:

$$C_0^{(4)} = 1, \ C_1^{(4)} = 4, \ C_2^{(4)} = 6, \ C_3^{(4)} = 4, \ C_4^{(4)} = 1$$

The formula (4) gives, for $n = 4$ and $m = 1, 2, 3, 4$,

$$C_1^{(4)} = 4/1 = 4, \ C_2^{(4)} = 4 \cdot 3/2 = 6, \ C_3^{(4)} = 4 \cdot 3 \cdot 2/6 = 4,$$

$$C_4^{(4)} = 4 \cdot 3 \cdot 2 \cdot 1/4! = 1$$

But for $m = 0$ the formula (4) does not work. This is why we have to modify it, creating a factorial in the numerator. This numerator $n(n - 1) \cdots (n - m + 1)$ is an incomplete n-factorial, and the factors of n-factorial missing in it are the following:

$$(n - m)(n - m - 1)(n - m - 2) \cdots 3 \cdot 2 \cdot 1$$

They form the $(n - m)$-factorial, which is denoted by $(n - m)!$ Therefore, multiplying both the numerator and denominator of $C_n^{(m)}$ by the factorial $(n - m)!$, we transform its numerator into n-factorial. Thus, the expression (4) can be also written as follows:

$$C_n^{(m)} = n!/[(n - m)! \, m!] \qquad (0 \leqslant m \leqslant n) \tag{5}$$

This form holds for $m = 0$ also: $C_0^{(n)} = n!/n! = 1$ because $0! = 1$.

To prove that the expression (5) holds for all values of n, we use the mathematical induction. Since we know that the expression (5) is true for $n = 2, 3, 4$, it is sufficient to prove that it possesses the hereditary property, that is, to prove that (5) holds for $n = k + 1$, if it is true for $n = k$.

We suppose that $\quad C_m^{(k)} = k!/[(k - m)! \, m!]$

and form $C_m^{(k+1)}$, using the relation (2):

$$C_m^{(k+1)} = C_m^{(k)} + C_{m-1}^{(k)} = k!/[(k - m)! \, m!] + k!/[(k + 1 - m)!(m - 1)!]$$

The common denominator of two fractions in the righthand member is $(k + 1 - m)!\,m!$ Reducing both fractions to this common denominator and adding, we obtain

$$(k + 1 - m)\,k!/[(k + 1 - m)!\,m!] + mk!/[(k + 1 - m)!\,m!]$$

$$= (k + 1 - m + m)\,k!/[(k + 1 - m)!\,m!]$$

where $(k + 1 - m + m)\,k! = k!(k + 1) = (k + 1)!$, so that the expression of $C_m^{(k+1)}$ follows the law (5).

$$C_m^{(k+1)} = (k + 1)!/[(k + 1 - m)!\,m!]$$

This is, indeed, the particular case of (5) for $n = k + 1$. Thus, the law (5) is justified for all integral values of n and $m \leqslant n$.

Pascal's triangle shows that the binomial coefficients $C_m^{(n)}$ are integers, so that the fractional expression (5) reduced to its lowest terms becomes an integer. Forming $C_{m+1}^{(n)}$, we prove easily that the quotient $C_{m+1}^{(n)}/C_m^{(n)}$ is equal to $(n - m)/(m + 1)$:

$$C_{m+1}^{(n)}/C_m^{(n)} = (n - m)!\,m!/[(n - m - 1)!\,(m + 1)!]$$

$$= (n - m)\,(n - m - 1)!\,m!/[(m + 1)\,(n - m - 1)!\,(m)!]$$

so that, indeed, $\qquad C_{m+1}^{(n)} = C_m^{(n)}(n - m)/(m + 1).$ (6)

We will now introduce an abbreviation for a sum of terms all of which have the same structure. Suppose that the expression of this law of structure for the $(m + 1)$-th term is denoted by u_m. Then, the first, second, third, etc. terms will be u_0, u_1, u_2, etc. and the sum of first $n + 1$ terms is

$$u_0 + u_1 + u_2 + u_3 + \cdots + u_{n-1} + u_n$$

Such a sum of terms of type u_m, from $m = 0$ (first term u_0) to $m = n$ (last term u_n) inclusive, will be denoted by Σ with the subscript $m = 0$ and the superscript $m = n$, followed by the general term u_m:

$$\sum_{m=0}^{m=n} u_m = u_0 + u_1 + u_2 + u_3 + \cdots + u_{n-1} + u_n$$

Thus, for example, noting that the general term in the expansion (1) of $(A + B)^n$ has the form $C_m^{(n)}A^{n-m}B^m$, we can write this expansion as follows:

$$(A + B)^n = \sum_{m=0}^{m=n} C_m^{(n)}A^{n-m}B^m$$

Replacing the coefficient $C_m^{(n)}$ by expressions (4) and (5) we also have

$$(A + B)^n = \sum_{m=0}^{m=n} n(n - 1) \cdots (n - m + 1)\, A^{n-m} B^m / m!$$

$$= \sum_{m=0}^{m=n} n!\, A^{n-m} B^m / [(n - m)!\, m!]$$

where, for $m = 0$, the expression $n(n - 1) \cdots (n - m) + 1)/m!$ by definition is equal to one. Indeed, we saw that

$$n(n - 1)\,(n - 2) \cdots (n - m + 1)/m! = n!/[(n - m)!\, m!]$$

for $m = 0$ becomes $n!/[n!\, 0!] = 1$ since $0! = 1$.

A very important particular case of (1) for $A = 1$ and $B = z$ is the binomial expansion of $(1 + z)^n$:

$$(1 + z)^n = \sum_{m=0}^{m=n} C_m^{(n)} z^m = 1 + nz/1! + n(n - 1)\, z^2/2! + \cdots + z^n \qquad (7)$$

For $z = 1$, it gives the value of the sum of all $n + 1$ coefficients $C_m^{(n)}$ of the binomial expansion (1). This value is $(1 + 1)^n = 2^n$:

$$(1 + 1)^n = 2^n = \sum_{m=0}^{m=n} C_m^{(n)} = 1 + n/1 + n(n - 1)/2 + \cdots + 1.$$

Very often the binomial coefficients $C_m^{(n)}$ is denoted also by $\binom{n}{m}$ so that the meaning of this new symbol $\binom{n}{m}$ is given by

$$\binom{n}{m} = \frac{n(n - 1) \cdots (n - m + 1)}{1 \cdot 2 \cdot 3 \cdots (m - 1)\, m} = \frac{n!}{m!(n - m)!} \qquad (0 \leqslant m \leqslant n)$$

If n is a positive integer, the symbol $\binom{n}{m}$ is meaningless for $m > n$, so that the integer m can vary only from zero to n. Later we will define and use the same symbol for any value of the number n, not necessarily an integer or positive. In this general case, the restriction $m \leqslant n$ does not apply; in all cases however, m in $\binom{n}{m}$ always denotes a non-negative integer.

We come now to an important property of binomial coefficients $C_m^{(n)} = \binom{n}{m}$ which we illustrate first on a numerical example. The sixth term in the binomial expansion of $(1 + z)^9$ is $C_5^{(9)}z^5$, where

$$C_5^{(9)} = \binom{9}{5} = 9!/(5!\,4!) = 126$$

On the other hand, $(1 + z)^9$ can be factored into a product of two powers, $(1 + z)^4$ and $(1 + z)^5$, of the same base $1 + z$

$$(1 + z)^9 = (1 + z)^4\,(1 + z)^5$$

These powers can also be expanded and their binomial expansions can be multiplied term by term, so that every coefficient of $(1 + z)^9$ will be obtained as a combination of coefficients $C_m^{(4)}$ and $C_m^{(5)}$ of these binomial expansions:

$$(1 + z)^4 = \sum_0^4 \binom{4}{m} z^m = \binom{4}{0} + \binom{4}{1} z + \binom{4}{2} z^2 + \binom{4}{3} z^3 + \binom{4}{4} z^4$$

$$(1 + z)^5 = \sum_0^5 \binom{5}{m} z^m \tag{8}$$

$$= \binom{5}{0} + \binom{5}{1} z + \binom{5}{2} z^2 + \binom{5}{3} z^3 + \binom{5}{4} z^4 + \binom{5}{5} z^5$$

Multiplying the righthand members of these expansions term by term, we are interested in the coefficient of z^5. The fifth power of z is obtained in five different partial products involving z^0z^5, z^1z^4, z^2z^3, z^3z^2, and z^4z^1 whose coefficients are

$$\binom{4}{0} \binom{5}{5},\ \binom{4}{1} \binom{5}{4},\ \binom{4}{2} \binom{5}{3},\ \binom{4}{3} \binom{5}{2} \quad \text{and} \quad \binom{4}{4} \binom{5}{1},$$

respectively. Therefore, the coefficient $\binom{9}{5}$ of z^5 in the expansion of $(1 + z)^9$ must be equal to their sum

$$\binom{9}{5} = \sum_{m=0}^{m=4} \binom{4}{m} \binom{5}{5 - m} = \binom{4}{0} \binom{5}{5}$$

$$+ \binom{4}{1} \binom{5}{4} + \binom{4}{2} \binom{5}{3} + \binom{4}{3} \binom{5}{2} + \binom{4}{4} \binom{5}{1} \tag{9}$$

It is easy to check this result, replacing the coefficients by their numerical values. We obtain indeed the following value:

$$1 \cdot 1 + 4 \cdot 5 + 6 \cdot 10 + 4 \cdot 10 + 1 \cdot 5 = 1 + 20 + 60 + 40 + 5 = 126$$

which is the value of the coefficient $\binom{9}{5}$.

This particular result suggests the following generalization: replacing the numbers 9 and 5 by $p + q$ and s, we consider the binomial coefficients $\binom{p+q}{s}$ on one hand and $\binom{p}{m}, \binom{q}{n}$ on the other. The expansion of $(1 + z)^{p+q}$ is equal to the product of the expansions of $(1 + z)^q$ and $(1 + z)^q$, so that any coefficient $\binom{p+q}{s}$ with $0 \leqslant s \leqslant p + q$ must be a sum of products $\binom{p}{m} \binom{q}{n}$ such that $m + n = s$ and, therefore, $n = s - m$. The products of this type, $\binom{p}{m} \binom{q}{s-m}$, have meaning only if their variable index m satisfies the following four inequalities:

$$m \leqslant p, \; m \leqslant s, \; m \geqslant 0, \; m \geqslant s - q$$

Therefore, m cannot exceed the smaller of two numbers p and s. Denoting it by minimum $(p, s) = \min (p, s)$, we note that the admissible values of m must verify the condition $m \leqslant \min (p, s)$. On the other hand, two other inequalities $m \geqslant 0, \; m \geqslant s - q$ show that m cannot be less than the greater of two numbers, zero and $s - q$. Denoting this number by maximum $(0, s - q) = \max (0, s - q)$, we note that $m \geqslant \max (0, s - q)$.

Thus, summing up the products of the type $\binom{p}{m} \binom{q}{s-m}$ to form $\binom{p+q}{s}$, we must consider all the values of m between $\max (0, s - q)$ and $\min (p, s)$, which gives the following formula:

$$\binom{p+q}{s} = \sum_{\max(0, s-q)}^{\min(p,s)} \binom{p}{m} \binom{q}{s-m} \tag{10}$$

To prove this relation, we replace all three powers of $(1 + z)$ in the identity

$$(1 + z)^{p+q} \equiv (1 + z)^p (1 + z)^q$$

by their binomial expansion

$$\sum_{s=0}^{s=p+q} \binom{p+q}{s} z^s \equiv \left\{ \sum_{m=0}^{m=p} \binom{p}{m} z^m \right\} \left\{ \sum_{n=0}^{n=q} \binom{q}{n} z^n \right\} \tag{11}$$

where s, m, and n vary from zero to $p + q$, p and q, respectively. Performing the multiplication of two sums term by term, we obtain

$(p + 1)(q + 1)$ terms of the general type $\binom{p}{m}\binom{q}{n} z^{m+n}$ with different m and n. Collecting those with the same power z^s of z, we add the terms with $m + n = s$, and their sum represents the term $\binom{p + q}{s} z^s$ of the lefthand member. The terms we chose are characterized by $m + n = s$, and in them, $n = s - m$, so that summing their coefficients we obtain precisely the formula (10) and thus achieve its proof.

Combinations

The binomial coefficient $C_m^{(n)} = \binom{n}{m}$, where m and n are integers and $0 \leqslant m \leqslant n$, has an important interpretation: *it expresses the number of different ways of selecting m items out of a set of n items.* These different ways have nothing to do with the order in which the m items are extracted or selected, but only with different groups of m items. are extracted or selected, but only with different groups of m items. Take, for instance, the set of six letters A, B, C, D, E, F. To select out of it all the different groups of three letters, we begin by taking six different choices of the *first* element $\Big[$observe that their number 6 can be represented as the binomial coefficient $C_1^{(6)} = \binom{6}{1}\Big]$.

$$A, B, C, D, E, F. \tag{12}$$

Adjoining a second element to each item in (12), we form five groups of two items with A as one of these two items:

$$AB, AC, AD, AE, AF;$$

four groups with B rather than five, since BA is already formed (listed as AB):

$$BC, BD, BE, BF;$$

three groups with C, namely CD, CE, CF; two groups with D, namely DE and DF, and, finally, one group EF, with E, while no new group can be formed with F in (12), because all five groups involving F are already formed (listed as AF, BF, CF, DF, EF).

Thus, in all, we have $5 + 4 + 3 + 2 + 1 = 15$ different ways of selecting two items out of six, and this number 15 is well represented by the binomial coefficient

$$C_2^{(6)} = \binom{6}{2} = 6 \cdot 5/2 = 15$$

The same result is obtained by observing that to each of six items in (12) we can associate one of five others, forming, thus, in all, $6 \cdot 5 = 30$ groups of two items. Then, however, each combination of two items, for example of A and B, will be formed twice, the first time in the order AB and the second time in the order BA. Therefore, the true number of different combinations of two items is $6 \cdot 5/2 = C_2^{(6)}$.

If we adjoin now to each combination of two items a third element chosen among four remaining elements, we can do it in four different ways, obtaining, in all, $6 \cdot 5 \cdot 4/2 = 60$ associations of three elements. In them, each combination of three elements is represented three times. Thus, for instance, three associations AB + C, BC + A, and CA + B represent *one and the same* combination ABC of three letters A, B, and C. Therefore, the number of different combinations of three items selected out of six is

$$20 = 60/3 = 6 \cdot 5 \cdot 4/3! = C_3^{(6)} = \binom{6}{3}$$

In general, if the number of different ways of selecting $m - 1$ items out of a collection of n different things is known to be equal to $C_{m-1}^{(n)}$, to find how many different ways there are of selecting m items out of this collection of n things, we adjoin to each combination of $m - 1$ items one of the remaining $n - (m - 1) = n - m + 1$ items. Thus, $n - m + 1$ associations of m items are formed out of each combination of $m - 1$ items, and a set of $(n - m + 1) C_{m-1}^{(n)}$ such associations is obtained, using all $C_{m-1}^{(n)}$ combinations of $m - 1$ items. In this set of associations, each particular combination of m items is represented exactly m times since it was formed in m different ways by adjoining as the last m-th item every one of its m elements.

Therefore, the number of all different combinations of m items selected out of n items is obtained dividing the number of all associations $(n - m + 1) C_{m-1}^{(n)}$ by m:

$$(n - m + 1) C_{m-1}^{(n)}/m = (n - m + 1) n!/[(n - m + 1)! (m - 1)! m]$$

$$= n!/[(n - m)! m!] = C_m^{(n)}$$

This result is based on the assumption that the number of different combinations of $m - 1$ items selected out of n items is equal to $C_{m-1}^{(n)}$. Since the number of different choices of one item out of a collection of n items is $n = C_1^{(n)}$, we prove, by mathematical induction, that the number of different ways of selecting m items out of n given items is equal to $C_m^{(n)}$ for $m \leqslant n$.

Since to every combination of m items chosen among n items there corresponds a combination formed by the remaining $n - m$ items, we conclude that the number of combinations of m items is equal to the number of combinations of $n - m$ items:

$$C_m^{(n)} = C_{n-n}^{(n)}$$

The interpretation of $C_m^{(n)}$ as the number of combinations of m items selected out of a given set of n items yields another proof of the binomial expansion. In this proof, the n-th power of the sum $x + a$ is considered as a particular case of the following product of n different linear factors:

$$Q_n(x) = (x + a_1)(x + a_2)(x + a_3 \cdots (x + a_{n-1})(x + a_n) \quad (13)$$

The first terms are all equal to x, while the second terms $a_1, a_2, a_3, \ldots, a_n$ are different. These second terms are any n numbers, so that in particular they all may be equal to a, and, in this case, the polynomial $Q_n(x)$ reduces to $(x + a)^n$.

In the general case, when the numbers a_k, $1 \leqslant k \leqslant n$, are different, the polynomial $Q_n(x)$ can be expanded into a sum of $n + 1$ terms of the general type $A_m x^m$, $0 \leqslant m \leqslant n$, and this expansion is obtained by performing the multiplication of n factors $x + a_k$, $1 \leqslant k \leqslant n$. The coefficients A_m in this sum

$$Q_n(x) = A_0 + A_1 x + A_2 x^2 + A_3 x^3 + \cdots + A_n x^n = \sum_{m=0}^{m=n} A_m x^m \quad (13^*)$$

are themselves sums of products of numbers a_k. Thus, $A_0 = a_1 a_2 \ldots a_n$, A_1 is a sum of n terms each of which is a product of $n - 1$ factors a_k, and A_2 is also a sum of terms each of which is a product of $n - 2$ numbers a_k, so that the number of terms in the sum A_2 is equal to the number of combinations of two items chosen among n items a_k, $1 \leqslant k \leqslant n$. To each product of $n - 2$ numbers a_k corresponds, indeed, a combination of two numbers a_k, namely, the combination formed by those two numbers a_k which are lacking in the product of $n - 2$ numbers of this set a_k, $1 \leqslant k \leqslant n$.

In general, the coefficient A_m of the term $A_m x^m$ in the polynomial $Q_n(x)$ is a sum of products of $n - m$ factors a_k because multiplying out the n linear factors in (13) we form a sum of products such that every product contains exactly n factors. Some of these factors are equal to x, while the others belong to the set of numbers a_k. Grouping together the like terms, for instance the terms with m factors x, we pick out the common factor x^m and call the sum of terms between the parentheses the coefficient A_m. These terms are products of numbers a_k, and in each of them there must be exactly $n - m$ factors a_k because, before picking out the factor x^m, there were n factors in each term, and x^m represents m factors.

Therefore, each term of the sum A_m being a product of $n - m$ factors a_k, corresponds to a combination of m items chosen among n numbers of the set a_k, $1 \leqslant k \leqslant n$, namely, the combination formed by m numbers a_k lacking in the product of $n - m$ numbers a_k. This proves that *the number of terms in the sum A_m is represented by $C_m^{(n)}$, which is the number of combinations of m items chosen among n elements of the set a_k, $1 \leqslant k \leqslant n$.*

Let us consider now the particular case when all the numbers a_k are equal to the same number a: $a_k = a$ for $k = 1, 2, 3, \ldots, n - 1, n$. In this case, the polynomial $Q_n(x)$ reduces to $(x + a)^n$, which we can write also as $(a + x)^n$. To find out what form its expansion takes in this patricular case, we must study what happens to the coefficients A_m. Each term of the sum A_m is a product of $n - m$ factors a_k, which now become equal factors so that their product reduces to a power of the base a with exponent $n - m$, that is, to a^{n-m}. Thus, each term of A_m becomes equal to the same power a^{n-m} and the sum A_m as a sum of equal terms is transformed into a product, namely, a^{n-m} times the number of equal terms. But we saw that the number of terms which compose the sum A_m is $C_m^{(n)}$, that is, the number of combinations of m items selected among n items. Therefore, the coefficient A_m is now equal to $C_m^{(n)} a^{n-m}$, and the expansion of the polynomial $Q_n(x)$ is transformed into the binomial expansion of the power $(a + x)^n$:

$$Q_n(x) = (a + x)^n = a^n + C_1^{(n)} a^{n-1} x + C_2^{(n)} a^{n-2} x^2 \cdots C_{n-1}^{(n)} a x^{n-1} + x^n$$

Thus, the binomial theorem is deduced from a more general expansion (13*).

Permutations

We bring now into consideration the idea of order, and, considering a particular combination or association of n items, distinguish between the different arrangements which can exhibit n elements associated in a combination, when they are *ordered* and form a certain *sequence* of n elements. Such a sequence of n elements, characterized not only by the choice of elements which participate in it but also by the order in which they follow each other, is called a *permutation* of n items.

Given a definite combination of n items chosen among N elements of a set of N items, we ask how many different permutations can be formed with the n elements of this combination? The answer is n-factorial, that is $n!$, and thus we arrive at an important practical interpretation of this product of the first n integers, called n-factorial and denoted by $n! = 1 \cdot 2 \cdot 3 \cdot 4 \cdots n$.

To prove it, let us denote the number of different permutations of n items by P_n. If $n = 1$, then $P_1 = 1$, while $P_2 = 2 = 2!$ because only two permutations AB and BA can be formed with two items A and B. We suppose now that the law $P_n = n!$ is true for all values of the integer n not exceeding N, and, considering a collection of $N + 1$ items, set out to evaluate the number P_{N+1} of different permutations which can be formed with $N + 1$ items.

Isolating an item of a collection of $N + 1$ items, we obtain a combination of N items, namely, the combination formed by N remaining elements. There are exactly $N + 1$ different ways of isolating an element among $N + 1$ items and there are $N + 1$ different combinations of N items chosen among $N + 1$ items, but we consider only one definite combination of N items. This particular combination of N items generates $P_N = N!$ different permutations of N items (here we use our assumption that the number of permutations of N items is known to be equal to $N!$). Choosing a particular perfectly determined permutation of N items, we can build with it a permutation of $N + 1$ items, inserting somewhere in it the isolated $(N + 1)$-th element of our collection of $N + 1$ items. This insertion can be performed in $N + 1$ different ways, *viz.*, before the first item, that is, at the beginning of the permutation of N items, between the first and second items, or between the second and third items, *etc.*, ... , between the second from the end and the last item and, finally, after the last item, that is, at the end of the permutation.

Thus, a single permutation of N items generates by this process $N + 1$ different permutations of $N + 1$ items. But we had $P_N = N!$ such permutations and all of them correspond to the same isolated element. Therefore, the total number of permutations of $N + 1$ items is equal to $(N + 1) P_N = (N + 1) N!$, that is,

$$P_{N+1} = (N + 1)!, \quad \text{if} \quad P_N = N!$$

The hereditary character of the evaluation $P_n = n!$ being proved, it is sufficient to apply mathematical induction to justify the law $P_n = n!$ for all values of the integer n because $P_1 = 1!$ and $P_2 = 2!$

This result $P_n = n!$ can be used to justify the expression

$$C_m^{(n)} = n!/[(n - m)!\, m!]$$

of the number of different combinations of m items selected among n elements of a collection of n items.

To any definite combination of m items selected from a set of n $(n > m)$ given items correspond $P_m = m!$ different permutations which can be formed with the aid of m elements of this combination, arranging them in different orders. A set of n items can be split in two combinations of m and $n - m$ items by choosing as the first combination any group of m elements, the remaining $n - m$ elements forming the second combination.

The choice of the first combination can be made in $C_m^{(n)}$ different ways, if the number of different combinations of m items chosen in a set of n items is denoted by $C_m^{(n)}$. At this moment, $C_m^{(n)}$ is nothing else than a symbol for the unknown number of combinations of m items selected in a given set of n items. Therefore, there are $C_m^{(n)}$ different ways of splitting a set of n elements into two combinations of m and $n - m$ items.

To every one of these $C_m^{(n)}$ ways correspond $P_m P_{n-m}$ different arrangements of all n elements involved in both juxtaposed combinations of m and of $n - m$ items, because any of P_m possible permutations of m elements of the first combination can be associated with any of P_{n-m} possible permutations of $n - m$ elements of the second combination.

Therefore, the number of different permutations of all n elements of our set generated with preservation of a particular splitting of the set in two combinations of m and of $n - m$ elements is equal to the product

$$P_m P_{n-m} = m!(n - m)!$$

On the other hand, all possible permutations of n items will be obtained, if all possible $C_m^{(n)}$ ways of splitting the set of n items into two combinations of m and $n - m$ items are considered. Therefore, the total number of all permutations of n items is expressed by the product

$$P_m P_{n-m} C_m^{(n)} = m!(n - m)!\, C_m^{(n)}$$

But, we know also that the same number is equal to $P_n = n!$ Thus for the unknown $C_m^{(n)}$, we have the equation

$$m!(n - m)!\, C_m^{(n)} = n!$$

Solving this equation for $C_m^{(n)}$, we find again the numerical value (5) of the m-th binomial coefficient of the expansion of $(A + B)^n$, namely,

$$C_m^{(n)} = n!/[m!(n - m]!) = \binom{n}{m} \qquad (0 \leqslant m \leqslant n)$$

Newton's Binominal Formula

We owe to Newton the generalization of the binomial expansion to the cases when the exponent n is no longer a positive integers. He was the first to consider and define the binomial coefficient $C_m^{(n)}$ for any value $n = t$ of the exponent by the same expression (4) which represents it for the positive integer n. Thus $\binom{t}{0} = C_0^{(t)} = 1$, and, for $m \geqslant 1$,

$$\binom{t}{m} = C_m^{(t)} = t(t - 1)(t - 2) \cdots (t - m + 1)/m! \qquad (m \geqslant 1) \quad (14)$$

This general formula yields $\binom{t}{m} = C_m^{(t)}$ for all values of t, complex as well as real, the symbol m always denoting a positive integer. It is important to emphasize that if t is not a positive integer, the numerator $t(t - 1)(t - 2) \cdots (t - m + 1)$ cannot vanish, and, therefore, the formula (14) defines in general an infinite sequence of coefficients.

$\binom{t}{m} = C_m^{(t)}$ for all values of $m = 1, 2, 3, \ldots$ Thus, the limitation $m \leqslant n$ holds only in the particular case, when the exponent t takes a positive and integral value $t = n$, and in this case the sequence of coefficients is finite.

Since

$$(A + B)^t = A^t[1 + (B/A)]^t = A^t(1 + z)^t \text{ with } z = B/A,$$

it is sufficient to write down the expansion of $(1 + z)^t$:

$$(1 + z) = 1 + tz + t(t - 1) z^2/2 + \cdots = \sum_{m=0}^{\infty} \binom{t}{m} z^m. \qquad (15)$$

where the coefficients are defined by (14). This expansion is essentially different from its particular case $t = n$ (n denoting a positive integer). Instead of a finite sum of $n + 1$ terms, we have in (15) an infinite series which converges for all values of the complex number z whose absolute value (modulus) is less than one: $|z| < 1$. In this respect, the expansion (15) behaves as the infinite series we studied under the name of geometric series. It can be shown that the condition $|z| < 1$ is sufficient to insure the convergence: if $|z| < 1$, the sum S_N of the first $N + 1$ terms of the series (15) approaches $(1 + z)^t$, when N tends to infinity, that is,

$$\lim_{N=\infty} S_N = \lim_{N=\infty} \sum_{m=0}^{N} \binom{t}{m} z^m = (1 + z)^t \qquad (|z| < 1)$$

In other words, the binomial expansion (15) represents the function $(1 + z)^t$ of the variable z in the form of a polynomial of infinite order. If t is equal to a positive integer n, the infinite series (15) reduces to a finite sum (7) because the coefficients $C_m^{(n)}$ with $m > t = n$ are equal to zero and the corresponding terms vanish.

Let us now study some examples of the general binomial expansion (15). Choosing first $t = -1$, we compute the coefficients $\binom{-1}{m}$ of the expansion of the function

$$(1 + z)^{-1} = 1/(1 + z)$$

The formula (14) gives for $t = -1$,

$$C_m^{(-1)} = \binom{-1}{m} = (-1)(-2)(-3)\cdots(-m)/m! = (-1)^m m!/m! = (-1)^m$$

so that the coefficients of even powers of z are equal to $+1$, while the coefficients of odd powers of z are equal to -1. Therefore,

$$(1+z)^{-1} = \sum_{m=0}^{\infty} (-1)^m z^m$$

$$= 1 - z + z^2 - z^3 + \cdots + (-z)^m + \cdots = \sum_{m=0}^{\infty} (-z)^m$$

This infinite series is a geometric progression $\sum_0^{\infty} r^m$ with $r = -z$.
Thus, geometric series is merely a particular case of binomial expansion, namely, the case when the exponent is equal to minus one. We state that the Newtonian binomial expansion represents a generalization of geometric series.

We consider now another particular case of (15) in which $t = -2$.
Replacing t by -2 in (14), we obtain the coefficients $\binom{-2}{m}$:

$$C_m^{(-2)} = \binom{-2}{m} = (-2)(-3)\cdots(-m)[-(m+1)]/m! = (-1)^m(m+1)$$

Applying this result in the expansion of $[1+(-z)]^{-2} = (1-z)^{-2}$ we have

$$1/(1-z)^2 = [1+(-z)]^{-2}$$

$$= \sum_{m=0}^{\infty} (-1)^m (m+1)(-z)^m = \sum_{m=0}^{\infty} (m+1) z^m$$

so that

$$1 + 2z + 3z^2 + 4z^3 + \cdots + (m+1) z^m + \cdots = 1/(1-z)^2$$

Expansion of a Power of a Sum of Three Terms

An extension of the binomial theorem in another direction is represented by the expansion of a power $(A+B+C)^n$ of a sum of *three* terms. Thus, for instance, we have for $n = 0, 1, 2, 3$ the formulae

$$(A+B+C)^0 = 1, \quad (A+B+C)^1 = 1A + 1B + 1C$$

$$(A+B+C)^2 = 1A^2 + 1B^2 + 1C^2 + 2AB + 2BC + 2CA$$

and

$$(A+B+C)^3 = 1A^3 + 1B^3 + 1C^3 + 3A^2B + 3B^2C + 3C^2A +$$

$$+ 3B^2A + 3C^2B + 3A^2C + 6ABC.$$

The law of coefficients can be represented with the aid of a triangular pyramid (see fig. 2) which plays, in the case of $(A + B + C)^n$, the role played by Pascal's triangle for $(A + B)^n$. Its three faces are Pascal's triangles, and the horizontal triangular sections replace the horizontal lines of Pascal's triangle. These horizontal sections correspond to different powers of the sum $A + B + C$, the n-th section from the vertex of the pyramid containing the coefficients of the expansion of $(A + B + C)^n$.

The units located at their vertices, that is, along three edges of the infinite pyramid, are coefficients of the highest powers A^n, B^n, C^n in the expansion of $(A + B + C)^n$. The numbers located in the interior of three faces are coefficients of terms involving powers of two among the three terms A, B, C of the sum $A + B + C$. Finally the numbers which are located inside the pyramid and thus belong to the interior of horizontal triangular sections of the pyramid, are coefficients of terms involving the powers of all three terms $A, B,$ and C. So, for instance, the third section (see fig. 2) corresponds to $(A + B + C)^3$,

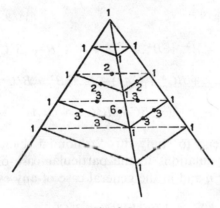

Fig. 9.2

and the number six located at its center is the coefficient of the unique term of the expansion involving all three terms, namely the coefficient of ABC.

The value of a coefficient located at an interior point of a horizontal section is the sum of three coefficients located above it in the previous horizontal section on three straight lines parallel to three edges of the pyramid. Thus, the coefficient six in the section represented on fig. 2 is equal to the sum $2 + 2 + 2$, and the lines passing through the point six and parallel to three edges meet in the previous section above the points marked by the numbers two. The rule just formulated generalizes Pascal's rule for the coefficients displayed in Pascal's triangle.

Applying this rule, we deduce and find the coefficients of the expansion $(A + B + C)^4$. Observing that displacements parallel to three edges of the pyramid correspond to multiplications by A, B, and C, we obtain the fifteen terms of the expansion of

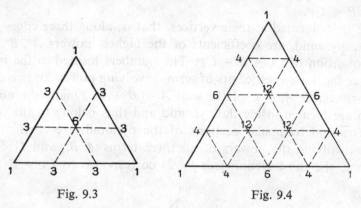

Fig. 9.3   Fig. 9.4

$$(A + B + C)^4 = A^4 + B^4 + C^4 + 4(A^3B + B^3C + C^3A + AB^3$$

$$+ BC^3 + CA^3) + 6(A^2B^2 + B^2C^2 + C^2A^2)$$

$$+ 12(A^2BC + B^2CA + C^2A)$$

We do not intend to study this "trinomial theorem". Instead, we state only its formulations in the particular case of an integral and positive exponent n and in the general case of any exponent t:

$$(A + B + C)^n = \sum_{m+k+l=n} n!/[m!k!l!]\, A^mB^kC^l \qquad (16)$$

$$= \sum_{m+k\leqslant n} n(n - 1)\cdots(n - m - k + 1)A^mB^kC^{n-m-k}/m!k!$$

and

$$(1 + x + y)^t = \sum_{m=0}^{\infty} \sum_{k=0}^{\infty} t(t - 1)(t - 2)\cdots(t - m - k + 1)x^my^k/m!k! \qquad (17)$$

where the summation extends to all integral values (zero included) of indices used in the latter, with the limitation $m + k + l = n$ in the case of the former, the negative values being excluded.

The infinite series (17) includes the finite sum (16) as a particular case and it reduces to the finite sum (16) if $t = n$, where n denotes, as usual, a positive integer. The number of terms in (16) is equal to $(n + 1)(n + 2)/2$, and the sum of all the coefficients is 3^n. It is obtained from (16) by substituting the number one for A, B, and C.

Applications of Binominal Theorem

The numerical computation of approximate values for radicals is often simplified and facilitated by the use of binomial expansion. Take, for instance, $\sqrt[5]{36}$, the value of which lies between two and three because $2^5 = 32$ and $3^5 = 243$. We observe that 36 is much nearer to 32 than to 243, and, therefore, $\sqrt[5]{36} = 2 + f$, where f must be a small fraction. To find the approximate value of f, with, say, four exact decimals after the dot, we can apply the binomial theorem to

$$\sqrt[5]{36} = (32 + 4)^t \text{ with } t = 1/5 = 0.2$$

Now, $32 + 4 = 32(1 + 1/8)$ and, thus,

$$\sqrt[5]{36} = \sqrt[5]{32}(1 + 1/8)^{1/5} = 2(1 + 1/8)^{1/5}$$

because $32 = 2^5$. The reason for the choice of 32 as first term in the decomposition of 36 into a sum of two terms is precisely the fact that 32 is the exact fifth power of an integer which is nearest to $\sqrt[5]{36}$. Likewise, for the radical $\sqrt[5]{220}$, we would use $220 = 243 - 23$ because the fifth power of three, namely $3^5 = 243$, is the nearest to 220.

Since $\sqrt[5]{36} = 2(1 + 1/8)^{1/5}$, the computation of the radical $\sqrt[5]{36}$ is reduced to that of $(1 + 1/8)^t$ with $t = 1/5$. To compute it we apply (15) with $t = 1/5$ and $z = 1/8$:

$$(1 + 1/8)^{1/5} = 1 + (1/5)(1/8) + (1/5)(-4/5)(1/8)^2/2$$

$$+ (1/5)(-4/5)(-9/5)(1/8)^3/6 + \cdots$$

$$= 1 + 0.025 - 0.00125 + 0.00009375 - \cdots$$

Though the expansion of $(1 + 1/8)^{1/5}$ as an infinite series contains an infinite number of terms, it is clear that its terms decrease very rapidly.

Therefore, the series converges so rapidly that all the terms except the first four can be neglected in computing the approximate value of $\sqrt[5]{1 + 1/8}$:

$$\sqrt[5]{1 + 1/8} \simeq 1 + 0.025 - 0.00125 + 0.00009375 = 1.02384375$$

Note that the terms of our series decrease in absolute value, being alternately positive and negative. Therefore, the error, committed considering instead of $\sqrt[5]{1 + 1/8}$ its approximate value 1.02384375, is surely less than the first term neglected, the approximate value being greater than the exact value because the first term neglected is negative. It is, indeed,

$$0.2(0.2 - 1)\,(0.2 - 2)\,(0.2 - 3)\,(1/8)^4/4! = -21/40^4 = -8203125/10^{12}$$

and, therefore, we have the inequalities

$$1.02383555 < \sqrt[5]{1 + 1/8} < 1.02384375$$

as well as

$$2.04767 < \sqrt[5]{36} = 2\sqrt[5]{1 + 1/8} < 2.04769$$

Finally, an approximate value 2.0476 for $\sqrt[5]{36}$ is obtained with four exact decimals.

Computation of $\sqrt{2}$

Different representations of the irrational number $2^{1/2}$ by infinite expressions were studied in Chapter 4. The binomial theorem yields a representation of $2^{1/2}$ in the form of an infinite series. To expand $2^{1/2}$ by binomial theorem, we write it as $(1 - 1/2)^{-1/2}$:

$$\sqrt{2} = 2^{1/2} = (2^{-1})^{-1/2} = (1/2)^{-1/2} = (1 - 1/2)^{-1/2}$$

Expanding $(1 - 1/2)^{-1/2}$, we apply the Newtonian expansion of $(1 + z)$ with $z = -1/2$ and $t = -1/2$. The coefficients of this expansion are computed with the aid of (14)

$$\binom{-1/2}{m} = C_m^{(-1/2)}$$
$$= (-1/2)\,(-1/2 - 1)\,(-1/2 - 2) \cdots (-1/2 - m + 1)/m!$$
$$= (-1)^m\, 1 \cdot 3 \cdot 5 \cdots (2m - 1)/(2^m\, m!).$$

Dropping the superscript $(-1/2)$, we obtain, for instance,

$$C_0 = 1, C_1 = -1/2, C_2 = 3/8, C_3 = -5/16, C_4 = 35/128 \cdots$$

The general term of our expansion is obtained multiplying the coefficient C_m by $(-1/2)^m = (-1)^m/2^m$, so that it is equal to

$$1 \cdot 3 \cdot 5 \cdot 7 \cdots (2m - 1)/(4^m m!).$$

Multiplying and dividing this expression by the product $2 \cdot 4 \cdot 6 \cdots (2m)$, we transform it as follows:

$$1 \cdot 3 \cdot 5 \cdot 7 \cdots (2m - 1)/4^m m! = 1 \cdot 2 \cdot 3 \cdot 4 \cdots (2m - 1)(2m)/4^m 2^m m! m!$$

$$= (2m)! \, (1/8)^m \, (m!)^{-2}$$

and this expression holds for all values of the integer m in the summation

$$\sqrt{2} = \sum_{m=0}^{\infty} (2m)! \, (m!)^{-2} \, 8^{-m} = 1 + 2!/8 + 4!/8^2 2^2 + 6!/8^3 6^2 + \cdots \quad (*)$$

All the terms of this infinite sum are known and we can compute $\sqrt{2}$ with any prescribed accuracy by computing a sufficient number of them. To prove the convergence of this infinite series, it is sufficient to observe that the terms of our series are smaller than the corresponding terms of a convergent geometric series. It is, indeed, easy to prove the inequality

$$1 \cdot 3 \cdot 5 \cdot 7 \cdots (2m - 1)/4^m m!$$

$$= (1/2) \, (3/4) \, (5/6) \cdots [(2m - 1)/(2m)] \, (1/2)^m < (1/2)^m$$

and the series with general term $(1/2)^m$

$$1 + (1/2) + (1/2)^2 + (1/2)^3 + \cdots + (1/2)^m + \cdots = 1/(1 - 1/2) = 2$$

is a convergent geometric series. A series of positive terms all of which are smaller than the terms of this geometric series is *a fortiori* a convergent series.

The computation of an approximate value of $2^{1/2}$ with the aid of the expansion (*) is a long and tedious process because the series (*) converges very slowly. So, for instance, the sum of its first eleven terms gives $\sqrt{2}$ with only three exact decimals. Denoting the sum of first $n + 1$ terms by s_n and the $(n + 1)$-th term by u_n, we have

n	u_n	s_n
0	1	1
1	$2^{-2} = 0.25$	1.25
2	$3 \cdot 2^{-5} = 0.093\,750$	1.343\,750
3	$5 \cdot 2^{-7} = 0.039\,062$	1.382\,812...
4	$35 \cdot 2^{-11} = 0.017\,089...$	1.399\,902...
5	$65 \cdot 2^{-13} = 0.007\,690...$	1.407\,593...
6	$231 \cdot 2^{-16} = 0.003\,535...$	1.411\,127...
7	$429 \cdot 2^{-18} = 0.001\,636...$	1.412\,764...
8	$6435 \cdot 2^{-23} = 0.000\,767...$	1.413\,531...
9	$12155 \cdot 2^{-25} = 0.000\,362...$	1.413\,893...
10	$46189 \cdot 2^{-28} = 0.000\,172...$	1.414\,065...

In practice, the computations are shortened by the use of a table of squares. We can write $2^{1/2}$ as $2000000^{1/2}/1000$, and in the table of squares we read $1414^2 = 1999396$, which is less than two million, and $1415^2 = 2002225$. Therefore, we conclude that $1.414 < 2^{1/2} < 1.415$ since 2000000 is between 1999396 and 2002225.

To find $2000000^{1/2}$ with the aid of the binomial theorem we represent the number 2000000 as follows:

$$2000000 = 1999396 + 604$$

$$= 1999396(1 + 604/1999396) = 1414^2(1 + z)$$

where $z = 0.000302/(1 - 0.000302) = 0.000\,302\,091\,32....$

Thus, $2000000^{1/2} = 1414(1 + z)^{1/2}$, and the binomial theorem yields the expansion

$$(1 + z)^{1/2} = 1 + z/2 - z^2/8 + z^3/16 - \cdots,$$

where the first three terms give a very accurate approximation because the fourth term, namely, $z^3/16$, is less than $0.000\,000\,000\,002$. The second and the third terms are equal to $0.000\,151\,045\,66$ and $0.000\,000\,001\,140$, respectively, so that the approximate value of $(1 + z)^{1/2}$ is equal to $1.000\,151\,034\,26$. Multiplying it by 1.414, we finally obtain an approximate value for $2^{1/2}$:

$$\sqrt{2} = 2^{1/2} = 1.414\,213\,562\,443...$$

which has eleven exact decimals.

Number e and its Powers

One of most important applications of the binomial theorem is the study of powers e^t of the irrational number e. This number is defined as the common limit for $n = \infty$ of two infinite sequences of rational numbers

$$M_n = (1 + 1/n)^n \quad \text{and} \quad H_n = M_n(1 + 1/n) = (1 + 1/n)^{n+1}$$

The first one is an *increasing* sequence and its terms M_n approach their limit e from below, so that $M_{n+1} > M_n$ and $M_n < e$ for all values of n. The second sequence is a *decreasing* sequence, and its terms approach e from above, so that for each n we have $H_{n+1} < H_n$ and $H_n > e$. Thus, the number e is for any n between M_n and H_n:

$$(1 + 1/n)^n = M_n < e < H_n = (1 + 1/n)^{n+1}$$

In other words, if we represent the number e by a point on the number axis, this point is an interior point of each interval I_n in the infinite sequence of nested interval $I_1, I_2, I_3, \ldots$ such that every interval is entirely contained in the interior of the previous interval and contains the next interval. The length d_n of the n-th interval I_n is equal to the difference $H_n - M_n = M_n/n$, and therefore it is less than e/n, which proves that d_n is infinitely small and approaches zero when n increases without limit:

$$\lim_{n=\infty} (H_n - M_n) = \lim_{n=\infty} d_n = 0.$$

Since at the limit the interval I_n vanishes, while the point representing the number e remains always in the interior of I_n, we conclude that when the interval I_n, vor $n \to \infty$, shrinks to a point, it can shrink only to the point which is the image of the number e on the number axis. Thus,

$$\lim_{n=\infty} M_n = \lim_{n=\infty} H_n = e$$

that is,

$$\lim_{n=\infty} (1 + 1/n)^n = e. \tag{18}$$

We must now prove that the numbers M_n form an increasing sequence, while the numbers H_n decrease when n increases. Expanding M_n

with the aid of the binomial theorem, we can write it as follows:

$$M_n = (1 + 1/n)^n = 1 + \sum_{m=1}^{n} n(n - 1) \cdots (n - m + 1)\, n^{-m}/m!$$

Observing that

$$n(n - 1)(n - 2) \cdots (n - m + 1)$$

$$= n^m(1 - 1/n)(1 - 2/n) \cdots [1 - (m - 1)/n],$$

we transcribe this expansion as

$$M_n = (1 + 1/n)^n = 1 + \sum_{m=1}^{n} (1 - 1/n)(1 - 2/n) \cdots [1 - (m - 1)/n]/m!$$

To compare M_{n+1} and M_n, we write down the same expansion for M_{n+1}. It is obtained from that for M_n, substituting $n + 1$ instead of n:

$$M_{n+1} = [1 + 1/(n + 1)]^{n+1} = 1 + \sum_{m=1}^{n+1} [1 - 1/(n + 1)]$$

$$[1 - 2/(n + 1)] \cdots [1 - (m - 1)/(n + 1)]/m!$$

Comparing the two expansions, we obtain $M_{n+1} > M_n$ since in the expansion of M_{n+1} the general term of the sum is greater than that in the expansion of M_n. We have, indeed, for each value of $m = 1, 2, 3, \dots,$ $n - 1, n,$

$$1 - m/(n + 1) > 1 - m/n \qquad (1 \leqslant m \leqslant n)$$

and, multiplying these inequalities, we prove that, in the case of M_{n+1}, the numerator of the general term is greater than that for M_n, the denominators being equal. Thus, the infinite sequence of inequalities $M_n < M_{n+1}$ is established.

To prove that the sequence of numbers H_n is a *decreasing* one, we will need Bernoulli's inequality:

$$(1 + p)^n > 1 + np \qquad (p > 0, n \geqslant 2)$$

proved in Chapter 3. Its righthand member represents the first two terms of the binomial expansion of the lefthand member $(1 + p)^n$. If p is positive, all the terms of this expansion are positive numbers. Omitting all the terms except the first two, we diminish the sum, and this fact constitutes another proof of Bernoulli's inequality.

It is sufficient to check that the ratio H_{n-1}/H_n exceeds one to prove that $H_{n-1} > H_n$. Let us therefore consider this ratio:

$$H_{n-1}/H_n = [1 + 1/(n - 1)]^n/(1 + 1/n)^{n+1}$$

$$= [n/(n - 1)]^n [n/(n + 1)]^n/(1 + 1/n)$$

$$= [n^2/(n^2 - 1)]^n/(1 + 1/n) = [1 + 1/(n^2 - 1)]^n/(1 + 1/n)$$

Applying now to the numerator $[1 + 1/(n^2 - 1)]^n$ Bernoulli's inequality with $p = 1/(n^2 - 1)$, we obtain

$$[1 + 1/(n^2 - 1)]^n > 1 + n/(n^2 - 1) > 1 + n/n^2 = 1 + 1/n$$

and this gives us the desired result:

$$H_{n-1}/H_n > (1 + 1/n)/(1 + 1/n) = 1$$

Computing some terms of these two sequences, we illustrate their convergence to the common limit e and obtain an approximate value for e:

Value of n	Value of H_n	Value of M_n
1	4	2
2	3.375	2.25
3	3.1604...	2.3703...
4	3.0517...	2.4414...
10	2.8531...	2.5937...
100	2.7318...	2.7048...
1 000	2.7196...	2.7169...
10 000	2.7184...	2.7181...

The convergence is very slow: only when n reaches 10 000 can we be sure of the first three decimals. The number e is indeed between 2.7181 and 2.7185, so that 2.718 can be considered as its approximate value with three exact decimals. To obtain more accurate approximate values for e, one needs tables of logarithms.

Representation of e by a Rapidly Convergent Series

The numerical computation of the important transcendental number e becomes much easier if this number is represented as the sum of a rapidly convergent numerical series. This representation of e can be easily obtained from its definition by the limit

$$e = \lim_{n=\infty} M_n$$

replacing in this definition the number $M_n = (1 + 1/n)^n$ by the binomial expansion already considered.

Thus, write the definition of e as follows:

$$e = \lim_{n=\infty} \left\{ 1 + \sum_{n}^{m=1} (1 - 1/n)(1 - 2/n)(1 - 3/n) \cdots [1 - (m-1)/n]/m! \right\}$$

and pass to the limit, replacing n in the expression of the general term by infinity. The $m - 1$ fractions $1/n$, $2/n$, $3/n$, ..., $(m - 1)/n$ vanish, and the numerator reduces to one, so that the general term takes at the limit a very simple form, namely $1/m!$. At the same time, the finite sum $\sum_{m=1}^{n}$ of n terms becomes an infinite expression $\sum_{m=1}^{\infty}$, that is, it is transformed into an infinite series. The final result is the following expression of e:

$$e = 1 + \sum_{m=1}^{\infty} 1/m! = 1 + 1/1! + 1/2! + 1/3! + \cdots + 1/m! + \cdots \quad (19)$$

Using this rapidly converging series, an approximate value of e can be computed without difficulty and with any prescribed accuracy. When more terms are used, more and more decimals become stabilized. Suppose that we want to know exactly the first six decimals, which means that we want an approximate value of e with an absolute error less than one millionth. Writing explicitly the first eleven terms

$$1 + 1 + 1/2 + 1/6 + 1/24 + 1/120 + 1/720 + 1/5040 + 1/40\,320$$
$$+ 1/362\,880 + 1/3\,628\,800,$$

we observe that they can be computed by recurrence: each term is equal to the previous one divided by the order number of this previous term. Therefore, the numerical value of each term is deduced from the value of the preceding one by a simple division. This rule is a corollary of the fact that the terms of our series are successive reciprocals of factorials $m!$. We have, indeed, for two such successive reciprocals, $1/m!$ and $1/(m + 1)!$, the relation

$$1/(m + 1)! = (1/m!)/(m + 1)$$

which is an algebraical expression of our rule. We give now the numerical results of the described computation:

n	Value of the n-th term	Sum of first n terms
1	1	1
2	1	2
3	$1/2! = 0.5$	2.5
4	$1/3! = 0.166\,666\,667$	2.666\,666\,667
5	$1/4! = 0.041\,666\,667$	2.708\,333\,333
6	$1/5! = 0.008\,333\,333$	2.716\,666\,667
7	$1/6! = 0.001\,388\,888$	2.718\,055\,555
8	$1/7! = 0.000\,198\,412$	2.718\,253\,968
9	$1/8! = 0.000\,024\,801$	2.718\,278\,770
10	$1/9! = 0.000\,002\,755$	2.718\,281\,526
11	$1/10 = 0.000\,000\,275$	2.718\,281\,801

To be sure of the precision with which the approximate value 2.718 281 is obtained, we must have an idea of the order of magnitude of the error we committed by neglecting an infinite number of terms of our series (19) which follow the last computed term $1/10!$. We are not interested in the exact value of their sum. It is sufficient for our purpose to verify that the addition of this sum to our approximate value 2.718 281 801 of the sum of first eleven terms cannot change the sixth decimal in 2.718 281.

Therefore, it is sufficient to find such an upper bound for the sum R of all neglected terms that it does not change the sixth decimal, being added to the sum of first eleven terms. The neglected terms form an infinite series beginning with the term $1/11!$, and this first term is a common factor of all the terms of the infinite series:

$$R = 1/11! + 1/12! + \cdots + 1/n! + \cdots$$

$$= (1/11!)\,[1 + 1/12 + 1/(12 \cdot 13) + \cdots]$$

Replacing the factors in the denominators of all terms by 12, we decrease the denominators and therefore increase the terms. Denoting the exact sum of the series of all neglected terms by R, we have, therefore, as an upper bound for this number R, the following geometric series:

$$R < (1/11!)\,(1 + 1/12 + 1/12^2 + 1/12^3 + \cdots + 1/12^n + \cdots).$$

The sum of the infinite geometric series is equal to $1/(1 - 1/12)$ $= 12/11$, that is, the upper bound of R is equal to $(1/11!)\,(12/11)$ $= (12/121)/10!$ which is less than 0.000000028.

We conclude that the number e is less than 2.718281801 (approximate value of the sum of first eleven terms) plus 0.000000028 (upper bound of the sum of all neglected terms), that is, it is less than 2.718281830. Thus, the approximate value 2.7182818 obtained for e by computing only first eleven terms of the infinite series is accurate to 0.00000003 and has seven exact decimals: the exact value of e is greater than the approximation 2.71828180 but less than 2.71828183.

Irrationality of e

The first definition of e as the limit of $(1 + 1/n)^n$ for $n = \infty$ does not allow the study of the nature of this number. It does not preclude the possibility that e may be a rational number: the limit of a sequence of rational numbers—[and the expression $(1 + 1/n)^n$ is rational for all integral values of n]—can also be a rational number.

The representation of e by the infinite series (19) not only allows its computation with any prescribed accuracy, but also provides an easy proof of the fact that e is an irrational number, so that no fraction M/N which is a quotient of two integers can be equal to e. This proof uses the indirect method, which consists in the refutation of a hypothesis which itself is contrary to the fact to be proved.

Suppose, therefore, that there is a fraction p/q whose value is the number e and whose denominator q is greater than one because we know that e lies between two and three and threrefore cannot be an integer, $q \geqslant 2$. If this is so, then the product

$$1 \cdot 2 \cdot 3 \cdot 4 \cdots (q - 1)\, qe = q!e$$

must be an integer. On the other hand, the value of this product can be found by multiplying the series (19) by q-factorial. We now study the nature of the number obtained by multiplying the series (19) by the factorial $q!$:

$$q![1 + 1/1! + 1/2! + 1/3! + \cdots 1/q!]$$

$$+ q![1/(q + 1)! + 1/(q + 2)! + \cdots]$$

The denominators of the first $q + 1$ terms in (19) admit of the factorial $q!$ as their common denominator. Therefore, the product of the first brackets by $q!$ is an integer which may be denoted by N. But the product of an infinite series (in the second brackets) and of $q!$ cannot be an integer. To prove this point, we open the brackets performing the multiplication of the series by $q!$:

$$1/(q + 1) + 1/(q + 1)(q + 2) + 1/(q + 1)(q + 2)(q + 3) \cdots$$

Denoting the sum of this infinite series by f, we can now prove that f is less than $1/2$. Since q is at least equal to two, $q + 1$ exceeds or at least is equal to three. Replacing in this infinite series all the factors in the denominators of all terms by three we decrease the denominators and increase each term, increasing therefore the sum of the series. An upper bound for the number f is thus obtained. This upper bound is the sum of the following series:

$$1/3 + (1/3)^2 + (1/3)^3 + (1/3)^4 + \cdots + (1/3)^n + \cdots$$

We recognize a geometric series without its first term one. The standard ratio is equal to $1/3$. Therefore, the sum of this series is

$$1/(1 - 1/3) - 1 = 1/(2/3) - 1 = 3/2 - 1 = 1/2$$

and, thus, $f < 1/2$.

The hypothesis that e is a rational number p/q leads us to the equality

$$q!e = q!p/q = (q - 1)!p = N + f \qquad (f < 1/2)$$

where the lefthand member $(q - 1)!p$ is an integer as well as the first term N of the righthand member, while the second term f is less than $1/2$, though it does not vanish. Such an equality is a nonsense because $N + f$, as a number different from any integer, cannot be equal to the integer $(q - 1)!p$.

Since our hypothesis $e = p/q$ leads to a contradiction, it cannot be true. This means that e cannot be a rational number and is, therefore, an irrational number.

The series (19) represents the number e with the aid of natural numbers 1, 2, 3, 4, ..., and all of them (an infinity of them) are used in this expression of e. There is another infinite expression which also uses only the fundamental integers. It is the continued fraction

$$e - 2 = \cfrac{1}{1 + \cfrac{1}{2 + \cfrac{2}{3 + \cfrac{3}{4 + \cdots}}}}$$

$$\cfrac{}{n + \cfrac{n}{(n + 1) + \cdots}}$$

which can be written also as follows:

$$e = 2 + \cfrac{1}{1 + \cfrac{2^{-1}}{1 + \cfrac{3^{-1}}{1 + \cfrac{4^{-1}}{1 + \cdots}}}}$$

$$\cfrac{}{1 + \cfrac{n^{-1}}{1 + \cdots}}$$

(for the proof of convergence see Appendix VI).

The computation of an approximate value for e may be achieved with either of these two continued fractions. The first one has all its denominators b_n given by the formula $b_n = n$, while the numerators are $a_n = n - 1$ for $n \geqslant 2$, but $a_1 = 1$. The sequence of its convergents P_n/Q_n begins with

$$P_1 = Q_1 = 1 \quad \text{and} \quad P_2 = 2, \, Q_2 = 3$$

and it is computed with the aid of formulas (16) Chapter 5:

$$P_{n+1} = (n + 1) P_n + n P_{n-1}$$

$$Q_{n+1} = (n + 1) Q_n + n Q_{n-1}$$

so that, for instance, $P_8 = 106{,}542$ and $Q_8 = 148{,}329$, which gives for the difference $e - 2$ an approximate value $P_8/Q_8 = 0.718281\ldots$ with first six decimals exact.

Generalized Definition of the Number e

In the first definition (18) the variable n is a discrete variable: it takes only integral values, and, every time it changes its value running through the infinite sequence of integers, it jumps one unit. The limit e of the sequence of rational numbers $(1 + 1/n)^n$ is also the ultimate value of another discrete variable $y_n = (1 + 1/n)^n$, which is a function of n.

But what can be said about the limit for $x = \infty$ of a *continuous* function $(1 + 1/x)^x$ of the *continuous* variable x, which increases without limit and becomes infinite, taking all real and positive numerical values without omitting any of them?

We shall see that the substitution into $(1 + 1/n)^n$ of the continuous variable x instead of the discrete variable n does not change the limit e, so that

$$\lim_{x=\infty} (1 + 1/x)^x = \lim_{n=\infty} (1 + 1/n)^n = e \tag{20}$$

To prove this proposition, we consider two integers N and $N + 1$ such that the value of x lies always between them, x being less than $N + 1$ but greater or at least equal to N. The integer N is clearly the integral part of the continuous variable x, and, therefore, when x increases, N cannot remain constant: at the moment when x, increasing continuously, reaches the value $N + 1$, its integral part jumps one unit and becomes $N + 1$, remaining again constant and equal to $N + 1$ until x reaches the value $N + 2$. Denoting the integral part of x by the symbol $N(x)$, we express the definition of this discrete variable $N(x)$ as follows:

$$N(x) \leqslant x < N(x) + 1. \tag{21}$$

From this we deduce another inequality:

$$\left\{ 1 + \frac{1}{N(x) + 1} \right\}^x < \left(1 + \frac{1}{x} \right)^x < \left[1 + \frac{1}{N(x)} \right]^x$$

Replacing in the lefthand member the exponent x by $N(x)$ and in the righthand member by $N(x) + 1$, we reinforce this double inequality because a power to a base greater than one varies in the same sense as its exponent. Thus,

$$\{1 + 1/[N(x) + 1)]\}^{N(x)} < (1 + 1/x)^x < [1 + 1/N(x)]^{N(x)+1}$$

When x becomes infinite, so does also its integral part $N(x)$. Therefore, $\lim\limits_{x=0} N(x) = \infty$, and it is not difficult to prove that the limits of the lefthand member,

$$\{1 + 1/[N(x) + 1]\}^{N(x)},$$

as well as that of the righthand member,

$$[1 + 1/N(x)]^{N(x)+1},$$

are both equal to the number e. We have, indeed,

$$\lim_{x=\infty} \{1 + 1/[N(x) + 1]\} = 1$$

so that, denoting the integer $N(x) + 1$ by m,

$$\lim_{x=\infty} \{1 + 1/[N(x) + 1]\}^{N(x)} = \lim_{x=\infty} \{1 + 1/[N(x) + 1]\}^{N(x)+1}$$

$$= \lim_{m=\infty} (1 + 1/m)^m = e$$

Discussing now the limit of the righthand member, we denote the integer $N(x)$ by n:

$$\lim_{x=\infty} [1 + 1/N(x)]^{N(x)+1} = \lim_{x=\infty} [(1 + 1/n)^n (1 + 1/n)]$$

$$= \lim_{n=\infty} (1 + 1/n)^n \cdot \lim_{n=\infty} (1 + 1/n) = e$$

Therefore, at the limit for $x = \infty$, the inequalities are transformed into equalities because the expression $(1 + 1/x)^x$, contained between two bounds which tend to the same limit e, must have the same limit e:

$$e = \lim_{x=\infty} (1 + 1/x)^x = e \tag{22}$$

This general definition can be expressed also in the following form:

$$\lim_{t=0} (1 + t)^{1/t} = \lim_{t=0} \sqrt[t]{(1 + t)} = e \tag{23}$$

Here, $t = 1/x$ is the reciprocal of x, and it is obvious that the reciprocal of a number increasing without limit, as does x, must vanish at the limit. The infinitely small quantity t approaches its limit zero from the right only because x is always positive and so is its reciprocal t.

To eliminate this limitation imposed on the behavior of the infinitely small t and to prove that the general definition (23) holds also when t

approaches zero from the left, taking negative values, we expand $(1 + t)^{1/t}$ using the binomial theorem. The general term of this expansion is as follows:

$$(1/t)\,(1/t - 1)\,(1/t - 2) \cdots (1/t - n + 1)t^n/n!$$

The numerator has n factors of the type $(1/t - m)$ and also the factor t^n. Performing the multiplication of each factor of the type $(1/t - m)$ by t, we transform the general term into

$$(1 - t)\,(1 - 2t)\,(1 - 3t) \cdots (1 - nt + t)/n!$$

so that

$$(1 + t)^{1/t} = 1 + 1/1! + \sum_{n=2}^{\infty} (1 - t) \cdots (1 - nt + t)/n! \qquad (24)$$

In this expression, t can take negative values also. Observing that the numerator of each term at the limit for $t = 0$ becomes equal to one, we find, without any limitation imposed on t, that by (19)

$$\lim_{t=0} (1 + t)^{1/t} = 1 + \sum_{n=1}^{\infty} 1/n! = e$$

We add that $(1 + t)^{1/t}$ is less than e, if t is positive, as the comparison of the expansions (19) and (24) shows, while for negative values of t, $(1 + t)^{1/t}$ is greater than e.

Exponential Function

Raising e to a power with variable exponent x, we construct a function e^x of x which is the mathematical equivalent of processes of *continuous growth* or *decay*. The idea of continuous growth is already embodied in the definition of e by the limit

$$\lim_{n=\infty} (1 + 1/n)^n = e$$

Let us first consider a discontinuous growth by sudden instantaneous jumps. Suppose that a plant one foot high becomes twice as high in one month by a sudden increase in height at the end of the month, so that the rate of increase is 100 per cent per month. If it grows at the same rate by two sudden increases at the end of the first and of the second half of the month, the jump each time represents 50 per cent of its height at the moment of discrete growth. Therefore, at the end of the first half of the month, its height abruptly changes from one foot to $1 + 1/2$ feet, while at the end of the second half of the month it increases again 50 per cent, becoming equal to $(1 + 1/2)(1 + 1/2)$ $= (1 + 1/2)^2 = 2.25$ feet instead of two feet.

Suppose now that the number of sudden increases in the process of discontinuous growth is n per month, the moments of these spasmodic growth's outbursts being distributed evenly during the month: at the end of each $(1/n)$-th part of the month the plant's height increases by $100/n$ per cent. Since an increase of $100/n$ per cent is represented by a multiplication by $1 + 1/n$, the initial height of one foot becomes at the end of the month equal to $(1 + 1/n)^n$. To prove this, we denote the height at the end of m/n of the month by H_m, so that H_0 represents the initial height of one foot. This H_m at the end of $(m + 1)/n$ of the month becomes H_{m+1}, and we know that during $1/n$ of the month H_m increased $1/n$ of it. Therefore, we obtain the recurrent relation

$$H_{m+1} = H_m(1 + 1/n)$$

which yields

$$H_n = H_0(1 + 1/n)^n = (1 + 1/n)^n.$$

When the number n of moments of spasmodic growth increases without limit, the dicontinuous growth approaches continuous growth at the same rate. At the limit for $n = \infty$, we obtain the continuous growth and find that

$$\lim_{n=\infty} (1 + 1/n)^n = e = 2.71828...$$

corresponds to the height attained by the plant at the end of a month of continuous growth whose speed is characterized by a rate of 100 per cent per month. In continuous growth, the instantaneous increase of height is always proportional to the height at the instant when it takes place, and at each moment there is such an instantaneous increase. The rate of 100 per cent per month or, in general, p per cent for a given interval of time plays the role of the coefficient of proportionality which is involved in the relation between the amount of instantaneous increase and the height at this moment. It is often called the *nominal rate*.

The general problem of continuous growth can be illustrated by the example of the growth of bacteria in a culture. The area of such a culture is proportional to the number of microorganisms, and the law of continuous growth expressed by the exponential function is confirmed by experiments. If N_0 and N_t denote the culture's areas at the moments $t_0 = 0$ and t, the nominal rate of growth being p per cent per hour, we approach the law of continuous growth in the usual way, by considering n spasmodic outbursts of growth per hour occuring each $(1/n)$-th part of the hour. At the assumed nominal rate of $p\%$ per hour, each such outburst incrases the actual area by p/n per cent, so that its new value is obtained by multiplying the actual value by $1 + p/100n$.

There are n such outbursts of growth per hour, and, therefore, after n multiplications by $1 + p/100n$, at the end of an hour the initial area N_0 grows to

$$N_1 = N_0(1 + p/100n)^n$$

In t hours, there will be nt outbursts of discontinuous growth and the area after t hours of growth becomes equal to

$$N_t = N_0(1 + p/100n)^{nt}.$$

The expression obtained for N_t is an approximation because bacteria do not wait $(1/n$-th) of an hour to multiply, and they proliferate continuously. Increasing the number of outbursts of growth per hour indefinitely, we approach the continuous growth, and the law of continuous growth is obtained from the approximate expression $N_0(1 + p/100n)^{nt}$ as its limit for $n = \infty$. The exact expression of the law is, thus, as follows:

$$N_t = \lim_{n=\infty} [N_0(1 + p/100n)^{nt}] = N_0 \lim_{n=\infty} (1 + p/100n)^{nt} \qquad (25)$$

We formulate the problem of computation thus raised in the following general way: find the limit of the expression $(1 + sx)^{1/s}$ for $s = 0$. Here, the exponent nt increases without limit, and it is replaced in our formulation by $1/s$, which tends also to infinity when s approaches zero. Since $nt = 1/s$, the base $1 + p/100n = 1 + pt/100nt$ can be written as $1 + pt/(100/s) = 1 + s(pt/100)$, so that in our formulation x replaces $pt/100$, namely $x = pt/100$.

We study now the limit of $(1 + sx)^{1/s}$ for $s \to 0$, x being any fixed number. Denoting the product sx by z, $z = sx$, where z approaches zero because a product vanishes if one of its two factors vanishes while the other remains bounded and finite, we can rewrite the expression $(1 + sx)^{1/s}$ as follows:

$$(1 + sx)^{1/s} = [(1 + sx)^{1/xs}]^x = [(1 + z)^{1/z}]^x$$

We know [see (23)] that $\lim_{z=0} (1 + z)^{1/z} = e$. Therefore, we have

$$\lim_{z=0} (1 + sx)^{1/s} = \lim_{z=0} \{[(1 + z)^{1z}]^x\} = [\lim_{z=0} (1 + z)^{1/z}]^x = e^x$$

We can now give the final expression of the law of continuous growth (25), namely:

$$N_t = N_0 e^{pt/100} \tag{26}$$

because $x = pt/100$.

Thus, the law of continuous grotwh finds mathematical expression in the exponential function e^{mx}, the exponent of which is proportional to the independent variable $x = t$ (time), the constant factor m representing the speed of growth and being expressed in per cent per unit of time.

The law (26) involves four quantities, namely the per cent p (speed of growth), the initial datum N_0, final amount N_t, and the interval of time t during which N_0 grows to N_t. Any three of these four quantities being given, the fourth quantity can be found with the aid of the law (26).

EXAMPLES: 1) The initial area of a culture being $N_0 = 12.5$ square inches and the nominal rate of growth being $p = 2$ per cent per minute, find the area at the end of the second hour. The unit of time is a minute and, therefore, $t = 120$. The product $pt/100$ is equal to 2.4 and, thus,

$$N_{120} = 12.5 e^{2.4} = 137.789 \cdots$$

square inches because $e^{2.4} = 11.023 \ldots$

2) Knowing that a culture grows four times greater in one hour, find the speed of its continuous growth. Here $t = 60$ and

$$N_{60}/N_0 = 4 = e^{0.6p},$$

taking a minute as the unit of time. Therefore, $0.6p = 1.3863\ldots$ because $4 = e^{1.3683}$, so that $p = 2.31$ per cent, which means that the nominal rate of continuous growth is 2.31 per cent per minute.

These two examples raise the question of computation of the exponential function e^x, when the exponent's value x is known. Before explaining how e^x was computed (there are excellent tables of exponential function), we shall see how e^x expresses the law of continuous decay.

The gradual vanishing of a radioactive substance is an excellent illustration of continuous decay. Suppose that its mass disintegrates at the nominal rate of p per cent per day. Replacing the continuous decay by an approximation, we consider n outbursts of disintegration per day, so that at the end of each $(1/n)$-th of a day the mass of this radioactive substance suddenly decreases, losing p/n per cent of the actual mass. This loss is expressed by a multiplication by $1 - p/100n$: the remaining mass is

$$M - Mp/100n = M(1 - p/100n)$$

if the mass before the outburst was M. During t days, there will be nt such outbursts of disintegration, and the final mass M_t will be expressed in terms of initial mass M_0 by the following approximate expression:

$$M_t = M_0(1 - p/100n)^{nt}$$

Again the continuous decay is obtained when the number n of outbursts of radioactivity per unit of time becomes infinite. Therefore, the exact law of continuous decay is represented by

$$M_t = M_0 \lim_{n=\infty} (1 - p/100n)^{nt}$$

This limit is computed exactly as the limit in (25), the unique difference between the growth and decay being the sign of p. This difference has no importance because the general definition (23) can be applied also for negative values of infinitely small t. We have indeed, using (23) for $nt = 1/z$:

$$\lim_{n=\infty} (1 - p/100n)^{-nt} = \lim_{z=0} [(1 - z)^{-1/z}]^x = e^x = e^{pt/100}$$

where $x = pt/100$. Therefore, taking the reciprocals,

$$\lim_{n=\infty} (1 - p/100n)^{nt} = e^{-pt/100}$$

so that the law of continuous decay is as follows:

$$M_t = M_0 e^{-pt/100}. \tag{27}$$

EXAMPLE: Knowing the half-life (period) T of a radioactive substance, express the speed of its decay in terms of T. By definition, the half-life T is equal to the interval of time during which the substance dissipates half the initial mass M_0. Thus, $M_T = 1/2M_0$, and this relation gives, with the aid of (27),

$$M_T/M_0 = 1/2 = e^{-pT/100} = e^{-0.693\,15} \quad \text{since } 1/2 = e^{-0.693\,15}$$

For the product $pT/100$ we find the equation $pT = 69.315$, which gives $p = 69.315/T$. For the radium, for instance, with a half-life of 1600 years p is equal to $69.315/1600 = 0.0433$ per cent per year

In a given interval of time and at the same rate, the total gain in a continuous growth is greater than in a discontinuos one, while the total loss in a continuous decay is less than the corresponding loss in a discontinuous one. In other words, the continuous growth is more rapid and the continuous decay is more slow than the discontinuous.

Exponential Series

Applying the definition of e by a passage to the limit, we obtained the exponential function e^x in the form of another limit, namely,

$$e^x = \lim_{s=0} (1 + sx)^{1/s} \tag{28}$$

On the other hand, the representation of e by the infinite series (19) was deduced combining its definition as a limit with the binominal theorem. Applying the binominal expansion to the expression under the symbol of the above limit in (28), we shall obtain a corresponding infinite series for e^x. The representation of e^x in the form of an infinite series, whose terms are powers of x, exponent in e^x, with numerical coefficients and integral positive exponents, is called the exponential series. Discovered by Euler, father of the number e, it is one of most important tools of pure and applied mathematics.

The binomial expansion of $(1 + sx)^{1/s}$ is as follows:

$$(1 + sx)^{1/s} = 1 + x/1!$$

$$+ \sum_{n=2}^{\infty} (1 - s)(1 - 2s)(1 - 3s) \cdots (1 - ns + s)\, x^n/n!$$

It is deduced from (15) writing in it $1/s$ instead of t and replacing z by sx. Passing now to the limit for $s = 0$, we find that the general term reduces to $x^n/n!$, so that the function e^x is now represented by the sum of the following infinite series:

$$e^x = \sum_{n=0}^{\infty} x^n/n! = 1 + x/1! + x^2/2! + x^3/3! + \cdots + x^n/n! + \cdots \quad (29)$$

The exponential series (29) converges for all values, real and complex of the variable x. The formula (29) means that e^x is the limit for $n = \infty$ of the sum s_n of first $n + 1$ terms of the series (29). It is therefore obtained by two successive passages to the limit for $s = 0$ and for $n = \infty$. We formulate the result omitting its justification, as we did for (19).

For $x = 1$ the series (29) reduces to (19) the sum of which is e. Substituting in e^x the series (19) for e, we find an astonishingly simple and bewildering property of the number e, that is, of the sum of reciprocals of all factorials:

$$\left[\sum_{n=0}^{\infty} 1/n! \right]^x = \sum_{n=0}^{\infty} x^n/n! \quad (30)$$

This transfer of x from the lefthand member, in which it is an *exponent*, to the numerators of all terms in the righthand member, where it becomes the *base* of powers x^n, is at least beyond expectation. It is an exceptional fact: for all infinite series of the most general type Σu_n it does not hold because their power with exponent x is *never* equal to $\Sigma u_n x^n$, and the corresponding inequality

$$\left[\sum_{n=0}^{\infty} u_n \right]^x \neq \sum_{n=0}^{\infty} u_n x^n \quad (31)$$

is true for all numerical series, except the series (19) which represents the number e. For this exceptional series the inequality (31) does not hold and it is replaced by the equality (30). In other words, the rule expressed by the relation (30), namely "To raise the series $\sum_{0}^{\infty} 1/n!$ to the power with exponent x multiply its successive terms by $x^0 = 1$, $x^1 = x$, x^2, x^3, etc. holds only for this exceptional series and it is wrong for all other numerical series.

Rotation Factor

We shall study now the application of exponential series to trigonometry. In this application, the exponent x of e^x must be considered as a complex number. Therefore, replacing it by $z = x + iy$, where x and y

are, by definition, two real quantities, we form the exponential e^z:

$$e^z = \lim_{s=0} (1 + sz)^{1/s} = 1 + z + z^2/2! + z^3/3! + \cdots = \sum_{n=0}^{\infty} z^n/n!$$

In particular, the complex exponent z may take purely imaginary values $z = it$. The even powers z^{2n} in this case are real since an even power of i is a real number: $i^{2n} = (-1)^n$, so that $i^{4m} = 1$ and $i^{4m+2} = -1$. The odd powers of i being purely imaginary, $i^{2n+1} = (-1)^n i$, the odd powers of $z = it$ are also imaginary. Therefore, substituting it instead of z in the expansion of e^z, we obtain in the righthand member (infinite series) two groups of terms, namely real and purely imaginary terms. Applying the principle of separation of real and imaginary, we conclude that e^{it} is a complex number:

$$e^{it} = [1 - t^2/2! + t^4/4! - t^6/6! + \cdots + (-1)^n t^n/(2n)! + \cdots]$$

$$+ i[t/1! - t^3/3! + t^5/5! + \cdots + (-1)^n t^{2n+1}/(2n+1)! + \cdots] \quad (32)$$

The function e^{it} of a real variable t plays an important role in mathematics because it represents the rotation factor through an angle t in a plane. In Chapter 5 the rotation factor through t was studied under the form $\cos t + i \sin t$, and the discovery of the identity

$$\cos t + i \sin t = e^{it} \quad (33)$$

is one of best results of Euler's work. It is called *Euler's Formula*, and it shows that the real part of the complex number e^{it} is nothing else than $\cos t$, while the coefficient of the imaginary part is $\sin t$.

Thus, two fundamental trigonometric functions, $\cos t$ and $\sin t$ are reunited in the exponential e^{it} and the identity (33) holds for all the values of the real variable t. In the left member t is the argument of a sine and a cosine and appears as an angle. In the right member t is the argument of the exponential e^{it}, in the expansion (32) of which powers of t are involved. A square or cube or a power of 30 or 60 degrees in general has no sense, and, therefore, we must interpret t in (33) as a pure number.

Radians and Degrees

We thus arrive at the conclusion that an angle t, which is always measurable in degrees, can also be represented by a pure number. This measurement of angles by pure numbers is based on the following geometric fact: the length of a circular arc AB is always proportional to the central angle $\overparen{AOB}$ subtended by this arc and having its vertex at the circle's center O, (see fig. 5). Drawing a second concentric circle of smaller radius $r = OC$, $r < R = OA$, we have two circular arcs of

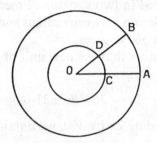

Fig. 9.5

different length CD and AB, which correspond to the same central angle $\overparen{AOB}$. The circular sectors COD and AOB are similar, their corresponding parts being proportional. Thus, we obtain a proportion

$$\text{arc } AB/\text{arc } CD = OA/OC \quad \text{that is} \quad \text{arc } AB/\text{arc } CD = R/r$$

It can also be written

$$\text{arc } AB/R = \text{arc } CD/r.$$

The length of a circular arc subtended by a given angle AOB depends on the radius of the circle to which this arc belongs, but the proportion arc $AB/R = $ arc CD/r proves that the ratio arc AB/R of an arc to its radius remains constant when the radius varies, provided the central angle does not change. If it does, the ratio AB/R varies too, and in its variation remains proportional to the central angle AOB. Therefore, this ratio of two lengths AB/R can be used as a measure of the size of angle AOB, and this ratio is a pure number.

The definition

$$t = \text{angle } AOB = \text{arc } AB/R$$

gives $t = 1$, if are $AB = R$, establishing a new unit of angle called a *radian*. Thus, in measuring angles by pure numbers, we use as the unit of angle the central angle subtended by an arc whose length is equal to the radius. The two systems of measurement of angles, in degrees and in pure numbers, are proportional to each other. To the whole circumference corresponds a central angle equal to four right angles, that is, expressed in degrees, to 360°. On the other hand, the length of the whole circumference is $2\pi R$, so that we can say that a central angle of 360° is subtended by an arc of length $2\pi R$. The ratio of this arc to the radius R is equal to the pure number $2\pi = 6.2831...$. The central angle we are considering is represented in two systems of measurement by 360° and by 2π. Therefore, the relation between radians and degrees is established: 2π radians are equal to 360 degrees.

This basic relation shows that the new unit of angle, the *radian*, contains $360/2\pi$ degrees:

$$\text{one radian} = 360°/2\pi = 360°/6.2831\cdots = 57°17'44.5''...$$

On the other hand, dividing 2π by 360, we obtain the equivalent of one degree in radians:

$$\text{one degree} = 1° = 2\pi/360 = 0.017453...$$

Dividing this number by 60, we deduce the equivalent in radians of a minute of angle which is equal to $0.000291...$ of a radian. We add that 0.1 radian contains $5°43'46''$; 0.01 radian is equal to $3'26''$ and 0.001 radian is equal to $21''$. To transform degrees into radians and *vice versa*, we use the relations

$$\theta = 360t/2\pi = 180t/\pi, \quad t = 2\pi\theta/360 = \theta\pi/180,$$

where t and θ are measures of the same angle in radians and in degrees.

It is interesting to recall that the measurement of angles in degrees is an inheritance of Babylonian culture. Babylonian scientists used as the unit of angle the central angle subtended by a side of the regular inscribed hexagon, that is by a *chord* whose length is equal to the radius. In the new system of measurement, the unit angle is subtended by an *arc* whose length is equal to the radius. Our degree of angle was for the Babylonians merely a subdivision, namely a sixtieth part of their unit of angle. The divisor sixty is in general, of Babylonian origin, and it is conserved in the division of a degree into 60 minutes and of one minute into 60 seconds of *angle*, as well as in the division of an hour into 60 minutes and of a minute into 60 seconds of *time*.

The old Babylonian unit angle of 60° is completely forgotten and out of use, but it is significant that both systems of measurement of angles are based on the comparison of a length with the length of radius; this basic length subtends the unit angle in both cases, the difference between two systems is in the *choice* of this subtending length. The Babylonians chose the *chord* and we chose the *arc*. In the old system, the angular space around a point, that is, the central angle corresponding to the whole circumference, is expressed by an integral number of unit angles, namely, by six unit angles. In our modern system, however, it is measured by an irrational number 2π. It is also equal to four right angles so that the radian measure of a right angle is $\pi/2$, a radian being equivalent to $2/\pi$ right angles.

The measurement of angles in radians is characterized by an important property which is missing in the old system of measurement in degrees or in right angles, a right angle being considered as the unit angle. The area A of a circular sector AOB (see fig. 5) is proportional to its central angle $t = AOB$, so that we can write $A = kt$, where k denotes the unknown coefficient of proportionality. To find the value of this unknown coefficient we apply the relation $A = kt$ to the whole circle, considering it as a circular sector with a central angle equal to four right angles, to 360° or, finally, to 2π, according to the system of measurement used.

The area of the circle being equal to πR^2, we obtain an equation for our unknown k, namely

$$\pi R^2 = 2\pi k, \quad \text{or} \quad \pi R^2 = 4kD$$

where D denotes a right angle, or, finally,

$$\pi R^2 = 360°k.$$

Among these three equations, only the first one, which gives $k = R^2/2$, has sense and ascribes to the coefficient k a geometrical meaning: k appears as an area, namely, one half the area of a square whose side is equal to the radius R. The second one yields $k = \pi R^2/4D$, and nobody can say what it means since it makes no sense to divide an area by four right angles. The third has no sense either since the quotient $\pi R^2/360°$ is again the nonsensical result of division of an area by degrees of angle.

Therefore, in the fundamental relation $A = kt$, the measure t of central angle *must* be expressed by a pure number, that is, in radiaus, and k then becomes an area, namely $k = R^2/2$, so that the final formula

$$A = (R^2/2) t = R^2 t/2$$

makes sense. Solving it for t, we obtain another form of the definition of radian measure of angles:

$$t = 2A/R^2$$

We formulate it as follows: The radian measure of a central angle is the ratio of the doubled area $2A$ of the corresponding circular sector to the area R^2 of a square whose side is equal to the radius R.

No other system of measurement can be used in the computation of areas of circular sectors. In addition to degree and right angle, other units of angle are sometimes used. Our globe performs a complete revolution about its axis in twenty-four hours, so that one hour of time appears to be equal to 15 degrees, or to one sixth of a right angle. One minute of time contains 15 minutes of angle, and the same holds for seconds of time and of angle. The Armed Forces use their own unit of angle, called a *mil*. It is defined as $1/1600$ of a right angle or $1/6400$ of the complete angular space around a point. Therefore, a mil is equal to $0°.05625 = 3'22.5''$ of angle $= 13.5$ seconds of time. The French Army uses the *grade* which is equal to 16 mils or to a hundredth of a right angle.

The coexistence of five different systems of measurement of angles is an excellent example of the chaotic confusion in the choice of units which characterizes many practical applications of mathematics. There are five different kinds of trigonometric tables of the same functions, sine, cosine, tangent, *etc.*, but in which angles are expressed in degrees, mils, grades, hours, and radians.

Euler's Formula

After this necessary digression, let us sketch the proof of Euler's formula (33). The rigorous proof can be found in Appendix VII. Here we shall try to reproduce only the reasoning which led Euler to this important discovery. Moivre's formula (14), Chapter 6, allows us to represent $\cos t + i \sin t$ as follows:

$$\cos t + i \sin t = [\cos (t/n) + i \sin (t/n)]^n \tag{34}$$

where n can take any integral value. We now ask what is the ultimate form of the relation (34) when n increase without limit? When n becomes infinite, the fraction t/n vanishes because the angle t is fixed. We cannot substitute zero for t/n into the righthand member of (34) because the result of such a direct substitution is an indeterminate expression

$$(\cos 0 + i \sin 0)^{\infty} = (1 + i \cdot 0)^{\infty} = 1^{\infty}.$$

It is not one since when n varies approaching infinity, $\cos (t/n) + i \sin (t/n)$ is not one but only approaches one. Therefore, we have a power whose base approaches one when the exponent increases without limit. To find out what happens to $[\cos (t/n) + i \sin (t/n)]^n$, when n becomes infinite, we shall use in this expression the approximate values of a cosine and of a sine of an infinitely small argument t/n.

The behavior of $\sin x$ when $x \to 0$ is very simple: $\sin x$ decreases with x and approaches zero in such a way that the ratio $\sin x/x$ approaches one. It simply means that, for exceedingly small values of x, the number $\sin x$ can hardly be distinguished from x, becoming exactly equal to x at the very moment when both vanish. Any table of values of the function $\sin x$ discloses this fact; suppose, for example, that the values of the argument x are given in radians, at intervals of 0.0001, while the values of $\sin x$ are tabulated to nine decimals. In such a table the first fifteen values of x, from 0.0000 to 0.0014, coincide exactly with the corresponding values of $\sin x$, and the first value of x for which a difference appears between it and the value of $\sin x$ is 0.0015; the table gives $\sin (0.0015) = 0.001499999$. We now give a proof of this important fact.

THEOREM: *The limit of the ratio $\sin x/x$ as $x \to 0$ is one.*

In a circle of radius $OA = 1$, fig. 6, we draw two straight lines OBE and OCF, forming with OA two equal central angles $AOB = AOC = x$, the chord BDC, and, through the point A, the tangent to the circle, FAE. Three areas are thus formed, namely, the triangular areas OBC and OEF and the circular sector $OCABO$. To evaluate them, we observe that the segments OD, DB, and AE are equal to $\cos x$, $\sin x$, and $\tan x$, respectively, because the radius is equal to one and the angle DOB is x. The central angle of the circular sector COB is equal to $2x$.

Therefore, the areas we are considering are given by

$$\text{area } OCB = \mathsf{OD} \cdot \mathsf{DB} = \sin x \cdot \cos x$$

$$\text{area } OCABO = 1^2 x = x$$

$$\text{area } OFE = \mathsf{OA} \cdot \mathsf{AE} = \tan x$$

On the other hand, the area OCB, included in that of the circular sector, is surely less than the area of this sector, which itself is less than the area of the triangle OFE. Thus, the inequalities

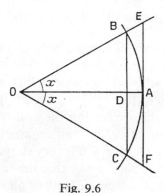

Fig. 9.6

$$\text{area } OCB < \text{area } OCABO < \text{area } OFE$$

translated into algebraical language, give the following results:

$$\sin x \cdot \cos x < x < \tan x = \sin x / \cos x \tag{35}$$

The first inequality, $\sin x \cdot \cos x < x$, can be improved. Multiplying it by two and applying to the product $2 \sin x \cos x$ the relation (29) Chapter 6, we find that $\sin (2x) < 2x$. But ,the angle $2x$ being an arbitrary acute angle, we conclude that the sine of *any* angle is less than this angle, so that, also, $\sin x < x$. The second inequality in (35) can be written as follows: $x \cos x < \sin x$. This form, indeed, can be obtained by multiplying the inequality $x < \sin x / \cos x$ by $\cos x$. We see, therefore, that

$$x \cos x < \sin x < x$$

Dividing all three members of these inequalities by x, we transform it into

$$\cos x < \sin x / x < 1 \tag{36}$$

Thus, for any acute angle x, the value of the ratio $\sin x/x$ is between $\cos x$ and one. Consider now the variable x in (36) as an infinitely small quantity approaching zero. At the limit, when x vanishes, $\cos x$ becomes equal to $\cos 0 = 1$, so that the lower bound (the lefthand member $\cos x$) becomes equal to the upper constant bound of one. The ratio $\sin x/x$, the value of which is between the lower and upper bounds, takes necessarily the value one when the lower bound becomes equal to the upper bound, that is, to one. We formulate this result as follows:

$$\lim_{x=0} (\sin x/x) = 1 \tag{37}$$

The theorem (37) just proved admits of an interesting geometrical interpretation. We know that the chord of a finite arc is always shorter than the arc since a segment of straight line is the shortest path between two points. On the other hand, if the size of the arc decreases and the arc becomes infinitely small our intuition suggests that it is impossible to distinguish the chord from the arc which means that their lengths tend to become equal when they approach zero. The limit formula (37) proves this guess in the case of a circle, thus justifying our intuition. Comparing the lengths BC and BC of a chord and its arc in fig. 6 we form the ratio BC/BC. It is expressed by

$$2 \sin x/(2x) = \sin x/x \quad \text{because} \quad \mathsf{BC} = 2DB = 2 \sin x$$

while BC is measured by the product of radius $\mathsf{OA} = 1$ and of its central angle $2x$, so that $BC = 2x$.

Therefore, the theorem (37) states that the ratio BC/BC approaches one when a circular arc BC tends to zero, and it becomes exactly equal to one at the very moment when the arc BC and its chord BC vanish. In other words, the curvature of a circular arc is a phenomenon characteristic essentially of *finite* arcs. An infinitely small (in length) circular arc can be considered also as an infinitely small segment of a straight line.

The same conclusion holds for arcs of any curve. At each point, of a continuous and sufficiently smooth curve there are many different circles tangent to the curve at this point, but only one of them, called the *osculating circle*, is the best tangent circle because it is not only tangent to the curve at the contact point, but it has also the same curvature as the curve at this point. In the immediate neighborhood of the contact point, the osculating circle and the curve coincide, so that an infinitely small arc of the curve is also an infinitely small arc on the osculating circle, and, therefore, the ratio of chord length to arc length at the limit becomes equal to one.

We now apply the result (37) to our problem which is related to the limit of the expression

$$[\cos (t/n) + i \sin (t/n)]^n \quad \text{for} \quad n = \infty.$$

For n infinitely large, that is, for vanishing t/n, $\cos (t/n)$ and $\sin (t/n)$ can be replaced by one and t/n, which are their asymptotic values:

$$\lim_{n=\infty} [\cos (t/n)/1] = 1, \quad \text{as well as} \quad \lim_{n=\infty} [\sin (t/n)]/(t/n) = 1$$

We conclude, therefore, that

$$\cos t + i \sin t = \lim_{n=\infty} [\cos (t/n) + i \sin (t/n)]^n = \lim_{n=\infty} (1 + it/n)^n = e^{it}$$

and, thus, the formula (33) is obtained. We insist that the reasoning just described does not constitute a rigorous proof of Euler's formula (see Appendix VII).

Thus, e^{it} is the rotation factor through an angle of t radians and the fact that two successive rotations about the same point are equivalent to a single rotation whose angle is the sum of angles of two component rotations finds its mathematical counterpart and expression in the multiplication rule for powers

$$e^{it} e^{is} = e^{it+is} = e^{i(t+s)}$$

In geometrical language, this multiplication rule of powers to the same base, which states that the exponents are to be added, can be read as follows: *The product of two rotation-factors through angles t and s is also a rotation-factor corresponding to a rotation through an angle equal to the sum t + s.*

Moivre's formula

$$(\cos x + i \sin x)^n = \cos (nx) + i \sin (nx)$$

now appears trivial since, writing the rotation-factors in their exponential form and applying the rule of exponents, $(a^m)^n = a^{mn}$, we obtain immediately

$$(\cos x + i \sin x)^n = (e^{ix})^n = e^{inx} = \cos (nx) + i \sin (nx)$$

A complex number $z = x + iy$, written in polar form, is now simply $z = re^{it}$, since the expressions $x = r\cos t$, $y = r\sin t$ carry with them

$$z = x + iy = r\cos t + ir\sin t = r(\cos t + i\sin t) = re^{it}$$

Computation of Tables of Trigonometric Functions

Combining Euler's formula (33) with the expansion (32) of the rotation factor e^{it} into the exponential series, we obtain a complex identity

$$\cos t + i\sin t = 1 - t^2/2! + t^4/4! - t^6/6! + \cdots$$
$$+ (-1)^n t^{2n}/(2n)! + \cdots + i[t/1! - t^3/3! + t^5/5!$$
$$+ \cdots + (-1)^n t^{2n+1}/(2n+1)! + \cdots]$$

Applying the principle of separation of real and imaginary to this identity, we obtain the expansions of the sine and cosine into infinite series:

$$\cos t = 1 - t^2/2! + t^4/4! - t^6/6! + \cdots + (-1)^n t^{2n}/(2n)! + \cdots$$
$$\sin t = t/1! - t^3/3! + t^5/5! - \cdots + (-1)^n t^{2n+1}/(2n+1)! + \cdots$$

(38)

They are convergent for all values of the independent variable t and represent their respective sums, $\cos t$ and $\sin t$, in the whole range of variation of t from $-\infty$ to $+\infty$:

$$-\infty < t < +\infty$$

We have studied how the numerical values of trigonometric functions sine, cosine, and tangent can be obtained with the aid of geometrical considerations. But this method works only for some particular numerical values of t such as

$$\pi/10 = 18°, \ \pi/6 = 30°, \ \pi/5 = 36°, \ \pi/4 = 45°, \ 3\pi/10 = 54°,$$
$$\pi/3 = 60°, \quad \text{and} \quad 2\pi/5 = 72°$$

We use in numerical computations tables of trigonometric functions and find in them values for any t. It is interesting to point out that the above series (38) were the fundamental tools with which these tables were computed. The angle t was given a sequence of numerical values expressed in radians, because in these series the variable t is a pure number.

The polynominals of infinite order (38) do not reflect such important properties of sine and cosine as their periodicity with a period equal to $2\pi = 360°$:

$$\cos (t \pm 2\pi) = \cos (t \pm 360°) = \cos t$$

$$\sin (t \pm 2\pi) = \sin (t \pm 360°) = \sin t$$

or the fundamental relations

$$\cos (\pi/2 - t) = \sin t, \ \sin (\pi/2) - t) = \cos t; \ \cos^2 t + \sin^2 t = 1$$

It would be extremely difficult, if not impossible, to discover the properties of sine and cosine by working uniquely with their expansions (38). The same remark is true for e^{it}. The most important feature of the exponential function e^{it}, namely, its periodicity with the period 2π, cannot be observed or deduced from either

$$e^{it} = \lim_{n=\infty} (1 + it/n)^n \quad \text{or} \quad e^{it} = \sum_{n=0}^{\infty} (it)^n/n!$$

It is Euler's formula which throws an unexpected light not only on $\cos t$ and $\sin t$, but also on e^{it}. Using the periodicity of the sine and cosine, we obtain immediately the corresponding property of the exponential function:

$$e^{it \pm 2\pi i} = e^{i(t \pm 2\pi)} = \cos (t \pm 2\pi) + i \sin (t \pm 2\pi) = \cos t + i \sin t = e^{it}$$

Thus, e^{it} considered as a complex function of a *real* variable t is a periodic function, and its period is the same as that of sine and cosine of t, namely, $2\pi = 360°$. This result, applied to the particular value $t = 0$, can also be written as follows:

$$e^{\pm 2\pi i} = e^0 = 1$$

which is equivalent to the form $e^{i(t \pm 2\pi)} = e^{it}$ because the lefthand member is equal to $e^{it} e^{\pm 2\pi i}$. The relation $e^{2\pi i} = 1$ shows that multiplication by $e^{2\pi i}$ does not change the multiplicand, which is not at all surprising, a rotation through 360° having no effect on the position of a vector and $e^{2\pi i}$ being nothing else than the rotation factor through 360°.

The value it of the complex exponent z in the general form of the exponential function $e^z = e^{x+iy}$, with which Euler's formula is concerned, is only a particular case. We now consider e^z as a complex function of a complex variable $z = x + iy$. It is also periodic, but its period is no longer a real number. We have, indeed,

$$e^{z+2\pi i} = e^z e^{2\pi i} = e^z \cdot 1 = e^z$$

which proves that the period of the function e^z is a purely imaginary number $2\pi i$:

$$e^{z+2\pi i} = e^z$$

This statement becomes trivial if we use a formal substitution, $it = z$, because then z increases by $2\pi i$, when t increases by 2π. But this substitution is, in our case, contradictory, and it cannot be used since t, by definition, is real and, therefore, $it = x + iy$ is possible only when $x = 0$, $y = t$. What is essential in both the cases of e^{it} and e^z is the fact that the increase of the exponent by $2\pi i$ does not change the value of the exponential function to the base e.

The rotation factors through $90°$ and $180°$, that is, the numbers i and -1, arc particular cases of the general expression e^{it} of the rotation factor through any angle t. They correspond to $t = \pi/2$ and $t = \pi$, so that these two familiar and fundamental units take new forms, namely,

$$i = e^{i\pi/2}; \quad -1 = e^{i\pi}$$

Raising the relation $i = e^{i\pi/2}$ to a power with exponent i, the number i^i is computed:

$$i^i = (e^{i\pi/2})^i = e^{i^2\pi/2} = e^{-\pi/2} = 1/e^{\pi/2} = 0.207\ldots$$

and a curious result is obtained: the number i^i is real, and its approximate value is equal to 0.207. This fact is a typical example of a general situation: the use of complex numbers in applied mathematics often leads to results expressed in real numbers.

Euler's formula establishes an intimate relation between the trigonometric functions sine and cosine on one hand and the exponential e^{it} on the other. Cos t and i sin t appear as real and imaginary parts of the complex number e^{it}. They can also be obtained as linear combinations of two exponential functions e^{it} and e^{-it}, the second complex expression being conjugate to the first.

We know that

$$\cos(-t) = \cos t, \quad \text{while} \quad \sin(-t) = -\sin t$$

Therefore, using Euler's formula, we can express e^{-it} as follows:

$$e^{-it} = e^{i(-t)} = \cos(-t) + i\sin(-t) = \cos t - i\sin t \qquad (39)$$

This relation is a conjugate form of Euler's formula

$$e^{it} = \cos t + i \sin t \qquad (33)$$

and it could be deduced from it directly, replacing in (33) i by $-i$.

Adding member by member (39) and (33) and dividing the result by two, we obtain the expression of $\cos t$ as a linear combination of e^{it} and e^{-it}:

$$\cos t = (e^{it} + e^{-it})/2 \qquad (40)$$

Subtracting (39) from (33) and dividing the difference by $2i$, we have a similar expression of $\sin t$:

$$\sin t = (e^{it} - e^{-it})/2i \qquad (41)$$

The relations (40) and (41) are useful in the study of the trigonometric functions sine and cosine. The exponential e^{-it} is the rotation factor through the angle $-t$, that is, if t is positive, through the angle t *clockwise*. Thus, $e^{it} \cdot e^{-it} = 1$ because there is no effect of two opposite rotations through equal angles. On the other hand, replacing both rotation factors by their trigonometric expressions, we obtain the fundamental relation

$$(\cos t + i \sin t)(\cos t - i \sin t) = \cos^2 t + \sin^2 t = 1$$

We conclude this chapter by an important example of the binomial expansion related to the theory of logarithms and which will be used in Chapter 11. Consider a difference $(1 + x)^t - 1$ for variable exponent t, but a fixed base $1 + x$, the number x being constant in our discussion. If the variable t takes the value zero, $(1 + x)^0$ becomes equal to one, and our difference vanishes. We want to know how does it vanish, that is, to what power of t it is comparable for infinitely small t. The binomial expansion of $(1 + x)^t$ begins with $1 + tx$, so that the difference $(1 + x)^t - 1$ surely contains the term tx which is proportional to t. Therefore, we find that our difference vanishes as t, being comparable to the first power of the infinitely small quantity t.

We now ask: what is the limit of the ratio $[(1 + x)^t - 1]/t$, obtained by dividing the difference we are studying by t, when t approaches and reaches zero? In other words, the problem raised consists in the determination of the value $F(x)$ of the following limit:

$$\lim_{t=0} \{[(1 + x)^t - 1]/t\} = F(x)$$

The unknown value of this limit is denoted by $F(x)$, which means "function of the variable x" because, in our reasoning, the constant x can be chosen as we please, so that, in fact, x can have any value which is then kept constant during the computation of the limit $F(x)$, but is arbitrary in itself. Thus, the result which we shall obtain will depend on the value of the variable x, defining the corresponding value $F(x)$ of the limit as a function of x. To find this unknown function of x, we expand $(1 + x)^t$ with the aid of the binomial theorem, transposing the first term 1 of this expansion in the lefthand member:

$$(1 + x)^t - 1 = (t/1) x + t(t - 1) x^2/2! + t(t - 1) (t - 2) x^3/3! + \cdots,$$

the general term of this infinite series having the following expression:

$$t(t - 1) (t - 2) \cdots (t - n + 1) x^n/n!$$

All the terms of this series have t as their common factor. Picking it out and replacing each factor of the type $(t - k)$ by $-(k - t)$, we rewrite the expansion as follows:

$$(1 + t)^t - 1 = t[x - (1 - t) x^2/2! + (1 - t) (2 - t) x^3/3!$$
$$- (1 - t) (2 - t) (3 - t) x^4/4! + ...]$$

The expression of the general term inside the brackets now becomes

$$(-1)^{n-1} (1 - t) (2 - t) (3 - t) \cdots (n - 1 - t) x^n/n!$$

Dividing both members by t and using the summation symbol Σ, we obtain the following expression of the ratio whose limit is being discussed:

$$[(1 + x)^t - 1]/t = \sum_{n=1}^{\infty} (-1)^{n-1}(1 - t)(2 - t)(3 - t)\cdots(n - 1 - t)x^n/n!$$

At the limit for $t = 0$, the general term of this series reduces to

$$(-1)^{n-1} 1 \cdot 2 \cdot 3 \cdots (n - 1) x^n/n! = (-1)^{n-1}x^n/n$$

so that, passing to the limit, we find the ultimate expression $F(x)$ of our ratio for $t = 0$:

$$F(x) = \lim_{t=0} \{[(1 + x)^t - 1]/t\} = \sum_{n=1}^{\infty} (-1)^{n-1}x^n/n$$
$$= x/1 - x^2/2 + x^3/3 - x^4/4 + x^5/5 - x^6/6 + \cdots \qquad (42)$$

The expansion of the limit $\lim_{t=0} \{[(1 + x)^t - 1]/t\}$ is convergent and has a sum $F(x)$ only if the range of variation of x is limited to the interior of the interval $(-1, 1)$, the admissible values of x being between -1 and 1 and satisfying the inequalities $-1 < x < 1$. Thus, for instance, if $x = 0.1$ the above expansion (42) reduces to the following numerical series:

$$F(0.1) = \lim_{t=0} \{[(1.1)^t - 1]/t\} = 0.1 - 0.005 + 0.000333333...$$

$$-0.000025 + 0.000002 - 0.000000166... = 0.09531018...$$

The series (42) diverges for $x = -1$ because the sum of all its terms becomes equal to $-\infty$ when $x = -1$. But it remains convergent and represents the numerical value of the limit $\lim [(2^t - 1/t]$ if $x = 1$:

$$\lim_{t=0} [(2^t - 1)/t] = 1 - 1/2 + (1/3) - 1/4 + (1/5) - (1/6) + \cdots$$

the approximate value of this limit (43) being equal to 0.69315....

CHAPTER 10

Determinants; Systems of Linear Equations with n Unknowns

The solution of two linear equations with two unknowns was discussed in Chapter 7. Consider now a system S_n of n equations with n unknowns $x_1, x_2, \ldots, x_n$. Denoting the constant coefficients by the letter a with two subscripts so that coefficient of x_j in the i-th equation is a_{ij}, we have in this system S_n n equations $(1 \leqslant i \leqslant n)$

$$\sum_{j=1}^{n} a_{ij}x_j = a_{i1}x_1 + a_{i2}x_2 + \cdots + a_{ik}x_k + \cdots + a_{in}x_n = b_i \qquad (S_n)$$

the righthand members being known constants b_i, $1 \leqslant i \leqslant n$.

The study of such a system necessitates the introduction of determinants. In fact, they were used already in Chapter 7, as, for instance, $d = a_1b_2 - a_2b_1$. A determinant is a number of a particular structure. Thus the determinant of second order d is a sum of two terms a_1b_2 and $-a_2b_1$ formed with a given set of four numbers a_1, b_1, a_2, b_2, called its elements. In Chapter 7, $a_1b_2 - a_2b_1$ has as elements the coefficients of two equations with two unknowns

$$a_1x + b_1y = c_1 \text{ and } a_2x + b_2y = c_2$$

This system is a particular case of the system (S_n) and we prefer to rewrite it as

$$a_{11}x_1 + a_{12}x_2 = b_1 \text{ and } a_{21}x_1 + a_{22}x_2 = b_2$$

so that the determinant of this system will be now $a_{11}a_{22} - a_{12}a_{21}$. It is denoted usually as follows:

$$\begin{vmatrix} a_{11} & a_{12} \\ a_{21} & a_{22} \end{vmatrix} = a_{11}a_{22} - a_{12}a_{21} \qquad (1)$$

It is seen that the rows of this square table correspond to equations

427

and the columns to unknowns. The determinant (1) is of second order because it has two rows and two columns. A determinant of first order would have only one element; it reduces to a number.

The square table of coefficients a_{ij} in the system (S_n) has n rows and as many columns, and the determinant D of all n^2 coefficients a_{ij} in (S_n) is said to be of n-th order. Sometimes it is denoted by det $|a_{ij}|_1^n$, but it may also be written as follows:

$$D = \begin{vmatrix} a_{11} & a_{12} & \cdots & a_{1n} \\ a_{21} & a_{22} & \cdots & a_{2n} \\ \cdots\cdots\cdots\cdots\cdots \\ \cdots\cdots\cdots\cdots\cdots \\ a_{n1} & a_{n2} & \cdots & a_{nn} \end{vmatrix},$$

the first notation det $|a_{ij}|_1^n$ being an abbreviation.

To answer the question how the numerical value of D is related to its elements a_{ij}, we have first to study the nature of permutations of the first n integers. When taken in natural order, they form the fundamental permutation symbolized by $[123 \cdots n]$ and characterized by the fact that in it the k-th element (which is k) precedes the m-th element if k is less than m. Any permutation can be denoted by $[i_1 i_2 i_3 \cdots i_n]$, where the elements i_k $(1 \leqslant k \leqslant n)$ are the first n integers from 1 to n, arranged in any order. In it, any pair of elements i_k and i_m which occupy the k-th and the m-th place are said to form a disarrangement when $i_k > i_m$ while $k < m$, which means that a larger integer i_k *precedes* the smaller one i_m. Thus, in [32541] we have six disarrangements. A disarrangement can be created or destroyed by a *transposition*, that is, by an exchange of two elements. Thus, [32514], obtained from [32541] by transposing 1 and 4, has five disarrangements, while [32541] has six. A transposition of two *adjacent* elements changes the number N of disarrangements in a permutation by one so that it becomes $N + 1$ or $N - 1$. Thus, the parity of N changes: N becomes even (odd) if it was odd (even). To study the effect on N of a transposition of two *non-adjacent* elements separated, say, by m elements, we denote these two elements by p and q, the m separating elements being denoted by $i_1, i_2, \ldots i_m$. Thus, before the transposition we had $P_1 = [a \cdots p i_1 i_2 \cdots i_m q \cdots w]$, while after the transposition $P_2 = [a \cdots q i_1 \cdots i_m p \cdots w]$ is obtained. Let us denote by α the number of disarrangements in P_1 formed by the element q with $i_1, i_2, \ldots i_m$ and by β the number of those formed by p with $i_1, i_2, \ldots i_m$. After the transposition of p and q, $\alpha + \beta$ disarrangements are destroyed, but new ones appear: the $m - \beta$ elements i_k which did not form disarrangements with p in the original permutation P_1 do form after the transposition as many disarrangements in P_2, and the same holds for $m - \alpha$ elements i_k with respect to q. Therefore,

$$m - \beta + m - \alpha = 2m - \alpha - \beta$$

new disarrangements appear. This proves that the variation of the number N of disarrangements in P_1 caused by the transposition of p and q and due to m elements i_k separating them is equal to

$$2m - \alpha - \beta - (\alpha + \beta) = 2(m - \alpha - \beta)$$

This variation is an even number so that it does not change the parity of N. But we have not yet considered the effect of permuting p and q: if $p < q$, the transposition created a disarrangement and if $p > q$, it destroyed one; thus, we come to the conclusion that *any transposition changes the parity of the number of disarrangements.*

Any permutation arises from the fundamental one by transpositions, and the parity of the number of disarrangements in a permutation is the same as the parity of the number of transpositions used.

A permutation obtainable from the fundamental permutation in an even number of transpositions is said to belong to the class of even permutations. We will call it an *even permutation.* It has an even number of disarrangements and can be retransformed back into $[123 \cdots n]$ by an even number of transpositions. The fundamental permutation has an even number, namely zero, of disarrangements and is therefore an even permutation.

Likewise, the class of odd permutations consists of all permutations with an odd number of disarrangements which are obtainable from or reducible to the fundamental permutation in an odd number of transpositions. It is obvious that *a transposition changes the class of a permutation.*

Returning to the definition of determinants, we call a determinant of n-th order the algebraic sum of all products of n factors a_{ij} chosen among n^2 elements a_{ij} ($1 \leqslant i \leqslant n$ and $1 \leqslant j \leqslant n$) in such a way that no two factors of a product belong to the same row or same column of the square table of elements a_{ij}. In other words, if a typical product thus defined is written as

$$\pm\, a_{i_1 j_1} \cdot a_{i_2 j_2} \cdots a_{i_n j_n}$$

then the set of first subscripts i_k and the set of second subscripts j_m form two permutations $[i_1 i_2 \cdots i_n]$ and $[j_1 j_2 \cdots j_n]$ of first n integers. The double sign $\pm$ means that one half of the products, terms of the determinant, are to be taken with the sign plus and the other half are to be taken with the sign minus. It remains to define the rule of sign to be affixed to each term.

Since the value of a product does not depend on the order of factors, we complete the definition of a determinant as an algebraic sum of typical products, stipulating that in each term of this sum the permutation of first subscripts is the fundamental one, namely $[123 \cdots n]$:

$$D = \det |a_{ij}|_1^n = \Sigma \pm a_{1j_1} a_{2j_2} a_{3j_3} \cdots a_{nj_n} \qquad (2)$$

where the sum-symbol Σ means that the summation extends to all $n!$ permutations $[j_1 j_2 j_3 \cdots j_n]$ of integers $1, 2, 3, \ldots, n$.

Now we state the rule of sign as follows: *The sign of a term in Σ depends on the nature of the permutation of its second subscripts; terms with an even permutation are taken with a plus sign, terms with an odd permutation have a minus sign.*

There are as many even permutations as odd ones since by performing one transposition in each even permutation we transform the class of all even permutations into the class of all odd permutations and *vice versa*. The total number of permutations of n objects is equal to $n!$ (see Chapter 9).

Therefore a determinant of n-th order is a sum of $n!$ terms of which $n!/2$ are taken with a plus sign and $n!/2$ with a minus sign.

EXAMPLES:
$$\begin{vmatrix} a_{11} & a_{12} \\ a_{21} & a_{22} \end{vmatrix} = \det |a_{ij}|_1^2 = a_{11}a_{22} - a_{12}a_{21}$$

Here the permutation of second subscripts in the first term, $[12]$, is an even one while in the second term $[21]$ is an odd permutation.

$$\begin{vmatrix} a_{11} & a_{12} & a_{13} \\ a_{21} & a_{22} & a_{23} \\ a_{31} & a_{32} & a_{33} \end{vmatrix} = \begin{cases} a_{11}a_{22}a_{33} + a_{12}a_{23}a_{31} + a_{13}a_{21}a_{32} - \\ - a_{11}a_{23}a_{32} - a_{12}a_{21}a_{33} - a_{13}a_{22}a_{31} \end{cases}$$

the permutations $[231]$ and $[312]$ being even, while $[132]$, $[213]$ and $[321]$ are odd.

A special notation used for the sign of a typical product is as follows:

$$(-1)^{[i_1 i_2 \cdots i_n]} = \begin{cases} +1 \\ -1 \end{cases} \text{ if } [i_1 i_2 \cdots i_n] \text{ is an } \begin{matrix} \text{even} \\ \text{odd} \end{matrix} \text{ permutation}$$

With this notation, we finally have

$$D = \det |a_{ij}|_1^n = \begin{vmatrix} a_{11} & a_{12} & \cdots & a_{1n} \\ \cdots\cdots\cdots\cdots\cdots \\ \cdots\cdots\cdots\cdots\cdots \\ \cdots\cdots\cdots\cdots\cdots \\ a_{n1} & a_{n2} & \cdots & a_{nn} \end{vmatrix} = \Sigma(-1)^{[j_1 j_2 \cdots j_n]} \cdot a_{1j_1}\ldots a_{nj_n} \tag{3}$$

Naturally, the terms in Σ could be rewritten rearranging the factors so that it is the permutation of *second* subscripts which becomes fundamental, while the first subscripts form permutations $[i_1 i_2 \cdots i_n]$:

$$D = \Sigma(-1)^{[i_1 i_2 \cdots i_n]} \cdot a_{i_1 1} a_{i_2 2} \cdots a_{i_n n} \tag{4}$$

It is important to observe that, in the new form of the general term of Σ the permutation $[i_1 i_2 \cdots i_n]$ belongs to the class of the permutation $P = [j_1 j_2 \cdots j_n]$. The new permutation was obtained from the fundamental one by the same number of transpositions (caused by the rearrangement of factors a_{ij} of general term) as the number of transpositions which retransformed P back to the fundamental permutation. The equivalence of these two expressions (3) and (4) proves that, in a determinant, rows and columns play the same role, so that what is true for rows is true also for columns. Reflecting the elements of the square table (3) in the principal diagonal $a_{11} - a_{nn}$, we transform rows into columns and *vice versa* and this operation does not change the determinant because the *order* of rows and columns remains unchanged. Such a transformation is called transposition, and the transposed determinant is denoted by $\tilde{D}$.

The definition (3) or (4) of a determinant as a sum of $n!$ terms is never used in the numerical computation of its value, but it allows an easy proof of its properties. In what follows, we often use the letter D as an abbreviation for the word determinant.

Properties of Determinants

Exchanging in a D any two rows (or columns) induces in (3) or in (4) a transposition in the exponent $[j_1 j_2 \cdots j_n]$ or $[i_2 i_2 \cdots i_n]$ of (-1). The transposition changes the parity of exponent and therefore changes the sign of all terms of the D. Thus

I) *Exchanging two rows or two columns in a determinant we change its sign.*

II) *If a determinant has two identical rows or two identical columns it vanishes:* exchanging them, we transform D into $-D$, but, on the other hand, it did not change at all, so that $-D = D$, that is, $D = 0$.

III) *A determinant vanishes if in it all the elements of a row R (or of a column) vanish.* This is a direct corollary of the definition of D which states that in each term of Σ one of its factors belongs to R.

IV) Considering a D as a function of the n elements of the i-th row a_{ij} (i is fixed, $1 \leqslant j \leqslant n$), we state that D is a linear and homogeneous function of $a_{i1}, a_{i2}, \ldots, a_{in}$. Arraying together the $(n - 1)!$ terms with the same factor a_{i1} and picking out the common factor a_{i1}, we can write this group of terms as $a_{i1}. (\ldots\ldots) = a_{i1}A_{i1}$, where A_{i1} denotes the sum of terms inside the parentheses. This expression A_{i1} is called *cofactor* of a_{i1}. Repeating the same procedure with a_{i2} and then $a_{i3}, a_{i4}, \ldots, a_{in}$, we define the cofactors A_{ij} of all the elements of the i-th row. Naturally, the same procedure can be applied to define the cofactor A_{ij} of any element a_{ij} of D. Using the n cofactors of elements of the i-th row, we transform (3) into an expansion of a D along its i-th row. There are n such expansions:

$$D = \sum_{j=1}^{n} a_{ij}A_{ij} \qquad (i = 1, 2, \ldots, n) \qquad (5a)$$

What is true for rows is also true for columns and we have n more expansions of D along its columns (j fixed):

$$D = \sum_{i=1}^{n} a_{ij}A_{ij} \qquad (j = 1, 2, \ldots, n) \qquad (5b)$$

With the aid of these expansions, the reader can easily verify and prove the following properties of a D:

Va) To multiply a D by a number c, it is sufficient to multiply by c *one and only one* of its rows or columns.

Vb) If in a D all the elements of a row or column have a common factor, it can be picked out.

VI) If in a row or column of a D all the elements are sums with equal number of terms, this D can be decomposed into a sum of the same number of D's.

EXAMPLE:

$$\begin{vmatrix} a_{11} & a_{12} & a_{13} + b_{13} \\ a_{21} & a_{22} & a_{23} + b_{23} \\ a_{31} & a_{32} & a_{33} + b_{33} \end{vmatrix} = \begin{vmatrix} a_{11} & a_{12} & a_{13} \\ a_{21} & a_{22} & a_{23} \\ a_{31} & a_{32} & a_{33} \end{vmatrix} + \begin{vmatrix} a_{11} & a_{12} & b_{13} \\ a_{21} & a_{22} & b_{23} \\ a_{31} & a_{32} & b_{33} \end{vmatrix}$$

Any determinant formed with the elements of a D, $|a_{ij}|_1^n$, by striking out in D an equal number m ($m < n$) of rows and columns, is called a *minor* of order $n - m$ of D. It is a *principal* minor if the omitted rows and columns intersect pairwise on the principal diagonal $a_{11} - a_{nn}$ of D. The n^2 minors of $(n - 1)$-th order, obtained by striking out one row and one column, correspond to n^2 elements of D and the minor M_{ij}, formed by omitting in D the i-th row and the j-th column, is said to correspond to a_{ij}, which stands on the intersection of the omitted row and column.

We will now establish a relation between the cofactor A_{ij} of an element a_{ij} and the corresponding minor M_{ij}. Let us first consider the minor M_{11} related to the element a_{11} at the left upper corner of D. By definition, it is

$$M_{11} = \det |a_{ij}|_2^n = \begin{vmatrix} a_{22} & a_{23} & \cdots & a_{2n} \\ a_{32} & a_{33} & \cdots & a_{3n} \\ \cdots & \cdots & \cdots & \cdots \\ a_{n2} & a_{n3} & \cdots & a_{nn} \end{vmatrix}$$

On the other hand, the cofactor A_{11} of a_{11} is defined by the relation

$$a_{11}A_{11} = \sum (-1)^{[1j_2j_3\cdots j_n]} a_{11}a_{2j_2}a_{3j_3} \cdots a_{nj_n}$$

where the summation is extended to all $(n - 1)!$ permutations $[j_2j_3 \cdots j_n]$ of $n - 1$ integers 2, 3, 4, ..., n. Now in $[1j_2j_3 \cdots j_n]$, the first element 1 cannot form a disarrangement with larger integers which follow it. Therefore, the parity of $[1j_2j_3 \cdots j_n]$ is the same as the parity of $[j_2j_3 \cdots j_n]$, and this proves that in A_{11} the sign $(-1)^{[1j_2j_3\cdots j_n]}$ can be replaced by the equal sign $(-1)^{[j_2j_3\cdots j_n]}$. Therefore, dividing by a_{11}, we have

$$A_{11} = \sum (-1)^{[j_2j_3\cdots j_n]} \cdot a_{2j_2}a_{3j_3} \cdots a_{nj_n}$$

where the summation is extended to all permutations $[j_2j_3 \cdots j_n]$ of $n - 1$ integers 2, 3, ..., $n - 1$, n. But such is also the definition of the determinant M_{11}, so that we find a very simple relation $A_{11} = M_{11}$ between the cofactor and the minor of a_{11}.

Kogbetliantz 28

Consider now the cofactor A_{ij} and the minor M_{ij} of any element a_{ij}. We could shift a_{ij} to the left upper corner of D by exchanging directly the first and the i-th rows as well as the first and the j-th columns. But then, striking out the new first row and first column, we would not obtain exactly the minor M_{ij} because the original order of rows and columns in D was perturbed by the direct exchange of first and i-th rows and of first and j-th columns.

Therefore, we will proceed by gradually exchanging at each step two *adjacent* rows or columns. Shifting thus the i-th row in $i - 1$ steps upward so that it becomes the first row and then moving the j-th column leftward in $j - 1$ steps to the position of first column, we obtain a determinant which is equal to D multiplied $i + j - 2$ times by (-1), namely,

$$D^* = (-1)^{i+j-2}D = \begin{vmatrix} a_{ij}a_{i1}a_{i2} \cdots a_{i,j-1} & a_{i,j+1} \cdots a_{in} \\ a_{1j}a_{11}a_{12} \cdots a_{1j-1} & a_{1,j+1} \cdots a_{1n} \\ \cdots\cdots\cdots\cdots\cdots\cdots\cdots\cdots\cdots \\ a_{i-1,j} \cdots a_{i-1,j-1} \; a_{i-1,j+1} \cdots a_{i-1,n} \\ a_{i+1,j} \cdots a_{i+1,j-1} \; a_{i+1,j+1} \cdots a_{i+1,n} \\ \cdots\cdots\cdots\cdots\cdots\cdots\cdots\cdots\cdots \\ \cdots\cdots\cdots\cdots\cdots\cdots\cdots\cdots\cdots \\ a_{nj}a_{n1}a_{n2} \cdots a_{n,j-1} & a_{n,j+1} \cdots a_{nn} \end{vmatrix}$$

Now, denoting the elements of the determinant D^* by a_{ij}^*, we have $a_{11}^* = a_{ij}$ as well as $M_{11}^* = M_{ij}$. The cofactor A_{11}^* of a_{11}^* in D^* is equal to $(-1)^{i+j-2} A_{ij}$ of a_{ij} in $(-1)^{i+j-2} D$. Thus, we have, multiplying it by $(-1)^{i+j}$,

$$A_{ij} = A_{11}^*(-1)^{i+j}$$

But we just proved that $A_{11}^* = M_{11}^* = M_{ij}$, and this yields the relation between A_{ij} and M_{ij}:

$$A_{ij} = (-1)^{i+j} M_{ij}$$

EXAMPLE: The expansion along the second row of

$$\begin{vmatrix} 3 & 2 & 1 \\ 0 & 7 & 5 \\ -1 & 4 & 2 \end{vmatrix} = a_{21}(-1)^3 M_{21} + a_{22}(-1)^4 M_{22} + a_{23}(-1)^5 M_{23}$$

$$= -0\begin{vmatrix} 2 & 1 \\ 4 & 2 \end{vmatrix} + 7\begin{vmatrix} 3 & 1 \\ -1 & 2 \end{vmatrix} - 5\begin{vmatrix} 3 & 2 \\ -1 & 4 \end{vmatrix}$$

$$= 7(6 + 1) - 5(12 + 2) = -21$$

yields the value -21 of this determinant.

Replacing in the expansion (5a) of a D along the i-th row,

$$D = \sum_{j=1}^{n} a_{ij} A_{ij}$$

the set of elements a_{ij} with $1 \leqslant j \leqslant n$ by a set of other numbers $c_1, c_2, \ldots, c_n$, we form another determinant

$$d = \sum_{j=1}^{n} c_j A_{ij}$$

In particular, replacing a_{ij} by the elements of another, say, of the m-th row ($m \neq i$) of D, a vanishing determinant is obtained because in it two rows are identical. Thus, an important property of cofactors is proved:

VII) *If cofactors of the elements of a row are multiplied by the elements of another row, the sum of such products vanishes.*

Naturally, the same holds for the cofactors of elements of a column, and we symbolize these results as follows:

$$\sum_{j=1}^{n} a_{mj} A_{ij} = 0, \quad \text{if} \quad m \neq i \quad \text{and} \quad \sum_{j=1}^{n} a_{im} A_{ij} = 0, \quad \text{if} \quad m \neq j \quad (6)$$

The property VII leads to the following:

THEOREM: *A determinant does not change when multiples of elements of a row or of a column are added or subtracted from the corresponding elements of another row or of another column.*

Adding to the elements of the i-th row (or j-th column) the elements of the m-th row (or m-th column) multiplied by a positive or negative number h, we transform a D into D^* in which the i-th row elements are now $a_{ij} + h a_{mj}$ with $1 \leqslant j \leqslant n$. Expanding D^* along this row, we have by (6):

$$D^* = \sum_{j=1}^{n} (a_{ij} + h a_{mj}) A_{ij} = \sum_{j=1}^{n} a_{ij} A_{ij} + h \sum_{j=1}^{n} a_{mj} A_{ij} = D + h0 = D$$

The same proof holds for the columns.

This theorem serves as basis for the computation of determinants. With its aid, we can make vanish all the elements, except one, of a predetermined row or column. Applying then the expansion of D along this row or column, we obtain only one term which is the product of a cofactor by the nonvanishing element. This cofactor is a determinant the order of which is one unit less than the order of D.

The same procedure is applied again and again until a determinant of order two is obtained.

EXAMPLE: Add to the first three columns the multiples of the last column, choosing the factors h in such a way that zeros are created in the last row:

$$D = \begin{vmatrix} 3 & 5 & 1 & 0 \\ 2 & 1 & 4 & 5 \\ 1 & 7 & 4 & 2 \\ 3 & -5 & 1 & 1 \end{vmatrix} = \begin{vmatrix} 3-0 & 5+0 & 1-0 & 0 \\ 2-15 & 1+25 & 4-5 & 5 \\ 1-6 & 7+10 & 4-2 & 2 \\ 3-3 & -5+5 & 1-1 & 1 \end{vmatrix}$$

$$= \begin{vmatrix} 3 & 5 & 1 & 0 \\ -13 & 26 & -1 & 5 \\ -5 & 17 & 2 & 2 \\ 0 & 0 & 0 & 1 \end{vmatrix} = \begin{vmatrix} 3 & 5 & 1 \\ -13 & 26 & -1 \\ -5 & 17 & 2 \end{vmatrix}$$

Add now the multiples of second row to the first and third rows to create zeros in the third column:

$$D = \begin{vmatrix} 3-13 & 5+26 & 1-1 \\ -13 & 26 & -1 \\ -5-26 & 17+52 & 2-2 \end{vmatrix} = \begin{vmatrix} -10 & 31 & 0 \\ -13 & 26 & -1 \\ -31 & 69 & 0 \end{vmatrix} = \begin{vmatrix} -10 & 31 \\ -31 & 69 \end{vmatrix} = 271$$

The theorem just stated proves that a D vanishes if in it the elements of a row (or column) are *proportional* to those of another row (or column). We can, indeed, create zeros in the row which is proportional to another row by subtracting from the first the elements of the second multiplied by the factor of proportionality. The determinant is not changed, but now it vanishes because all the elements of a row vanish.

The determinants have many applications. Here, we will discuss only the solution of systems of linear equations with many unknowns. Before studying this important question, we mention some applications of determinants in geometry. Thus, the area of a parallelogram formed by two vectors $\mathbf{u}(a_{11}, a_{12})$ and $\mathbf{v}(a_{21}, a_{22})$ is equal to the determinant of second order:

$$\begin{vmatrix} a_{11} & a_{12} \\ a_{21} & a_{22} \end{vmatrix}$$

provided the vector $\mathbf{v}$ standing in the second row follows $\mathbf{u}$, when the perimeter of parallelogram is described in the positive, counterclockwise direction so that the area remains to the left of $\mathbf{u}$.

In a three-dimensional space, three non-coplanar vectors $\mathbf{u}_1(a_{11},$ $a_{12}, a_{23})$, $\mathbf{u}_2(a_{21}, a_{22}, a_{23})$, and $\mathbf{u}_3(a_{31}, a_{32}, a_{33})$ define a parallele-piped, and, again, its volume is equal to the third-order determinant $\det |a_{ij}|_1^3$.

In an n-dimensional space, the measure of the part of this space interior to the hyper-parallelepiped constructed on n vectors $\mathbf{U}_j(a_{1j}, a_{2j}, \ldots, a_{nj})$, $1 \leqslant j \leqslant n$, is again expressed by the determinant of n-th order, $\det |a_{ij}|_1^n$. From this point of view, the vanishing of a determinant corresponds to zero measure of the part of space enclosed by the hyper-parallelepiped built on the n vectors defined by n rows of the determinant. Thus, for instance, if $n = 3$ the fact that $\det |a_{ij}|_1^3 = 0$ means that there is no volume and therefore no parallelepiped formed by three vectors $\mathbf{U}_1, \mathbf{U}_2, \mathbf{U}_3$. In other words, these three vectors, the components of which form a vanishing determinant, belong to one and the same plane, one of them being a linear combination of two others: $\mathbf{U}_3 = \alpha \mathbf{U}_1 + \beta \mathbf{U}_2$. Therefore, these three vectors are not independent.

Determinants are also useful when equations of geometric loci are to be formed. Thus, to determine the equation of a straight line through two given points with coordinates x_1, y_1 and x_2, y_2, it is sufficient to write

$$\begin{vmatrix} x & y & 1 \\ x_1 & y_1 & 1 \\ x_2 & y_2 & 1 \end{vmatrix} = 0$$

where x and y are running coordinates of any point on this line.

Likewise, the equation of a plane defined by three given points (x_1, y_1, z_1), (x_2, y_2, z_2) and (x_3, y_3, z_3) is simply

$$\begin{vmatrix} x & y & z & 1 \\ x_1 & y_1 & z_1 & 1 \\ x_2 & y_2 & z_2 & 1 \\ x_3 & y_3 & z_3 & 1 \end{vmatrix} = 0$$

Finally, in Chapter 7 we defined and discussed the vector-multi-plication of two vectors $\mathbf{U}(a, b, c)$ and $\mathbf{V}(r, s, t)$ in a tridimensional space. The vector- or cross-product $[\mathbf{U}, \mathbf{V}]$ is a vector, the components of which are $bt - cs$, $cr - at$ and $as - br$. We recognize in them determinants of second order. Using the unit-vectors i, j, k, we have the representation of a cross-product by a determinant of third order, namely:

$$[ai + bj + ck, ri + sj + tk] = \begin{vmatrix} i & j & k \\ a & b & c \\ r & s & t \end{vmatrix}$$

Determinants of same order can be multiplied, and the product of two determinants is a determinant of the same order. The condition of being of same order is not a limitation because it is easy to increase the order of a D by adding new rows and columns without changing its value. This is done by adding units on the principal diagonal and zeros as off-diagonal elements of new rows and columns.

EXAMPLE: A D of second order can be written as a D of fourth order as follows:

$$\begin{vmatrix} a_{11} & a_{12} \\ a_{21} & a_{22} \end{vmatrix} = \begin{vmatrix} a_{11} & a_{12} & 0 & 0 \\ a_{21} & a_{22} & 0 & 0 \\ 0 & 0 & 1 & 0 \\ 0 & 0 & 0 & 1 \end{vmatrix}$$

Rule of Multiplication

Given two D's of the n-th order, $A = \det |a_{ij}|_1^n$ and $B = \det |b_{ij}|_1^n$, the elements c_{ij} of their product $C = AB = \det |c_{ij}|_1^n$ are defined by the rule

$$c_{ij} = \sum_{k=1}^{n} a_{ik} b_{kj} \tag{7}$$

Thus, the element c_{ij} in the i-th row and j-th column of the product $C = AB$ is the scalar product of the i-th row of the first factor A and of the j-th column of the second factor B, considered as vectors in a n-dimensional space.

For instance, the first row of C is formed by multiplying the first row of A successively by all the columns of B, the product of first row of A by the j-th column of B being the j-th element in the first row of C.

We know that the rows and columns play the same role. Therefore, there are three more versions of our rule (7):

$$c'_{ij} = \sum_{k=1}^{n} a_{ik} b_{jk}; \quad c''_{ij} = \sum_{k=1}^{n} a_{ki} b_{jk}; \quad c'''_{ij} = \sum_{k=1}^{n} a_{ki} b_{jk} \tag{8}$$

They can be deduced from our rule (7) observing that the transposition of a D does not change its value, so that $\widetilde{A} = A$ and $\widetilde{B} = B$. Applying (7) to $C = A\widetilde{B} = \widetilde{A}B = \widetilde{A}\widetilde{B}$, we obtain the three versions (8). More important is the fact that the multiplication of D's is commutative, that is, $AB = BA$. To prove this point let us denote the product BA by $C^* = BA = \det |c_{ij}^*|_1^n$, where

$$c_{ij}^* = \sum_{k=1}^{n} b_{ik}a_{kj}.$$

Transposing C^*, we obtain $C^* = \widetilde{C}^* = \det |c_{ji}^*|_1^n$ with

$$c_{ji}^* = \sum_{k=1}^{n} b_{jk}a_{ki} = c_{ij}''.$$

Therefore, $BA = C^* = C = AB$.

The rule of multiplication can be deduced from the definition of D's. We show, using the example of determinants of second order, how it is done and omit the general case of n-th order determinants. In the chapter on matrices, the proof of this rule in the general case is easily obtained as a particular case of the rule of matrix multiplication.

In the case $n = 2$, the proof develops as follows:

$$C = \begin{vmatrix} c_{11} & c_{12} \\ c_{21} & c_{22} \end{vmatrix} = \begin{vmatrix} a_{11}b_{11} + a_{12}b_{21} & a_{11}b_{12} + a_{12}b_{22} \\ a_{21}b_{11} + a_{22}b_{21} & a_{21}b_{12} + a_{22}b_{22} \end{vmatrix}$$

$$= \begin{vmatrix} a_{11}b_{11} & a_{11}b_{12} \\ a_{21}b_{11} & a_{21}b_{12} \end{vmatrix} + \begin{vmatrix} a_{11}b_{11} & a_{12}b_{22} \\ a_{21}b_{11} & a_{22}b_{22} \end{vmatrix} + \begin{vmatrix} a_{12}b_{21} & a_{11}b_{12} \\ a_{22}b_{21} & a_{21}b_{12} \end{vmatrix}$$

$$+ \begin{vmatrix} a_{12}b_{21} & a_{12}b_{22} \\ a_{22}b_{21} & a_{22}b_{22} \end{vmatrix} = b_{11}b_{12} \begin{vmatrix} a_{11} & a_{11} \\ a_{21} & a_{21} \end{vmatrix} + b_{11}b_{22} \begin{vmatrix} a_{11} & a_{12} \\ a_{21} & a_{22} \end{vmatrix}$$

$$+ b_{21}b_{12} \begin{vmatrix} a_{12} & a_{11} \\ a_{22} & a_{21} \end{vmatrix} + b_{21}b_{22} \begin{vmatrix} a_{12} & a_{12} \\ a_{22} & a_{22} \end{vmatrix}$$

The determinants in the first and the last terms of the second member vanish as having two identical rows. Those in the second and third are equal to A and $-A$, respectively. Therefore,

$$C = b_{11}b_{22}A - b_{12}b_{21}A = A(b_{11}b_{22} - b_{12}b_{21}) = AB$$

EXAMPLE: Given a determinant A of order n, we consider the set of all n^2 cofactors A_{ij} of the elements a_{ij} of A. They form a determinant B of order n with the elements $b_{ij} = A_{ij}$. Multiplying the determinants $A = \det |a_{ij}|$ and $B = \det |A_{ij}|$, a third determinant $C = AB$ is formed. It is related to A, and it is natural to expect that its value C is a function of the value A of the original $\det |a_{ij}| = A$. To find this value, we compute the elements of C. A diagonal entry (the elements of a determinant very often are called *entries*) c_{kk}, when computed as c'_{ij} in (8), is equal to A by the definition of cofactors:

$$c_{kk} = \sum_{s=1}^{n} a_{ks}A_{ks} = A$$

All off-diagonal entries c_{ij} with $i \neq j$ vanish. We have, indeed, by (6):

$$c_{ij} = \sum_{s=1}^{n} a_{is}A_{js} = 0$$

We see therefore that $C' = A\widetilde{B}$ is a so-called *diagonal* determinant in which all off-diagonal entries vanish, so is also $C'' = \widetilde{A}B$. The value of such a determinant is equal to the product of its diagonal elements and, thus, $C = A^n$. Now we can find the value of B, determinant of cofactors A_{ij}. From $C = AB$, we conclude that $B = A^{n-1}$.

Up to now we did not exclude the case in which $A = 0$, but suppose from now on that A does not vanish. We can then form a determinant, the value of which is the reciprocal of A, that is, A^{-1}. The entries of such a determinant, which is also denoted by A^{-1} and is called determinant reciprocal to A, are simply ratios A_{ij}/A, that is, quotients of divisions of cofactors by the value A of the determinant A. The reader can easily verify the following numerical example:

$$\text{If } A = \begin{vmatrix} 1 & 0 & 1 \\ 3 & 2 & -3 \\ -2 & 0 & -1 \end{vmatrix} = 2, \text{ then } B = \begin{vmatrix} -2 & 9 & 4 \\ 0 & 1 & 0 \\ -2 & 6 & 2 \end{vmatrix} = 4,$$

$$C = AB = \begin{vmatrix} -4 & 15 & 6 \\ 0 & 11 & 6 \\ 6 & -24 & -10 \end{vmatrix}, \text{ while}$$

$$C' = \widetilde{A}B = \begin{vmatrix} 2 & 0 & 0 \\ 0 & 2 & 0 \\ 0 & 0 & 2 \end{vmatrix} = C'' = A\widetilde{B} \text{ and } C''' = \widetilde{A}\widetilde{B} = \begin{vmatrix} 17 & 3 & 12 \\ 17 & 2 & 12 \\ -33 & -3 & -22 \end{vmatrix}$$

All four determinants, products of A and B, have the same value, $8 = 2^3$, because here $n = 3$, $A = 2$, and $C = A^n = 2^3$. The determinant of cofactors is equal to A^{n-1} and, indeed $B = 4 = 2^2$. The diagonal products C' and C'' correspond to the multiplication of columns by columns and of rows by rows, respectively, while $C = AB$ and $C''' = \tilde{A}\tilde{B}$ correspond to multiplication of rows by columns and columns by rows. The reciprocal determinant A^{-1} is obtained by transposing the cofactors determinant B and dividing each of its entries by A. Since all rows of $\tilde{B} = A^{n-1}$ were divided by A, the determinant itself is divided by A^n, and this gives it the value $A^{n-1}/A^n = A^{-1}$. In our numerical example A^{-1} is

$$A^{-1} = \begin{vmatrix} -1 & 0 & -1 \\ 9/2 & 1/2 & 3 \\ 2 & 0 & 1 \end{vmatrix} = 1/2 \text{ and indeed, } AA^{-1} = \begin{vmatrix} 1 & 0 & 0 \\ 0 & 1 & 0 \\ 0 & 0 & 1 \end{vmatrix} = 1$$

In a vanishing determinant its minors of various orders may also vanish. It may happen that not only the determinant itself, but also *all* its minors of a certain order vanish. Then all the minors of higher orders also vanish because they contain, when expanded, the minors of this particular order. Thus, the vanishing of a determinant may have different causes. If, for instance among its minors of order $n - 1$ some minors do not vanish, then the fact that $D = 0$ cannot be ascribed to the behaviour of minors of D. But if all minors of order $n - 1$ vanish, then naturally D vanishes because all its minors of order $n - 1$ vanish. The order of a vanishing determinant does not describe the behaviour of its minors and, to characterize completely the structure of a vanishing determinant, we need another concept related to the behavior of minors. Such is the concept of *rank*:

DEFINITION: the *maximum* order of non-vanishing minors of a determinant is called the *rank* of the determinant.

Since a D can be considered as its own minor of order n, the rank of a non-vanishing determinant is equal to its order. If the rank r of a determinant of order n is less than its order, $r < n$, then not only the determinant but also all its minors of orders greater than the rank r vanish, while among its minors of order r at least one minor is different from zero. It may happen that in a D all minors of second order vanish, but some of its entries are not equal to zero. Then, the rank of such a determinant is equal to one because an entry can be considered as a minor of order one. Finally, a determinant, all the entries of which are zeros, is of the rank zero.

Systems of Linear Equations with n Unknowns

We begin with the simplest case when the number of equations is equal to the number of unknowns and, moreover, the determinant of coefficients of unknowns in the lefthand members of equations does not vanish. In such a case, there is only one solution, and this unique solution is described by the classical

CRAMER'S RULE: The system (S) of n equations

$$\sum_{j=1}^{n} a_{ij}x_j = a_{i1}x_1 + a_{i2}x_2 + \cdots + a_{in}x_n = y_i \qquad (1 \leqslant i \leqslant n) \text{ (S)}$$

with a non-vanishing determinant $D = \det |a_{ij}| \neq 0$ has as the only solution

$$x_k = (1/D)\sum_{s=1}^{n} A_{sk}y_s = (A_{1k}y_1 + \cdots + A_{nk}y_n)/D \qquad (1 \leqslant k \leqslant n) \text{ (9)}$$

In it, the symbol A_{sk} denotes, as usual, the cofactor of a_{sk} in D. The rule (9) is easy to prove using (5) and (6). Postulating the existence of n numbers x_k, $1 \leqslant k \leqslant n$, which satisfy (S), we multiply each i-th equation $(1 \leqslant i \leqslant n)$ by A_{ik} and then add them, summing up in i from 1 to n. Inverting the order of two summations and summing up first in i, we can write

$$\sum_{i=1}^{n}\sum_{j=1}^{n} A_{ik}a_{ij}x_j = \sum_{j=1}^{n} x_j \sum_{i=1}^{n} A_{ik}a_{ij} = \sum_{i=1}^{n} A_{ik}y_i$$

Observing that the summation with respect to i yields zero for all $j \neq k$, while for $j = k$ the first sum gives the value of the determinant D, we have

$$\sum_{j=1}^{n} x_j \sum_{i=1}^{n} A_{ik}a_{ij} = x_k D = \sum_{i=1}^{n} A_{ik}y_i = \sum_{s=1}^{n} A_{sk}y_s$$

which is (9). Substituting for the dummy index of summation i another letters s does not matter.

The existence of solution was postulated. Therefore, a justification is needed. To justify (9) we substitute these expressions of x_k into the equations of the system (S), and this substitution proves the existence of the solution (9) because, as we will see, the equations (S) are satisfied.

Take, for instance, the i-th equation, the integer i being, of course, any number from 1 to n:

$$\sum_{j=1}^{n} a_{ij}x_j = \sum_{j=1}^{n}\sum_{s=1}^{n} (a_{ij}/D) A_{sj}y_s = \sum_{s=1}^{n}(y_s/D) \sum_{j=1}^{n} a_{ij}A_{sj} = y_i$$

because, summing up with respect to j, zeros are obtained for all $s \neq i$, but for $s = i$ the summation in j yields the determinant D of the system (S).

It is customary to represent the values (9) of $x_1, x_2, ..., x_n$ by quotients of two determinants, the determinant D of the system being in the denominator of the fraction thus obtained. The sum $\sum_{s=1}^{n} A_{sk}y_s$ can indeed be interpreted as the expansion (5b) of a determinant D_k which differs from the determinant of the system D in its k-th column only. The determinant D_k is obtained by replacing in D the entries $a_{1k}, a_{2k}, ..., a_{nk}$ of the k-th column by the righthand members $y_1, y_2, ..., y_n$ of equations (S):

$$D_k = \begin{vmatrix} a_{11} \cdots a_{1,k-1} & y_1 & a_{1,k+1} \cdots a_{1n} \\ a_{21} \cdots a_{2,k-1} & y_2 & a_{2,k+1} \cdots a_{2n} \\ \cdots\cdots\cdots\cdots & & \cdots\cdots\cdots\cdots \\ \cdots\cdots\cdots\cdots & & \cdots\cdots\cdots\cdots \\ a_{n1} \cdots a_{n,k-1} & y_n & a_{n,k+1} \cdots a_{nn} \end{vmatrix}.$$

Thus, the solution (9) now becomes

$$x_1 = D_1/D, \ x_2 = D_2/D, \ ..., \ x_n = D_n/D \tag{10}$$

EXAMPLE: Find the solution of the system (S_3):

$$x + y + 3z = 6; \quad 3x - 2y - z = 3; \quad 7x - 3y + 4z = 18 \tag{S_3}$$

Computing the four determinants D, D_x, D_y, D_z, we find:

$$D = -15; \quad D_x = -15; \quad D_y = 15; \quad D_z = -30$$

Therefore,

$$x = D_x/D = 1, \ y = D_y/D = -1, \text{ and } z = D_z/D = 2$$

COROLLARY: A system of linear equations in which the constant terms y_i all vanish is called *homogeneous* because a linear equation is homogeneous in x_k if its constant term is equal to zero. If the determinant D of coefficients of a homogeneous system of n equations with n unknowns is different from zero, $D \neq 0$ then, applying Cramer's Rule, we conclude that the only solution of such a system is the so-called *trivial* solution, $x_1 = x_2 = x_3 = \cdots = x_n = 0$: the homogeneous equations obviously are satisfied when all the unknowns vanish, and there is no other possibility. But, if the determinant of a homogeneous system vanishes, then—as we will see below—there are other, nontrivial, solutions of the system.

Elimination Method

This method of solution consists in the gradual reduction of the number of equations and unknowns by forming equivalent systems. It is based on the fact that any new equation obtained as a linear combination of equations of (S) is also satisfied by the solution of (S). It is therefore possible to replace any equation in (S) by such a linear combination. We illustrate the application of this method on our previous numerical example.

Multiplying the first equation, $x + y + 3z = 6$, by -3 and adding to the second equation, we form a new equation, $5y + 10z = 15$. It does not contain x, and, dividing by 5, we write it as $y + 2z = 3$. Likewise, adding to the third equation the first multiplied by -7, a second equation without x is obtained. The new system thus obtained:

$$y + 2z = 3; \quad 10y + 17z = 24$$

is equivalent to (S$_3$) and the number of unknowns and equations is reduced by one. Solving it by Cramer's Rule, we obtain

$$y = \begin{vmatrix} 3 & 2 \\ 24 & 17 \end{vmatrix} : \begin{vmatrix} 1 & 2 \\ 10 & 17 \end{vmatrix} = 3 : (-3) = -1$$

$$\text{and } z = \begin{vmatrix} 1 & 3 \\ 10 & 24 \end{vmatrix} : \begin{vmatrix} 1 & 2 \\ 10 & 17 \end{vmatrix} = (-6) : (-3) = 2$$

The third unknown x is now given by the first equation of (S):

$$x = 6 - y - 3z = 6 + 1 - 6 = 1.$$

The two methods just studied are impractical when the number of equations is large. The solutions of large systems are computed, in general, by successive approximations. There are several iterative methods based on the idea of successive approximations. In all of them, beginning with an *arbitrary* set $[x_k^{(0)}]$ of initial values for the set of unknowns $[x_k]$, a sequence of sets $[x_k^{(1)}), [x_k^{(2)}], \ldots, [x_k^{(n)}], \ldots$ is formed such that, although none of them satisfies the equations, the n-th approximation $[x_k^{(n)}]$ tends, for $n \to \infty$, to the solution $[x_k]$.

These various methods differ in the definition of iteration rule which is applied in computing the next, better approximation $[x_k^{(r+1)}]$ from the known (because already computed) previous approximation $[x_k^{(r)}]$.

As an example of successive approximations, we define and describe the so-called Gauss–Seidel Iteration often used in programming for electronic computers the solution of a large system of linear equations. Let us suppose that the values $x_1^{(r)}, x_2^{(r)}, \ldots, x_n^{(r)}$ which form the set of r-th approximations were already computed and we want to compute the $(r + 1)$-th approximation $[x_k^{(r+1)}]$, using the known set $[x_k^{(r)}]$. In the Gauss–Seidel method, the system

$$a_{i1}x_1 + a_{i2}x_2 + a_{i3}x_3 + \cdots + a_{in}x_n = y_i \quad (1 \leqslant i \leqslant n) \quad \text{(S)}$$

s rewritten as system (S*):

$$a_{i1}x_1^{(r+1)} + \cdots + a_{ii}x_i^{(r+1)} + a_{i,i+1}x_{i+1}^{(r)} + \cdots + a_{in}x_n^{(r)} = y_i \quad (1 \leqslant i \leqslant n)$$
$$\text{(S*)}$$

so that the first equation contains one unknown $x_1^{(r+1)}$ only, the second—two unknowns, the third—three unknowns, *etc.* In the i-th equation first i variables $x_1, x_2, \ldots, x_i$ are replaced by their $(r + 1)$-th *unknown* approximations, while the remaining variables beginning with x_{i+1} are replaced by *known*, already computed r-th approximations $x_k^{(r)}$, with $i + 1 \leqslant k \leqslant n$. The solution of the new system (S*) is easy: its equations are solved one after another in the same order in which they are written, and at each step there is one unknown only in each equation. Thus, when we come to the i-th equation which involves $x_1^{(r+1)}, x_2^{(r+1)}, \ldots, x_{i-1}^{(r+1)}, x_i^{(r+1)}$, the first $i - 1$ numbers are already known because the first $i - 1$ equations were already solved, and, therefore, we have to compute $x_i^{(r+1)}$ only from the equation

$$a_{ii}x_i^{(r+1)} = y_i - a_{i1}x_1^{(r+1)} - \cdots - a_{i,i-1}x_{i-1}^{(r+1)} - a_{i,i+1}x_{i+1}^{(r)} - \cdots - a_{in}x_n^{(r)}$$

In practical applications such iteration methods raise many specific questions relative to the accumulation of rounding off errors, the speed of convergence of successive approximations towards the exact solution, etc. We do not intend to continue their study since they belong to applied mathematics and numerical analysis.

We saw that the important condition $D = \det |a_{ij}| \neq 0$ insures the existence of a unique solution of a linear system with as many equations as there are unknowns. Very often we have to deal with systems for which this condition is not satisfied. If $D = 0$, a system may have no solution at all because its equations are incompatible and create contradictions. Take, for instance, the system

$$5x + 10y + 5z = 15; \quad 3x + y - z = 2; \quad 2x + 9y + 6z = 18 \quad (11)$$

the determinant of which vanishes. Adding the second and the third equations and subtracting the first one, an impossible corollary of this system $0 = 5$ is obtained. Thus, no set of three numbers x, y, z can be found which could satisfy the system (11).

Another complication which may arise when $D = 0$ consists in the existence of an *infinite* number of solutions, so that in the absence of an extraneous supplementary condition it is impossible to fix the choice of a perfectly determined particular solution. Suppose, to take an example, that a point is asked such that its three coordinates x, y, z satisfy the system

$$3x + 2y + z = 4; \quad 9x + y - z = 2; \quad 2x + 3y + 2z = 6 \quad (12)$$

In geometrical language, the unknown point is defined as the intersection point of three planes, the equations of which are given by the above system (12). Let us try to find its coordinates by the elimination method. Cramer's Rule cannot be used because $D = 0$ and the division by zero has no meaning. From the second equation, we have $z = 9x + y - 2$, which transforms the first equation into $y = 2 - 4x$. Now, $z = 9x + 2 - 4x - 2 = 5x$. To find x, we substitute $y = 2 - 4x$ and $z = 5x$ in the third equation. The result is $0 = 0$. The method breaks down because the system (12) consists in reality of only two "true" equations and the number of unknowns is three. Indeed, the first equation is a linear combination of two others; multiplying the third equation by 3 and then adding to it the second one, $15x + 10y + 5z = 20$ is obtained, and, after the division by 5, this gives the first equation. The first plane contains the intersection line of the second and third planes, or, better, the three planes (12) pass through the same straight line. Therefore, all the points of this straight line answer the question, and, since every one of them represents a solution of (12), there are an infinite number of solutions. Since there are only two independent equations, all that can be done to find the solutions of the system (12) is to consider one of three coordinates, x for instance, as an indeterminate and variable parameter and to solve the two equations for two other unknowns. The result, $y = 2 - 4x$ and $z = 5x$, proves that to each choice of a numerical value for x corresponds a solution of the system (12). Thus, for instance, the point $x = 1, y = -2$, $z = 5$ is a solution and it is on the straight line which represents the infinite totality of points (x, y, z) satisfying the conditions (12). The solution $y = 2 - 4x$, $z = 5x$ indeed describes this same line and represents the equations of the line as defined now by the intersection of the plane $y = 2 - 4x$, which is parallel to the z-axis, with the plane $z = 5x$ parallel to y-axis.

The two examples just discussed prove that it is necessary to explore the meaning of the condition $D \neq 0$ in the general case of the system (S). Let us consider $x_1, x_2, \ldots, x_n$ as n independent *variables*. The lefthand members of (S) are n linear expressions in these variables with constant coefficients a_{ij} ($1 \leqslant i, j \leqslant n$). Denoting them by f_i

$$f_i = \sum_{j=1}^{n} a_{ij}x_j = a_{i1}x_1 + a_{i2}x_2 + \cdots + a_{in}x_n \qquad (1 \leqslant i \leqslant n) \ (13)$$

we will call them *forms*, an abbreviation for linear forms in variables x_k.

Multiplying them by constant factors c_k and then adding the products, we can build linear combinations of forms $f_1, f_2, \ldots, f_n$ of the type

$$\sum_{k=1}^{n} c_k f_k = c_1 f_1 + c_2 f_2 + c_3 f_3 + \cdots + c_n f_n \qquad (14)$$

which are also linear forms in x_k but are dependent on $f_1, f_2, \ldots, f_n$.

DEFINITION: If it is possible to find n such constant and not all vanishing real factors c_k with

$$\sum_{k=1}^{n} c_k^2 = c_1^2 + c_2^2 + c_3^2 + \cdots + c_n^2 > 0 \qquad (15)$$

that the form (14) vanishes identically, that is,

$$\sum_{k=1}^{n} c_k f_k = c_1 f_1 + c_2 f_2 + c_3 f_3 + \cdots + c_n f_n \equiv 0 \qquad (16)$$

for *all* values of n independent variables $x_1, x_2, \ldots, x_n$, then the n forms $f_1, f_2, \ldots, f_n$ are, by *definition*, not independent.

In this case, at least one of them is a linear combination of other forms. Indeed, by (15) it is clear that at least one of n real constants c_k is different from zero. Let it be c_r. Then we conclude from (16) that

$$f_r = - \sum_{k=1, \neq r}^{n*} (c_k/c_r) f_k \qquad (k \neq r) \ (17)$$

so that f_r is a linear combination of other forms. Now the condition $D \neq 0$ expresses precisely the fact that the n forms (13) are independent. In other words, if $D \neq 0$, no such n constants c_k with

$$c_1^2 + c_2^2 + c_3^2 + \cdots + c_n^2 > 0$$

can be found that the identity (16) holds. We now formulate the following

THEOREM: *det $|a_{ij}| \neq 0$ is a sufficient and necessary condition of independence of n forms $f_1, f_2, f_3, \ldots, f_n$ defined by* (13).

To prove that this condition is necessary, we suppose that the forms are not independent, so that the identity (16) holds together with (15). The independent variables x_k can take any values. We will give the value one to one of them and zero values to other $n - 1$ variables. This can be done in n different ways giving the value one first to x_1, then to x_2, and so on, up to $x_n = 1$. The forms f_k have the values a_{km} when it is x_m which takes the value *one* while the other variables vanish. Because the forms by hypothesis are not independent, the identity (17) holds, and it reduces now to n relations:

$$a_{rm} = - \sum_{k=1}^{n*} (c_k/c_r) a_{km} \qquad (m = 1, 2, \ldots, n; k \neq r) \ (18)$$

where in Σ^* the index k does not take the value $k = r$. This result shows that all the entries a_{rm}, $1 \leqslant m \leqslant n$, of the r-th row in the determinant D are linear combinations of corresponding entries of $n - 1$ other rows. Therefore, adding to the r-th row the multiple c_1/c_r of the first row, then c_2/c_r times the second row, and so on, up to c_n/c_r times the last row, we make vanish all the entries of the r-th row without affecting the value of D. Now we see that $D = 0$, for it has a vanishing row. Thus, $D = 0$ is the corollary of our hypothesis that the forms (13) are not independent, and this proves the necessity of the condition $D \neq 0$ for the independence of forms (13).

Assume now that $D = \det |a_{ij}| \neq 0$ and that (15) and (16) hold true, so that the forms f_k are not independent. Substituting their expressions (13) in the identity (16), we rewrite it explicitly as follows:

$$\sum_{i=1}^{n} c_i f_i = \sum_{i=1}^{n} \sum_{j=1}^{n} c_i a_{ij} x_j = \sum_{j=1}^{n} x_j \sum_{i=1}^{n} c_i a_{ij} \equiv 0 \qquad (19)$$

The identity (19) holds for *all* values of variables x_k. We apply it to n cases already considered, when one variable only takes a non-vanishing value, say, $x_j = 1$, while all other $n - 1$ variables vanish. Thus, taking successively $x_1 = 1$, $x_2 = 1$, ..., $x_n = 1$, we obtain from (19) a system of n homogeneous equations with n unknowns $c_1, c_2, c_3, ..., c_n$:

$$\sum_{i=1}^{n} c_i a_{ij} = c_1 a_{1j} + c_2 a_{2j} + \cdots + c_n a_{nj} = 0 \qquad (1 \leqslant j \leqslant n) \ (20)$$

By assumption, this system has a non-vanishing determinant, and we solve it by Cramer's rule. The solution is given by (10):

$$c_1 = D_1/D, \ c_2 = D_2/D, \ ..., \ c_n = D_n/D$$

But in our case, all the numerators D_k, $1 \leqslant k \leqslant n$, vanish because zeros in the righthand members of the homogeneous system (20) fill up a column in every one of n determinants D_k. Thus, the trivial solution $c_1 = c_2 = \cdots = c_n = 0$ is obtained, and this contradicts the assumption that (15) holds true. The incompatibility of the condition $D \neq 0$ with (15) and (16) proves that $D \neq 0$ is a sufficient condition of the independence of forms (13).

COROLLARY: We can now prove that in a vanishing determinant the columns (and also the rows) are not independent. Assume that $D = \det |a_{ij}| = 0$. Then, the forms (13) are not independent and (17) holds. But we know that (17) contains (18) as its particular case and (18) proves that at least one column (row) of $D = 0$ is a linear combination of other $n - 1$ columns (rows).

Consider now a vanishing determinant $D = 0$, the rank r of which is less than $n - 1$ so that not only $D = 0$, but also all its minors of orders greater than r vanish, while at least one of minors of order r is not zero. The r columns (rows) of this non-vanishing minor M are independent, for otherwise this minor would vanish. This fact proves that the corresponding r columns (rows) of D itself are also independent. Otherwise, all n entries of at least one column (row) among them should be linear combinations of entries of others and then the r entries of the same column (row) in M would be linear combinations also and this is impossible since $M \neq 0$. Therefore, in a vanishing determinant, the number of independent columns or rows is at least equal to the rank of the determinant. We prove now that it cannot be greater than the rank.

In $D = 0$, there is at least one column which is a linear combination of other columns. Striking out this column and one of rows, we obtain a minor of order $n - 1$. This minor also vanishes. So we repeat the procedure and strike out the column which is not independent together with a row, obtaining a minor of order $n - 2$. It vanishes again provided $r < n - 2$. Continuing this procedure as long as the order of remaining minors exceeds r, we can strike out $n - r$ dependent columns because there are $n - r$ orders greater than r: $n, n - 1, ...,$ $r + 2, r + 1$. Therefore, there are at least $n - r$ dependent columns, and it is clear that the number of independent columns cannot exceed r. Thus, *in a vanishing determinant the number of independent columns or rows is equal to its rank.*

General Case

We discussed systems with as many independent equations as unknowns; in general, however, the number m of equations is not equal to the number n of unknowns, and the coefficients a_{ij} form a rectangular table or *matrix* with m rows and n columns:

$$\begin{pmatrix} a_{11} & a_{12} & \cdots & a_{1n} \\ a_{21} & a_{22} & \cdots & a_{2n} \\ \multicolumn{4}{c}{\dotfill} \\ a_{m1} & a_{m2} & \cdots & a_{mn} \end{pmatrix}, \tag{21}$$

the system of m equations being the system (S):

$$f_i = \sum_{j=1}^{n} a_{ij} x_j = b_i \qquad (i = 1, 2, ... m - 1, m) \text{ (S)}$$

Denote by p the smaller of two integers m and n: $p = m$, if $m < n$ and $p = n$, if $m > n$. With the rows and columns of the matrix (21) various determinants of order p can be formed. If at least one of them does not vanish, the rank r of the matrix (21) is equal to p, but it may happen that the maximum order of their non-vanishing minors is less than p. Then, by definition, the rank of the matrix (21) is equal to this maximum order r. Naturally, $r \leqslant m$ and $r \leqslant n$.

Given a system (S) with a matrix (21) of rank r, we can always bring the non-vanishing minor or order r into the left upper corner of the matrix by renumbering the unknowns and rearranging the order of equations in (S). This determinant, $D = \det |a_{ij}|_1^r \neq 0$, formed by the first r rows and the first r columns of the matrix (21), is called the *principal* determinant of the system (S), and the first r equations in (S), with $1 \leqslant i \leqslant r$, are *principal* equations of (S).

Characteristic Determinants of (S)

In the example of the system (11) given on page 446, we saw that the equations of a system may be incompatible. If the rank of a system is equal to the number of its equations, $r = m$, which means that all m equations are independent equations, the question of compatibility does not arise and the system has solutions. But, if $r < m$, then it is important to know a criterion of compatibility and to apply this criterion before looking for a solution. Such a criterion is supplied by the so-called characteristic determinants of the system: *If all $m - r$ characteristic determinants of a system of rank r vanish, then the m equations of the system are compatible, and the problem of solving them has a meaning.*

Before proving this statement, we have to define and describe the determinants in question. The equations (S) were divided in two groups: first r equations, called principal equations, and the remaining $m - r$ equations:

$$f_{r+s} = \sum_{j=1}^{n} a_{r+s,j} x_j = b_{r+s} \qquad (s = 1, 2, \ldots, m - r) \quad (22)$$

To each of these equations (22), that is, to each value of $s = 1, 2, \ldots, m - r$, corresponds a characteristic determinant D_s of order $r + 1$. It is formed by adding to the principal determinant

$$D = \begin{vmatrix} a_{11} & a_{12} & \cdots & a_{1r} \\ a_{21} & a_{22} & \cdots & a_{2r} \\ \cdots\cdots\cdots\cdots\cdots \\ a_{r1} & a_{r2} & \cdots & a_{rr} \end{vmatrix}$$

the $(r + 1)$-th row and the $(r + 1)$-th column. The $r + 1$ entries of the new row are the first r coefficients and the constant term b_{r+s} of the equation considered, while the r entries of the new column above b_{r+s} are the constant terms $b_1, b_2, ..., b_r$ of principal equations:

$$D_s = \begin{vmatrix} & & & b_1 \\ & D & & \vdots \\ & & & b_r \\ \hline a_{r+s,1} & \cdots & a_{r+s,r} & b_{r+s} \end{vmatrix} \quad (s = 1, 2, ..., m - r)$$

To prove the criterion of compatibility, we have to consider another set of $m - r$ determinants of order $r + 1$ related to (S) which will be denoted by $\varDelta_s$ with $1 \leqslant s \leqslant m - r$. For each value of s, the determinant $\varDelta_s$ is obtained by replacing in D_s the last column $b_1, b_2, ..., b_r, b_{r+s}$ by the linear forms $f_1, f_2, ..., f_r, f_{r+s}$, which stand in the lefthand members of principal equations and of the s-th equation (22):

$$\varDelta_s = \begin{vmatrix} & & & f_1 \\ & D & & \vdots \\ & & & f_r \\ \hline a_{r+s,1} & \cdots & a_{r+s,r} & f_{r+s} \end{vmatrix}$$

It is not difficult to find out that all $m - r$ determinants $\varDelta_s$ vanish. In a $\varDelta_s$, the entries of the last column are sums of n terms since

$$f_k = \sum_{j=1}^{n} a_{kj} x_j.$$

Therefore, $\varDelta_s$ itself is also a sum of n determinants which differ in their last columns only. Each one of them has in its last column a common factor x_j with $1 \leqslant j \leqslant n$. Picking out these common factors, we have

$$\varDelta_s = \sum_{j=1}^{n} d_{sj} x_j \text{ with } d_{sj} = \begin{vmatrix} & & & a_{1j} \\ & D & & \cdot \\ & & & a_{rj} \\ \hline a_{r+s,1} & \cdots & a_{r+s,r} & a_{r+s,j} \end{vmatrix}$$

If $j \leqslant r$, then $d_{sj} = 0$ because it has two identical columns. If $j > r$, than again $d_{sj} = 0$ as a minor of order greater than the rank r of the matrix (21).

Therefore, subtracting $\varDelta_s$ from D_s does not change D_s. This subtraction is performed by substracting the last column of $\varDelta_s$ from that of D_s because their first r columns are identical.

Now we rewrite D_s as $D_s - \Delta_s$:

$$D_s = \begin{vmatrix} & D & & b_1 - f_1 \\ & & & \cdots\cdots \\ & & & \cdots\cdots \\ & & & b_r - f_r \\ a_{r+s,1} & \cdots & a_{r+s,r} & b_{r+s} - f_{r+s} \end{vmatrix}$$

Expanding D_s along the elements of its last column, we arrive at important relations between the equations (22) and characteristic determinants of (S):

$$D_s = \sum_{k=1}^{r} c_{sk}(b_k - f_k) + D(b_{r+s} - f_{r+s}), \quad (s = 1, 2, \ldots, m - r) \quad (23)$$

where c_{sk} are cofactors of the first r entries of the last column.

We emphasize the fact that D_s are *numbers* which do not depend on variables x_k, although they seem to involve these variables through f_k.

Assume now that the equations of (S) are compatible so that there is a solution $x_j = \alpha_j$ with $1 \leqslant j \leqslant n$. Substituting into (S) the set of n numbers α_j instead of x_j makes the m differences $b_k - f_k$ vanish simultaneously. The relations (23) show then that all determinants D_s of a system (S), the equations of which are compatible, vanish. Thus, the criterion is a necessary one.

To prove that it is also sufficient, assume that all D_s vanish. We will prove that the equations of (S) are compatible by constructing a solution of the system (S) with vanishing characteristic determinants D_s.

Since the determinant D of the subsystem formed by r principal equations does not vanish, we can solve this subsystem for the first r unknowns, $x_1, x_2, \ldots, x_r$ applying Cramer's Rule. Rewriting the principal equations as

$$f_k = \sum_{j=1}^{r} a_{kj}x_j = b_k^* \text{ with } b_k^* = b_k - \sum_{j=r+1}^{n} a_{kj}x_j, \quad (1 \leqslant k \leqslant r) \quad (24)$$

we consider $n - r$ variables x_j with $r + 1 \leqslant j \leqslant n$, as parameters. These parameters are free to vary, and the solutions of the principal equations (24)

$$x_k = a_k + \sum_{s=1}^{n-r} \beta_{sk}x_{r+s} \quad (1 \leqslant k \leqslant r) \quad (25)$$

are linear functions of $n - r$ parameters x_{r+s}, $1 \leqslant s \leqslant n - r$. Fixing their values, we obtain a particular solution of (24) and the number of solutions is illimited. In other words, the system (24) has an infinite number of solutions if $r < n$. Such is always the case when the number r of independent equations is less than the number n of unknowns. The number m of equations is involved only in the *existence* of solutions: if $r = m$, the system consists of independent equations only, and there are no characteristic determinants, all the equations being principal equations. But, if $r < m$, the criterion of compatibility must be satisfied, otherwise there are no solutions at all.

It remains to prove that the criterion $D_s = 0$, with $1 \leqslant s \leqslant m - r$ is a sufficient condition of compatibility. Giving fixed values to parameters x_{r+s}, we construct a solution of r principal equations for which the differences $b_k - f_k$ vanish for $k = 1, 2, \ldots, r$. But, if $D_s = 0$, then the relations (23) prove that the equations (22) are satisfied since

$$f_{r+s} = b_{r+s} + (1/D) \sum_{k=1}^{r} c_{sk}(b_k - f_k) = b_{r+s} \qquad (1 \leqslant s \leqslant m - r)$$

Thus, if the criterion of compatibility is satisfied and if the r principal equations are solved, then their solution satisfies also $m - r$ equations of the second group (22). Thus, any solution of the principal equations is a solution of the system (S), and this proves the compatibility of all equations in (S).

We note that a system of m equations with n unknowns has a unique perfectly determined solution if $r = n < m$ and $D_s = 0$ for $1 \leqslant s \leqslant m - r$.

EXAMPLES: 1) The system of five equations with three unknowns

$$-x + 3y + 2z = 1; \quad 2x + y - 4z = 3; \quad x + 4y - 2z = 4$$
$$5x + 6y - 10z = 10; \quad 7x + 7y - 14z = 13 \qquad (S_1)$$

has a matrix of coefficient

$$A = \begin{pmatrix} -1 & 3 & 2 \\ 2 & 1 & -4 \\ 1 & 4 & -2 \\ 5 & 6 & -10 \\ 7 & 7 & -14 \end{pmatrix}$$

the rank of which is equal to two: all six determinants of third order it contains vanish, but the principal minor of order two, namely, $D = \begin{vmatrix} -1 & 3 \\ 2 & 1 \end{vmatrix} = -7$, does not vanish. There are three $(m - r = 3)$

characteristic determinants of third order ($r + 1 = 3$):

$$D_1 = \begin{vmatrix} -1 & 3 & 1 \\ 2 & 1 & 3 \\ 1 & 4 & 4 \end{vmatrix} = 0; \quad D_2 = \begin{vmatrix} -1 & 3 & 1 \\ 2 & 1 & 3 \\ 5 & 6 & 10 \end{vmatrix} = 0; \quad D_3 = \begin{vmatrix} -1 & 3 & 1 \\ 2 & 1 & 3 \\ 7 & 7 & 13 \end{vmatrix} = 0$$

All of them vanish, and to solve the principal equations, we rewrite them in the form (24)

$$-x + 3y = 1 - 2z; \quad 2x + y = 3 + 4z$$

For this system,

$$D = -7, \quad D_x = \begin{vmatrix} 1 - 2z & 3 \\ 3 + 4z & 1 \end{vmatrix} = -14z - 8, \quad D_y = \begin{vmatrix} -1 & 1 - 2z \\ 2 & 3 + 4z \end{vmatrix} = -5$$

so that

$$x = D_x/D = 2z + 8/7 \quad \text{and} \quad y = D_y/D = 5/7.$$

This solution represents all the points on a straight line in the plane $y = 5/7$ which passes through the point $x_0 = 8/7$, $y_0 = 5/7$, $z_0 = 0$ and has a slope equal to 2 with respect to the z-axis in this plane. It is easy to check that this solution also satisfies the last three equations of the system (S_1).

2) Consider also a *homogeneous* system (S_2) of three equations with five unknowns s, t, u, v, w:

$$-s + 2t + u + 5v + 7w = 0; \quad 3s + t + 4u + 6v + 7w = 0 \quad (S_2)$$

$$2s - 4t - 2u - 10v - 14w = 0$$

It is related to the system (S_1) of the first example for the matrix $\tilde{A}$ of its coefficients

$$\tilde{A} = \begin{pmatrix} -1 & 2 & 1 & 5 & 7 \\ 3 & 1 & 4 & 6 & 7 \\ 2 & -4 & -2 & -10 & -14 \end{pmatrix}$$

is simply the *transposed* matrix A of the system (S_1): the rows and columns of A became columns and rows in the transposed matrix $\tilde{A}$. The homogeneous system (S_2) is called *adjoint* to the system (S_1). Its equations are compatible: in homogeneous equations the righthand terms are zeros, and, therefore, characteristic determinants vanish. The rank of $\tilde{A}$ is equal to two because a transposition does not change the rank of a matrix. Solving (S_2) with respect to two unknowns s and t, we obtain $s = -u - v - w$ and $t = -u - 3v - 4w$, the number of parameters being equal to $n - r = 5 - 2 = 3$, as it should.

Here we introduce a new concept, namely, the concept of *independent* or *fundamental* solution of a homogeneous system. Particular solutions are obtained giving fixed values to parameters. If a particular solution was obtained by giving a non-vanishing value to only one parameter and zero values to all other parameters, it is, by definition, a fundamental solution. Thus, in our case, we can construct three fundamental solutions: the first one, $s = 1$ and $t = 1$, corresponds to $u = -1$ and $v = w = 0$; the second, $s = 1$ and $t = 3$, is obtained for $u = w = 0$ and $v = -1$; finally, to construct the third fundamental solution, we take $u = v = 0$ and $w = -1$ and obtain $s = 1$ and $t = 4$.

The fact that (S_2) is a homogeneous system entails the possibility of so-called superposition of particular solutions: any linear combination of particular solutions is, *eo ipso*, also a solution of the system. Such a solution is not an independent solution because it depends on solutions of which it is a linear combination. But fundamental solutions, once they are constructed, are independent, and any other solution can be expressed as a linear combination of these independent solutions. In our example, each one of them is a set of five numbers: $\sigma_1 = (1, 1, -1, 0, 0)$; $\sigma_2 = (1, 3, 0, -1, 0)$; and $\sigma_3 = (1, 4, 0, 0, -1)$, in the order s, t, u, v, w. Using geometrical language, we can call them vectors of a five-dimensional space. Such vectors have five components s, t, u, v, w along five coordinate axes. Any other particular solution $\sigma = (\alpha + \beta + \gamma, \ \alpha + 3\beta + 4\gamma, \ -\alpha, \ -\beta, \ -\gamma)$, obtained giving to u, v, w the fixed values $-\alpha, -\beta, -\gamma$, is, indeed, the linear combination $\sigma = \alpha\sigma_1 + \beta\sigma_2 + \gamma\sigma_3$ of three fundamental solutions $\sigma_1, \sigma_2, \sigma_3$.

Now, after having formed these three fundamental solutions of (S_2), we have right to expect that they should be related in some way to the system (S_1) because the system (S_2) is adjoint to (S_1). There is, indeed, a relation between them and the righthand members of (S_1). These last five numbers can also be considered as five components of a vector **B** $(1, 3, 4, 10, 13)$ and the relation between the vector **B** and three vectors $\sigma_1, \sigma_2, \sigma_3$ can best be described in geometrical language as follows: *the vector* **B** *is perpendicular to three vectors* $\sigma_1, \sigma_2, \sigma_3$. We defined in Chapter 6 the concept of scalar product of two vectors in three-dimensional space. We also saw that this scalar product is related to the angle formed by two vectors, factors of the scalar product. Indeed, the value of a scalar product was shown to be equal to the product of the lengths of two vector factors times the cosine of their angle. We now generalize these definitions and relations to n-dimensional space in which each vector has n components. Given two such n-dimensional vectors $\mathbf{A}(a_1, a_2, \ldots, a_n)$ and $\mathbf{B}(b_1, b_2, \ldots, b_n)$, their scalar product $(\mathbf{A}, \mathbf{B})$ is, by definition, equal to the sum of all n products $a_k b_k$, $1 \leqslant k \leqslant n$, of their corresponding components:

$$(\mathbf{A}, \mathbf{B}) = \sum_{k=1}^{n} a_k b_k = a_1 b_1 + a_2 b_2 + a_3 b_3 + \cdots + a_n b_n.$$

It can be shown that this product is related to the cosine of the angle of two vectors $\mathbf{A}$ and $\mathbf{B}$ in the same way as in a three-dimensional case, and we accept this fact omitting the proof. It follows that the scalar product vanishes if two vectors are perpendicular, for the cosine of a right angle is equal to zero, and *vice versa*: if the scalar product of two vectors is zero, then the vectors are perpendicular.

Applying these generalities to our example, we compute the scalar products the vector $\mathbf{B}$ forms with each one of three vectors $\sigma_1, \sigma_2, \sigma_3$:

$$(\mathbf{B}, \sigma_1) = b_1 + b_2 - b_3 = 1 + 3 - 4 = 0$$
$$(\mathbf{B}, \sigma_2) = b_1 + 3b_2 - b_4 = 1 + 9 - 10 = 0$$
$$(\mathbf{B}, \sigma_3) = b_1 + 4b_2 - b_5 = 1 + 12 - 13 = 0.$$

The relation just described between the righthand members of the system (S_1) and the fundamental solutions of its adjoint homogeneous system is a general one. As it will be proved below, it is completely equivalent to the criterion of compatibility.

Homogeneous Systems

We know that a system of n homogeneous equations with n unknowns has only the trivial solution (when all the unknowns vanish), if the rank of the matrix of coefficients is equal to n, all the equations of the system being, in this case, independent equations. The geometrical interpretation of this fact is worth studying. We begin with the cases $m = n = r = 2$ or 3. In the first case, we have two unknowns, x and y, which we interpret as two components of a vector $\mathbf{V}$ in a *plane*. The coefficients a_{ij} in the system $a_{11}x + a_{12}y = 0$ and $a_{21}x + a_{22}y = 0$

admit the same interpretation, and we consider two known vectors $V_I = (a_{11}, a_{12})$ and $V_{II} = (a_{21}, a_{22})$. The rank of the system is two and $D = a_{11}a_{22} - a_{12}a_{21} \neq 0$. This condition insures the independence of two vectors V_I and V_{II}. From it, we deduce indeed that $a_{12}/a_{11} \neq a_{22}/a_{21}$ so that their slopes are unequal and, thus neither can be proportional to the other.

Now the system

$$a_{11}x + a_{12}y = 0, \quad a_{21}x + a_{22}y = 0$$

means that the scalar products (V, V_I) and (V, V_{II}) vanish. This means that in trying to solve the system in question we are looking for a vector $V(x, y)$ which belongs to the same plane as V_I and V_{II} and at the same time is perpendicular to both vectors V_I and V_{II}. Clearly such a vector cannot be found because V_I and V_{II} are not parallel. The trivial solution $x = y = 0$ is an algebraic counterpart of this geometric impossibility. We need indeed a third dimension to find a vector perpendicular to two vectors which define a plane.

The same situation is encountered in space when we try to solve three homogeneous equations:

$$a_{11}x + a_{12}y + a_{13}z = 0; \quad a_{21}x + a_{22}y + a_{23}z = 0;$$

$$a_{31}x + a_{32}y + a_{33}z = 0$$

with a determinant $D \neq 0$. Here we have three known vectors $V_1(a_{11}, a_{12}, a_{13})$, $V_2(a_{21}, a_{22}, a_{23})$, $V_3(a_{31}, a_{32}, a_{33})$ and a unknown vector $V(x, y, z)$ which belongs to the same space as the three vectors V_k, $1 \leqslant k \leqslant 3$. The condition $D \neq 0$ expresses the fact that these three known vectors are not coplanar: neither of them is a linear combination of two others. They are independent, and the set of all their linear combinations $\alpha V_1 + \beta V_2 + \gamma V_3$ spans whole the space when α, β, γ vary. Thus, interpreting the equations of the system as vanishing scalar products:

$$(V, V_1) = (V, V_2) = (V, V_3) = 0$$

we meet the same impossibility: no vector perpendicular to three independent vectors of a three-dimensional space can be found *inside* this space. The trivial solution $x = y = z = 0$ says it in algebraical language.

In the general case of a system of m $(m > 3)$ homogeneous linear equations, our geometrical intuition cannot help. Based on the sensual perception of physical environment as a space of three dimensions only, our imagination cannot picture the spatial relationship between vectors with more than three components. But algebra does not know such limitations, and we saw that the properties of solutions of linear systems do not depend on the number of unknowns. It is customary to paraphrase the result of study of systems with n unknowns in geometrical language, and so we will speak about vectors of an m-dimensional space though we cannot "see" them. In the last volume we will have to study some properties of four-dimensional figures and we will see that the geometry of four-dimensional space is as natural a generalization of solid geometry as the last is of plane geometry. In the sequel we will denote an m-dimensional space by S_m.

In an S_m the system of orthogonal Cartesian coordinates is formed by m pairwise perpendicular axes. Projecting a vector located in S_m on these axes, its m components are obtained exactly as for a vector in a S_3. Now let $n > m$ and consider in S_m a set of n vectors $V_k = (a_{1k}, a_{2k}, \ldots, a_{mk})$, $1 \leqslant k \leqslant n$, where a_{ij} denotes the i-th component of the j-th vector V_j.

The vectors V_k are said to be linearly dependent if n real constants c_k can be found such that, firstly, not all of them vanish,

$$\sum_1^n c_1^2 + c_2^2 + \cdots + c_n^2 > 0$$

and, secondly,

$$\sum_{k=1}^{k=n} c_k V_k = c_1 V_1 + c_2 V_2 + \cdots + c_n V_n = 0 \tag{26}$$

If so, then at least one of vectors V_k is a linear combination of $n - 1$ other vectors. Projecting the vectorial identity (26) on either one of m coordinate axis of S_m, we obtain the equivalent system of m homogeneous equations:

$$
\begin{aligned}
a_{11}c_1 + a_{12}c_2 + \cdots + a_{1n}c_n &= 0 \\
a_{21}c_1 + a_{22}c_2 + \cdots + a_{2n}c_n &= 0 \\
&\cdots\cdots\cdots\cdots\cdots \\
&\cdots\cdots\cdots\cdots\cdots \\
a_{m1}c_1 + a_{m2}c_2 + \cdots + a_{mn}c_n &= 0
\end{aligned}
\tag{27}
$$

In the general case, the rank r of this system is at most equal to m, $r \leqslant m$. In our case, $m < n$ and the rank r is less than the number of unknowns n, $r < n$. Therefore, there are non-trivial solutions with $\sum_1^n c_k^2 > 0$. Thus, it becomes clear that in an S_m there can be at most m independent vectors because n vectors will be always dependent if $n > m$.

If $n = m$, the answer depends on the value of the determinant $D = \det |a_{ij}|^m$. If $D \neq 0$, there is the trivial solution only: all c_k vanish and this proves that m vectors in S_m are independent, provided the determinant of their components does not vanish. To give an example, we now prove that the set of m pairwise perpendicular vectors is a set of independent vectors in an S_m. But first we must answer the question: is it possible to find m pairwise perpendicular directions in an S_m? Using mathematical induction, we first state that in a three dimensional space S_3 we know three pairwise perpendicular directions. It will be sufficient to prove that the existence of $m - 1$ such directions in an S_{m-1} entails the existence of m pairwise perpendicular directions in S_m. Suppose it is true for S_{m-1} and denote by d_k, $1 \leqslant k \leqslant m - 1$, these directions in S_{m-1}. To build S_m around S_{m-1}, it is sufficient to draw through all points of S_{m-1} straight lines parallel to a direction *not contained* in S_{m-1}.

Although issued from points belonging to S_{m-1}, these straight lines are not in it: either one of them has in common with S_{m-1} one point only. Moreover, their common direction can be chosen so as to be perpendicular to whole the space S_{m-1} in exactly the same way as a direction not contained in a plane can be chosen to be perpendicular to whole the plane. Thus, we can draw from a point of S_{m-1} a straight line d perpendicular to the whole space S_{m-1} and therefore perpendicular to all straight lines through the same point and located in S_{m-1}. In particular d is perpendicular to $m - 1$ directions d_k, $1 \leqslant k \leqslant m - 1$, described above. Together with them, the new line d forms in S_m a set of m pairwise perpendicular directions. We see that the mathematical induction works, and, therefore, the proposition in question is proved: *It is possible to find in a S_m exactly m but not more directions which are pairwise perpendicular.*

Vectors belonging to such a set are also pairwise perpendicular. Assuming now that these m vectors are not independent, we can prove that this assumption leads to a contradiction. This contradiction, once established, will be a sufficient proof of the existence in S_m of m *independent* vectors. By assumption, m real constants c_k, $1 \leqslant k \leqslant m$, can be found such that

$$\sum_1^m c_k^2 = c_1^2 + c_3^2 + \cdots + c_m^2 > 0 \tag{28}$$

and

$$\sum_1^m c_k \mathbf{V}_k = c_1 \mathbf{V}_1 + c_2 \mathbf{V}_2 + \cdots + c_m \mathbf{V}_m = 0 \tag{29}$$

The vectors $\mathbf{V}_k$ are pairwise perpendicular. Therefore, the scalar products of any two of them vanish, but the scalar square $(\mathbf{V}_k, \mathbf{V}_k) = |\mathbf{V}_k|^2$ does not: $(\mathbf{V}_i, \mathbf{V}_j) = 0$; $(\mathbf{V}_k, \mathbf{V}_k) > 0$. Multiplying the identity (29) scalarly by $\mathbf{V}_j$ we obtain $c_j = 0$ because

$$\sum_1^m c_k(\mathbf{V}_k, \mathbf{V}_j) = c_j(\mathbf{V}_j, \mathbf{V}_j) = 0$$

while $(\mathbf{V}_j, \mathbf{V}_j) > 0$. Repeating this procedure m times for $j = 1, 2, 3,$ ..., m, we prove that in (29) all c_k vanish, and this contradicts our assumption (28). Therefore, the set $\mathbf{V}_k$ of m pairwise perpendicular vectors is an example of m independent vectors in an m-dimensional space S_m. Taking one of such sets as a coordinate system in S_m, we norm the vectors $\mathbf{V}_k$, giving them unit length. Let us denote these new unit-vectors by e_k so that $e_k = \mathbf{V}_k/|\mathbf{V}_k|$. Any vector W in S_m with components $w_1, w_2, ..., w_m$ is now a sum of vectors $w_k e_k$ on coordinate axes. But if the initial length of $\mathbf{V}_k$ was $l_k = |\mathbf{V}_k|$, then $l_k e_k = \mathbf{V}_k$, and each term $w_k e_k$ can be written as $a_k \mathbf{V}_k$ with $a_k = w_k/l_k$:

$$\mathbf{W} = a_1 \mathbf{V}_1 + a_2 \mathbf{V}_2 + a_3 \mathbf{V}_3 + \cdots + a_m \mathbf{V}_m$$

Thus, in an S_m, the set of all linear combinations of m independent vectors spans the whole space in the sense that any vector in S_m is, *eo ipso*, a member of this set. We proved it for m independent vectors which are pairwise perpendicular, but it holds true for any set of m independent vectors, orthogonal to each other or not.

The system

$$a_{i1}x_1 + a_{i2}x_2 + \cdots + a_{in}x_n = 0 \qquad (i = 1, 2, ..., m) \tag{30}$$

of m homogeneous equations with n unknowns is a particular case of the system (S) in which $b_i = 0$ for $1 \leqslant i \leqslant m$. Assume that the rank r of (30) is less than n, $r < n$. Solving (30) with respect to r principal unknowns $x_1, x_2, ..., x_r$, we express them as linear functions of $n - r$ other variables $x_{r+1}, x_{r+2}, ..., x_n$ which remain free to vary and are considered as parameters:

$$x_k = \sum_{j=1}^{n-r} \beta_{jk} x_{r+j} \qquad (1 \leqslant k \leqslant r) \quad (31)$$

The general solution (31) is obtained from (25) because the constant terms a_k in (25) vanish when all b_k are zeros, which is the case of homogeneous equations (30).

Fixing the parameters x_{r+j}, particular solutions of (30) are obtained. Among them, *fundamental* solutions correspond to zero values of all parameters, except one which is given the value one. Thus, $n - r$ different fundamental solutions are obtained. Either one is a set of values of n variables $x_1, x_2, ..., x_n$. Thus, the j-th fundamental solution X_j which corresponds to $x_{r+j} = 1$ and $x_{r+s} = 0$ with $s \neq j$, is the set

$$X_j = (\beta_{j1}, \beta_{j2}, ..., \beta_{jr}, \underbrace{0, 0, ..., 0}_{j-1 \text{ zeros}}, 1, \underbrace{0, 0, ..., 0}_{n-j-r \text{ zeros}}) \quad (1 \leqslant j \leqslant n - r)$$

since (31) now yields $x_k = \beta_{jk}, 1 \leqslant k \leqslant r$.

Interpreting $x_1, x_2, ..., x_n$ as n components of a vector in S_n, we have $n - r$ vectors $X_j, 1 \leqslant j \leqslant n - r$, as fundamental solutions of (30). They are independent: their last $n - r$ components form a non-vanishing determinant (with zeros as off-diagonal entries and units as diagonal elements), and, therefore, neither one of them can be a linear combination of $n - r - 1$ other vectors.

Multiplying each vector X_j by the variable parameter x_{r+j}, adding these $n - r$ products, and applying (31), we give to the general solution of (30) the form of a vector $\mathbf{X}$ in an n-dimensional space S_n:

$$\mathbf{X} = x_{r+1}\mathbf{X}_1 + x_{r+2}\mathbf{X}_2 + \cdots + x_n\mathbf{X}_{n-r} \qquad (32)$$

Thus, it is established that this set (32) of all solutions of (30) obtained when the parameters $x_{r+1}, x_{r+2}, ..., x_n$ vary from $-\infty$ to $+\infty$, can be interpreted as a set of all vectors located in a subspace S_{n-r} of S_n, where S_{n-r} denotes an $(n - r)$-dimensional space defined and spanned by $n - r$ independent vectors $X_j, 1 \leqslant j \leqslant n - r$, which are fundamental solutions of our system (30).

An interesting question now arises: how can we explain the fact that the vectors of S_n which are solutions of (30) occupy and fill up a *part* only of this n-dimensional space S_n, namely, its $(n - r)$-dimensional subspace S_{n-r}?

The answer to this question is found by analyzing the geometrical meaning of the system (30) itself. The set of n coefficients in any one of m equations (30) can be interpreted as n components of a known vector. Thus, for $i = 1, 2, ..., m$, we define m vectors A_i with components $a_{i1}, a_{i2}, ..., a_{in}$. The fact that the rank of (30) is equal to r means that the r first vectors $\mathbf{A}_1, \mathbf{A}_2, ..., \mathbf{A}_r$ among them are independent, while the other $m - r$ vectors $\mathbf{A}_j$, $r < j \leqslant m$, are simply linear combinations of these r independent vectors.

The vectors $\mathbf{A}_1, \mathbf{A}_2, ..., \mathbf{A}_r$ define a subspace S_r of r dimensions which is a part of S_n. All linear combinations of r independent vectors A_k, $1 \leqslant k \leqslant r$, belong to S_r, and *vice versa* any vector located in S_r is a linear combination of the principal vectors $\mathbf{A}_1, \mathbf{A}_2, ..., \mathbf{A}_r$. Therefore, the $m - r$ known vectors $\mathbf{A}_{r+1}, \mathbf{A}_{r+2}, ..., \mathbf{A}_m$ also are in S_r.

Now the solution $\mathbf{X}$ of (30) given by (32) is a vector in S_n which satisfies certain conditions expressed by the equations (30). The lefthand members of these equations are scalar products of the vector $\mathbf{X}$ and of m known vectors $\mathbf{A}_i$, $1 \leqslant i \leqslant m$. The meaning of these equations is plain: vector $\mathbf{X}$ must be perpendicular to m vectors $\mathbf{A}_i$ since the scalar products vanish. The solution-vector $\mathbf{X}$ was determined as solution of the first r principal equations so that, by definition, it is perpendicular to r principal vectors $\mathbf{A}_1, \mathbf{A}_2 ..., \mathbf{A}_r$ and, therefore, perpendicular to whole the space S_r spanned by the principal vectors. The fact that $\mathbf{X}$ is perpendicular to the space S_r means that it is perpendicular to all vectors located in S_r. In particular, it is perpendicular to the vectors $\mathbf{A}_{r+1}, \mathbf{A}_{r+2}, ..., \mathbf{A}_m$ all of which are in S_r. But this means that the $m - r$ non-principal equations of the system (30) are satisfied by the solution of the first r principal equations. Thus, we have the geometrical picture of the compatibility of the equations (30).

The answer to the question formulated above is now as follows: the solution-vectors $\mathbf{X}$ are those vectors of S_n which are perpendicular to S_r and therefore *exterior* to this subspace of S_n. They are, of necessity, located in the complement of S_r, and this complement, which together with S_r forms the whole space S_n, must have $n - r$ dimensions. To illustrate this situation, it is sufficient to point out that in S_3 vectors perpendicular to a plane S_2 are parallel and therefore belong to one and the same straight line which is an one-dimensional space S_1. The straight line S_1 and the plane S_2 define the whole space S_3, and in S_3 the line S_1 and the plane S_2 are two mutually exclusive and complementary subspaces of S_3.

It is thus shown that the rank r of our system (30) gives the number of dimensions of that part of S_n which is defined by m known vectors A_i, $1 \leqslant i \leqslant m$, limiting the solutions of (30) to the complementary part of S_n which is therefore a subspace S_{n-r} of $n - r$ dimensions.

It remains to discuss the geometrical interpretation of the criterion of compatibility, that is, of the vanishing of characteristic determinants, when the equations of the system are not homogeneous:

$$f_i = \sum_{j=1}^{n} a_{ij}x_j = b_i \qquad (1 \leqslant i \leqslant m) \quad (33)$$

Transposing the matrix (21) of coefficients of (33), we consider together with (33) the adjoint *homogeneous* system

$$\sum_{j=1}^{m} a_{ji}y_j = 0 \qquad (1 \leqslant i \leqslant n) \quad (34)$$

which consists of n equations with m unknowns y_j. The rank of a determinant or a matrix does not change by transposition, and the adjoint system (34) has the same rank r as the system (33). Therefore, the adjoint homogeneous system (34) has $m - r$ independent fundamental solutions. These solutions are represented by $m - r$ vectors

$$\mathbf{Y}_{r+s} = (y_{s1}, y_{s2}, \ldots, y_{sr} \overbrace{0, 0, \ldots, 0}^{s-1\ \text{zeros}}, 1, \overbrace{0, 0, \ldots, 0}^{m-r-s\ \text{zeros}}), \qquad (1 \leqslant s \leqslant m - r)$$

where y_{sj}, $1 \leqslant j \leqslant r$, are components of the s-th solution of r principal equations in the adjoint homogeneous system (34), while 1 stands for the $(r + s)$-th component of $\mathbf{Y}_{r+s}$. These vectors $\mathbf{Y}_{r+s}$ are located in an m-dimensional space S_m because they have m components. On the other hand, the righthand members b_i, $1 \leqslant i \leqslant m$, of equations (33) can be interpreted as m components of a known vector $\mathbf{B}$ in the same space S_m: $\mathbf{B}\,(=b_1, b_2, \cdots b_m)$.

Let us study the scalar products of this vector $\mathbf{B}$ with the $m - r$ fundamental solution-vectors $\mathbf{Y}_{r+s}$ of the *adjoint* system (34). The scalar product $(\mathbf{B}, \mathbf{Y}_{r+s})$ involves m components of $\mathbf{Y}_{r+s}$. We denote them y_{sj} also for $j = r + 1, r + 2, \ldots, m$, so that $y_{sj} = 0$ for $r < j < r + s$ and also for $r + s < j \leqslant m$. Therefore, since $y_{s,r+s} = 1$,

$$(\mathbf{B}, \mathbf{Y}_{r+s}) = b_1 y_{s1} + \cdots + b_r y_{sr} + b_{r+s} = \sum_{i=1}^{r} b_i y_{si} + b_{r+s} \quad (35)$$

The components y_{sj} of $\mathbf{Y}_{r+s}$ satisfy, for $1 \leqslant j \leqslant r$, the system of principal equations of (34) in which the parameters y_j, with $j > r$, all vanish except $y_{r+s} = 1$, so that we can find y_{sj} from the system

$$\sum_{j=1}^{r} a_{ji} y_{sj} = a_{1i} y_{s1} + a_{2i} y_{s2} + \cdots + a_{ri} y_{sr} = -a_{r+s,\,i} \tag{36}$$

Denoting the principal determinant of (33) by D, $D \neq 0$, and applying Cramer's Rule, we have

$$y_{sj} = d_j / \tilde{D} = d_j / D \qquad\qquad (1 \leqslant j \leqslant r)$$

for $\tilde{D} = D$, a transposition having no effect on the value of a determinant. Here the determinant d_j is obtained replacing in $\tilde{D}$ the j-th column by the column of righthand members of (36):

$$d_j = - \begin{vmatrix} a_{11} \cdots a_{j-1,1} a_{r+s,1} a_{j+1,1} \cdots a_{r1} \\ \cdots\cdots\cdots\cdots\cdots\cdots\cdots\cdots\cdots \\ \cdots\cdots\cdots\cdots\cdots\cdots\cdots\cdots\cdots \\ \cdots\cdots\cdots\cdots\cdots\cdots\cdots\cdots\cdots \\ a_{1r} \cdots a_{j-1,r} a_{r+s,r} a_{j+1,r} \cdots a_{rr} \end{vmatrix}$$

Shifting the j-th column through $r - j$ columns to the right and then transposing, we have

$$d_j = (-1)^{r-j+1} d_j^* = (-1)^{r+j+1} d_j^*$$

where

$$d_j^* = \begin{vmatrix} a_{11} \cdots\cdots\cdots\cdots\cdots a_{1r} \\ \cdots\cdots\cdots\cdots\cdots\cdots\cdots \\ a_{j-1,1} \cdots\cdots\cdots\cdots a_{j-1,r} \\ a_{j+1,1} \cdots\cdots\cdots\cdots a_{j+1,r} \\ \cdots\cdots\cdots\cdots\cdots\cdots\cdots \\ a_{r1} \cdots\cdots\cdots\cdots\cdots a_{rr} \\ a_{r+s,1} \cdots\cdots\cdots\cdots a_{r+s,r} \end{vmatrix}$$

Now we can express $(\mathbf{B}, \mathbf{Y}_{r+s})$ as follows:

$$(\mathbf{B}, \mathbf{Y}_{r+s}) = \sum_{j=1}^{r} (-1)^{r+j+1} b_j d_j^* / D + b_{r+s}$$

On the other hand, expanding the characteristic determinant D_s

$$D_s = \begin{vmatrix} a_{11} \cdots\cdots\cdots a_{1r} & b_1 \\ \cdots\cdots\cdots\cdots\cdots \\ \cdots\cdots\cdots\cdots\cdots \\ a_{r1} \cdots\cdots\cdots a_{rr} & b_r \\ a_{r+s,1} \cdots\cdots a_{r+s,r} b_{r+s} \end{vmatrix}$$

along the elements of its last column, we obtain

$$D_s = \sum_{j=1}^{r} (-1)^{r+j+1} b_j d_j^* + b_{r+s}D = D \cdot (\mathbf{B}, \mathbf{Y}_{r+s})$$

The final result of this discussion is

$$(\mathbf{B}, \mathbf{Y}_{r+s}) = D_s/D \qquad (1 \leqslant s \leqslant m - r)$$

This result proves that *the scalar products* $(\mathbf{B}, \mathbf{Y}_{r+s})$ *and the characteristic determinants D_s vanish together.* Therefore, using the geometric language, we can formulate the *criterion* of compatibility as follows: *The orthogonality of the vector $\mathbf{B}$ of righthand members of the system* (33) *to $m - r$ fundamental solutions of the adjoint system* (34) *is a necessary and sufficient condition of the existence of solutions of* (33).

To terminate this chapter, we consider a system

$$-\lambda x_1 + x_2 = b_1$$

$$x_{j-1} - 2x_j + x_{j+1} = b_j \qquad (2 \leqslant j \leqslant n - 1) \quad (37)$$

$$x_{n-1} - \lambda x_n = b_n$$

encountered in the analysis of propagation of heat through the walls of a manned re-entry vehicle subject in its flight through the atmosphere to moderate heating for long periods of time. The vehicle's interior is protected by a series of n parallel plates in radiation equilibrium, the top plate being subject to a constant heat flux while the bottom plate radiates to a zero temperature medium. The unknown x_j denotes the fourth power of the temperature of the j-th plate, and b_j is due to the absorption of heat by this plate. The parameter λ is free to vary so that the determinant the system of (37) which depends on λ, vanishes for certain critical values of λ. This determinant of order n is

$$D(\lambda) = \begin{vmatrix} -\lambda & 1 & & & & \\ 1 & -2 & 1 & & & \\ & 1 & -2 & 1 & & \\ & & \cdots\cdots & & & \\ & & & \cdots\cdots & & \\ & & & 1 & -2 & 1 \\ & & & & 1 & -\lambda \end{vmatrix}$$

where the omitted terms vanish. Expanding $D(\lambda)$, we obtain a quadratic polynomial in λ:

$$D(\lambda) = d_{n-2}\lambda^2 + 2d_{n-3}\lambda + d_{n-4}$$

where d_n denotes a determinant of order n defined as follows:

$$d_n = D(2).$$

To find the critical values of λ, we have to solve the quadratic equation $D(\lambda) = 0$. Therefore, the first thing to do is to find the value of d_n. Now it is easy to check that $D(1) = 0$, and this proves that the numbers d_n satisfy the recurrent relation

$$d_n + 2d_{n-1} + d_{n-2} = 0$$

Computing directly d_3 and d_4, we find that $d_3 = -4$ and $d_4 = 5$. This result suggests that, probably, $d_n = (-1)^n (n + 1)$. And, indeed, by direct substitution of this guess into the recurrent relation, we justify it. Now, solving the equation

$$(-1)^n \cdot D(\lambda) = (n - 1)\lambda^2 - 2(n - 2)\lambda + (n - 3) = 0$$

we determine the critical values $\lambda_1 = 1$ and $\lambda_2 = (n - 3)/(n - 1)$ of λ for which Cramer's Rule is out of question since $D(\lambda)$ vanishes for $\lambda = \lambda_1$ and $\lambda = \lambda_2$.

We consider first the general case, when λ is not equal to a critical value: $\lambda \neq 1$ and $\lambda \neq (n - 3)/(n - 1)$.

We could apply Cramer's Rule, but the computation of n determinants in the numerators of (10) is long and tedious. In many cases, transforming the equations to new variables by substitution facilitates the computation of solution and such is precisely the case of the system (37). Substituting in the place of x_k new unknowns z_k related to old unknowns by $z_1 = x_1$ and

$$z_k = x_k - \sum_{s=1}^{k-1} (k - s) b_s \qquad (2 \leqslant k \leqslant n)$$

the equations (37), except for the last one, are transformed into

$$-\lambda z_1 + z_2 = 0 \qquad (38)$$

$$z_{j-1} - 2z_j + z_{j+1} = 0, \qquad (2 \leqslant j \leqslant n - 1)$$

while the last equation is now

$$z_{n-1} - \lambda z_n = (\lambda - 1)(nM_0 - M_1) + M_0 \qquad (38^*)$$

with
$$M_0 = b_1 + b_2 + b_3 + \cdots + b_n$$
and
$$M_1 = b_1 + 2b_2 + 3b_3 + \cdots + nb_n = \sum_{s=1}^{n} sb_s$$

From (38) it follows that all z_j for $j > 1$ are proportional to z_1: $z_2 = \lambda z_1$, $z_3 = (2\lambda - 1)z_1$, and, in general,
$$z_j = (A_j\lambda + B_j)z_1$$

where the constant coefficients A_j and B_j satisfy the same recurrent relation (38) as z_j. Knowing $A_2 = 1$, $A_3 = 2$, $B_2 = 0$, and $B_3 = -1$, we conclude that $A_j = j - 1$, while $B_j = 2 - j$. Therefore, we find that
$$z_j = [1 + (j - 1)(\lambda - 1)]z_1. \tag{39}$$

Using in (38*) the values (39) of z_{n-1} and z_n, we obtain z_1:
$$z_1 = [(\lambda - 1)(nM_0 - M_1) + M_0]/\{(1 - \lambda)[(n - 1)(\lambda - 1) + 2]\}$$

The denominator in the expression of z_1 is equal to
$$(n - 1)(\lambda_1 - \lambda)(\lambda - \lambda_2)$$

as it should be, taking into consideration that
$$D(\lambda) = (-1)^n (n - 1)(\lambda - \lambda_1)(\lambda - \lambda_2).$$

The solution takes now the form
$$x_j = [1 + (j - 1)(\lambda - 1)]z_1 + \sum_{s=1}^{j-1}(j - s)b_s \tag{40}$$

CASE $\lambda = 1$. The system (38) yields in this case $z_1 = z_2 = \cdots = z_n$, if the last equation (38*) is satisfied. The existence of solution depends, however, on whether or not the criterion of compatibility is satisfied. Taking this criterion in its geometrical form, we build the adjoint homogeneous system (34) and—in this case—find the same lefthand members as in the system (37) because the matrix of coefficients a_{ij} is in our case a symmetric one: $a_{ji} = a_{ij}$. Therefore, the only difference between (37) and its adjoint homogeneous system consists in the replacement of righthand members b_j by zeros. Since, moreover, $\lambda = 1$, the solution of the adjoint system is simply $y_1 = y_2 = \cdots = y_n$. The rank of the system is $n - 1$ so there is only one condition imposed on the vector $\mathbf{B}(b_1, b_2, \ldots, b_n)$, namely it must be perpendicular to the solution-vector $\mathbf{Y}(1, 1, \ldots, 1)$ of the adjoint system.

The scalar product $(\mathbf{B}, \mathbf{Y})$ is equal to M_0, and, therefore, if $\lambda = 1$, the system (37) has solutions only when $M_0 = 0$; otherwise, it is inconsistent. The solution, when it does exist, is obtained from (40) for $\lambda = 1$:

$$x_j = z_1 + \sum_{s=1}^{j-1} (j - s) b_s$$

where this time z_1 is an arbitrary constant.

CASE $\lambda = (n - 3)/(n - 1)$. This time the fundamental solution of the adjoint homogeneous system obtained for $y_1 = 1$ is as follows:

$$y_j = [(n - 2j + 1)/(n - 1)] y_1 \qquad (1 \leqslant j \leqslant n)$$

and the criterion of compatibility yields the condition of existence of solutions in the form

$$(n - 1) (\mathbf{B}, \mathbf{Y}) = \sum_{j=1}^{n} (n - 2j + 1) b_j = 0$$

which can be written also as

$$(n + 1) M_0 - 2M_1 = 0$$

Suppose it is satisfied. Then,

$$x_j = (n - 2j + 1) z_1/(n - 1) + \sum_{s=1}^{j=1} (j - s) b_j$$

where again z_1 is an arbitrary constant.

CHAPTER 11

Logarithms

Introduction

Planning is an absolute necessity in our industrialized society. Every planned step of human activity is based on numerical computations. The total amount of computations performed, say, in one year in laboratories, administrative and industrial offices, plants, insurance companies, banks, *etc.* exceeds all that the wildest imagination can picture.

How such an enormous computational work can be done? Partly with the aid of computing machines, but mostly by using a very powerful tool which bears the modest name of tables of logarithms. It can be said without exaggeration that our modern cities with their bridges, railroads, factories, power installations, skyscrapers, in short, all our highly artificial environment, built by mankind during the last century or two, and which implies an enormous amount of numerical computations, would be impossible without the tables of logarithms.

Without these tables the numerical computations which were required to build these things would represent a task impossible to perform in a hundred years, they would necessitate many centuries, if not millenaries of computational work. In these tables once for all, "forever" as said in the 17th century by John Napier, inventor of logarithms and author of *A Description of the Wonderful Law of Logarithms* (*Mirifici Logarithmorum Canonis Descriptio*, published in 1614), human thought has performed all possible kinds of numerical computations reducing them to the simplest. An enormous economy of work and time was thus achieved for the future applications of numbers in everyday life.

The marvellous tool created in computing, once for all, the tables of logarithms, replaces multiplication and division by much easier and more rapid operations of addition and subtraction. Exponentiation and extraction of roots are reduced to multiplication and division and, therefore, to addition and subtraction.

But that is not all. Any numerical operations involving trigonometric functions and all other mathematical expressions are too enormously simplified and accelerated by the use of logarithms.

The invention of logarithms was an important event in the history of mankind because, by achieving enormous economy of time and effort in dealing with numbers, it opened a large way to their practical use and thus permitted the industrialization of human society.

The fundamental fact underlying the use of logarithms is simple and it was known already to Archimedes. It consists of one-to-one correspondence between the numerical values N of powers a^n of a fixed number a (called *base*) and the exponents n (called *logarithms*) of these powers. To take an example suppose that we compute the values N of some powers to the base 5 with different exponents n ranging from -3 to $+3$:

Power	N.	n.	Power	N.	n.
5^{-3}	0.008	-3	$5^{0.5}$	2.236 ...	0.5
$5^{-2.5}$	0.0179 ...	-2.5	5^1	5.00	1
5^{-2}	0.0400	-2	$5^{1.5}$	11.18 ...	1.5
$5^{-1.5}$	0.0894 ...	-1.5	5^2	25.00	2
5^{-1}	0.2000	-1	$5^{2.5}$	55.87 ...	2.5
$5^{-0.5}$	0.4472 ...	-0.5	5^3	125.00	3
5^0	1.0000	0			

Using this small table and the rules of exponentiation,

$$a^n a^m = a^{n+m} \quad \text{and} \quad a^n/a^m = a^{n-m}$$

we can replace the multiplication of any two numbers N in our table by the addition of corresponding exponents n. Take for instance the product 0.4472×55.87 which is equal to $5^{-0.5} \cdot 5^{2.5}$. Applying the rule $a^n a^m = a^{n+m}$, we find that ist must be equal to $5^{2.5-0.5} = 5^2$ so that $0.4472 \times 55.87 \approx 25$. Thus the direct multiplication is avoided and replaced by the addition of exponents: $2.5 - 0.5 = 2$.

The same simplification applies to the division. Instead of dividing directly 11.18 by 0.0894 we can consider this operation as division of $5^{3/2}$ by $5^{-3/2}$ so that

$$11.18 \div 0.0894 \approx 5^{3/2} \div 5^{-3/2} = 5^3 = 125$$

Again a division can be performed in the form of a subtraction of exponents, if we have at our disposal the table of powers of 5. The base 5 was chosen arbitrarily and the same results can be achieved with any number chosen as base of powers, except 1 and zero.

This idea of Archimedes was not developed and completely forgotten because at his time mankind did not know how to use numbers and did not feel a need for their computation. Fifteen centuries later, in the thirteenth century, Iranian astronomers used the same idea to simplify their numerical work and computed some simple tables of correspondence between values of powers and exponents.

Their work also was lost and forgotten and the logarithms were rediscovered for the third time in Europe by John Napier, who was the first to compute sufficiently detailed tables for this correspondence between values of powers and corresponding exponents to be able to represent any given number N as the value of some power to the base a, $N = a^n$. It was John Napier who gave to the exponent n the name of logarithm of the number N to the base a, denoting it $\log_a N$, so that, if $N = a^n$, then $n = \log_a N$ and *vice versa*.

The computation of tables of logarithms necessitated an enormous amount of work, but this herculean task was to be done only once and when it was done the tool was created. Henceforth and forever all the numerical computations were greatly simplified, facilitated and abbreviated.

In this chapter we study the logarithms introducing them as the solution of the exponential equation $a^x = N$, where a and N are two given and known numbers.

Definition of a Logarithm

The operation of exponentiation $a^b = N$ admits of two different inverse operations. The first one, which corresponds to the equation $x^b = N$, leads to radicals $x = \sqrt[b]{N} = N^{1/b}$ and it was studied in Chapter 4. In this chapter we introduce the second inverse operation defined as follows: suppose that among three numbers base a, exponent b and value N of $a^b = N$, the base a and the value N of the power a^b are two given and known numbers, but the exponent is considered as unknown and therefore replaced by x. The unknown value x of the exponent must be found and by definition it is such that equation $a^x = N$ is satisfied.

In general, any complex values a and N being given, the exponent x can be found and has also a complex value, but first we consider the equation $a^x = N$ with a positive base a and a positive value of the righthand member N.

This limitation is motivated by the desire to avoid, in this first part of the chapter, complex values of x. It is not necessary to consider all positive values of the base a because equations of the type $a^x = N$ with a base a smaller than one, $a < 1$, are reducible to those with $a > 1$. Suppose for a moment that in $d^t = N$ the base d is less than 1 and denote ist reciprocal $1/d$ by a: $d = 1/a$, where $a > 1$ because $d < 1$. The equation $d^t = N$ can be written

$$(1/a)^t = a^{-t} = N.$$

Introducing, instead of the unknown exponent t, its symmetrical number $-t = x$, we see that $d^t = N$, $(d < 1)$, is equivalent to the equation $a^x = N$, with $a > 1$, if $t = -x$. Therefore, we will study the solution of the equations $a^x = N$ under the hypothese $a > 1$ and $N > 0$. The value $a = 1$ of the base a is precluded because the equation $1^x = N$ is impossible for $N \neq 1$, and meaningless, if $N = 1$.

The solution x of the equation $a^x = N$ is called *logarithm* of the number N with respect to the base a and is denoted by $\log_a N$. This definition raises an important question: is the condition $N > 0$ sufficient to insure the existence of a solution and, if so, is this solution unique or are there many real numbers x which do satisfy the same equation $a^x = N$? We will prove that there is one and only one real number x, such that a raised to a power with exponent x is equal to N, provided that $a > 1$ and $N > 0$. This unique solution is called logarithm of N to the base a. In other words the exponent x in $a^x = N$ is equal to $\log_a N$ and the definition of $\log_a N$ may be stated as follows:

$$a^{\log_a N} = N \tag{1}$$

Note that the same number N can be represented as a power of different bases and for each base it has a different logarithm. Thus, for instance,

$$256 = 2^8 = 4^4 = 16^2$$

so that

$$\log_2 256 = 8, \quad \log_4 256 = 4, \quad \log_{16} 256 = 2$$

Existence Problem

When the number N is a power of the base with an integral exponent (as in the preceding examples) the existence of $\log_a N$ is clear, but given the equation $a^x = N$ with any known positive numbers $a > 1$ and $N > 0$ we must first of all show the existence of the unique solution x such that $a^x = N$. In general this number x is irrational and we have to prove that there is a regular procedure which allows the computation of any decimal, in particular of the n-th decimal, b_n, in the representation of $x = \log_a N$ as an infinite decimal fraction.

Forming first the increasing sequence (we always suppose $a > 1$)

$$\ldots, 1/a^3 = a^{-3},\ 1/a^2 = a^{-2},\ 1/a = a^{-1},\ a^0 = 1, a, a^2, a^3, \ldots \quad \text{(S)}$$

and, comparing the number N with its terms, we find a positive or negative integer c such that N belongs to the interval (a^c, a^{c+1}):

$$a^c \leqslant N < a^{c+1}. \qquad\qquad (a > 1)$$

Replacing N in it by a^x, we get

$$a^c \leqslant a^x < a^{c+1} \qquad\qquad (2)$$

and since powers of the base a greater than one, $a > 1$, increase with the exponent, we conclude from (2) the inequality

$$c \leqslant x = \log_a N < c + 1$$

Thus the integral part c of $x = \log_a N$ is found. It is denoted c because it has a special name. Integral part c of a logarithm is called its *characteristic*: it "characterizes" the interval $(c, c + 1)$ to which $\log_a N$ belongs. It is never given in the tables of logarithms and must be found by direct comparison of N with the sequence of positive and negative integral powers of the base a. Thus, if $a = 3$ and $N = 17$ we see that

$$3^2 = 9 < 17 < 27 = 3^3$$

and therefore the characteristic of $\log_3 17$ is $c = 2$. The value of $\log_3 17$ is comprised between 2 and 3: $\log_3 17 = 2\ldots$ with the decimals after the dot remaining to be found.

The characteristic c can be zero or negative too. Thus, if $a = 10$ and $N = 7$ we have

$$10^0 = 1 < 7 < 10^1 = 10$$

and therefore $\log_{10} 7$ is a positive number less than one, $0 < \log_{10} 7 < 1$ and for it $c = 0$. To illustrate the case when c is negative we consider $a = 5$ and $N = 0.03$. Here

$$5^{-3} = 0.008 < 0.03 < 5^{-2} = 0.04$$

Thus, $\log_5 (0.03)$ satisfies the inequality

$$c = -3 < \log_5 (0.03) < -2 = c + 1$$

and for it $c = -3$. The fractional part of $\log_5 (0.03)$ is therefore positive and this is always so for all logarithms regardless of the sign or the value of the characteristic c.

The inequality $a^c \leqslant N < a^{c+1}$ is a definition of c. The existence of c may be illustrated by the geometric picture

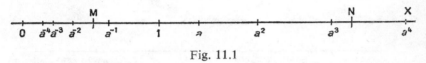

Fig. 11.1

which shows that the real positive half-axis OX is subdivided into intervals by the terms of the sequence (S) and therefore a real positive number N *must* belong to one of these intervals:

$$N \geqslant a^c, \quad \text{but} \quad N < a^{c+1}$$

On the figure $c = 3$ for $\log_a N$ and $c = -2$ for $\log_a M$.

Now we consider the quotient N/a^c. Dividing the inequality (2) by a^c we transform it into

$$1 \leqslant N/a^c < a$$

The interval $(1, a)$ can be subdivided into ten subintervals by nine points $a^{k/10}$, $1 \leqslant k \leqslant 9$

$$a^{0.1} = \sqrt[10]{a}, a^{0.2} = \sqrt[10]{a^2}, a^{0.3} = \sqrt[10]{a^3}, \dots a^{0.9} = \sqrt[10]{a^9}$$

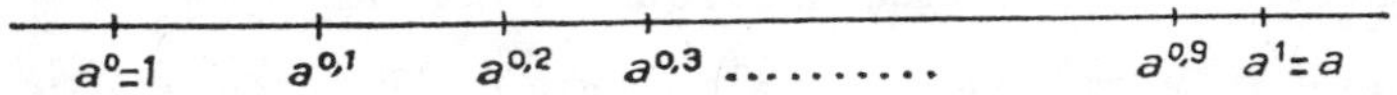

Fig. 11.2

The number N/a^c belongs to the interval $(1, a)$ and therefore it is necessarily within one of these ten subintervals. Denoting by $b_1/10$

the exponent of the power of a which corresponds to the left end of the subinterval containing N/a^c, we express the fact that N/a^c belongs to this subinterval $[a^{b_1/10}, a^{(b_1+1)/10}]$ by the inequality

$$\sqrt[10]{a^{b_1}} = a^{b_1/10} = a^{0.b_1} \leqslant N/a^c < a^{0.(b_1+1)} = a^{(b_1+1)/10} = \sqrt[10]{a^{b_1+1}}$$

where b_1 is one of ten digits 0, 1, 2, 3, 4, 5, 6, 7, 8, 9. Dividing this inequality by its lefthand member $a^{0.b_1}$, we transform it again into

that is

$$1 \leqslant N/(a^c a^{0.b_1}) < a^{0.1}$$

$$1 \leqslant N/a^{c.b_1} < a^{0.1}$$

which proves that the number $N/a^{c.b_1}$ belongs to the interval $(1, a^{0.1})$. We continue the same approximation process further and subdivide the interval $(1, a^{0.1})$ into ten smaller intervals by points

$$a^{0.01} = \sqrt[100]{a}, \ a^{0.02} = \sqrt[100]{a^2}, \ a^{0.03} = \sqrt[100]{a^3}, \ ... \ a^{0.09} = \sqrt[100]{a^9}$$

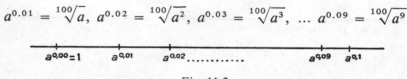

Fig. 11.3

The number $N/a^{c.b_1}$, interior to $(1, a^{0.1})$, necessarily belongs to some one of the subintervals. We denote by b_2 the significant digit in the exponent of power of a which corresponds to the left extremity of the subinterval to which $N/a^{c.b_1}$ belongs, so that

$$a^{b_2/100} = a^{0.0b_2} \leqslant N/a^{c.b_1} < a^{0.0(b_2+1)} = a^{(b_2+1)/100}$$

Dividing this inequality by $a^{b_2/100} = a^{0.0b_2}$, we have again

$$1 \leqslant N/a^{c.b_1b_2} < a^{0.01}$$

In these first three steps we have formed three intervals $(1, a)$; $(1, a^{0.1})$; $(1, a^{00.1})$ e in which the three quotients N/a^c, $N/a^{c.b_1}$ and $N/a^{c.b_1b_2}$ respectively are included. It is clear that the lengths of these three intervals form a decreasing sequence because

$$a > a^{0.1} = \sqrt[10]{a} > a^{0.01} = \sqrt[100]{a}$$

so that the numbers a^c, $a^{c.b_1}$, $a^{c.b_1b_2}$ form a sequence approaching the number N. We can continue this process of successive approximations as far as we want. Suppose that after $n + 1$ steps we have formed the approximate value $a^{c.b_1b_2\cdots b_n}$ such that the quotient $N/a^{c.b_1b_2\cdots b_n}$ belongs to the interval $(1, a^{0.00\cdots01} = a^{10^{-n}})$, that is

$$1 \leqslant N/a^{c.b_1b_2\cdots b_n} < a^{10^{-n}} = \sqrt[10^n]{a} = a^{\overbrace{0.00\cdots001}^{n\ \text{zeros}}}$$

We now subdivide the last interval $(1, \sqrt[10^n]{a})$ again into ten subintervals by points:

$$a^{10^{-n-1}}, (a^{10^{-n-1}})^2, (a^{10^{-n-1}})^3, \ \ldots \ (a^{10^{-n-1}})^9$$

and conclude that the quotient $N/a^{c.b_1b_2\cdots b_n}$ *must* belong to some one of these ten subintervals. Denoting it by $[a^{b_{n+1}.10^{-n-1}}, a^{(b_{n+1}+1).10^{-n-1}}]$, we have the inequality

$$a^{10^{-n-1}.b_{n+1}} \leqslant N/a^{c.b_1b_2\cdots b_n} < a^{10^{-n-1}.(b_{n+1}+1)}$$

Dividing this inequality by $a^{10^{-n-1}.b_{n+1}}$, we obtain a better approximate value for N since

$$1 \leqslant N/a^{c.b_1b_2\cdots b_nb_{n+1}} < a^{10^{-n-1}} = \sqrt[10]{a^{10^{-n}}}$$

This process of successive approximations stops only if, at some of its steps, we find a *finite* decimal expression $c.b_1b_2 \cdots b_m$ such that $a^{c.b_1b_2\cdots b_m} = N$. Then we conclude that $\log_a N = c.b_1b_2 \cdots b_m$ exactly, and the process is discontinued. But in general the fractional part of a logarithm is represented by an infinite decimal fraction and the process does not stop. Since we have a regular process which allows us to deduce the next, $(n + 1)$-th, decimal b_{n+1}, if the preceding one, n-th decimal b_n, was already computed, we conclude the existence of such an infinite decimal fraction

$$M = c.b_1b_2b_3 \cdots b_nb_{n+1} \cdots$$

that for any positive integer n as large as we want, the following inequality is satisfied:

$$1 \leqslant N/a^{c.b_1b_2\cdots b_n} < a^{10^{-n}} = a^{\overbrace{0.00\cdots001}^{n\ \text{zeros}}}$$

Denoting the finite exponent $c.b_1b_2 \cdots b_n$ by M_n

$$M_n = c.b_1b_2 \cdots b_{n-1}b_n$$

we rewrite this inequality as follows:

$$1 \leqslant N/a^{M_n} < a^{10^{-n}}, \tag{3}$$

where $\lim\limits_{n=\infty} M_n = M$.

We can now pass to the limit for $n = \infty$ and the interval $(1, a^{10^{-n}})$, to which the ratio N/a^{M_n} belongs, shrinks at the limit to a single point 1 since, as we will see.

$$\lim_{n=\infty} a^{10^{-n}} = \lim_{n=\infty} \sqrt[10^n]{a} = 1 \qquad (4)$$

Therefore, passage to the limit gives

$$\lim_{n=\infty} [N/a^{M_n}] = N/\lim_{n=\infty} a^{M_n} = N/a^{\lim_{n=\infty} M_n} = N/a^M = 1$$

and the existence of $\log_a N = M$ is proved, as well as its uniqueness, insofar as the *real* values of logarithms are considered.

It remains for us to show that (4) is true. To prove (4) we denote the value of the radical $a^{10^{-n}} = \sqrt[10^n]{a}$ by $1 + t_n$:

$$\sqrt[10^n]{a} = 1 + t_n$$

Raising this equality to the power with exponent 10^n, we have

$$a = (1 + t_n)^{10^n} \qquad (t_n > 0).$$

Bernoulli's inequality $(1 + p)^k > 1 + pk$ now gives

$$a = (1 + t_n)^{10^n} < 1 + 10^n \cdot t_n$$

Solving for t_n, we obtain $10^n \cdot t_n > a - 1$ and thus

$$0 < t_n < (a - 1)/10^n$$

When $n \to \infty$ the denominator increases without limit, $10^n \to \infty$, but the numerator $a - 1$ is a fixed positive number $(a > 1)$, so that $\lim_{n=\infty} t_n = 0$. Therefore

$$\lim_{n=\infty} \sqrt[10^n]{a} = \lim_{n=\infty} (1 + t_n) = 1 + \lim_{n=\infty} t_n = 1$$

Thus, the existence of the unique exponent

$$M = \lim_{n=\infty} M_n = c.b_1 b_2 \cdots b_n \cdots \quad \text{such that} \quad a^M = N$$

is proved. This exponent is represented by an infinite decimal fraction and it is the solution $\log_a N$ of the equation $a^x = N$. Thus, the existence and uniqueness of solution for $a^x = N$ is established, and the definition of $\log_a N$ is justified. Its value appears as an infinite convergent series

$$\log_a N = c + \sum_{n=1}^{\infty} b_n/10^n = c + b_1/10 + b_2/100 + \cdots + b_n/10^n + \cdots$$

The decimal fraction $0.b_1b_2 \cdots b_n \cdots$ has a *positive* value, which is between zero and one, and is called the *mantissa* of the logarithm. The tables of logarithms give the mantissas only. A logarithm is, therefore, a sum of an integral part, *characteristic*, and of a fractional part, *mantissa*. The first, characteristic, can be negative, zero, or positive. If N is greater than the base a, $N > a$, then $\log_a N$ exceeds one since

$$N = a^{\log_a N} > a^1$$

and its characteristic is positive. If N is greater than one, but less than a, $1 < N < a$, then

$$1 = a^0 < a^{\log_a N} < a^1$$

and the value of $\log_a N$ is positive but smaller than one, which means that the characteristic c is zero. Finally, if N is a positive number smaller than one, then $\log_a N$ is negative and its characteristic c must be negative too:

Number N	Characteristic c
$0 < N < 1$	negative
$1 \leqslant N < a$	zero
$a \leqslant N$	positive

Since $a^0 = 1$ we conclude that $\log_a 1 = 0$ regardless of the value of the base. A second remarkable property of logarithm is $\log_a a = 1$, since $a = a^1$.

Variation of Logarithm

If the number N increases, its logarithm increases too, provided that the base a is greater than one, which is the case of both kinds of logarithms used in practice. We do not need two different systems of logarithms to two different bases, but is is a tradition to use the so-called *common logarithms* to the base ten in addition to the *natural logarithms* to the base $e = 2.71828\ldots$ In both cases the base is greater than one and therefore the logarithm of a number and this number vary in the same sense: both increase or decrease together. Now suppose that the number N increases without limit, $N \to \infty$, what happens to its $\log_a N$ $(a > 1)$? We know first that $\log_a N$ increases with N and second, that a finite value of the number $N = a^{\log_a N}$ corresponds to a finite value of a logarithm. Therefore $\log_a N$ must become infinite, when N becomes infinite and $\log_a (\infty) = +\infty$.

To illustrate this point observe that the *common logarithm* (that is, logarithm to the base 10) of 10^n is equal to n:

$$\log_{10} 10^n = n$$

and when $n \to \infty$ the number $10^n \to \infty$ too. Now we will consider the logarithm of a decreasing number N, smaller than one, $N < 1$, and approaching zero, $N \to 0$. The $\log_a N$ is negative, since $N < 1$, and it decreases because N decreases, which means that its absolute value increases. To find its limit, $\log_a 0$, we represent N as $N = 1/M$ where M, reciprocal of N, increases. Now $N = a^{\log_a N}$ and at the same time $1/N = M = a^{\log_a M}$ by definition. Multiplying the identities

$$N = a^{\log_a N} \quad \text{and} \quad 1/N = a^{\log_a M}$$

member by member, we obtain

$$1 = a^{\log_a N} a^{\log_a M} = a^{\log_a N + \log_a M}$$

But $1 = a^0$ and therefore the logarithms of two reciprocal numbers N, M always satisfy the relation

$$\log_a N + \log_a M = 0, \quad \text{if} \quad MN = 1. \tag{5}$$

Now, when $N \to 0$, its reciprocal $M = 1/N$ approaches infinity, $M \to \infty$, and therefore its logarithm too increases without limit

$$\lim_{N=0} (\log_a M) = +\infty$$

The relation (5) gives $\log_a N = -\log_a M$ and we find the limiting value of $\log N$, when $N \to 0$:

$$\lim_{N=0} (\log_a N) = -\lim_{N=0} (\log_a M) = -\infty$$

that is, $\log_a 0$ is equal to $-\infty$:

$$\log_a 0 = -\infty.$$

We can now formulate the law of variation of $\log_a N$ to the base a greater than one, $a > 1$, as follows: *Provided that the base a of logarithms is greater than one, the logarithm $\log_a x$ increases from $-\infty$ to $+\infty$ when the number x increases from zero to $+\infty$.*

We can represent the result of this discussion by a graph of the function $y = \log_a x$ by plotting the values of the logarithm as ordinates and those of the number x, argument of the logarithm, as abcissas: the logarithmic curve starts at minus infinity on the y-axis, which corresponds to $x = 0$, then rises continuously, passing through the points A ($x = 1$, $y = \log_a 1 = 0$) and B ($x = a$, $y = \log_a a = 1$). The first point, A, corresponds to $y = \log_a 1 = 0$ and the second, B, to $y = \log_a a = 1$.

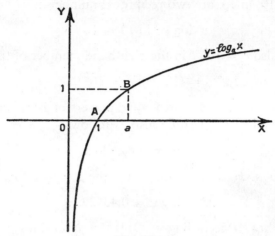

Fig. 11.4

Common and Natural Logarithms

Natural and common logarithms are proportional and the coefficient of proportionality, called *modulus* and denoted by M, is defined by

$$\log_{10} x = M \cdot \log_e x \tag{6}$$

To avoid subscripts we will denote common logarithms simply by log, omitting the subscript 10, and natural logarithms by ln, so that (6) may be written also as follows

$$\log x = M \ln x \tag{7}$$

It is important to evaluate the modulus M, but first we must prove that $\log x$ and $\ln x$ are proportional, the modulus M being a constant regardless of the variation of x. By definition (1) we have

$$10^{\log x} = x = e^{\ln x} \tag{8}$$

On the other hand, we have, by definition, also

$$10 = e^{\ln 10} \quad \text{and} \quad e = 10^{\log e}$$

Substituting for e in the first relation its value $10^{\log e}$, we obtain

$$10 = (10^{\log e})^{\ln 10} = 10^{\log e \cdot \ln 10}$$

Therefore the common logarithm of the number e, $\log e$, and the natural logarithm of 10, $\ln 10$, are two reciprocal numbers:

$$\log e \cdot \ln 10 = 1 \tag{9}$$

Substituting also $e = 10^{\log e}$ in the righthand member of (8), we obtain

$$10^{\log x} = (10^{\log e})^{\ln x} = 10^{\log e \cdot \ln x}$$

Comparing the exponents of two equal powers of 10 we conclude that (7) is proved and can be written also as follows

$$\log x = \log e \cdot \ln x \tag{10}$$

Therefore, the *modulus M* is found. It is the common logarithm of the number e:

$$M = \log e = 0.43429\ldots \tag{11}$$

The reciprocal of M according to (9) is the natural logarithm of 10

$$1/M = \ln 10 = 2.30258\ldots \tag{12}$$

The numerical values (11) and (12) of M and $1/M$ will be justified later. We note that, as a parallel to (10), we also have

$$\ln x = (1/M) \log x = 2.30258 \cdots \log x \tag{13}$$

The result (10) has a great practical importance. As we will see in the next section, natural logarithms are much easier to compute and therefore the table of natural logarithms is calculated first, and the table of common logarithmus is deduced from it by multiplying the natural logarithms by the constant factor $M = 0.43429\ldots$

Computation of Natural Logarithms

By definition of logarithms we have

$$e^{\ln x} = x$$

The power e^u of the number e is defined by (see Chapter 9, form. (28))

$$e^u = \lim_{t=0} (1 + ut)^{1/t}$$

Using this definition in $e^{\ln x}$, we obtain

$$x = e^{\ln x} = \lim_{t=0} [1 + t(\ln x)]^{1/t}.$$

The difference between $[1 + t(\ln x)]^{1/t}$ and x is a function $f(t)$ of t which is infinitely small for $t \to 0$, and we can rewrite this relation as follows:

$$[1 + t(\ln x)]^{1/t} = x + f(t), \tag{14}$$

where $f(t)$ is infinitely small, when $t \to 0$ so that

$$\lim_{t=0} f(t) = 0.$$

Raising both members of (14) to a power with exponent t, we transform it into

$$1 + t(\ln x) = [x + f(t)]^t$$

and thus, solving for $\ln x$:

$$\ln x = \{[x + f(t)]^t - 1\}/t \tag{15}$$

Since $f(t)$ vanishes for $t = 0$, the relation (15) suggests that

$$\ln x = \lim_{t=0} [(x^t - 1)/t] \tag{16}$$

but this important formula is not yet proved. To prove it, we study the limit in question. Because $x = e^{\ln x}$, we write $x^t - 1$ as $e^{t\ln x} - 1$ and express the exponential function as the exponential series (29) Chapter 9:

$$x^t - 1 = e^{t\ln x} - 1 = t\ln x + t^2 (\ln x)^2/2! + \cdots + t^n(\ln x)^n/n! + \tag{17}$$

In the righthand member of (17) $t^2(\ln x)^2$ is a common factor of all terms except the first term. Picking it out

$$x^t - 1 = t \ln x + t^2(\ln x)^2 (1/2 + \cdots)$$

we obtain between parentheses an infinite series $1/2 + \cdots$, the sum $s(t)$ of which is a finite number because the series converges for all t. Thus,

$$x^t - 1 = t \ln x + t^2(\ln x)^2 \cdot s(t)$$

Dividing both members by t and passing to the limit for $t = 0$, we have

$$\lim_{t=0} [(x^t - 1)/t] = \ln x + \lim_{t=0} [t(\ln x)^2 \cdot s(t)]$$

Now the limit of the product $t.s(t)$ for $t = 0$ is zero because the first factor, t, vanishes while the second factor remains finite: $s(t)$ tends to $1/2$ when $t \to 0$. Since $\ln x$ is a constant we see that

$$\lim_{t=0} [t(\ln x)^2 \, s(t)] = 0$$

and this achieves the proof of the relation (16) which can be considered as a direct definition of natural logarithm.

If we replace in (16) the continuous infinitely small t by a discontinuous infinitesimal $1/n$, which tends to zero when the integer n increases without limit, $n \to \infty$, a particular case of (16) is obtained:

$$\ln x = \lim_{n=\infty} [n(x^{1/n} - 1)] = \lim_{n=\infty} [n(\sqrt[n]{x} - 1)] \qquad (18)$$

This shows that the natural logarithm is related to radicals since it is the limit for $n = \infty$ of an expression involving $\sqrt[n]{x}$.

At the end of Chapter 7 we deduced, with the aid of binomial expansion, an infinite series representing the limit for $t = 0$ of the quotient $[(1 + u)^t - 1]/t$:

$$\lim_{t=0} \{[(1 + u)^t - 1]/t\}$$
$$= u/1 - u^2/2 + u^3/3 - \cdots + (-1)^{n-1} u^n/n + \cdots$$

On the other hand, we have just proved that

$$\lim_{t=0} \{[(1 + u)^t - 1]/t\} = \ln(1 + u)$$

which is obtained, if we replace x by $1 + u$ in (16). Thus, the natural logarithm of the number $1 + u$ can be computed by using its representation by the infinite series

$$\ln (1 + u) = u/1 - u^2/2 + u^3/3 + \cdots + (-1)^{n-1} u^n/n + \cdots \qquad (19)$$

This series converges for $-1 < u < 1$ and also for $u = 1$. In the last case we obtain the sum of the numerical series we met at the end of Chapter 9:

$$\ln 2 = 1 - 1/2 + 1/3 - 1/4 + 1/5 - 1/6 + \cdots \qquad (20)$$

This result is remarkable. It is an illustration of the fundamental fact that all numbers are nothing more than results of operations performed with natural integers 1, 2, 3, etc., so that all numbers in principle must admit of explicit expressions in terms of natural integers only. The discovery of such expressions is not easy, and this one produced a deep impression, when it was obtained for the first time.

Though the series (20) converges, its convergence is so slow that it cannot be used to compute ln 2. If ln 2 with five exact decimals is required, more than fifty thousand terms must be effectively computed and added to obtain ln 2 with an error smaller than 0.00001. The same circumstance prevents the practical use of the series (19) except for exceedingly small values of u.

But both obstacles, divergence for $|u| > 1$ and slow convergence for $u \leqslant 1$, can be easily overcome. Changing the sign of u, we obtain another infinite series which represents $\ln(1 - u)$:

$$\ln (1 - u) = -u/1 - u^2/2 - u^3/3 - \cdots - u^n/n - \cdots \qquad (21)$$

Subtracting it from series (19), we obtain

$$\ln (1+u) - \ln (1-u) = 2[u/1 + u^3/3 + \cdots + u^{2n+1}/(2n+1) + \cdots]$$

since the terms with even exponents cancel and those with odd exponents are doubled. The difference and the sum of two logarithms can be replaced by a single logarithm. We have indeed

$$A = a^{\log_a A}, \; B = a^{\log_a B}$$

and thus:

$$A/B = a^{\log_a A}/a^{\log_a B} = a^{\log_a A - \log_a B}$$

as well as

$$AB = a^{\log_a A} a^{\log_a B} = a^{\log_a A + \log_a B}$$

But, on the other hand, by definition,

$$A/B = a^{\log_a (A/B)}; \quad AB = a^{\log_a (AB)}.$$

Therefore, in general

$$\log A - \log B = \log (A/B) \quad \text{and} \quad \log A + \log B = \log (AB) \qquad (22)$$

In particular, if the number e is the base ($a = e$):

$$\ln A - \ln B = \ln (A/B)$$

$$\ln A + \ln B = \ln (AB)$$

In our case $A = 1 + u$, $B = 1 - u$ and thus

$$\ln (1 + u) - \ln (1 - u) = \ln [(1 + u)/(1 - u)]$$

so that the final result is: *The natural logarithm of a positive number N is represented by the infinite convergent series*

$$\ln N = 2[u/1 + u^3/3 + u^5/5 + \cdots + u^{2n+1}/(2n + 1) + \cdots] \quad (23)$$

where

$$N = (1 + u)/(1 - u), \text{ that is } u = (N - 1)/(N + 1).$$

Therefore, $|u| < 1$, so the series always converges.

As an example we compute the modulus $M = \log e$ by evaluating its reciprocal

$$1/M = \ln 10$$

Since $10 = 2 \cdot 5$, we have

$$10 = e^{\ln 2} e^{\ln 5} = e^{\ln 2 + \ln 5}$$

that is:

$$\ln 10 = \ln 2 + \ln 5$$

We need Ln 2 and Ln 5.

If $N = 2$, then

$$u = (N - 1)/(N + 1) = 1/3$$

so that

$$\ln 2 = 2[1/3 + 1/81 + 1/1215 + 1/15309 + 1/177147 + \cdots]$$

It is sufficient to transform only the first five terms into decimal fractions and add them to find $\ln 2$ correct to five decimal places:

$$1/3 = 0.3333333\ldots$$

$$1/81 = 0.0123456\ldots$$

$$1/1215 = 0.0008230\ldots$$

$$1/15309 = 0.0000653\ldots$$

$$1/177147 = 0.0000057\ldots$$

Adding the decimal fractions and multiplying the sum by 2, we obtain

$$\ln 2 = 0.693146\ldots$$

where only the sixth decimal is wrong, since a better approximate value of $\ln 2$, correct to eight decimals, is $0.69314718\ldots$ In five-place logarithmic tables we read 0.69315 and this approximate value can be deduced from our result since the omitted terms are all positive and they could only increase the sixth decimal.

But there is a better and easier way of computing ln 2. By direct multiplication we find 7.389056 as an approximate value of e^2 correct to five decimals and observe that $2^3 = 8$ is very near to it. We therefore take $N = 2^3/e^2$ and obtain, for the corresponding value of its function $u = (N - 1)/(N + 1)$, the following expression:

$$u = (8e^{-2} - 1)/(8e^{-2} + 1) = (8 - e^2)/(8 + e^2) = 0.610944/15.389056$$

Thus the values of u and $u^3/3$ corresponding to $N = 2^3/e^2$ are:

$$u = 0.03970...$$

$$u^3/3 = 0.00002...$$

all other terms being so small that their sum is negligible. Thus the series for $\ln(2^3 e^{-2})$ is much more rapidly convergent than the series for ln 2. Adding $u + u^3/3$ and multiplying by 2 we obtain 0.07944 correct to five decimal places:

$$\ln(2^3 e^{-2}) = 0.07944...$$

But, on the other hand, the logarithm of a power of N, $\log(N^k)$, is equal to the logarithm of N times the exponent k of the power N^k:

$$\log_a(N^k) = k(\log_a N) \tag{24}$$

To prove (24) it is sufficient to substitute for N in $\log_a(N^k)$ its representation as a power of the base a: $N = a^{\log_a N}$. Thus:

$$\log_a(N^k) = \log_a[(a^{\log_a N})^k] = \log_a(a^{k \log_a N}) = k \log_a N$$

Applying (24) and (23) to $\ln(2^3 e^{-2})$, we obtain:

$$(\ln 2^3 e^{-2}) = \ln(2^3) + \ln(e^{-2}) = 3 \ln 2 - 2 \ln e$$

But $\ln e = 1$ and therefore

$$3 \ln 2 - 2 = 0.07944...$$

Solving this linear equation for the unknown ln 2, we have finally

$$\ln 2 = 0.693147...$$

correct to six decimals.

The second method proves that it is possible to abbreviate the computations by taking as N the ratio of such integral powers of e and of the given number, whose logarithm is to be computed, that the value of the ratio does not differ much from one.

We continue our computation of ln 10 by computing ln 5. Since $e^3 \approx 20.0855$ and $20 = 5 \cdot 4$, we choose $N = e^3/20$:

$$\ln N = \ln e^3 - \ln 20 = 3 \ln e - \ln 5 - \ln 4$$

$$= 3 - \ln 5 - 2(0.693147) = 1.613706 - \ln 5$$

since $\ln 4 = \ln 2^2 = 2 \ln 2$. Thus, if $N = e^3/20$,

$$\ln 5 = 1.613706 \ldots - \ln N$$

Now, if $N = e^3/20$, then

$$u = (e^3/20 - 1)/(e^3/20 + 1) = (e^3 - 20)/(e^3 + 20)$$

that is

$$u = 0.0855/40.0855 = 0.002133$$

Therefore,

$$u^3/3 = 0.0000000033\ldots$$

is negligible, the first term $2u$, alone, already giving five exact decimals:

$$\ln N = 2 \cdot 0.002133 = 0.004266$$

so that

$$\ln 5 = 1.613706 - 0.004266 = 1.609440\ldots$$

Adding ln 2 and ln 5, we obtain $1/M$:

$$M^{-1} = 1/M = \ln 10 = 0.693147 + 1.609440 = 2.302587\ldots$$

and

$$M = 1/M^{-1} = 0.43429\ldots$$

We compute also ln 3 and ln 7. The ratio $N = 3/e$ is convenient for the first logarithm and for $N = 3/e$, we get

$$u = (3/e - 1)/(3/e + 1) = (3 - e)/(3 + e)$$

$$= 0.28172 \ldots /5.71828 = 0.0492666\ldots;$$

$$u^3/3 = 0.00003986\ldots$$

so that

$$\ln N = \ln 3 - 1 = 2 \cdot 0.04930652 = 0.09861304\ldots$$

and

$$\ln 3 = 1.09861\ldots$$

To compute ln 7 we choose

$$N = e^2/7 \text{ and } u = (N - 1)/(N + 1) = (e^2 - 7)/(e^2 + 7)$$

Substituting $e^2 = 7.38905$, we obtain

$$u = 0.38905/14.38905 = 0.027038$$
$$u^3/3 = 0.000007$$
$$\overline{u + u^3/3 = 0.027045}$$

so that

$$\ln (e^2/7) = 0.054090 = 2 - \ln 7$$

which gives

$$\ln 7 = 1.94591...$$

Now taking into consideration the relations $\log 4 = 2 \log 2$, $\log 6 = \log 2 + \log 3$, $\log 8 = 3 \log 2$, $\log 9 = 2 \log 3$, which hold for logarithms to any base, we have the table of first nine logarithms:

N	Approximate values of	
	Natural ln N	Common log N
1	0.00000	0.00000
2	0.69315	0.30103
3	1.09861	0.47712
4	1.38629	0.60206
5	1.60944	0.69897
6	1.79176	0.77815
7	1.94591	0.84510
8	2.07944	0.90309
9	2.19722	0.95424
10	2.30259	1.00000

Common logarithms are easily obtained multiplying the natural logarithms by the modulus $M = 0.43429...$ because

$$\log N = M \cdot \ln N$$

To continue and complete this table another infinite series can be used, namely the series for

$$\ln [(N + 1)/N] = \ln (N + 1) - \ln N$$

which allows the computation of the increment (amount of increase) to be added to ln N, when N is replaced by the next integer $N + 1$.

This series is deduced from the series (23) by replacing u by $u = 1/(2N + 1)$: if $u = 1/(2N + 1)$, then the number $(1 + u)/(1 - u)$ is equal to

$$(1 + u)/(1 - u) = [(2N + 2)/(2N + 1)]/[2N/(2N + 1)] = (N + 1)/N$$

so that the series (23) is transformed into:

$$\ln[(N + 1)/N] = 2\{1/(2N + 1) + (1/3)\cdot 1/(2N + 1)^3 + \cdots\}$$

that is, picking out the first term as common factor of all terms:

$$\ln(N + 1) = \ln N + 2(2N + 1)^{-1}\{1 + (1/3)\cdot(2N + 1)^{-2} + \cdots\}$$

The series

$$1 + (2N + 1)^{-2}/3 + (2N + 1)^{-4}/5 + \cdots + (2N+1)^{-2m}/(2m +1) + \cdots$$

converges very rapidly. So, for instance if $N = 10$, we obtain

$$\ln 11 = \ln 10 + (2/21)\{1 + 1/1323 + 1/972405 + \cdots\}$$

and the third term is negligible. The sum of the first two terms $2/21 + 2/27783$ is transformed easily into the decimal fraction $0.09531\ldots$ and the result is

$$\ln 11 = 2.30259\ldots + 0.09531\ldots = 2.39790\ldots$$

The table is completed by inserting rational numbers between the integers and thus obtaining a more dense set of values for the powers of e. For instance, if $\ln 2.1$ is to be computed one can observe that $(2.1)/2 = 1.05$ and thus

$$\ln 2.1 - \ln 2 = \ln 1.05$$

But, for $\ln 1.05$ we can use the series (19) with $u = 0.05$:

$$\ln 1.05 = 0.05 - 0.0025/2 + 0.000125/3 - 0.00000625/4\ldots$$

$$= 0.04879\ldots$$

so that

$$\ln 2.1 = 0.69315\ldots + 0.04879\ldots = 0.74194\ldots$$

Use of Tables of Common Logarithms

Having explained how the tables of logarithms were computed, we now show how to use them.

First we restate the properties of logarithms which simply express the laws of exponentiation in another form. Because $\log_a N = n$ is equivalent to $N = a^n$ we formulate, omitting for the sake of brevity the subscript a (base), the known laws of exponentiation as follows:

Powers	Logarithms
$MN = a^m a^n = a^{m+n}$	$\log(MN) = \log M + \log N$
$M/N = a^m/a^n = a^{m-n}$	$\log(M/N) = \log M - \log N$
$N^k = (a^n)^k = a^{nk}$	$\log(N^k) = k \log N$
$\sqrt[k]{N} = (a^n)^{1/k} = a^{n/k}$	$\log(\sqrt[k]{N}) = (\log N)/k$

The tabular numbers N have only four significant figures and the common logarithms of all numbers with the same four significant figures have the same mantissa. The characteristics are necessarily different, because their values depend on the position of the decimal points. Take for instance 471100, 47.11, 4.711, 0.04711. The common mantissa of the logarithms of all these numbers is 67311. Their characteristics are different: the characteristic of $\log 4.711$ is zero since $10 > 4.711 > 1$ and therefore $\log 4.711 = 0.67311$. But the characteristic of $\log 471100$ is equal to 5 because $10^5 < 471100 < 10^6$ and $\log 471100 = 5.67311$.

In general a number with $n + 1$ digits to the left of the dot is contained between 10^{n+1} and 10^n, and the characteristic of its logarithm is therefore equal to n. Abbreviating the expression "characteristic (or mantissa) of the logarithm of a number N" to "characteristic (or mantissa) of N", we have thus:

RULE I: The characteristic of any number greater than one is one less than the number of digits before the decimal point. Thus

$$\log 47110 = 4.67311 \text{ and } \log 47.11 = 1.67311$$

Note that the tables contain only mantissas, and the characteristics are to be found according to the position of the decimal point. Now what about the characteristic of 0.04711? We observe that

$$0.01 = 10^{-2} < 0.04711 < 10^{-1} = 0.1$$

Therefore, the characteristic is equal to -2 since it is defined by the inequality (2) which here becomes $10^c < 0.04711 < 10^{c+1}$ with $c = -2$ and $c + 1 = -1$. Now we write the logarithm of 0.04711 as

$$\log 0.04711 = -2 + 0.67311 = \overline{2}.67311 \qquad (25)$$

It is important to emphasize the fact that the mantissa (fractional part of a logarithm) is always positive in the tabular form $\overline{2}.67311$ of logarithm. But the numerical value of this logarithm is equal to -1.32689 and, if we write

$$\log 0.04711 = -1.32689,$$

we use the so-called *non-tabular* form of a logarithm. This non-tabular form has no interest for us and it is preferable to use exclusively the tabular form in which, for negative logarithms of numbers smaller than one, the negative integral part is noted as $\overline{2}, \overline{3}$, *etc.*, the sign minus above the absolute value of the negative characteristic having no relation to the positive mantissa.

In general, if the significant figures of a number smaller than one are preceded by m zeros, as for instance in

$$\overbrace{0.00 \cdots 00}^{m \text{ zeros}}4711$$

we conclude that this number is contained between $\overbrace{0.00 \cdots 00}^{m \text{ zeros}}1 = 10^{-m}$ and $\overbrace{0.00 \cdots 0}^{m-1 \text{ zeros}}1 = 10^{-m+1}$:

$$10^{-m} < \overbrace{0.00 \cdots 0}^{m \text{ zeros}}4711 < 10^{-m+1}.$$

Thus its characteristic is equal to $-m$. Hence, the second rule is:

RULE II: The characteristic of a number less than one is negative and its absolute value is equal to the number of zeros before the first significant figure. Thus

$$\log 0.00004711 = \overline{5}.67311$$

EXAMPLES: 1) Find $\log (3/701)$. Because $\log 3 = 0.47712$ and $\log 701 = 2.84572$, we have

$$\log (3/701) = 0.47712 - 2.84572 = \overline{3}.63140$$

2) Find $\log \sqrt[3]{1/7}$. Since $\log 7 = 0.84510$ and $\log 1 = 0$, we obtain

$$\log (\sqrt[3]{1/7}) = (-\log 7)/3 = (-0.84510)/3 = -0.28170 = \overline{1}.71830$$

Note that -0.28170, value of the logarithm, cannot be considered as the final answer since it is a non-tabular form of the logarithm and must be transformed into $-1 + 0.71830 = \overline{1}.71830$ which has the negative characteristic $\overline{1}$ and the mantissa 71830, while 28170 in -0.28170, being negative, cannot be considered as a mantissa.

We have described how to find the common logarithm of a number having as many significant figures as the table we have to use. But in many cases the number will have more significant digits than have the tabular numbers. In such a case the method of interpolation is used, and we will explain it on the example of a table, where the numbers have four significant figures.

The characteristic is determined according to Rules I and II and we have to study how to find the mantissa by interpolation. Let us first study a numerical example. If $\log 47.1145$ is asked for, the position of the decimal point proves that the characteristic is one. We can now shift the decimal point since the mantissa does not change if the decimal point is shifted. Thus, instead of the given number $N^* = 47.1145$ we will consider $N' = 4711.45$ which has four significant digits before the dot, as have tabular numbers. Our number N' does not appear in the table, but it belongs to the interval $4711 - 4712$ formed by two successive tabular numbers $N = 4711$ and $N + 1 = 4712$ enclosing N'. The mantissas $M = 67311$ and $M + \Delta M = 67403$ correspond to them, with the difference $\Delta M = 67403 - 67311 = 92$. Therefore, the unknown mantissa M^* of $N' = 4711.45$ must be included between M and $M + \Delta M$. It has the value $M + \delta M$, if we denote by δM the increment of M, when N increases and becomes equal to N'. We sum up this discussion in the following short table:

Numbers	Mantissas
$N = 4711$	$M = 67311$
$N' = 4711 \cdot 45$	$M^* = M + \delta M = ?$
$N + 1 = 4712$	$M + \Delta M = 67403$

Now we plot two points P_1, P_2 whose coordinates are 4711 and 67311 for P_1 and 4712; 67403 for P_2:

The variation of the mantissa from 67311 to 67403, when the number increases from 4711 to 4712, cannot be represented by the straight line P_1P_2, its graph being, in general, a curve. But the table of mantissas does not and cannot give their exact values because they are represented

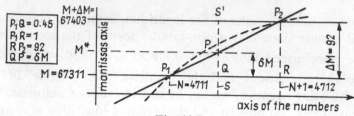

Fig. 11.5

by infinite decimal fractions. The exact value of the mantissa M^* of the number 4711.45 is not asked: all that we need is its approximate value correct to four decimal places with the fifth decimal sometimes correct, sometimes rounded off to reduce the difference between the exact and the approximate values below one-half of the last decimal unit, that is below 0.000005. Therefore, it is sufficient to replace the unknown graph of mantissa between the points P_1 and P_2 by its chord, joining the points P_1 and P_2 by a straight line P_1P_2. This straight line intersects the parallel SS' to the vertical mantissa axis through the point S, corresponding to the number 4711.45, on the number axis, at a point P in Figure 1 which can be considered as the point image of the mantissa of $N' = 4711.45$. Drawing a parallel P_1R to the horizontal number axis through the point P_1, we define a point Q as the intersection point of SP and P_1R. Now the horizontal line P_1QR corresponds to the value 67311 of the mantissa and the mantissa of 4711.45 is represented by the sum $67311 + QP$. To find it we must determine the length of the segment QP. It can be done with the aid of two similar triangles P_1QP and P_1RP_2: in them QP, $P_1Q = 0.45$, $P_1R = 1$, and $RP_2 = 67403 - 67311 = \Delta M = 92$ form the proportion $QP/RP_2 = P_1Q/P_1R$, that is

$$QP/92 = 0.45/1 = 0.45$$

Solving it for QP, we find that

$$\delta M = QP = 92 \cdot 0.45 = 41.4 \sim 41$$

and therefore the mantissa M^* of 4711.45 is equal to $67311 + 41$
$= 67352$.

Thus M^* was found by adding to the mantissa $M = 67311$ of
$N = 4711$ the proportional part δM of the difference $\Delta M = 92$ between the mantissas of tabular numbers $N = 4711$ and $N + 1 = 4712$
which enclose the number $N' = 4711.45$.

Generalizing, we formulate the interpolation method as follows. The
given number N^*, whose logarithm must be computed, is transformed
by shifting its decimal point into N', which belongs to the tabular
interval $(N, N + 1)$. The tabular mantissas of N and $N + 1$ are M
and $M + \Delta M$ respectively, where ΔM denotes their tabular difference.
The mantissa M^* of N' is represented by the sum $M + \delta M$, where δM
denotes the unknown increment of M, when the number N increases
to N'. To compute $M^* = M + \delta M$, it is sufficient to determine δM
and the interpolation with the aid of a straight line shows that $\delta M/$
$\Delta M = (N' - N)/1$, that is

$$\delta M = (N' - N)\,\Delta M \qquad (26)$$

In our example $N' - N = 0.45$, while $\Delta M = 92$.

Interpolation is needed also in the inverse problem: find the number N^*, knowing its logarithm. We begin again by studying a numerical
example. Suppose that $\log N^* = 2.34917$, so that the given mantissa
is $M^* = 34917$. The value 2 of the characteristic indicates that in N^*
there are three digits before the decimal point, but the significant digits
are to be found by using the value 34917 of the given mantissa M^*.
This mantissa 34917 does not appear in the table and it is enclosed by
the next smaller $M = 34908$ and the next larger mantissa $M + \Delta M$
$= 34928$:

	Mantissas	Numbers	
	$M = 34908$	$N = 2234$	
$\Delta M = 20$	$M + \delta M = M^* = 34917$	$N' = ?$	
$\delta M = 9$	$M + \Delta M = 34928$	$N + 1 = 2235$	

The number N' belongs to the interval (2234; 2235) and it has the
same digits as the unknown number N^*, differing from it only by the
position of the decimal point. The same relation (26), namely
$\delta M = (N' - N)\,\Delta M$, applies to the inverse problem, but now the
unknown is the increment $N' - N$ which affects the number N,
when its mantissa M increases by δM, the variation ΔM of the same

mantissa M being equal to the tabular difference between two mantissas enclosing the given mantissa M^*. In our example $\Delta M = 20$ and $\delta M = 9$, so that

$$N' - N = \delta M / \Delta M = 9/20 = 0.45$$

and therefore $N' = N + 0.45 = 2234.45$. Now the characteristic of $\log N^*$ being equal to 2, we find that $N^* = 223.445$. In general we have:

RULE III: If the characteristic c is zero or positive, place the decimal point after the first $c + 1$ significant digits counted from the left to the right.

RULE IV: If the characteristic c is negative, prefix $|c|$ zeros to the left of the first significant digit, and place the decimal point after the first zero.

The practical importance of common logarithms consists in the fact that shifting the decimal point in a number does not change the mantissa of its logarithm. The displacement of the dot corresponds to the multiplication of the number by a power of 10, and because the base of common logarithms is equal to the base 10 of our system of decimal numeration, this multiplication alters only the characteristic of the logarithm. This fact was the reason for the use of common logarithms in all numerical computations, introduced by Briggs in 1617 when the first edition of his tabes *Logarithmorum Chilias Prima* was published.

The logarithm can be considered as an operator which, when applied to a number x, transforms it into another number $y = \log x$. This operation may be repeated and thus double, triple, *etc* logarithms can be generated. We have, for instance, the double common logarithm of 2:

$$\log \log 2 = \log 0.30103 \ldots = \bar{1}.47861 \ldots$$

But, if we want to compute

$$\log \log \log 2 = \log (\bar{1}.47861\ldots) = \log (-0.52130\ldots)$$

we meet the common logarithm of a *negative* number, and this logarithm cannot be a real number: when the exponent x in 10^x increases from $-\infty$ to $+\infty$, running through all real values, the value 10^x of the power increases from zero to $+\infty$ and is *never* negative. Therefore, logarithms of negative and of complex numbers must be complex numbers, if they can be expressed as such numbers.

This question is related to the operation of exponentiation with complex exponents, which we have not yet studied. It is plain that if a complex number $\alpha + i\beta$ can be represented as a power of e or of 10 with a complex exponent, this exponent will be the natural or common logarithm of $\alpha + i\beta$.

Before studying these two related questions we note the application of logarithms to the solution of exponential equations. To solve an equation of this type

$$a^x = b \qquad\qquad (a > 0, b > 0)$$

where a and b are two positive numbers, we first apply the operation of taking logarithms of both sides:

$$\log (a^x) = \log b$$

But $\log (a^x) = x \log a$. Thus

$$x \log a = \log b$$

and the solution appears in the form of a ratio of two logarithm: $x = \log b/\log a$. In practice the value of x is found with the aid of double logarithms since

$$\log x = \log \log b - \log \log a$$

EXAMPLE: Given $7^x = 3$. The solution is $x = \log 3/\log 7$ and

$$\log x = \log \log 3 - \log \log 7 = \log 0.477\,12 - \log 0.845\,10$$

$$= \overline{1}.678\,63 - \overline{1}.926\,91 = -0.248\,28 = \overline{1}.751\,72$$

that is

$$x = \log_7 3 = 0.564\,57 \ldots$$

which means that

$$3 = 7^{0.564\,57\ldots}$$

Natural Logarithms of Complex Numbers

In the domain of real numbers $\ln 1 = 0$, and this real value of $\ln 1$ is unique. But, if we extend the number domain and consider the complex values of $\ln 1$, we find that besides the real value zero there are an infinite set of other, purely imaginary values, so that the symbol

Kogbetliantz 32

ln 1 is manyvalued in the domain of complex numbers. To prove it we recall that Euler's Formula

$$\cos x + i \sin x = e^{ix}$$

gives, for $x = 2\pi m$ ($m =$ any integer, negative, positive or zero)

$$1 = \cos 2\pi m + i \sin 2\pi m = 1 + i \cdot 0 = e^{2\pi mi}$$

Taking the logarithms of both members, we have the announced result

$$\ln 1 = 2\pi mi \qquad (m = 0, \pm 1, \pm 2, ...)$$

If $m = 0$, then we have the real value ln 1 = 0, but for $m \neq 0$ all other values are purely imaginary. The same applies to common logarithm $\log_{10} 1$ since $\log_{10} 1 = M \ln 1$. The real value zero of ln 1 is called its *principal value* and is denoted by log 1. From now on the principal value of any ln will be denoted by log. Thus,

$$\ln 1 = \log 1 + 2\pi mi, \qquad [m = E(m)]$$

where $E(m)$ denotes the integral part of the number m. If m is an integer, then $E(m) = m$ and *vice versa* $m = E(m)$ indicates that m is an integer without specifying its sign and value. We can now see that the logarithm of any real and positive number N, $N > 0$, is also a manyvalued symbol, if considered in the field of complex numbers. Indeed, denoting the *real* logarithm of N by log N and taking into consideration the fact that $N = N \times 1$, we have

$$\ln N = \log N + \ln 1 = \log N + 2\pi mi$$

Here again log N is called the principal value of the many valued ln N. All other values of ln N are complex numbers whose imaginary parts $2\pi mi$ are multiples of $2\pi i$.

We met manyvalued functions, when we studied the radicals of complex numbers such as $\sqrt[n]{a + ib}$ with $n = E(n)$. The n-th root $\sqrt[n]{N}$ has a finite number n of different values, but each logarithm has an infinite number of values. If we recall that

$$\ln x = \lim_{n = \infty} [n(\sqrt[n]{x} - 1)]$$

we can explain the fact that the logarithm has an infinite set of values. In the complex number-domain $n(\sqrt[n]{x} - 1)$ has n different values and its limit for $n = \infty$, ln x, must have an infinite set of values.

The natural logarithm was defined as an operation inverse to exponentiation and the function $y = \ln x$ appears as the inverse function to the exponential function $x = e^y$ which is periodic, its period being $2\pi i$. The value x of e^y does not change, if a multiple $2\pi mi$ of the period $2\pi i$ is added to the exponent y:

$$x = e^y = e^{y+2m\pi i}$$

Taking the logarithms of both sides, we deduce again that $\ln x$ is a many-valued function, namely:

$$\ln x = y + 2m\pi i$$

Therefore, the fact that $\ln x$ is a many-valued function is related to the periodicity of the exponential function and we see that a function inverse to a periodic function must be many-valued.

We will now study the logarithms of negative numbers. A negative number $N < 0$ can be represented by the product $(-1)\,|N|$. We have indeed $|N| = -N$ so that

$$N = -\,|N| = (-1)\,|N| \qquad\qquad (N < 0)$$

with $|N| > 0$. Taking the logarithms, we obtain

$$\ln N = \ln |N| + \ln (-1).$$

Here

$$\ln |N| = \log |N| + 2\pi ki \qquad\qquad [k = E(k)] \quad (27)$$

where $\log |N|$ is the principal, real value of the natural logarithm of a real and positive number $|N|$. To find $\ln (-1)$ we apply Euler's Formula

$$\cos x + i \sin x = e^{ix}$$

with $x = 180° = \pi$. Since $\sin \pi = 0$ and $\cos \pi = -1$, it gives, for $x = \pi$,

$$-1 = e^{i\pi}$$

and therefore

$$\ln (-1) = i\pi + 2\pi mi \qquad\qquad [m = E(m)] \quad (28)$$

Here $i\pi$ is the principal value, $\log (-1)$, of $\ln (-1)$. We obtain now, adding (27) and (28):

$$\ln N = \log |N| + (2n + 1)\,\pi i \qquad\qquad [n = E(n)]$$

where $n = m + k = E(n)$.

EXAMPLE:

$$\ln (-2) = \log 2 + (2n + 1)\, \pi i \qquad\qquad [n = E(n)]$$

with

$$\log 2 = 0.693\ldots \text{ and } \log (-2) = 0.693\ldots + \pi i.$$

We now pass to the general case and compute $\ln (a + ib)$. First we transform $a + ib$ into its polar form $Re^{i\theta}$, where

$$R = \sqrt{a^2 + b^2} > 0 \text{ and } \tan \theta = b/a$$

so that

$$\ln (a + ib) = \ln (Re^{i\theta}) = \ln R + i\theta$$

But

$$\ln R = \log R + 2m\pi i \qquad\qquad [m = E(m)]$$

and thus, replacing R by $(a^2 + b^2)^{1/2}$:

$$\ln (a + ib) = (1/2) \log (a^2 + b^2) + i\theta + 2m\pi i \qquad (29)$$

with $\tan \theta = b/a$. The angle θ is such that its tangent is equal to b/a. A special notation exists in mathematics for an angle defined by its tangent. Since each angle can be plotted as a central angle in a circle of radius one, the arc subtended by the angle θ has the same radian measure θ and instead of angle θ we can speak of the arc θ. Thus θ is an arc such that its tangent is equal to b/a. This is abbreviated into "arctan (b/a)" which means "arc whose tangent is equal to b/a". Now arctan y (read "arctangent y") can also be considered as an operation applied to the number y, transforming it into $x = \arctan y$. This relation between two variables x and y is equivalent to $y = \tan x$, since $x = \arctan y$ means angle (arc) x such that its tangent has the value y: $\tan x = y$. Using the function arctan y, inverse to the function $\tan x$, we can write $\theta = \arctan (b/a)$, because $\tan \theta = b/a$ and the formula (29) now takes the form

$$\ln (a + ib) = (1/2) \log (a^2 + b^2) + i \arctan (b/a) + 2m\pi i \quad (30)$$

But, the function $\tan x$ is periodic and its period is π:

$$y = \tan x = \tan (x + k\pi) \qquad\qquad [k = E(k)]$$

Therefore, the inverse function arctan y is again many-valued and has an infinite number of different values for a given value of y. One of them, which belongs to the interval $(-\pi/2, \pi/2)$, is denoted by Arctan y, and called the principal value:

$$x = \arctan y = \text{Arctan } y + k\pi \qquad\qquad [k = E(k)]$$

as it is illustrated on fig. 2, where the angles $AOB = x = $ Arctan y and $AOC = x + \pi$ can be increased or decreased by multiples of $\pi = 180°$ without changing the value $y = \mathsf{AP}$ of their tangent.

In applying the function arctangent to the representation of $\ln (a + ib)$, we observe that in the formula (30) arctan (b/a) denotes the *amplitude* (also called *phase* and *argument*) of the complex number $a + ib$ and therefore the different values of $\theta = $ arctan (b/a) to be used in (30) can differ only by multiples of 2π, but not by multiples

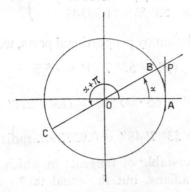

Fig. 11.6

of π. Denoting a special value of θ by arctan* (b/a), we emphasize that arctan* (b/a) is an angle in the first, second, third, or fourth quadrant, according to the signs of a and b, that is, according to $(b > 0, a > 0)$, $(b > 0, a < 0)$, $(b < 0, a < 0)$, and $(b < 0, a > 0)$, respectively. In (30) we can have, therefore,

$$\theta = \text{arctan} (b/a) = \text{arctan*} (b/a) + 2n\pi i \qquad [n = E(n)]$$

and the term $2n\pi i$ is absorbed by $2m\pi i$.

Summing up this discussion, we see that in the final form of the $\ln (a + ib)$, as it is given by (30), the arctangent of b/a, arctan* (b/a), must not be considered as many-valued, its value being defined by the signs of $\sin \theta = b/R$ and $\cos \theta = a/R, R > 0$.

EXAMPLE: Find $\ln (3 - 4i)$. Here

$$a = 3, b = -4, R = \sqrt{a^2 + b^2} = |a + ib| = 5, \text{ and } \tan \theta = -4/3$$

with

$$b/R = \sin \theta < 0 \text{ and } a/R = \cos \theta > 0$$

so that the amplitude θ of $3 - 4i$ belongs to the fourth quadrant: $-\pi/2 < \theta < 0$. To find θ, it is sufficient to compute its absolute value $|\theta|$, which is an acute positive angle $|\theta| = \text{Arctan}\,(4/3)$, since

$$\tan |\theta| = 4/3 = 1.33333\ldots$$

The table of tangents now gives

$$\left.\begin{array}{l} \tan 53°\,7' = 1.33268 \\ \tan |\theta| = 1.33333 \\ \tan 53°\,8' = 1.33349 \end{array}\right\} \begin{array}{l} 65 \\ \\ \end{array} \left.\begin{array}{l} \\ 81 \\ \end{array}\right.$$

Applying the interpolation by proportional parts, we form the equation

$$(|\theta| - 53°\,7')/1' = 65/81$$

so that

$$|\theta| - 53°\,7' = 65 \cdot 60''/81 = (1300/27)'' = 48''\ldots$$

and

$$|\theta| = 53°\,7'\,48'' = 0.92729\ldots \text{ radians}$$

We could use another table of tangents in which the angles are expressed directly in radians, but the usual tables do not use radian measure of angles and thus impose a supplementary work of transforming the degrees, minutes and seconds of angle into radians. This transformation is facilitated by special tables which give the values of degrees, minutes and seconds of angle in radians and *vice versa*.

We now have the numerical value of

$$\theta = \text{arctan}^* \,(-4/3) = \text{amplitude}\,(3 - 4i) = -0.92729$$

On the other hand, $\log R = \log 5 = 1.60944$ and thus, applying (30):

$$\ln (3 - 4i) = 1.60944 - 0.92729 \cdot i + 2m\pi i \qquad (31)$$

The term $2m\pi i$ expresses the fact that the natural logarithm is a many-valued expression, and it is the same in all natural logarithms. The value of $\ln (3 - 4i)$ corresponding to $m = 0$ is called *principal value* and is denoted by log:

$$\log (3 - 4i) = 1.60944\ldots - 0.92729\ldots \cdot i$$

In general, for any complex number $a + ib$ the principal value $\log (a + ib)$ of its natural logarithm expressed in (29) is equal to

$$\log (a + ib) = 1/2 \log (a^2 + b^2) + i \cdot \text{arctan}^* \,(b/a)$$

so that

$$\ln (a + ib) = \log (a + ib) + 2m\pi i.$$

Logarithms can solve the algebraic equations with complex exponents, such as

$$z^i = i$$

The fact that this equation has only real and positive roots is easy to prove, solving $z^i = i$ with the aid of logarithms. First we observe that Euler's Formula

$$\cos x + i \sin x = e^{ix}$$

carries with it

$$\log (\cos x + i \sin x) = ix$$

In the particular case, when $x = \pi/2$, we obtain $\cos (\pi/2) = 0$, $\sin (\pi/2) = 1$ and therefore $i = e^{i\pi/2}$, that is

$$\log i = i\,\pi/2 \tag{32}$$

Taking the logarithms of both sides of $z^i = i$, we transform it into the equivalent equation

$$i \ln z = \ln i = i\,\pi/2 + 2m\pi i$$

since $\ln i = \log i + 2m\pi i$. Dividing by i we obtain

$$\ln z = \pi/2 + 2m\pi$$

and, reverting to numbers,

$$z = e^{\pi/2 + 2m\pi}, \tag{33}$$

where $m = 0, \pm 1, \pm 2, \pm 3, \ldots$ runs through all integers from $-\infty$ to $+\infty$.

Therefore, the equation $z^i = i$ has an infinite number of positive and real roots given by (33) and no complex roots at all. The principal root $z_0 = e^{\pi/2} = 4.81\ldots$ corresponds to $m = 0$. All other roots $z_m (m \neq 0$ and $m \gtreqless 0)$ are deducible from z_0 by multiplying it by $e^{2\pi m}$:

$$z_m = e^{\pi/2} e^{2m\pi} = z_0 e^{2m\pi} = z_0 z_0^{4m} = z_0^{4m+1}$$

Since $\log_{10} (e^{2\pi}) = 2.728\,75$, we have $e^{2\pi} = 535.49\ldots$ and thus

$$z_m = z_0 (535.49)^m = 4.81\ldots (535.49)^m = (4.81\ldots)^{4m+1}$$

We have proved in Chapter 9 that the value of i^i is real, namely

$$i^i = (e^{i\pi/2})^i = e^{-\pi/2} = 1/e^{\pi/2} = 1/4.81\ldots = 0.207\,88\ldots$$

But in Chapter 9 we used only the principal value $i\pi/2$ of $\ln i$.

The power i^i is many-valued since

$$\ln i = \log i + 2m\pi i = i\pi/2 + 2m\pi i$$

and therefore

$$i^i = [e^{i(\pi/2 + 2m\pi)}]^i$$

which gives

$$i^i = e^{-\pi/2 - 2m\pi} = e^{-\pi/2}\, e^{-2m\pi} = (0.207\,88\ldots)\, e^{-2m\pi} = 0.207\,88/(535.49\ldots)^m$$

with $m = E(m) \gtrless 0$, or $m = 0$.

Exponentiation with complex exponents is a many-valued operation, as was exponentiation with fractional exponents. To compute the complex power $(a + ib)^{c + id}$ of a complex number $a + ib$, we represent this number $a + ib$ as a power of e:

$$a + ib = e^{\ln(a + ib)} \tag{34}$$

Now $\ln(a + ib) = \log(a + ib) + 2m\pi i$, and raising both members of (34) to a power with exponent $c + id$:

$$(a + ib)^{c + id} = [e^{\log(a + ib) + 2m\pi i}]^{c + id} = e^{(c + id)\log(a + ib)}\, e^{2mc\pi i - 2m\pi d}$$

The natural logarithm $\log(a + ib)$ is equal to $\log r + i\theta$, if $a + ib = re^{i\theta}$, and thus

$$(c + id)\log(a + ib) = (c + id)(\log r + i\theta)$$

$$= c \log r - d\theta + i(d \log r + c\theta)$$

Therefore, we obtain

$$(a + ib)^{c + id} = e^u e^{iv} = e^u(\cos v + i \sin v)$$

where the two *real* numbers u and v are expressed in terms of $c, d, r = (a^2 + b^2)^{1/2}$, and $\theta = $ amplitude $(a + ib) = \arctan^* (b/a)$ by:

$$u = c \log r - d\theta - 2m\pi d$$
$$v = d \log r + c\theta + 2m\pi c \qquad [m = E(m)]\ (35)$$

the integer m running through all integers from $-\infty$ to $+\infty$. The final result is

$$(a + ib)^{c + id} = e^u \cos v + i e^u \sin v.$$

EXAMPLE: Find $(\sqrt{3} + i)^{1 - i}$.

Here
$$a = \sqrt{3}, b = 1, r = 2, \tan \theta = b/a = 1/\sqrt{3}$$
and
$$\theta = 30° = \pi/6, c = 1, d = -1, \log r = \log 2 = 0.69315...$$

so that the expressions (35) for u and v become:

$$u = 0.69315... + \pi/6 + 2m\pi, v = \pi/6 - 0.69315... + 2m\pi,$$

that is
$$u = 2m\pi + 1.21675..., v = 2m\pi - 0.16955...$$

To compute $\cos v = \cos(-0.16955...) = \cos(0.16955...)$ and $\sin v = \sin(-0.16955...) = -\sin(0.16955...)$ we transform 0.16955 radians into $9°42'52''$, so that $\cos v = 0.98569$ and $\sin v = -0.16874$. Further

$$e^u = e^{2m\pi}e^{1.21675} = (e^{2\pi})^m 3.3777... = (535.49...)^m 3.3777$$

Since
$$3.3777 \cos v = 3.3294; \quad 3.3777 \sin v = -0.5727$$

we can write

$$(\sqrt{3} + i)^{1-i} = (3.3294 - 0.5727i)(535.49)^m \quad [m = E(m)]$$

The principal value of $(\sqrt{3} + 2)^{1-i}$ is obtained for $m = 0$.

The important point to emphasize is this: the study of logarithms and powers of complex numbers proves that all three direct operations, addition, multiplication, exponentiation, and their four inverse operations (there are two inverse operations to exponentiation), performed with complex numbers do not lead us outside the complex number domain in the sense that their results are again only complex numbers.

Thus the evolution and extension of the number concept, motivated by the impossibility of performing certain operations within a narrower number domain, which culminates in the concept of complex number, is terminated: since the results of all operations performed on complex numbers are complex numbers, the complex number appears as a perfect self-sufficient number. The further extension of the number concept arises from the necessity of applying numbers to geometry and physics.

Gregory's Series

Euler's formulas

$$e^{i\theta} = \cos\theta + i\sin\theta, \qquad\qquad e^{-i\theta} = \cos\theta - i\sin\theta$$

divided member by member give

$$e^{i\theta}/e^{-i\theta} = e^{2i\theta} = (\cos\theta + i\sin\theta)/(\cos\theta - i\sin\theta)$$

Dividing the numerator and the denominator of the righthand member by $\cos\theta$ and remembering that $\sin\theta/\cos\theta$ is $\tan\theta$, we obtain

$$e^{2i\theta} = (1 + i\tan\theta)/(1 - i\tan\theta)$$

Taking the logarithms of both sides

$$2i\theta = \ln[(1 + i\tan\theta)/(1 - i\tan\theta)]$$

and replacing $\tan\theta$ by x and θ by arctan x, we express an arctangent as a logarithm: $\qquad 2i \cdot \arctan x = \ln[(1 + ix)/(1 - ix)] \qquad\qquad$ (36)

Both members in (36) are many-valued functions of x. The principal value of $\ln[(1 + ix)/(1 - ix)]$ for $x = 0$ is that of log 1, that is zero. Therefore,

$$\ln[(1 + ix)/(1 - ix)] = \log[(1 + ix)/(1 - ix)] + 2m\pi i$$

where $\log[(1 + ix)/(1 - ix)]$ is that branch of many-valued $\ln[(1 + ix)/(1 - ix)]$ *which* for $x = 0$ *becomes equal to zero.*

On the other hand $\qquad \arctan x = \text{Arctan } x + k\pi \qquad\qquad [k = E(k)]$

where Arctan x, principal value of arctan x, is defined by the condition

$$-\pi/2 \leqslant \text{Arctan } x \leqslant \pi/2.$$

Therefore, it is also zero for $x = 0$.

If we introduce the principal values in (36), we can write it as follows

$$2i \text{ Arctan } x + 2k\pi i = \log[(1 + ix)/(1 - ix)] + 2m\pi i \qquad (37)$$

It is an identity, as are Euler's formulas from which (36) was derived. The integers k and m can vary, but they cannot be independent: choosing $x = 0$, in (37) we cancel the Arctan x and log x, since

$$\text{Arctan } 0 = \log 1 = 0$$

Thus, $2k\pi i = 2m\pi i$, so that $k = m$ and the identity (37) becomes now a relation between the principal values

$$2i \text{ Arctan } x = \log [(1 + ix)/(1 - ix)] \qquad (38)$$

Here we have an example of the importance of complex numbers: in the domain of real numbers there is no relation between the logarithm and the inverse trigonometric function arctangent. They appear as two *separate* functions having no link whatsoever. In reality Arctan x and logarithm are one and the same function, since, if $z = (1 + ix)/(1 - ix)$,

$$\log z = \log [(1 + ix)/(1 - ix)]$$

is identical to $2i$ Arctan x. *Vice versa*, solving $z = (1 + ix)/(1 - ix)$ with respect to x, we have $x = i(1 - z)/(1 + z)$ and

$$2i \text{ Arctan} [i(1 - z)/(1 + z)]$$

is nothing else than $\log z$.

Now we can deduce Gregory's Series which represents the principal value Arctan x of the function arctan x as an infinite series of odd powers of the variable x, in other words as an odd polynomial in x of infinite order. To write this series it is sufficient to apply to $\log [(1 + ix)/(1 - ix)]$ the expansion (23), replacing u in it by ix: the number N becomes $(1 + ix)/(1 - ix)$ and thus

$$\log [(1 + ix)/[1 - ix)]$$
$$= 2 \{ix/1 + (ix)^3/3 + (ix)^5/5 + \cdots + (ix)^{2n+1}/(2n + 1) + ...\}$$

Dividing both sides by $2i$ and taking into consideration (38), we have Gregory's Series:

$$\text{Arctan} x = x/1 - x^3/3 + x^5/5 - \cdots + (-1)^n x^{2n+1}/(2n + 1) + ... \qquad (39)$$

It is interesting to emphasize that this *real* series is obtained by using *complex* numbers.

The discovery of the series (39) is ascribed to the Scotch mathematician James Gregory (1638–1675). It is famous in the history of mathematics because Gregory deduced from it the first *exact* expression of the number π, substituting 1 for x. We have indeed Arctan $1 = \pi/4$ since the tangent of the angle $\pi/4 = 45°$ is equal to one. Thus

$$\pi/4 = 1 - 1/3 + 1/5 - 1/7 + 1/9 - 1/11 + \cdots \qquad (40)$$

This numerical series is sometimes also called Leibnitz's series, since Leibnitz obtained it independently from Gregory's work. It converges but extremely slowly, so that it cannot be used for practical computation of π. Its convergence is improved, if we group the terms by pairs and perform the subtraction. Thus $1 - 1/3 = 2/(1 \times 3)$, $1/5 - 1/7 = 2/(5 \times 7)$, *etc.* so that

$$\pi/8 = 1/(1 \times 3) + 1/(5 \times 7) + 1/(9 \times 11)$$

$$+ \cdots + 1/[(4n + 1)(4n + 3)] + \cdots$$

but even this series of positive terms converges too slowly.

The best method of using the series (39) for the computation of π consists of representing $\pi/4$ as follows:

$$\pi/4 = 4 \operatorname{Arctan} (1/5) - \operatorname{Arctan} (1/239) \tag{41}$$

and using the series (39) with $x = 1/5$ and $x = 1/239$. To prove (41) it is necessary to apply the duplication formula for tangent, that is to express the tangent of double angle $2A$ in terms of the tangent of the simple angle A. The tangent of a double angle, $\tan 2A$, is by definition the ratio $\sin 2A/\cos 2A$ of the sine and cosine of a double angle. According to Euler's formula the numerator and the denominator of this ratio are involved in two terms of the rotation factor through $2A$:

$$e^{2Ai} = \cos 2A + i \sin 2A$$

Dividing both sides by

$$\cos 2A = \cos^2 A - \sin^2 A$$

we obtain

But

$$e^{2Ai}/(\cos^2 A - \sin^2 A) = 1 + i \tan 2A \tag{42}$$

$$e^{2Ai} = (e^{Ai})^2 = (\cos A + i \sin A)^2 = \cos^2 A - \sin^2 A + 2i \sin A \cos A \tag{43}$$

Dividing by $\cos^2 A - \sin^2 A$, we transform (43) into

$$e^{2Ai}/(\cos^2 A - \sin^2 A) = 1 + 2i \sin A \cos A/(\cos^2 A - \sin^2 A).$$

The righthand member can be expressed in terms of $\tan A = \sin A/\cos A$ and to do it we divide the numerator and denominator of the last term by $\cos^2 A$:

$$e^{2Ai}/(\cos^2 A - \sin^2 A) = 1 + 2i \tan A/(1 - \tan^2 A). \tag{44}$$

Comparing (42) and (44), we obtain finally the duplication formula

$$\tan 2A = 2 \tan A/(1 - \tan^2 A) \qquad (45)$$

Here is an example of (45): If $A = 30°$, then

$$\tan A = \tan 30° = 1/\sqrt{3} \text{ and } \tan 2A = \tan 60° = \sqrt{3}$$

so that, indeed,

$$2 \tan 30°/(1 - \tan^2 30°) = 2/[\sqrt{3}(1 - 1/3)] = 3/\sqrt{3} = \sqrt{3} = \tan 60°$$

The most interesting particular case of (45) is $A = 45°$, when $\tan A = 1$ and $\tan 2A = \tan 90° = \infty$. And, indeed, the numerator and denominator of the righthand member in (45) are, for $A = 45°$, two and zero, respectively, so that $\tan 90° = \infty$.

Having established the duplication formula, we can apply it twice and deduce the expression of $\tan 4A$ in terms of $\tan A$. Considering $4A$ as a double angle and $2A$ as a simple angle, we can write (45) as follows:

$$\tan 4A = 2 \tan 2A/(1 - \tan^2 2A)$$

Now we substitute for $\tan 2A$ its value in terms of $\tan A$ given by (45). Thus, after some algebraic computations left to the reader as useful exercise, we obtain the desired result:

$$\tan 4A = 4 \tan A(1 - \tan^2 A)/(1 - 6 \tan^2 A + \tan^4 A) \quad (46)$$

We now choose angle A in such a way that $\tan A = 1/5$, that is

$$A = \text{Arctan} (1/5)$$

and apply the relation (46):

$$\tan 4A = 4(1/5) (1 - 1/25)/[1 - 6(1/25) + 1/625] = 120/119$$

which proves that the angle $4A$ is very near to $\pi/4$ since

$$\tan (\pi/4) = 1 \text{ and } \tan 4A = 120/119.$$

We can therefore represent $4A$ as $\pi/4 + x$: $4A = \pi/4 + x$ and, if we can find x, the value of $\pi/4$ will be represented by the difference $4A - x$:

$$\pi/4 = 4A - x = 4 \text{ Arctan} (1/5) - x \qquad (47)$$

Note that $4A = 4$ Arctan $(1/5)$ is the first term in the expression (41) of $\pi/4$. Therefore the relation (41) will be established, if we can show that

$$x = \text{Arctan } (1/239) \qquad (48)$$

To prove this it is sufficient to verify that

$$\tan x = 1/239$$

But

$$x = 4A - \pi/4 \text{ and } \tan x = \tan (4A - \pi/4)$$

so that we must compute the tangent of a difference $4A - \pi/4$, knowing the tangents of each term of this difference:

$$\tan 4A = 120/119 \quad \text{and} \quad \tan (\pi/4) = 1.$$

Here we meet with an important problem which has wide practical applications, since the sum and the difference of two angles arise as a result of two successive rotations in the same sense (sum of two rotation angles) or in two opposite directions (difference of rotation angles). Trigonometric functions sine, cosine, tangent are nothing more than indirect characterizations of angles; therefore sine, cosine, and tangent of a sum or difference of two angles play important roles in applied mathematics. Since

$$\tan (A + B) = \sin (A + B)/\cos (A + B)$$

we begin by deducing the expressions of $\sin (A + B)$ and $\cos (A + B)$. Euler's formula is again the source of these expressions:

$$e^{i(A+B)} = e^{iA+iB} = e^{iA}e^{iB} = (\cos A + i \sin A)(\cos B + i \sin B)$$

so that performing the multiplication $(i^2 = -1)$:

$$e^{i(A+B)} = \cos A \cos B - \sin A \sin B + i(\sin A \cos B + \cos A \sin B)$$

On the other hand,

$$e^{i(A+B)} = \cos (A + B) + i \sin (A + B)$$

Comparing the two expressions of $e^{i(A+B)}$, we obtain a complex identity

$$\cos (A + B) + i \sin (A + B)$$

$$= \cos A \cos B - \sin A \sin B + i(\sin A \cos B + \sin B \cos A)$$

Splitting it into two real identities, we find the following expressions for cosine and sine of $A + B$:

$$\cos (A + B) = \cos A \cos B - \sin A \sin B \qquad (49)$$

$$\sin (A + B) = \sin A \cos B + \sin B \cos A \qquad (50)$$

Dividing the second identity by the first one, member by member, we deduce the corresponding formula for $\tan (A + B)$:

$$\tan (A + B)$$

$$= (\sin A \cos B + \sin B \cos A)/(\cos A \cos B - \sin A \sin B) \quad (51)$$

The second member of (51) is expressed in terms of sine and cosine of angles A and B, but it is easy to express it in terms of $\tan A$ and $\tan B$. To achieve this transformation we divide the numerator and the denominator of the second member by the product $\cos A \cdot \cos B$ which does not change the value of the fraction. Now

$$(\sin A \cos B)/(\cos A \cos B) + (\sin B \cos A)/(\cos A \cos B)$$

$$= \tan A + \tan B$$

$$(\cos A \cos B)/(\cos A \cos B) - (\sin A \sin B)/(\cos A \cos B)$$

$$= 1 - \tan A \tan B$$

and our goal is attained:

$$\tan (A + B) = (\tan A + \tan B)/(1 - \tan A \tan B) \qquad (52)$$

The three formulas (49), (50) and (52):

$$\sin (A + B) = \sin A \cos B + \cos A \sin B$$

$$\cos (A + B) = \cos A \cos B - \sin A \sin B$$

$$\tan (A + B) = (\tan A + \tan B)/(1 - \tan A \tan B)$$

express the effect of addition of two angles on the trigonometric functions and they are called "addition formulas". Changing the sign of B, that is replacing B by $-B$, we transform them into equivalent formulas dealing with differences of angles:

$$\sin (A - B) = \sin A \cos B - \sin B \cos A$$

$$\cos (A - B) = \cos A \cos B + \sin A \sin B \qquad (53)$$

$$\tan (A - B) = (\tan A - \tan B)/(1 + \tan A \tan B)$$

since

$$\sin(-B) = -\sin B, \quad \cos(-B) = \cos B$$

and

$$\tan(-B) = \sin(-B)/\cos(-B) = -\tan B$$

Now we revert to our problem of computing π and apply the last formula (53) to $\tan x = \tan(4A - \pi/4)$:

$$\tan x = [\tan 4A - \tan(\pi/4)]/[1 + \tan 4A \tan(\pi/4)]$$

The substitution in the expression of $\tan x$ of the values $\tan 4A = 120/119$ and $\tan(\pi/4) = 1$ transforms it into

$$\tan x = (120/119 - 1)/(1 + 120/119) = 1/239$$

and therefore (48) is justified:

$$x = \text{Arctan}(1/239)$$

The numerical value of $\pi/4 = 4A - x$ given in (47) is now:

$$\pi/4 = 4 \arctan(1/5) - \text{Arctan}(1/239).$$

Using Gregory's Series (39) for $x = 1/5$ and $x = 1/239$, we obtain the following evaluation for $\pi/4$:

$$\pi/4 = 4[1/5 - 1/375 + 1/125^2 - 1/(7 \cdot 5^7) + \cdots]$$
$$- [1/239 - 1/(3 \cdot 239^3) + \cdots] \qquad (54)$$

Already the fourth term of the first series for arctan $(1/5)$ is small: $1/(7 \cdot 5^7) = 0.0000018328...$ since its common logarithm is equal to

$$- (\log 7 + 7 \log 5) = -0.84510 - 7.(0.69897) = -5 \cdot 73689 = \overline{6}.26311$$

while the fifth, omitted, term is

$$1/(9 \cdot 5^9) = 0.0000000 5689...$$

because

$$\log[1/(9 \cdot 5^9)] = -0.95424 - 6.29073 = \overline{8}.75503...$$

The terms of the first series are alternately positive and negative. Therefore the error made by retaining only the first four terms is less than the fifth term. Their sum is

$$1/5 - 1/375 + 1/15625 - 1/546875 = 0.1973955006$$

Thus, the value of the terms in the first brackets is 0.1973955... with seven exact decimals. The third, omitted, term in the second brackets is $1/(5 \cdot 239^5)$ and its value is less than 10^{-12}:

$$1/(5 \cdot 239^5) < 0.000000000001$$

Therefore
$$1/239 - 1/(3 \cdot 239^3) = 0.004184076$$

and
$$\pi/4 = 0.789582 - 0.004184 = 0.785396...$$

which gives $\pi = 3.141592...$ with six exact decimals.

We see that logarithmic series (19) and the result of its transformation (39), the expansion of arctan x, can be used in numerical computations notwithstanding their slow convergence, if they are applied to cases which are dealing with small values of variables.

The logarithmic series (19), when applied to a complex variable $u = re^{i\theta}$, generates two real series whose terms involve trigonometric functions sine and cosine of θ and its multiples 2θ, 3θ, 4θ, ..., $n\theta$ .... Substituting in (19) $u = r^{i\theta}$, we obtain

$$\log (1 + re^{i\theta}) = re^{i\theta}/1 - r^2 e^{2i\theta}/2 + r^3 r^{3i\theta}/3$$
$$- r^4 r^{4i\theta}/4 + \cdots + (-1)^{n-1} r^n e^{in\theta}/n + \cdots \quad (55)$$

The numerators can be split into their real and imaginary parts with the aid of Euler's formula:

$$r^n e^{in\theta} = r^n \cos n\theta + i r^n \sin n\theta \qquad (56)$$

On the other hand we know that

$$\log [1 + re^{i\theta}] = \log R + i\theta$$

if R and ω denote the absolute value and the amplitude (argument, phase) of the complex number

Now
$$1 + re^{i\theta} = 1 + r \cos \theta + i r \sin \theta = Re^{i\omega}$$
$$R = [(1 + r \cos \theta)^2 + r^2 \sin^2 \theta]^{1/2} = (1 + 2r \cos \theta + r^2)^{1/2}$$
and
$$\tan \omega = r \sin \theta/(1 + r \cos \theta)$$
so that
$$\omega = \text{Arctan} [r \sin \theta/(1 + r \cos \theta)]$$
Therefore,
$$\log (1 + re^{i\theta}) = \log (1 + 2r \cos \theta + r^2)^{1/2}$$
$$+ i \, \text{Arctan} [r \sin \theta/(1 + r \cos \theta)] \quad (57)$$

Using (56), we also have from (55)

$$\log (1 + re^{i\theta}) = r \cos \theta/1 - r^2 \cos 2\theta/2 + r^3 \cos 3\theta/3 - \cdots$$
$$+ i(r \sin \theta/1 - r^2 \sin 2\theta/2 + r^3 \sin 3\theta/3 - \cdots) \quad (58)$$

Comparing (57) and (58) and separating real from imaginary, we obtain two real expansions in infinite series

$$(1/2) \log (1 + 2r \cos \theta + r^2)$$
$$= r \cos \theta - r^2 \cos 2\theta/2 + r^3 \cos 3\theta/3 - \cdots \quad (59)$$

$$\text{Arctan } [r \sin \theta/(1 + r \cos \theta)]$$
$$= r \sin \theta - r^2 \sin 2\theta/2 + r^3 \sin 3\theta/3 - \cdots \quad (60)$$

In particular, for $\theta = \pi/2$ we have

$$\cos (\pi/2) = 0, \ \sin (\pi/2) = 1, \ \sin (2\pi/2) = \sin \pi = 0,$$
$$\sin (3\pi/2) = -1, etc$$

so that we come back again to Gregory's Series for Arctan r:

$$\text{Arctan } r = r/1 - r^2/3 + r^5/5 - r^7/7 + \cdots$$

Thus (60) appears as a generalization of Gregory's Series.

The interesting particular cases of (59) and (60) are those in which $r = 1$. If $r = 1$, $1 + 2r \cos \theta + r^2$ reduces to

$$2 + 2 \cos \theta = 2(1 + \cos \theta) = 4 \cos^2 (\theta/2)$$

and $(1/2) \log (1 + 2r \cos \theta + r^2)$ to

$$(1/2) \log [4 \cos^2 (\theta/2)] = (1/2) \log \{[2 \cos (\theta/2)]^2\}$$
$$= \log [2 \cos (\theta/2)]$$

while Arctan $[r \sin \theta/(1 + r \cos \theta)]$ becomes equal to $\theta/2$ since

$$\sin \theta/(1 + \cos \theta) = 2 \sin (\theta/2) \cos (\theta/2)/[2 \cos^2 (\theta/2)] = \tan (\theta/2)$$

so that
$$\text{Arctan } [\sin \theta/(1 + \cos \theta)] = \text{Arctan } [\tan (\theta/2)] = \theta/2$$

two inverse operations *Arctan* and *tan* cancelling each other. Thus, we obtain

$$\log [2 \cos (\theta/2)] = \cos \theta - \cos 2\theta/2 + \cos 3\theta/3 - \cos 4\theta/4 + \cdots \quad (61)$$
$$\theta/2 = \sin \theta - \sin 2\theta/2 + \sin 3\theta/3 - \sin 4\theta/4 + \cdots \quad (62)$$

In all these transformations of the logarithmic series the angle $\theta/2$ as an Arctangent is between $-\pi/2$ and $\pi/2$. Thus, the essential condition of validity for both series (61) and (62) is $-\pi < \theta < \pi$.

The numerical series (20) and (40) are particular cases of these two series: for $\theta = 0$, as well as for $\theta = 90°$, the first series gives

$$\log 2 = 1 - 1/2 + 1/3 - 1/4 + 1/5 - \cdots \tag{20}$$

and for $\theta = \pi/2 = 90°$ the second becomes

$$\pi/4 = 1 - 1/3 + 1/5 - 1/7 + 1/9 - \cdots \tag{40}$$

We know that $\sin x/x$ tends to *one* for $x \to 0$. Therefore, for any fixed n we have also

$$\lim_{\theta=0} \sin (n\theta)/n\theta = 1$$

Dividing the series (62) by θ and passing to the limit for $\theta = 0$, we get

$$1/2 \sim 1 - 1 + 1 - 1 + 1 - 1 + 1 - \cdots \tag{63}$$

where the sign of equality, $=$, is replaced, by the sign of equivalence, $\sim$, because the series (63) diverges. We met it already, when dealing with the geometrical series, since the formula

$$1 + q + q^2 + q^3 + q^4 + \cdots + q^n + \cdots = 1/(1 - q)$$

reduces for $q = -1$ to the series (63), ascribing to this divergent series the value $1/2$. Note that if the series (63) does represent a number s

$$s \sim 1 - 1 + 1 - 1 + 1 \tag{64}$$

this number can be equal only to $1/2$ because (64) gives

$$s \sim 1 - (1 - 1 + 1 - 1 + 1 - \cdots) \sim 1 - s$$

and the equation $s = 1 - s$ yields $s = 1/2$. This explains the persistent association of the number $1/2$ with the divergent series (63).

We do not know yet *how* a divergent series can represent a number, if the limit $\lim_{n=\infty} S_n$ of the sum S_n of its first n terms for $n \to \infty$ does not exist, and we will discuss this important question in Chapter 12.

Generalization of Limit Concept and Summation of Divergent Series

The concept of limit leads to the representation of numbers or functions by convergent series. We have already studied some of them as, for instance, the geometric series (Chapter 4):

$$\sum_1^\infty q^n = 1 + q + q^2 + q^3 + \cdots + q^n + \cdots = 1/(1 - q) \qquad (1)$$

which converges for $-1 < q < 1$, but diverges for $|q| \geq 1$, and the series

$$\sum_1^\infty (-1)^{n-1} x^n/n = x - x^2/2 + x^3/3 - x^4/4 \cdots + (-1)^{n-1} x^n/n \ldots$$
$$= \log (1 + x) \qquad (2)$$

convergent also for $|x| < 1$, as well as for $x = 1$, but not for $x = -1$ and $|x| > 1$.

The convergence of an infinite series

$$\sum_0^\infty u_n = u_0 + u_1 + u_2 + u_3 + \cdots + u_n + \cdots = s$$

means, as we know, the existence, for $n \to \infty$, of the limit $\lim s_n = s$, where the so-called *partial* sums

$$s_0, s_1, s_2, s_3, \ldots, s_n, \ldots \to s \qquad (3)$$

are defined by

$$s_n = \sum_0^n u_k = u_0 + u_1 + u_2 + \cdots + u_n$$

s_n being the sum of the first $n + 1$ of the series. The number s represented by a convergent series is computed with the aid of the limit $s = \lim_{n=\infty} s_n$ of the convergent sequence (3).

We now consider a much more general class of infinite series for which the limit $\lim_{n=\infty} s_n$ does not exist, the series being divergent. Their study is important because divergent series are now used with the same success as convergent series in the practical applications of mathematics. The fundamental fact is that divergent series may represent perfectly determined numbers as well as do convergent series, notwithstanding the non-existence of $\lim_{n=\infty} s_n$. The lack of this limit eliminates the possibility of computing the number represented by a divergent series by $\lim_{n=\infty} s_n$, and the use of divergent series is based on the generalization of this classical limit concept. The new concept of *generalized limit* in itself represents an important and relatively recent extension of the classical passage to the limit.

Let us first discuss some particular divergent series in order to study the generalized limit on these examples. In them we will use the complex variable $z = re^{it}$. In Chapter 11 we have applied the principle of permanency to the series (2) substituting in it re^{it} for x. We have also seen there how the separation of real and imaginary in both members of the identity

$$\log (1 + re^{it}) = re^{it} - r^2 e^{2it}/2 + r^3 e^{3it}/3 - \cdots$$

$$= \sum_{1}^{\infty} (-1)^{n-1} r^n e^{int}/n$$

yields two real infinite series

$$\log (1 - 2r \cos t + r^2) = r \cos t - r^2 \cos 2t/2 + r^3 \cos 3t/3 - \cdots \quad (4)$$

$$\text{Arctan } [r \sin t/(1 + r \cos t)] = r \sin t - r^2 \sin 2t/2 + r^3 \sin 3t/3 - \cdots \quad (5)$$

which converge for $0 < r < 1$ and $0 \leqslant t \leqslant 2\pi$. The coefficients of these polynominals of infinite order in the real variable r are the trigonometric functions of multiplies nt of t. For this reason the expansions (4) and (5) are called *trigonometric series* of functions

$$\log (1 - 2r \cos t + r^2) \quad \text{and} \quad \text{Arctan } [r \sin t/(1 + r \cos t)]$$

respectively, these functions being considered as functions of t. When they are considered as functions of r, their expansions (4) and (5) are called *power series* in r.

We apply now the same transformation to the geometric series (1). Replacing in it q by re^{it}, we study first the complex number $1/(1 - re^{it})$.

Using Euler's formula $e^{it} = \cos t + i \sin t$, we write $1/(1 - q)$ as follows:

$$(1 - re^{it})^{-1} = (1 - r\cos t - i\sin t)^{-1} \cdot (1 - r\cos t + i\sin t)^{-1}$$
$$\times (1 - r\cos t + i\sin t)$$

The product of first two factors can be written as $(1 - 2r\cos t + r^2)^{-1}$ for

$$(1 - r\cos t - i\sin t)(1 - r\cos t + i\sin t)$$
$$= (1 - r\cos t)^2 + (r\sin t)^2 = 1 - 2r\cos t + r^2 = T$$

where T is an abbreviation for the trinomial $1 - 2r\cos t + r^2 = T$. Thus, if $q = re^{it}$, then

$$(1 - q)^{-1} = (1 - r\cos t)/T + ir\sin t/T \tag{6}$$

On the other hand,

$$q^n = r^n e^{int} = r^n \cos(nt) + ir^n \sin(nt)$$

which gives, splitting each term of (1) into its real and imaginary parts:

$$(1 - q)^{-1} = \sum_0^\infty r^n \cos(nt) + i\sum_0^\infty r^n \sin(nt)$$

$$= 1 + r\cos t + r^2\cos(2t) + \cdots \tag{7}$$
$$+ i[r\sin t + r^2\sin(2t) + \cdots]$$

Comparing (6) and (7), we derive the following two important series:

$$(1 - r\cos t)/(1 - 2r\cos t + r^2)$$
$$= 1 + r\cos t + r^2\cos(2t) + \cdots + r^n\cos(nt) + \cdots \tag{8}$$

$$r\sin t/(1 - 2r\cos t + r^2)$$
$$= r\sin t + r^2\sin(2t) + r^3\sin(3t) + \cdots + r^n\sin(nt) + \cdots \tag{9}$$

They converge for $0 < r < 1$ and $0 \leqslant t \leqslant 2\pi$, that is, within the circle of radius *one* and center at the origin of coordinates.

Subtracting one half from both members of the series (8), we have also

$$\tfrac{1}{2}(1 - r^2)/(1 - 2r\cos t + r^2)$$
$$= 1/2 + r\cos t + r^2\cos(2t) + \cdots + r^n\cos(nt) + \cdots \tag{10}$$

If r is less than *one*, the series (9) and (10) converge and represent the lefthand members of these two identities.

We ask now what happens to them if r becomes equal to *one*? Do the infinite series

$$\sin t + \sin (2t) + \sin (3t) + \cdots + \sin (nt) + \cdots \qquad (11)$$

$$1/2 + \cos t + \cos (2t) + \cos (3t) + \cdots + \cos (nt) + \cdots \qquad (12)$$

derived from (9) and (10) by replacing r by *one*, represent the functions of the variable t which are the limits for $r = 1$ of the lefthand members in (9) and (10)?

If the denominator of these lefthand members, $T = 1 - 2r \cos t + r^2$, does not vanish for $r = 1$, their limits are equal to zero for (10) and to

$$\sin t/[2(1 - \cos t)] = 2 \sin (t/2) \cos (t/2)/[4 \sin^2 (t/2)]$$

$$= \tfrac{1}{2} \cotan (t/2)$$

But the denominator $1 - 2r \cos t + r^2$ can vanish for $r = 1$, if the variable t has at the same time special values. To find these exceptional values of t we must solve the equation

$$1 - 2r \cos t + r^2 = 0. \qquad (13)$$

This equation cal also be written as follows:

$$[\cos^2 (t/2) + \sin^2 (t/2)] (1 + r^2) - 2r[\cos^2 (t/2) - \sin^2 (t/2)]$$

$$= (1 - 2r + r^2) \cos^2 (t/2) + (1 + 2r + r^2) \sin^2 (t/2)$$

since

$$\cos t = \cos^2 (t/2) - \sin^2 (t/2)$$

Finally our equation (13) becomes

$$[(1 - r) \cos (t/2)]^2 + [(1 + r) \sin (t/2)]^2 = 0$$

A sum of two squares of real quantities can vanish if and only if each one of its two non-negative terms vanishes separately. Therefore, if the equation (13) is satisfied, r and t must satisfy two equations

$$(1 - r) \cos (t/2) = 0 \quad \text{and} \quad (1 + r) \sin (t/2) = 0$$

But $1 + r > 0$ and the second equation reduces to $\sin (t/2) = 0$ which gives $t = 0$ or $t = 2\pi$. Therefore, $\cos (t/2)$ in the first equation is equal to *one* or to *minus one*, so that $\cos(t/2) \neq 0$. The first equation reduced to $1 - r = 0$ gives $r = 1$.

We thus see that, when $r = 1$, the limits 0 and $1/2 \cot(t/2)$ of the lefthand members of (10) and (9) are defined for all values of t in the interval $(0, 2\pi)$, except the two boundary values $t = 0$ and $t = 2\pi$, for which $\sin(t/2) = 0$. The end-points $t = 0$ and $t = 2\pi$ of the range of variation of the variable t must be discarded, if r becomes equal to *one*. Note that $1/2 \cot(t/2)$ is infinite for $t = 0$ and $t = 2\pi$.

Our question now becomes more precise: do infinite series (11) and (12) represent $1/2 \cot(t/2)$ and zero respectively, when $0 < t < 2\pi$, the values $t = 0$ and $t = 2\pi$ being eliminated once and for all from consideration?

We emphasize that both series are divergent series for any value of t. To prove this assertion we observe that the general term u_n of a convergent series must vanish at the limit for $n = \infty$. In other words, $\lim_{n=\infty} u_n = 0$ is a *necessary condition* of convergence for the series

$$\sum u_n = u_0 + u_1 + u_2 + u_3 + \cdots + u_n + \cdots \qquad (14)$$

If this condition is not satisfied, the series is surely divergent. For a convergent series we have, indeed, $s_n = s + e_n$ with $\lim_{n=\infty} e_n = 0$ because by definition, $\lim_{n=\infty} s_n = s$ does exist. Forming the difference $s_n - s_{n-1}$ we find that

$$u_n = s_n - s_{n-1} = e_n - e_{n-1}$$

because $s_n - s_{n-1} = (s + e_n) - (s + e_{n-1})$, which proves that

$$\lim_{n=\infty} u_n = 0$$

The example of the *harmonic series*

$$\sum_1^\infty 1/n = 1 + 1/2 + 1/3 + \cdots + 1/n + \cdots$$

the terms of which do tend to zero when $n \to \infty$ because $\lim_{n=\infty}(1/n) = 0$, and which nevertheless diverges, proves also that the necessary condition of convergence

$$\lim_{u=\infty} u_n = 0 \qquad (15)$$

is by no means sufficient to ensure the convergence of a series.

Applying the condition (15) to the series (11) and (12), we prove their divergence for all values of t since the ordinary, classical limits $\lim_{n=\infty} \cos(nt)$ and $\lim_{n=\infty} \sin(nt)$ do not exist. When $n \to \infty$, the angle $nt = AOP_n$ increases without limit, and for $n = \infty$ there cannot be a last fixed position for the point P_n on the circumference of the circle with center at 0. The symbols $\lim_{n=\infty} \cos(nt)$ and $\lim_{n=\infty} \sin(nt)$ are meaningless, the condition (15) is not satisfied and the series (11) and (12) diverge. Their

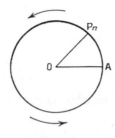

Fig. 12.1

partial sums do not approach fixed, definite numbers, when the number of terms increases without limit, and for them the sequence (3) diverges.

Before explaining how these divergent series can represent definite numbers or functions, we want to show that if they represent something they can represent only $1/2 \cot(t/2)$ and zero. In other words, assuming that (11) and (12) represent s and σ, we shall find that $s = 1/2 \cot(t/2)$ and $\sigma = 0$. To symbolize the representation of a number by a divergent series, we use the sign $\sim$ instead of the sign $=$, which is reserved for the representation of a number by a convergent series. Thus, we write by hypothesis

$$s \sim \sum_1^\infty \sin(nt)$$

$$= \sin t + \sin(2t) + \sin(3t) + \cdots + \sin(nt) + \cdots \qquad (16)$$

$$\sigma \sim 1/2 + \sum_1^\infty \cos(nt)$$

$$= 1/2 + \cos t + \cos(2t) + \cos(3t) + \cdots + \cos(nt) + \cdots \qquad (17)$$

where $s = s(t)$ and $\sigma = \sigma(t)$ are two unknown functions of t to be found.

To form the series which represents the expression $\sigma - is$, we multiply the series (16) by $(-i)$ and add it, term by term, to the series (17). Using in the result Euler's formula

$$\cos(nt) - i \sin(nt) = e^{-int}$$

we obtain

$$\sigma - is \sim 1/2 + e^{-it} + e^{-2it} + \cdots + e^{-int} + \cdots$$

$$= 1/2 + e^{-it}[1/2 + (1/2 + e^{-it} + e^{-2it} + \cdots + e^{-int} + \cdots)]$$

Therefore, $\sigma - is$ satisfies the equation

$$\sigma - is = 1/2 + e^{-it}(1/2 + \sigma - is)$$

Multiplying both members of this equation by $e^{it/2}$, we transform it into

$$e^{it/2}(\sigma - is) = (e^{it/2} + e^{-it/2})/2 + e^{-it/2}(\sigma - is)$$

Transposing to the left the second term of the righthand member and remembering that

$$2i \cdot \sin(t/2) = e^{it/2} - e^{-it/2}, \; 2\cos(t/2) = e^{it/2} + e^{-it/2} \quad (18)$$

we obtain the relation

$$2i \sin(t/2)\,(\sigma - is) = \cos(t/2)$$

Divided by $2i \sin(t/2)$, it gives

$$\sigma - is = -i/2 \cotan(t/2)$$

and this is equivalent to $\sigma = \sigma(t) = 0$ and $s = s(t) = 1/2 \cotan(t/2)$.

This reasoning does not constitute a proof of the fact that the series (11) and (12) do represent $1/2 \cotan(t/2)$ and zero. For the moment we know only representations of numbers and functions by convergent series and both series (11) and (12) diverge. Moreover, for $t = 0$ and $t = 2\pi$ there is a disagreement between these series and the functions $1/2 \cotan(t/2)$ and zero they represent for $0 < t < 2\pi$. Namely, if $t = 0$ or 2π, (12) becomes the numerical series

$$1/2 + 1 + 1 + 1 + \cdots + 1 + \cdots$$

for which $\lim\limits_{n=\infty} s_n = \infty$ although $\sigma(t) = 0$ for every $t > 0$ and thus $\lim\limits_{t=0} \sigma(t) = 0$, as well as $\lim\limits_{t=2\pi} \sigma(t) = 0$. The same discrepancy appears in the case of the series (11) which, for $t = 0$ and $t = 2\pi$, becomes a series of zeros and therefore converges and represents zero, although the function $s(t) = 1/2 \cotan (t/2)$ represented by (11) for $0 < t < 2\pi$, becomes infinite for $t = 0$ and $t = 2\pi$. These facts justify the exclusion of two boundary values $t = 0$ and $t = 2\pi$ of t.

Limiting henceforth the variation of t to the interior of the interval $(0, 2\pi)$ so that $0 < t < 2\pi$, we proceed now to the computation of an explicit expression in terms of n and t for the partial sums of series (11) and (12). Denoting by $S_n(t)$ and $C_n(t)$, respectively, the sums of the first n and $n + 1$ terms of series (11) and (12)

$$S_n(t) = \sum_1^n \sin (mt) = \sin t + \sin (2t) + \cdots + \sin (nt)$$

$$C_n(t) = 1/2 + \sum_1^n \cos (mt) = 1/2 + \cos t + \cos (2t) + \cdots + \cos (nt)$$

and forming the combination $C_n(t) + iS_n(t) + 1/2$, we have

$$1/2 + C_n(t) + iS_n(t) = 1 + q + q^2 + q^3 + \cdots + q^n$$
$$= (q^{n+1} - 1)/(q - 1),$$

where we used the symbol q as the abbreviation for $e^{it} = q$.

To find C_n and S_n the righthand member

$$(q^{n+1} - 1)/(q - 1) = [e^{i(n+1)t} - 1]/(e^{it} - 1)$$

must take the complex form $A + iB$ with A and B real. Now multiplying the first relation (18) by $e^{it/2}$, we see that

$$e^{it} - 1 = 2ie^{it/2} \sin (t/2) \tag{19}$$

Replacing in this result the variable t by $(n + 1) t$, we have also

$$e^{i(n+1)t} - 1 = 2ie^{i(n+1)t/2} \sin [(n + 1) t/2] \tag{20}$$

Dividing (20) member by member by (19), we obtain

$$(q^{n+1} - 1)/(q - 1) = e^{int/2} \sin [(n + 1) t/2]/\sin (t/2)$$

Euler's formula

$$e^{int/2} = \cos (nt/2) + i \sin (nt/2)$$

yields:

$$1/2 + C_n(t) + iS_n(t) = [\cos (nt/2) + i \sin (nt/2)]$$
$$\times \sin [(n + 1) t/2]/\sin (t/2)$$

Separating real and imaginary parts, we obtain finally

$$1/2 + C_n(t) = \cos (nt/2) \sin [(n + 1) t/2]/\sin (t/2) \qquad (21)$$

$$S_n(t) = \sin (nt/2) \sin [(n + 1) t/2]/\sin (t/2) \qquad (22)$$

Expressions (21) and (22) allow us to conclude the divergence of series (11) and (12) directly from the behavior of their partial sums C_n and S_n for $n \to \infty$. It is obvious, indeed, that the limits of C_n and S_n for $n = \infty$ do not exist because the factors in their numerators have no limits for n: the trigonometric functions in them oscillate, when n increases indefinitely, between -1 and 1 without tending to definite limits.

In order to prepare the generalization of the limit concept, with the aid of which it becomes possible to deduce from the divergent sequences

$$C_0, C_1, C_2, ..., C_n, ... \quad \text{and} \quad S_0, S_1, S_2, ..., S_n, ...$$

the functions $\sigma(t) = 0$ and $s(t) = 1/2 \cotan (t/2)$ they represent for $0 < t < 2\pi$, we transform the expressions (21) and (22) further.

To do this, we need the trigonometric relations which express the product of two sines or two cosines as well as the product of a sine and a cosine in the form of a sum of two terms, each of which is a sine or a cosine:

$$2 \sin A \sin B = \cos (A - B) - \cos (A + B) \qquad (23)$$

$$2 \cos A \cos B = \cos (A - B) + \cos (A + B) \qquad (24)$$

$$2 \sin A \cos B = \sin (A - B) + \sin (A + B) \qquad (25)$$

To prove them, we observe that, adding to the lefthand member of (24) that of (25) multiplied by i and picking out the common factor $2 \cos B$, we have with the aid of Euler's formula

$$2 \cos B(\cos A + i \sin A) = (e^{iB} + e^{-iB}) e^{iA} = e^{i(A+B)} + e^{i(A-B)}$$

$$= \cos (A + B) + i \sin (A + B) + \cos (A - B) + i \sin (A - B)$$

$$= \cos (A - B) + \cos (A + B) + i[\sin (A - B) + \sin (A + B)]$$

Separating the real and imaginary proves both (24) and (25). To justify (23), we replace in (24) the angles A and B by their complementary angles $90° - A$ and $90° - B$. This substitution transforms (24) into (23) since $\cos (90° - A) = \sin A$, $\cos (90° - B) = \sin B$ and $\cos (180° - A - B) = - \cos (A + B)$.

Applying (25) with $A = (n + 1) t/2$ and $B = nt/2$ to the numerator in (21), we obtain

$$\cos (nt/2) \sin [(n + 1) t/2] = \tfrac{1}{2} \sin (t/2) + \tfrac{1}{2} \sin [(n + 1/2) t],$$

so that (21) yields the expression of $C_n(t)$

$$C_n(t) = \sin [(n + 1/2) t]/2 \sin (t/2) \qquad (26)$$

Applying likewise (23) to (22), we find that

$$S_n(t) = \{\cos (t/2) - \cos [(n + 1/2) t]\}/2 \sin (t/2) \qquad (26^*)$$

and therefore

$$\tfrac{1}{2} \cotan (t/2) - S_n(t) = \cos [(n + 1/2) t]/2 \sin (t/2) \qquad (27)$$

We can now see by analyzing the relations (26) and (27) that the non-existence of definite limits of $C_n(t)$ and $S_n(t)$ for $n \to \infty$ is due to the indetermination of $\cos [(n + 1/2) t]$ and $\sin [(n + 1/2) t]$ for $n = \infty$.

At the same time these relations show that the series (11) and (12) are related in some way to $1/2 \cotan (t/2)$ and zero respectively, although they do not represent them in the same sense in which convergent series represent their sums. The expressions (26) and (27) of C_n and S_n belong to the same type of expressions which characterize the partial sums of convergent series. Take, for instance, the sum of first $n + 1$ terms of a geometric series

$$1 + q + q^2 + q^3 + \cdots + q^k + \cdots + q^n = (1 - q)^{-1} - q^{n+1}/(1 - q)$$

The first term, $(1 - q)^{-1}$, is independent of n, and it represents the sum of a convergent series, if $|q| < 1$, while the second term depends on n and tends to zero when $n \to \infty$, so that the series converges for $|q| < 1$.

Likewise, the first term in (26*), that is, in

$$S_n(t) = \tfrac{1}{2} \cotan (t/2) - \cos [(n + 1/2) t]/2 \sin (t/2) \qquad (28)$$

is precisely the function represented by the divergent series (11) and it does not depend on n. It is, indeed, the limit for $r = 1$ of the function $r \sin t/(1 - 2r \cos t + r^2)$ represented for $r < 1$ by the convergent series (9), which generates our divergent series (11) when r becomes equal to *one*.

Were the second term in (28), which depends on n, namely the term

$$\cos\left[(n + 1/2)\, t\right]/2 \sin (t/2)$$

at the limit for $n = \infty$, to represent zero in some sense different from the sense of usual passage to the limit, the correlation between the divergent series (11) and the function $\frac{1}{2} \cotan (t/2)$ could be established on a solid foundation.

The question raised here is of utmost importance for pure and applied mathematics as well as for applied sciences in general. Almost all practical computations are based on the use of infinite series. On the other hand, were their application limited to the use of convergent series only, the majority of cases where infinite series could be applied would become eliminated: it is a known fact that convergence is an exception, divergence being the general case with infinite series.

In other words, the concept of ordinary classical limit reveals itself as too narrow and weak when applied to infinite series, and we need a generalization of this fundamental concept.

Infinite series were introduced in the seventeenth century and were used for 200 years without any distinction between convergent and divergent series. This first period in their history was marked by great discoveries and at the same time by some paradoxical results owing to a lack of precision in the definition of limit.

The work of Cauchy and Abel at the beginning of the nineteenth century established, for the first time in the history of mathematics, a clear-cut distinction between convergent series and those series for which the limit $\lim_{n=\infty} s_n$ does not exist. As a final result, the divergent series were completely expelled from mathematics and were considered as empty symbols, unable to represent a number or a function.

During the nineteenth century, only convergent series were admitted and used. But toward the end of the century, in 1890, the Italian mathematician Cesaro suggested, for the first time after the discovery of the passage to the limit, a generalization of the classical limit concept. Applied to divergent series, this generalization establishes a correlation between a divergent series and the number or the function represented by it, enabling its deduction from the series.

Cesaro's Extension of the Limit Concept

Cesaro's extension of the classical limit concept is based on the use of arithmetic means. Given any $n + 1$ quantities $a_0, a_1, a_2, \dots a_n$, which can be considered also as first terms of an infinite sequence

$$a_0, a_1, \dots, a_n, a_{n+1}, \dots \tag{a}$$

we can form their average value by dividing the sum $a_0 + a_1 + a_2 + \dots + a_n$ by the number $n + 1$ of terms. Denoting the quotient by A_n:

$$A_n = (a_0 + a_1 + a_2 + \dots + a_n)/(n + 1) = \left(\sum_{k=0}^{n} a_k\right)/(n + 1) \tag{29}$$

we will call it the arithmetic mean of $n + 1$ quantities a_k, $0 \leqslant k \leqslant n$.

EXAMPLE: If $a_k = k$, that is, $a_0 = 0$, $a_1 = 1$, $a_2 = 2$, etc., then

$$A_n = (0 + 1 + 2 + 3 + \dots + n)/(n + 1)$$

$$= n(n + 1)/2(n + 1) = n/2.$$

Suppose now that the above infinite sequence (a) is given. The definition (29) of A_n may be applied for every value of the integer $n = 0, 1, 2, 3, \dots$ and thus, another infinite sequence

$$A_0, A_1, A_2, \dots, A_n, A_{n+1}, \dots \tag{A}$$

of arithmetic means of one, two, three, etc. terms of the original infinite sequence (a), is built. By definition, we have

$$A_0 = a_0, \quad A_1 = (a_0 + a_1)/2, \quad A_2 = (a_0 + a_1 + a_2)/3, \quad \text{etc.}$$

This new sequence (A) is generated by the original sequence (a). It is a *transformation* of (a) and, thus, every infinite sequence can be transformed into the sequence of its own arithmetic means. We will study the relation between the limits of the original sequence (a) and of the sequence of its successive arithmetic means (A). Given an infinite series (14), to study its convergence and to find the number represented by it, the first thing to do is to form, with the aid of terms of the series, the *sequence* (s) of its partial sums:

$$S_0, S_1, S_2, \dots, S_n, S_{n+1}, \dots \tag{s}$$

defined by

$$s_0 = u_0 \,; \quad s_1 = u_0 + u_1 \,; \quad s_2 = u_0 + u_1 + u_2, \text{ etc.}$$

and, in general,

$$s_n = u_0 + u_1 + u_2 + u_3 + \cdots + u_n$$

If the limit $\lim\limits_{n=\infty} s_n$ does exist, we say that the infinite sequence (s) converges towards the number $s = \lim\limits_{n=\infty} s_n$ and also that the infinite series

$$\sum_0^\infty u_n = u_0 + u_1 + u_2 + \cdots + u_n + u_{n+1} + \cdots \qquad (14)$$

converges and represents the number s, i.e. has the *sum s*. The number s is called the sum of the series although it is not a result of additions. We cannot, indeed, perform an infinite number of additions, and the sum s of a convergent series is not really a true sum of terms, but a limit, namely, the limit of a convergent sequence (s). Therefore, the infinite series (14) is simply a conventional notation for the limit of a convergent sequence, when the series (14) does converge.

Suppose now that the sequence (s) converges and transform it into the sequence (S)

$$S_0, S_1, S_2, \ldots, S_n, \ldots \qquad (S)$$

of successive arithmetic means defined by

$$S_n = (s_0 + s_1 + s_2 + \cdots + s_n)/(n + 1)$$

What happens to the limit $\lim\limits_{n=\infty} s_n = s$ when the sequence (s) is replaced by the sequence (S) of its arithmetic means? In other words does the limit $\lim\limits_{n=\infty} S_n$ exist, and, if so, how is it related to the limit s of the sequence (s)? Does the transformation of a convergent sequence (s) into (S) change its limit s or not?

The answer is "no": if the sequence (s) converges, its transform (S) converges too, and the limit does not change:

$$\lim_{n=\infty} S_n = \lim_{n=\infty} s_n = s \qquad (30)$$

Therefore, for the convergent series and sequences the passage to the limit in $\lim\limits_{n=\infty} S_n$ can be used instead of $\lim\limits_{n=\infty} s_n$ to compute the number represented by a convergent series. But the same transformation of (s) into (S) can be applied to a divergent series for which the sequence (s) has no limit. It can happen that the transformation will have no effect, that is, the sequence of arithmetic means (S) will diverge too, but it may happen also that it will converge, although the original sequence (s) is a divergent sequence.

In such a case, a generalization of the limit concept is achieved: a divergent sequence (s) is transformed into a convergent sequence (S) such that its limit can be considered as the number represented by the divergent sequence (s), that is, as its *generalized limit*. Although this number cannot be found by classical passage to the limit in $\lim_{n=\infty} s_n$, it is determined, nevertheless, with the aid of a new, more general, and more powerful procedure $\lim_{n=\infty} S_n$. This limit is a true generalization of the ordinary limit $\lim_{n=\infty} s_n$ because $\lim_{n=\infty} S_n$ yields the same results as $\lim_{n=\infty} s_n$, if the last does exist, while in many cases it yields a perfectly determined number $s = \lim_{n=\infty} S_n$, even when $\lim_{n=\infty} s_n$ does not exist at all. Therefore, we formulate Cesaro's definition of generalized limit of s_n as follows:

DEFINITION: *The ordinary limit* $\lim_{n=\infty} S_n$, *where S_n denotes the arithmetic mean of first $n + 1$ terms of an infinite divergent sequence* (s), *defines, provided it exists, the generalized limit of* s_n:

$$\text{genlim}_{n=\infty} s_n = \lim_{n=\infty} S_n \qquad (31)$$

To justify all the foregoing, we must prove the assertion (30), namely, we must deduce the limit $\lim_{n=m} S_n = s$ from the hypothesis $\lim_{n=\infty} s_n = s$. Granted that $\lim_{n=\infty} s_n = s$, we can write $s_n = s + e_n$ and, since the difference, $s_n - s$ is infinitely small for $n \to \infty$, we have $\lim_{n=\infty} e_n = 0$. Thus substituting in the definition of S_n

$$S_n = (s_0 + s_1 + s_2 + \cdots + s_n)/(n + 1) \qquad (32)$$

instead of $s_0, s_1, s_2, ..., s_n$ their expressions

$$s_0 = s + e_0, s_1 = s + e_1, s_2 = s + e_2, ..., s_n = s + e_n$$

we transform (32) into

$$S_n = [(n + 1) s + (e_0 + e_1 + e_2 + \cdots + e_n)]/(n + 1)$$

$$= s + E_n$$

34 Kogbetliantz

where E_n denotes the arithmetic mean of quantities e_k, $0 \leqslant k \leqslant n$:

$$E_n = (e_0 + e_1 + e_2 + \cdots + e_n)/(n + 1) \qquad (33)$$

To prove that $\lim\limits_{n=\infty} S_n = s$, it is sufficient to show that E_n is infinitely small for $n \to \infty$, that is, $\lim\limits_{n=\infty} E_n = 0$. On the other hand, the sequence (e)

$$e_0, e_1, e_2, ..., e_n, ... \to 0 \qquad (e)$$

not only is a convergent sequence, but it converges to zero. Thus, we have to prove that its transform (E) by arithmetic means

$$E_0, E_1, E_2, ..., E_n, ... \qquad (E)$$

is also a convergent sequence with the same limit zero. To prove it, we will show that, given an arbitrarily small positive fixed number h, a sufficiently large integer N can be found such that for all $n > N$ we have $|E_n| < h$. Now if an arbitrarily small h is chosen, we are sure that a sufficiently large N can be assigned such that, for $n > N$, we shall have

$$-h/2 < e_n < h/2 \qquad (n > N)$$

or, what is the same, $|e_n| < h/2$ since we know that $\lim\limits_{n=\infty} e_n = 0$.

We suppose that such N is assigned and that $n > N$. In the above expression (33) of E_n we subdivide the $n + 1$ terms of the sum

$$e_0 + e_1 + e_2 + \cdots + e_N + \cdots + e_n$$

into two groups of terms. The first one is the group of the first $N + 1$ terms and its value C_N does not depend on the value of n. This number C_N, defined by

$$C_N = e_0 + e_1 + e_2 + \cdots + e_N$$

s a *constant* and does not change when n increases. It does depend on h since the choice of N depends on the value of h, but in our reasoning h and N were chosen once for all and thereafter remain fixed.

In the second group we put all e_k whose subscripts k are greater than N. There will be $n - N$ terms in the second group, and we want to evaluate the upper bound of the absolute value of their sum D_n, defined by

$$D_n = e_{N+1} + e_{N+2} + \cdots + e_n$$

The absolute value of a sum is less than the sum of absolute values of its terms, or, at most, it is equal to the sum of absolute values, if all the terms are positive or all are negative. Therefore, we have

$$|D_n| \leqslant |e_{N+1}| + |e_{N+2}| + \cdots + |e_n|$$

On the other hand, the absolute value of each term in the righthand member is surely less than $h/2$ because their subscripts are greater than N. Their number being $n - N$, we have, thus,

$$|D_n| < (n - N) h/2 < (n + 1) h/2$$

The expression (33) now gives

$$|E_n| = |C_N + D_n|/(n + 1) < |C_N|/(n + 1) + |D_n|/(n + 1)$$

The first term, $|C_N|/(n + 1)$, decreases when $n \to \infty$: its numerator $|C_N|$ is a *fixed* number, while its denominator becomes infinite when $n \to \infty$. Therefore, it approaches zero, and, choosing a sufficiently large value of n, we can make the first term as small as we want. For instance, we can find an integer M such that for $n > M$ we will have

$$|C_N|/(n + 1) < h/2 \qquad\qquad (n > M)$$

The numerator $|D_n|$ of the second term was shown to be less than $(n + 1) h/2$, and therefore the second term is also less than $h/2$. Thus, for $n > N^*$, where $N^* > N$ and $N^* > M$, we have

$$|E_n| < h/2 + h/2 = h$$

and this is a sufficient proof of $\lim\limits_{n=\infty} E_n = 0$ since our h was arbitrarily small. The inequality $|E_n| < h$ for $n \to \infty$ would be impossible if $\lim\limits_{n=\infty} E_n$ were different from zero.

We have found for S_n the expression $S_n = E_n + s$, and the result, $\lim\limits_{n=\infty} E_n = 0$, is equivalent to $\lim\limits_{n=\infty} S_n = s$. Thus, the hypothesis $\lim\limits_{n=\infty} s_n = s$ entails also $\lim\limits_{n=\infty} S_n = 0$. This proves our assertiont that *Cesaro's transformation does not destroy the convergence of a sequence and does not change its limit.*

We have stated also that there are divergent sequences for which the Cesaro's transformation succeeds, that is, $\lim\limits_{n=\infty} S_n$ exists although $\lim\limits_{n=\infty} s_n$

is non-existent. To justify our statement, let us consider the particular sequence

$$1, -1, 1, -1, \dots, (-1)^n, \dots \tag{34}$$

which is the sequence of partial sums of the following series:

$$1 - 2 + 2 - 2 + 2 - 2 + \dots + (-1)^n 2 + \dots \tag{35}$$

We obtain, indeed,

$$s_0 = 1, \; s_1 = 1 - 2 = -1, \; s_2 = s_1 + 2 = -1 + 2 = 1, \textit{etc.}$$

so that the sequence (34) appears as the sequence $s_0, s_1, s_2, \dots, s_n, \dots$ of partial sums of the divergent series (35). The last series cannot converge because its general term $(-1)^n \cdot 2$ does not tend to zero for $n \to \infty$. Its divergence is also perfectly recognizable in the behavior of the sequence (34) which oscillates between -1 and $+1$ without converging to a limit. Thus, in the case of this sequences (34) the limit $\lim\limits_{n=\infty} s_n$ does not exist and has no meaning.

To transform (34) into the sequence of its successive arithmetic means, we observe that

$$s_0 = s_2 = s_4 = \dots = s_{2n} = 1$$

while

$$s_1 = s_3 = \dots = s_{2n+1} = -1$$

The terms of even order are all equal to plus one and those of odd order are all equal to minus one. Therefore, if the last term s_n of the sum $s_0 + s_1 + \dots + s_n$ is of an odd order, the number of terms being even, the value of this sum is zero. The definition (32) of S_n proves in this particular case that all arithmetic means of odd order are equal to zero:

$$S_1 = S_3 = S_5 = \dots = S_{2n+1} = \dots = 0$$

since their numerators are zeros.

But, if the last term of the sum $s_0 + s_1 + \dots + s_n$ is of an even order, $n = 2m$, then this last term s_{2m} gives the value of the entire sum. But s_{2m}, as we have seen, is equal to *plus one*. Thus, the arithmetic means of even order $2n$, are expressed as follows:

$$S_{2n} = 1/(2n + 1), \quad \text{while} \quad S_{2n+1} = 0$$

Thus, the divergent sequence (34) is transformed into the following sequence of its arithmetic means:

$$1, 0, 1/3, 0, 1/5, 0, 1/7, 0, \dots, 0, 1/(2n + 1), 0, \dots \tag{36}$$

This sequence is no longer divergent: it converges to zero since

$$S_{2n+1} = 0 \quad \text{entails} \quad \lim_{n=\infty} S_{2n+1} = 0$$

and also

$$\lim_{n=\infty} S_{2n} = \lim_{n=\infty} 1/(2n + 1) = 0$$

so that, in general,

$$\lim_{n=\infty} S_n = 0$$

It is important that the limits of both subsequences $\{S_{2n}\}$ and $\{S_{2n+1}\}$ are equal: a sequence can converge only if *all* its subsequences have the same limit. We express now the final result in stating that the divergent series (35) represents zero. Though divergent, it is summable by the arithmetic means or by Cesaro's method of summation.

The example of the series (35) has an interesting history. Dividing all its terms by two, we obtain again a series which diverges, but represents zero

$$0 \sim 1/2 - 1 + 1 - 1 + 1 - \cdots + (-1)^n + \cdots \qquad (37)$$

since the sequence of arithmetic means of its partial sums is

$$1/2, 0, 1/6, 0, 1/10, 0, 1/14, 0, \cdots \to 0 \qquad (38)$$

which is (36) divided by two. Adding 1/2 to the first term of the series (37), another divergent series

$$1/2 \sim \sum_0^\infty (-1)^n = 1 - 1 + 1 - 1 + 1 - \cdots + (-1)^n + \cdots \qquad (39)$$

is obtained, and it represents one half since the addition of 1/2 to the first term of (37) increases all partial sums and, therefore, their arithemtic means, by one half. Thus, as it can be verified by direct computation, the generalized limit ascribes to the divergent but summable series (39) the number one half as its value.

It is interesting to mention that the divergent series (39) appears for the first time in a paper by the monk Guido Grandi in 1703. Grandi considers it as a particular case of geometric series

$$\sum_{n=0}^\infty q^n = 1 + q + q^2 + q^3 + \cdots + q^n + \cdots = 1/(1 - q)$$

for $q = -1$. The series (39), is, indeed, obtained from the geometric series, if -1 is substituted instead of q. The sum $1/(1 - q)$ of a geometric series is equal to one half if $q = -1$, and Grandi ascribed to (39) a sum equal to onehalf. He tried to justify this result by the following story: Two brothers inherit a beautiful jewel. They can neither sell it nor divide it in two because this is forbidden by the testament. The brothers then decide to keep the jewel and use it alternatively, one year at a time.

Grandi says that by sharing possession of the jewel during an eternity each brother would realize his right to one half of it. On the other hand, each brother would receive it (which corresponds to the term $+1$ in the series) and give it back the (term -1 of the series) an infinite number of times, so that indeed the number represented by (39) is equal to one half.

Our result for the series, (39), namely, $\lim_{n=\infty} S_n = 1/2$, agrees well with the fact that this series, considered as a particular case of geometric series appears to be related to the number one half. Grandi's reasoning, repeated later by Euler, has found, more than one hundred and fifty years after it was published, an experimental justification which is worthwhile to narrate.

The elegant and sometimes very high steel towers of radio stations are now quite familiar to all of us. They girdle the globe and number in the thousands. The first tower of this type which opened the way for such constructions by proving that they were possible, is the famous 1050 feet high Eiffel Tower built in 1889 by Gustave Eiffel at the Champ-de-Mars in Paris.

Before erecting a new type of metallic structure, it is necessary to compute the shape and dimensions of all its parts to ensure stability and solidity. A high steel tower may collapse under its own weight if its parts are too thick and, therefore, too heavy. On the other hand, if they are too light and thin, the resistance of this high structure to the wind pressure becomes so slight that a strong wind can bend it too much, destroying the equilibrium and causing its collapse.

In considering these two opposite dangers and as a result of his computations to determine the shape and weight of his tower, Eiffel obtained the series (39). He was unable to solve his problem using convergent series only, and it was an extremely bold idea for his time when he resolutely substituted for the divergent series (39) the number one half as its meaning and value.

When the French Government sent Eiffel's project to a jury, the members of this jury unanimously discarded it, arguing that such a tower could not be stable. In their opinion, it was not at all safe to try to build it: this tower must collapse since a divergent series, which can have neither meaning nor value, was used in the computations. Thus, the whole project was declared by competent specialists as completely unfounded.

With the aid of friends who were neither mathematicians nor engineers, but who had personal confidence in him, Eiffel succeeded in realizing his project, and the tower he dreamed of was built. The fact that the Eiffel Tower has stood safely for over seventy years is tangible proof of the usefulness of divergent series and of generalized limits in applied mathematics. Instead of saying with the mathematicians of the nineteenth century that an infinite sequence or infinite series must converge towards s in order to represent this number s, we now use a more general definition:

A divergent sequence represents the number s if it possesses a generalized limit s.

It is important to emphasize that the definition just stated does not say how the limit concept was generalized, so that Cesaro's generalized limit, which is based on the ordinary limit of arithmetic means, appears as only a *particular case* of generalized limits.

And, indeed, modern mathematics knows and uses many different generalizations of limit concept. They are all based on some regular method of transformation of divergent sequences into convergent ones. A method is called a regular transformation method if it preserves the convergence and the value of the ordinary limit for all infinite convergent sequences. Cesaro's summation method by arithmetic means is now the weakest one, but the work of Cesaro was an important contribution to mathematics, and its influence on the development of the theory and use of divergent but summable series was enormous.

Divergent but summable series are now widely applied in all computations, and they are as useful as are convergent series. We must add that there are divergent series which cannot be used since no regular summation method can transform their divergence into convergence. Such are, for instance, the harmonic series

$$1 + 1/2 + 1/3 + 1/4 + 1/5 + \cdots + 1/n + \cdots$$

or the geometric progression with $q = 1$

$$1 + 1 + 1 + 1 + 1 + \ldots + 1 + \ldots$$

Returning now to the divergent series (12)

$$1/2 + \sum_1^\infty \cos(nt) = 1/2 + \cos t + \cos(2t) + \cdots + \cos(nt) + \cdots$$

we consider its partial sums $C_n(t)$, which are given by (26)

$$C_n(t) = \sin[(n + 1/2)\,t]/2\sin(t/2) \qquad (26)$$

To compute their generalized limit we will form the arithmetic means $M_n(t)$ of partial sums $C_n(t)$. The definition (32) of arithmetic means shows that the numerator of $M_n(t)$ is the sum of the first $n + 1$ expressions $C_m(t)$ for $m = 0, 1, 2, \ldots, n - 1, n$. Denoting this sum by $T_n(t)$, we have by (32)

$$(n + 1)\,M_n(t) = T_n(t) = \sum_0^n C_m(t) = C_0(t) + C_1(t) + \cdots + C_n(t).$$

To facilitate the computation of the sum $T_n(t)$ we transform (26) as follows: multiplying $C_m(t)$ by $4\sin^2(t/2)$ and applying in the righthand member the relation (23), we obtain

$$4\sin^2(t/2)\cdot C_m(t) = 2\sin[(m + 1/2)t]\sin(t/2) = \cos(mt) - \cos[(m + 1)t]$$

We now give to the variable subscript m the values $0, 1, 2, \ldots,$ $n - 1, n$, write the corresponding expressions of the products $4\sin^2(t/2)\cdot C_m(t)$ and then add them:

$$4\sin^2(t/2)\sum_0^n C_m(t) = \sum_0^n \{\cos(mt) - \cos[(m + 1)\,t]\}$$

$$= 1 - \cos t + \cos t - \cos(2t) + \cos(2t)$$

$$- \cos(3t) + \cos(3t) - \cdots + \cos(nt) - \cos[(n + 1)\,t]$$

In the lefthand member we have $4\sin^2(t/2)\,T_n(t)$. In the righthand member all the terms, except the first and the last, cancel out and there remains only the difference

$$1 - \cos[(n + 1)\,t] = 2\sin^2[(n + 1)\,t/2]$$

Observing that $T_n(t) = (n + 1)\,M_n(t)$, we have therefore

$$M_n(t) = \{\sin[(n + 1)\,t/2]/\sin(t/2)\}^2/(n + 1) \leqslant \sin^{-2}(t/2)/(n + 1)$$

The above expression proves that, for a fixed t, positive and less than 2π, the numerator of $M_n(t)$ remains less than the constant $\sin^{-2}(t/2)$, while the denominator $n + 1$ increases with n indefinitely. Therefore, the generalized limit of $C_n(t)$ is equal to zero, provided $0 < t < 2\pi$:

$$\lim_{n=\infty} M_n(t) = \operatorname{gen\,lim}_{n=\infty} C_n(t) = 0 \qquad (0 < t < 2\pi)$$

We add that the arithmetic means are all positive and tend to zero from the right, when $n \to \infty$. We now see that the divergent series (12) represents zero for all values of t within the interval $(0, 2\pi)$.

We pass now to our second divergent series (11)

$$\sum_1^\infty \sin(nt) = \sin t + \sin(2t) + \cdots + \sin(nt) + \cdots$$

The partial sums of this series $S_m(t)$, as given by (27), are:

$$S_m(t) - \tfrac{1}{2}\cotan(t/2) = -\cos[(m + 1/2)\,t]/2\sin(t/2)$$

Multiplying both sides by $4\sin^2(t/2)$ and applying (24), we obtain

$$4\sin^2(t/2)\,[S_m(t) - \tfrac{1}{2}\cotan(t/2)] = -2\sin(t/2)\cos[(m + 1/2)\,t]$$

$$= \sin(mt) - \sin[(m + 1)\,t]$$

Writing down these $n + 1$ relations for $m = 0, 1, 2, \ldots, n - 1, n$ and adding them, the following expression for the arithmetic mean $R_n(t)$ of $S_n(t)$ is obtained:

$$4(n + 1)\,\sin^2(t/2)\,[R_n(t) - \tfrac{1}{2}\cotan(t/2)] = -\sin[(n + 1)\,t]$$

Dividing by $4(n + 1)\sin^2(t/2)$, we finally have for $R_n(t)$

$$R_n(t) = \tfrac{1}{2}\cotan(t/2) - \sin[(n + 1)\,t]/[4(n + 1)\sin^2(t/2)]$$

For $0 < t < 2\pi$, the second term of this expression tends to zero when n increases indefinitely, so that

$$\lim_{n=\infty} R_n(t) = \operatorname{gen\,lim}_{n=\infty} S_n(t) = \tfrac{1}{2}\cotan(t/2) \qquad (0 < t < 2\pi)$$

This result proves that, indeed, the series (11) does represent the function $s(t) = \tfrac{1}{2}\cotan(t/2)$ in the interior of the interval $(0, 2\pi)$.

Arithmetic Means of Second Order

The success of the summation of series (11) and (12) illustrates well the importance of simple arithmetic means, called means of first order, in the theory and use of divergent series. But it may also happen that the sequence of partial sums diverges too strongly to be transformed into a convergent sequence with the aid of means *of first order*. In other words, it may happen that not only the sequence (s)

$$s_0, s_1, s_2, \ldots, s_n, \ldots \tag{s}$$

but also the sequence of its arithmetic means (S') of the first order

$$S_0', S_1', S_2', \ldots, S_n', \ldots \tag{S'}$$

are both divergent sequences.

In such a case, one can try to apply again Cesaro's method to the sequence (S') and form, with respect to the sequence (s), the arithmetic means *of second order*. Denoting them by S_n'', we have, by definition,

$$S_n'' = (S_0' + S_1' + S_2' + \cdots + S_n')/(n + 1)$$

To take an example, let us consider the divergent series

$$\sum_0^\infty (-1)^n (n + 1) = 1 - 2 + 3 - 4 + 5 - 6 + 7 - \cdots$$
$$+ (-1)^n)(n + 1) + \cdots \tag{40}$$

with its sequence of partial sums $s_0 = 1, s_1 = -1$, etc.:

$$1, -1, 2, -2, 3, -3, 4, -4, 5 \cdots \tag{s}$$

The general expression of s_n has two forms: the sums of an even order are positive, $s_{2m} = m + 1$, while those of an odd order are negative, $s_{2m+1} = -(m + 1)$.

Forming the sequence (S') of means of first order, we find

$$1, 0, 2/3, 0, 3/5, 0, 4/7, 0, 5/9, 0, 6/11, 0, \ldots \tag{S'}$$

Their general expressions are

$$S_{2m+1}' = 0; \quad S_{2m}' = (m + 1)/(2m + 1). \tag{41}$$

This sequence (S') comprises two subsequences, (S_{2m}') and (S_{2m+1}'). Both of them converge but their limits are different. The expression of the means S'_{2m} of even order

$$(m + 1)/(2m + 1) = (1 + 1/m)/(2 + 1/m) \to 1/2$$

proves that their limit is one half, but the means S'_{2m+1} of odd order have the limit zero since they all are equal to zero. Therefore, the complete sequence of means of first order (S') is a *divergent* sequence: the original sequence (s) of partial sums evidences so strong an oscillation (the amplitude of its oscillation increases *without limit*, when n increases, and becomes infinite for $n = \infty$) that means of the first order cannot suppress it but can only smooth the oscillation, reducing its infinite interval $(-\infty, +\infty)$ to the finite interval $(0, 2/3)$.

We will see now that the means of second order, that is the arithmetic means of the sequence (S'), form a convergent sequence whose limit is equal to one fourth. In other words, the divergent series (40), non-summable by means of first order, can be summed up with the aid of means of second order, whose limit, one fourth, is the value of this divergent series, that is, the number represented by it.

To prove our assertion, namely to prove that

$$\lim_{n=\infty} S''_n = 1/4$$

we give, first of all, the expressions of the means S''_n for n even, $n = 2m$, and for n odd, $n = 2m + 1$. Using the expressions (41) of means of first order, we form first the sum

$$S'_0 + S'_1 + S'_2 + \cdots + S'_{2n} = \tfrac{1}{4}(n + 1) + \tfrac{1}{2} \sum_{m=0}^{n} 1/(2m + 1)$$

and then the expressions of means of second order:

$$S''_{2n} = \tfrac{1}{2}(n + 1)/(2n + 1) + \tfrac{1}{2} \left[\sum_{0}^{n} 1/(2m + 1) \right]/(2n + 1)$$

$$S''_{2n+1} = S''_{2n}(2n + 1)/(2n + 2)$$

$$= \tfrac{1}{2}(n + 1)/(2n + 2) + \tfrac{1}{2} \left[\sum_{0}^{n} 1/(2m + 1) \right]/(2n + 2)$$

Denoting the second term of the righthand member in the expression of S''_{n2} by R_n, we can also write

$$S''_{2n} = 1/4 + (1/4)/(2n + 1) + R_n$$

$$S''_{2n+1} = 1/4 + (2n + 1) R_n/(2n + 2)$$

where the symbol R_n is defined by

$$R_n = \tfrac{1}{2} \left[\sum_0^n 1/(2m + 1) \right] / (2n + 1)$$

Thus, it becomes clear that, to prove our assertion

$$\lim_{n=\infty} S''_{2n} = \lim_{n=\infty} S''_{2n+1} = 1/4$$

it is sufficient to show that $\lim_{n=\infty} R_n = 0$. To evaluate the limit of R_n, we need the inequality

$$1/(2m + 1) < \tfrac{1}{2}\log\left[(m + 1)/(m)\right] \tag{42}$$

which is deduced from the logarithmic series (23), Chapter 11

$$\tfrac{1}{2}\, \text{Log}\, [(1 + x)/(1 - x)] = x + x^3/3 + x^5/5 + \cdots \tag{23}$$

This series converges for $-1 < x < 1$, and all its terms are positive, if x is positive. Therefore, for x positive and less than *one*, the sum of this series is greater than its first term

$$\tfrac{1}{2}\log\left[(1 + x)/(1 - x)\right] > x \qquad (0 < x < 1) \tag{43}$$

Substituting into this inequality $1/(2m + 1)$ instead of x, we transform the lefthand member of it into

$$\tfrac{1}{2}\log\left\{[1 + 1/(2m + 1)]/[1 - 1/(2m + 1)]\right\}$$

$$= \tfrac{1}{2}\log\left[(2m + 1 + 1)/(2m + 1 - 1)\right]$$

$$= \tfrac{1}{2}\log\left[(m + 1)/m\right].$$

Thus, our inequality (42) is proved. Using it for $m = 1, 2, 3, \ldots, n$, we deduce from it another inequality

$$0 < \sum_1^n 1/(2m + 1) < \tfrac{1}{2}\sum_1^n \log\left[(m + 1)/m\right]$$

The righthand member can be simplified using the fact that a sum of logarithms is equal to the logarithm of the product:

$$\log A_1 + \log A_2 + \log A_3 + \cdots + \log A_n$$

$$= \log (A_1 A_2 A_3 \cdots A_n)$$

Therefore,

$$\sum_{1}^{n} \log\,[(m + 1)/m]$$

$$= \log 2 - \log 1 + \log 3 - \log 2 + \log 4$$

$$- \log 3 + \cdots + \log (n + 1) - \log n$$

$$= \log (n + 1)$$

The last inequality takes now the form,

$$\sum_{1}^{n} 1/(2m + 1) < \tfrac{1}{2} \log (n + 1) \tag{44}$$

It is fundamental in many questions concerning logarithms. It gives a lower bound of $\log (n + 1)$. An upper bound for $\log (n + 1)$ can be deduced from the inequality

$$\tfrac{1}{2} \log\,[(m + 1)/m] < 1/(2m - 1) \tag{45}$$

which completes the inequality (42). To prove (45) we consider again the series (23) for x positive and less than *one*. We increase the sum of this series by decreasing the denominators of all its terms, except the first one:

$$\tfrac{1}{2}\log\,[(1 + x)/(1 - x)] < x + x^3/1 + x^5/3 + x^7/5 + \cdots$$

Picking out in all terms of the second member (except the first term) their common factor x^2, we rewrite our inequality as follows

$$\tfrac{1}{2}\log\,[(1 + x)/(1 - x)] < x + x^2(x + x^3/1 + x^5/5 + \cdots)$$

$$= x + x^2 \tfrac{1}{2}\log\,[(1 + x)/(1 - x)]$$

Transposing the second term of the righthand member into the left-hand member and dividing both sides by $(1 - x^2)$, we arrive at the inequality

$$\tfrac{1}{2}\log\,[(1 + x)/(1 - x)] < x/(1 - x^2) \qquad (0 < x < 1)$$

Substitute now in this result $x = 1/(2m + 1)$. The lefthand member becomes equal to $(1/2) \log\,[(m + 1)/m]$, while the righthand member is now less than $1/(2m - 1)$. We have indeed

$$[1/(2m + 1)]/[1 - 1/(2m + 1)^2]$$

$$= (2m + 1)/[2m(2m + 2)] < 1/2m < 1/(2m - 1)$$

Therefore, (45) is justified. Writing down this inequality (45) n times, for $m = 1, 2, \ldots, n$, and then adding these n inequalities member by member, we finally obtain

$$\tfrac{1}{2}\log (n + 1) < \sum_{1}^{n} 1/(2m - 1) < \sum_{0}^{n} 1/(2m + 1) \tag{46}$$

The inequalities (44) and (46) allow us to evaluate the lower and the upper bounds of the sum $\sum_{0}^{n} 1/(2m + 1)$, that is of $2 (2n + 1) R_n$, as follows:

$$\tfrac{1}{2}\log (n + 1) < \sum_{0}^{n} 1/(2m + 1) < 1 + \tfrac{1}{2}\log (n + 1)$$

and, therefore,

$$[\tfrac{1}{2}\log(n + 1)]/(2n + 1) < 2R_n < 1/(2n + 1) + [\tfrac{1}{2}\log(n + 1)]/(2n + 1) \tag{47}$$

We saw that it is sufficient to prove the ultimate vanishing of R_n for $n = \infty$, in order to justify the limit $\lim_{n=\infty} S_n'' = 1/4$. Now the inequality (47) proves that $\lim_{n=\infty} R_n = 0$, because the limits of the lower and upper bounds of R_n are equal to zero. This is obvious for $\lim_{n=\infty} 1/(2n + 1) = 0$, but must be proved for the limit of $[\log (n + 1)]/(2n + 1)$. This last point can be deduced from the limit $\lim_{x=\infty} [\log x]/x = 0$. Assuming that $\lim_{x=\infty} [\log x]/x = 0$, which will be justified below, it is clear that

$$0 < [\log (n + 1)]/(2n + 1) < [\log (2n + 1)]/(2n + 1)$$

and $\lim_{n=\infty} [\log (2n + 1)]/(2n + 1) = 0$, if $\lim_{x=\infty} [\log x]/x = 0$.

By definition of logarithms $x = e^{\log x}$. Denoting $\log x$ by t and expanding $e^{\log x} = e^t$ in the exponential series

$$x = e^t = 1 + t + t^2/2 + t^3/6 + \cdots + t^n/n! + \cdots,$$

we observe that for $x \to \infty$, $t = \log x$ also tends to infinity and therefore all the terms of this series are positive since t itself is positive. The sum of the series, that is e^t, is greater than any one of its term. In particular, e^t exceeds $t^2/2$. Thus, the quotient t/e^t is less than $t/(t^2/2)$, that is, less than $2/t$ and this gives the inequality

$$0 < \log x/x = t/e^t < 2/t = 2/\log x$$

At the limit for $x = \infty$, when also $\log x = \infty$, we obtain the justification of the limit zero of $\log x / x$:

$$0 \leqslant \lim_{x=\infty} \log x / x \leqslant \lim_{x=\infty} (2/\log x) = 0$$

Now the proof of $\lim\limits_{n=\infty} R_n = 0$ is completed and we can state that the arithmetic means of second order formed for the divergent series (40) converge to one fourth. The speed with which they converge to their limit 0.25 can be judged from the following numerical table:

n	s_n (partial sums)	S_n' (first means)	S_n'' (second means)	$S_n'' - 1/4$
1	-1	0	0.5	0.250
2	2	0.666	0.555	0.305
3	-2	0	0.416	0.166
5	-3	0	0.377	0.127
10	6	0.545	0.358	0.108
25	-13	0	0.293	0.043
50	26	0.509	0.280	0.030
101	-51	0	0.264	0.014

The table shows how the formation of arithmetic means smooths in S_n' the violent flluctuation of the divergent sequence s_n and then eliminates it completely in the means of second order S_n'', the sequence of which is not only convergent but also *monotonic* that is its terms decrease regularly, approaching their limit from above.

We add that arithmetic means of any order k can be formed. They are defined by a recurrent rule: ordinary arithmetic means of arithmetic means *of* order k are called means of the next order $k + 1$. The power of arithmetic means to smooth the oscillations of a divergent sequence increases with their order. Thus, there are series non-summable with the aid of arithmetic means of any given order k, but summable by arithmetic means of the order $k + 1$. Such is, for instance, the divergent series

$$\sum_0^\infty (-1)^n (n + 1)^k = 1 - 2^k + 3^k - 4^k + 5^k - 6^k + \cdots$$

$$+ (-1)^n (n + 1)^k + \cdots$$

It is interesting to mention that the divergent series (40) is related to the function $f(q) = (1 - q)^{-2} = 1/(1 - q)^2$. Applying the Binomial Theorem, we expand $f(q)$ into the following power series:

$$f(q = (1 - q)^{-2} = \sum_{0}^{\infty} C_n^{(-2)}(-q)^n$$

that is,

$$= \sum_{0}^{\infty} (-2)(-3) \cdots (-n)[-(n + 1)](-1)^n q^n/n!$$

$$f(q) = 1/(1 - q)^2 = \sum_{0}^{\infty} (n + 1) q^n$$

$$= 1 + 2q + 3q^2 + 4q^3 + \cdots + (n + 1) q^n + \cdots \quad (48)$$

It can be proved that the expansion (48) converges for $-1 < q < 1$, but becomes divergent if $|q| \geqslant 1$. Therefore, for $|q| < 1$, the values of the function $f(q) = (1 - q)^{-2}$ are represented by the convergent series (48).

If now -1 is substituted instead of q in the righthand member of (48), the convergence is destroyed, and the divergent series (40) is obtained. The function $f(q) = (1 - q)^{-2}$ in the lefthand member takes for $q = -1$ the value $(1 + 1)^{-2} = 1/4$. Thus, the summation of the divergent series (40) ascribes to it a value which is precisely the value of $f(q)$ for $q = -1$. This relationship between purely numerical series and functions is not new for us. We have already seen in Chapter 4 that every decimal periodic fraction is a numerical infinite convergent series related to the function $(1 - q)^{-1}$ since it is a particular case of the geometric series for some numerical value of q which is less than one. What is new here is the fact that this relationship is not limited to convergent series. The relation established between a function and its expansion into a convergent series holds also for those values of the variable for which the expansion becomes divergent.

Abel's Summation Method

This fact can be taken as the basis for another summation method invented about one hundred and fifty years ago by the French mathematician Poisson and known as Abel's summation method, although neither man conceived of it as a summation method in the modern sense of this term. Poisson has formulated the operations used in this method and Abel had proved its regularity, that is, the fact that this method, when applied to convergent series, yields their sums. In the opinion of Abel divergent series did not have a meaning and should not be used.

To apply Abel's method to a given numerical series

$$\sum_0^\infty u_n = u_0 + u_1 + u_2 + u_3 + \cdots + u_n + \cdots \tag{49}$$

which by hypothesis is supposed to be a divergent series, we must first transform it into a power series. The transformation consists in the multiplication of each term u_n by the corresponding power r^n of an auxiliary variable r with exponent equal to the subscript (number order of the term) of this term. Thus, u_0 remains unchanged since $r^0 = 1$, but u_1 is replaced by $u_1 r$, u_2 by $u_2 r^2$, u_3 by $u_3 r^3$, and so on. The power series

$$\sum_0^\infty u_n r^n = u_0 + u_1 r + u_2 r^2 + u_3 r^3 + \cdots + u_n r^n + \cdots \tag{50}$$

thus deduced from (49) may converge or diverge, its behaviour depending on the value of the parameter r. So, for instance, it is divergent if $r = 1$ since we obtain for $r = 1$ the given series (49), which by hypothesis diverges. But (50) may converge for values of $r < 1$ sufficiently small in absolute value to ensure the convergence.

Let us denote by R the number which separates the values of $|r|$ such that (50) is convergent from those for which it diverges. It is clear that the convergence corresponds to values which are less than R, while (50) diverges for $|r| > R$. In other words, R is the upper bound of all numbers $|r|$ for which the series (50) remains convergent, while, for $|r| > R$, it becomes divergent. Its behavior for $|r| = R$ does not matter.

We know that R cannot be greater than one since, the interval of convergence being $-R < r < R$ and the series (49) being divergent, we must have $R \leqslant 1$. In the case when R is less than one, the series (50) ceases to be convergent before r reaches the value one and no conclusions, which hold for $r = 1$, can be drawn from the behaviour of the convergent series (50) in the interval of convergence if $R < 1$.

Therefore, we consider only the case when $R = 1$ and the series (50) is convergent for all positive values of r less than one. In such cases, its sum is a known function of the variable r which certainly does exist for $|r| < 1$. Denoting this function by $F(r)$, we can write

$$F(r) = \sum_0^\infty u_n r^n = u_0 + u_1 r + u_2 r^2 + \cdots + u_n r^n + \cdots \qquad (51)$$

and in this relation the sign of equality is valid for all values of r less than one in absolute value, $-1 < r < 1$.

When the variable r now approaches one from the left, at the limit for $r = 1$, two cases are possible: the function $F(r)$ represented for $|r| < 1$ by the series (51) may become infinite or indetermined for $r = 1$, so that $\lim_{r=1} F(r)$ does not exist at all, or it may happen that this limit does exist and the symbol $\lim_{r=1} F(r)$ defines a perfectly determined number s: $\lim_{r=1} F(r) = s$. In the last case, it is plain that the divergent series (49) is related to this number s and must represent it though $\lim_{n=\infty} s_n$ does not exist. This conclusion leads us to another definition of a generalized limit, definition known under the name of Abel's summation method:

$$\operatorname*{genlim}_{n=\infty} s_n = \lim_{r=1} F(r) = \lim_{r=1} \left[\sum_0^\infty u_k r^k \right] \qquad (52)$$

This definition presupposes two things: on the one hand, the series (50) remains convergent for all r less than one, and, on the other hand, the sum of this series, $F(r)$, has a limit for $r = 1$. Thus, for instance, returning to our example (40),

$$\operatorname*{genlim}_{n=\infty} \left\{ \sum_0^n (-1)^k (k + 1) \right\} = \lim_{r=1} \left\{ \sum_0^\infty (-1)^k (k + 1) r^k \right\}$$

$$= \lim_{r=1} [(1 + r)^{-2}] = 1/4$$

It is known (Abel's Theorem) that this definition is regular one, that is, if a series $\sum_0^\infty u_n$ converges, then the generalized limit (52) of s_n is equal to the limit $\lim_{n=\infty} s_n = s$:

$$\lim_{r=1} \left\{ \sum_0^\infty u_k r^k \right\} = \sum_0^\infty u_n = s$$

Moreover, it is known that Abel's method is more powerful than Cesaro's method, so that we have always Abel's generalized limit, if

Cesaro's generalized limit of any order k does exist. In other words, a divergent series summable by arithmetic means of any order is *a fortiori* summable by Abel's method, and the two generalized limits are equal.

On the other hand, there are divergent series non-summable by arithmetic means of order as large as we want, but summable by Abel's method. Therefore, Abel's method is more powerful in dealing with divergent series than are Cesaro's arithmetic means of all orders.

Frege's Definition of the Number Concept and Russell's Paradox

At the end of the nineteenth century, Frege proposed the following definition of the number concept: let us call "class" the abstract idea of a collection, finite or infinite. Two classes are said to be *similar* if their members can be correlated by a one-to-one correspondence. Consider, together with a given class C, all possible classes similar to C. They form an entity which is again a class S whose members are the given class C and all classes similar to it. This new class S can be called "class of all similar classes", and to such a class of all classes similar to C corresponds an integer which is the number of members in C as well as in any class similar to it. Frege proposed that the cardinal number be defined as the class of all similar classes.

His definition was accepted and considered for a while as a valid logical definition of the number concept until 1908 when Russell discovered a flaw in it. The concept of a "class of all similar classes" is indeed fallacious from a purely logical point of view, as Russell established in his famous Paradox. Let us see how this Paradox develops.

First, observe that some classes contain themselves as one of their elements. Here are two examples of such an extraordinary class: consider a class A, defined as a collection of all classes definable by an English phrase of less than twenty words. This class A, being defined itself by an English phrase of less than twenty words, is at the same time one of its own elements.

Likewise the class B of all abstract notions is itself an abstract notion. Therefore, the class of all abstract notions contains itself as one of its elements. Let us call classes such as A and B *extraordinary*.

Most classes—we will call them ordinary—do not contain themselves as one of their elements. Consider, for instance, the class of all integers;

obviously the aleph-null totality of all integers, being infinite, cannot be an integer, because every integer must necessarily be finite. Thus, the class of all integers is ordinary.

Having defined the concepts of *ordinary class* and *extraordinary class*, we note that they are mutually exclusive. A class may contain itself as one of its elements, and thus be extraordinary; or it may not contain itself, and then it is ordinary. But the third possibility, namely a class which is neither ordinary nor extraordinary, is logically impossible (principle of the excluded middle).

Reverting to Frege's definition of the number-concept as the class of all similar classes, we note that in it the similar classes (members of the class of all similar classes) are ordinary classes because they are finite collections. Only classes having an infinite number of members can be extraordinary. To justify this point, consider a class C_n which has a finite number n of elements $e_1, e_2, e_3, ..., e_{n-1}, e_n$, each of these elements being distinct from the class C_n; suppose now that C_n is extraordinary. Since it does include itself as its own element, we are obliged to consider it as having $n + 1$ elements $e_1, e_2, e_3, ..., e_n$ and C_n. Thus, a new collection is formed which is different from C_n and, therefore, must be denoted by a new symbol, say C_{n+1}. Since $C_n \neq C_{n+1}$ this new collection, which by hypothesis is the extraordinary class we are considering, must include itself as its own element. Therefore, we add C_{n+1} to $e_1, e_2, e_3, ..., e_n, C_n$ and form C_{n+2} with $n + 2$ elements $e_1, e_2, e_3, ..., e_n, C_n, C_{n+1}$, and so on. The same argument can be repeated *ad infinitum*.

Thus, the number of elements of a finite extraordinary collection is increasing without limit. This contradiction between the hypothesis of an extraordinary class with finite number of elements and the conclusion that their number is growing without limit proves that all finite collections are ordinary classes. In particular, Frege's similar classes are ordinary classes.

Therefore, in Frege's definition of the number-concept, the concept of class of all similar classes is included in the more general concept of class of all ordinary classes. If this larger concept of class of all ordinary classes is contradictory and therefore nonexistent from a logical point of view, then its particular case (class of all similar classes) cannot be used safely in a logical definition. Thus, in this case Frege's definition of the number-concept fails.

This is precisely the case since the logical existence of a class T of all ordinary classes is doubtful. We have seen that a class must belong to ordinary classes if it is not extraordinary, and to extraordinary classes if it is not ordinary; otherwise its definition is contradictory. Let us study the nature of class T, the class of all ordinary classes.

If T is ordinary, it must contain itself as one of its elements since T is the class of *all* ordinary classes; but if it does contain itself, then it is extraordinary—a contradiction. Therefore T cannot be ordinary.

Suppose now that T is extraordinary and thus by definition does contain itself as one of its elements. All of its elements being ordinary by definition, T as its own element must be ordinary; again we are led to a contradiction. Therefore, T cannot be extraordinary either.

The conclusion that T is neither ordinary nor extraordinary is equivalent to the proof of the logical nonexistence of the class T. If a class does exist, it must be ordinary or extraordinary—there is no third possibility (principle of the excluded middle).

This analysis proves that the concept of class of *all* ordinary classes cannot be used. The obstacle seems to be in the word *all* which is a disguised use of infinity and the source of paradoxes in the classical, essentially finite, logic. We prefer to describe the concept of the integral cardinal number as an ideal set of abstract units, leaving aside all discussions of the logical nature of this concept. Perhaps logicians will succeed in finding a perfect definition of the number concept, perhaps not. It seems that in dealing with the number concept we necessarily meet concept of infinity undefinable in terms of a logic of finite collections.

Definition of limit and the concept of actual infinity

The usual definition of $\lim_{n=\infty} e_n = 0$, which is repeated in all textbooks, is carefully phrased in such a way that use of the concept of actual infinity seems unnecessary and, seemingly, only that of potential infinity is involved.

A close analysis of this definition will reveal, nevertheless, the necessity of a "jump into actual infinity" to eliminate the possibility of a non-vanishing $\lim_{n=\infty} e_n$ compatible with the assumptions stated in the definition.

The usual definition is stated as follows: "If, given any positive number h however small, a sufficiently large integer N_h (depending on h) can be found such that for all values of n which are greater than N_h

$$-h < e_n < h, \qquad\qquad (n > N_h),$$

then we say that e_n tends to the limit zero as n tends to infinity and write

$$\lim_{n=\infty} e_n = 0"$$

It is obvious that it is not sufficient to say that the limit is zero. This statement must be justified by proving that $\lim_{n=\infty} e_n$ cannot be different from zero. From the assumptions made in the definition it does not follow necessarily that the ultimate value of e_n, namely $\lim_{n=\infty} e_n$, is zero. What if this ultimate value is a fixed number different from zero though exceedingly close to it?

The justification usually proceeds as follows. The words "given any positive number h" used in the definition are interpreted to mean an infinite decreasing sequence of given *constant* numbers:

(H) $$h_1 > h_2 > h_3 > \cdots > h_k > \cdots \qquad (h_k \to 0)$$

and the definition states the existence of another infinite sequence (which is an increasing sequence) of integers N_k:

(N) $N_1 < N_2 < N_3 < \cdots < N_k < \cdots$ ($N_k \to \infty$)

such that to every value of the subscript k running through the infinite sequence (K) of all natural numbers:

(K) $1, 2, 3, \ldots, k, \ldots$

and thus to every h_k in (H) there corresponds an integer N_k in (N) and an inequality:

$$-h_k < e_n < h_k \qquad \text{(for } n > N_k)$$

Therefore the true meaning of the usual definition finds its expression in the following *infinite* sequence of inequalities:

$$
\begin{aligned}
-h_1 &< e_n < h_1 && \text{(for } n > N_1) \\
-h_2 &< e_n < h_2 && \text{(for } n > N_2) \\
\text{(S)} \qquad -h_3 &< e_n < h_3 && \text{(for } n > N_3)
\end{aligned}
$$

Translating this definition into geometrical language, we interpret each inequality $-h_k < e_n < h_k$ as a fixed interval $A_k B_k$ of length $2h_k$, symmetrical about the origin O (Fig. 1), and such that the points E_n defined by $\overline{OE_n} = e_n$ are interior to it, if $n > N_k$. Among them, only a finite number, namely the points E_n with $n \leq N_k$, may be found outside of the interval $A_k B_k$.

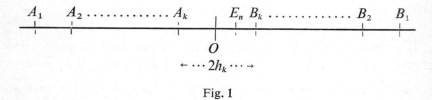

Fig. 1

An infinite sequence (I) of nested intervals $I_k = A_k B_k$

(I) $I_1 \supset I_2 \supset I_3 \supset \cdots \supset I_k \supset \cdots$

is thus obtained such that any one of them, I_k, is completely interior to its predecessor I_{k-1}, the interval I_k, comprising at the same time in its interior the next interval I_{k+1}. It is this property of mutual inclusion which is expressed by the adjective "nested".

Moreover, because h_k decreases when k increases and can be chosen as small as we please provided k is sufficiently large, the lengths $2h_k$ of these nested intervals decrease and they shrink to zero when k tends to infinity.

The question of existence of the unique and vanishing limit of e_n for n tending to infinity takes now the following geometrical form: Can an infinite sequence (I) of nested intervals, whose lengths shrink to zero, define at the limit one and only one point interior to *all* of them?

If this geometrical question is answered in the affirmative, then the unique point defined by the sequence (I) is necessarily the origin O which, by construction, is interior to all of them. Thus, the points E_n tend to the point O when n increases without limit; that is, $\lim_{n=\infty} e_n = 0$.

Therefore, to justify the definition of the limit $\lim_{n=\infty} e_n = 0$ we must prove (1) the *existence* of the limit-point and (2) the *uniqueness* of this limit-point defined by the infinite sequence of nested intervals (I).

If the existence of the limit-point is proved, then its uniqueness follows easily: Would there be two such limit-points x_1, x_2 the length of the interval I_k could not tend to zero because it is greater than $|x_2 - x_1| > 0$.

As early as 1882 the German mathematician Paul Du Bois Raymond raised a well justified objection to the idea that the use of potential infinity only (embodied in the infinite sequence (I)), is sufficient to prove the existence of the limit-point interior to *all* intervals of (I). Says Du Bois Raymond:

"Large or small, an interval between two points remains always an interval. If abruptly, without a logical justification, we let a point appear instead of an interval, it is an action which introduces arbitrarily a new concept without deducing it from what preceeds... A slow and gradual fusion of two points (two extremities of a shrinking interval) into one is perfect nonsense. The points are either separated by an interval, or there is only one point. An intermediate situation cannot exist."

The words of Du Bois Raymond clearly concern the use of potential infinity. If an interval keeps shrinking, it remains an interval as long as its shrinking continues. An interval, however small its length, always has two end-points. When and if the passage to the limit is *achieved*, the length of the interval abruptly disappears and there is suddenly only one limit-point. What has happened is this: the increasing integer k ceases to be an integer and, by jump, becomes actually infinite; its increase stops because the growth of k has exhausted the set of all integers (K).

It is interesting to notice that the logical discontinuity involved in the classical definition of limit which we are discussing is not at all easy to perceive. In general, it escapes attention. Thus, for instance, Friedrich Waismann in his valuable book on mathematical thinking[1]) says: "When an interval shrinks, it is gradually transformed into a point," while on another page he states that a convergent sequence never reaches its limit, which means that a shrinking interval continues forever to shrink and is never transformed into a point.

We now reproduce the usual reasoning by which one tries to justify the definition of the passage to the limit.

To prove that the origin is the limit-point of an infinite sequence of nested intervals, suppose—as it is done always—that to the contrary $\lim_{n=\infty} e_n = z$, where z is positive, otherwise we could consider $\lim_{n=\infty} (-e_n)$. We have now to show that this hypothesis, namely $z > 0$, is inconsistent with the assumptions as they are expressed in the infinite sequence of inequalities (S). For any positive fixed z a sufficiently large integer k can be found such that the corresponding h_k is less than $z/2$, because the sequence (H) approaches zero as close as we please. For all $n > N_k$ we have $-h_k < e_n < h_k$, as well as $h_k < z/2$, so that *a fortiori* we have

$$-z/2 < e_n < z/2 \qquad\qquad (n > N_k)$$

Therefore, only a finite number of e_n, namely those e_n for which $n \leqq N_k$, can lie outside of the interval $(-z/2, z/2)$. On the other hand the point z lies outside of this interval $(-z/2, z/2)$ and thus it becomes clear that z cannot be equal to $\lim_{n=\infty} e_n$ because the point representing this limit must be interior to the interval $(-z/2, z/2)$.

The inconsistency in question is proved and, to all appearances, it seems that this proof is complete and the concept of actual infinity is not involved in the definition of limit. Such is the point of view of many textbooks reprinted from generation to generation and restated without critical analysis.

The fallacy in this proof lies in the implicit substitution (in the con-

---

[1]) *Einführung in das mathematische Denken, Vienna.* **1936**, page 167.

clusion) of an undetermined (practically variable) z to a *fixed* perfectly determined number z with which the reasoning begins. The conclusion pretends that *all* possible nonvanishing values of $z = \lim\limits_{n=\infty} e_n$ are eliminated by this proof as inconsistent with the assumption $-h_k < e_n < h_k$ for $n > N_k$. In reality, all that is proved is the inconsistency of a *special, fixed, perfectly determined* (because *chosen*) value $z_0 = \lim\limits_{n=\infty} e_n$, as well as of all values greater than z_0.

How, indeed, can a sufficiently small h_k be *chosen*, such that $h_k < z/2$, if z is not beforehand a fixed, perfectly determined number? Therefore, the classical reasoning (which follows Weierstrass) precludes in one step of thought some one previously fixed and perfectly determined, nonvanishing value z of $\lim\limits_{n=\infty} e_n$, but not *all* of them at a time. The meaning of the word "*any*" in the sentence "for any fixed z an integer k can be found" is that we are completely free in our choice of this fixed value $z > 0$ for $\lim\limits_{n=\infty} e_n$ whose inconsistency we want to prove. But once we have chosen z we cannot change its value and are bound to apply our reasoning to it only. On the other hand, the word "*any*" also implies our freedom to *repeat* this reasoning indefinitely, choosing at every step of thought another eventual nonvanishing, and smaller, value for $\lim\limits_{n=\infty} e_n$. Thus, in reality, we can build an infinite sequence of decreasing eventual values

$$\text{(Z)} \qquad\qquad z_1, z_2, z_3, \ldots, z_k, \ldots \qquad\qquad (z_k \to 0)$$

where $z_k \to 0$ when k increases without limit, such that $\lim\limits_{n=\infty} e_n < z_k$. If we repeat our argument and continue the reasoning, we soon realize that the number of steps of thought necessary to reach our goal (that is, to prove the inconsistency of the hypothesis $\lim\limits_{n=\infty} e_n = z$ with our assumptions *for all non-vanishing values of z*) is actually infinite. Observe that, if the inconsistency is proved for $z = z_k$, all that we can do is to choose another smaller number z_{k+1} interior to the interval $(-z_k/2, z_k/2)$ in which necessarily lies $\lim\limits_{n=\infty} e_n$. Repeating the same reasoning as with z_k, we conclude that this time $\lim\limits_{n=\infty} e_n$ cannot be equal to z_{k+1} nor to a number greater than z_{k+1}. Thus, every step of thought reveals itself as insufficient, and a new link must be added to our logical chain *whose growth is unlimited.*

Therefore, even postulating the existence of the limit $\lim\limits_{n \to \infty} e_n$, an *infinite* chain of arguments is needed to preclude all possible non-vanishing values of $\lim e_n$, that is, to prove that there can be only one limit-point defined as common interior point for all intervals of an infinite sequence of nested intervals whose lengths shrink to zero.

Once this important point is established, the potential infinity is clearly insufficient for reaching a definite conclusion. If we apply the Greek thinking and try to reach a conclusion, passing continuously and successively through all the links of our infinite chain of arguments, we will never reach an end in our reasoning because *there is no last integer*. In his own way of thinking Zeno was right: using only the concept of potential infinity it is impossible to understand motion, just as it is impossible to create the passage to the limit and all the modern mathematical tools based on it.

To outthink the infinite divisibility of space (which is, perhaps, an attribute rather of our mind than of space), to prove that there is only *one* point common to all nested intervals shrinking to zero, we must use the concept of actual infinity and "jump" to the conclusion, as Paul Du Bois Raymond suspected eighty years ago.

Rational sequences approximating square roots of integers

Hero of Alexandria, inventor of the first steam turbine (first century B.C.), devised an ingenious and very simple method for computing the square root $N^{1/2}$ of any integer N by successive approximations. His method is based on:

Theorem: Given a rational number R_1, exceeding the square root $N^{1/2}$ so that $R_1^2 > N$, there exist two infinite rational sequences $[r_n]$ and $[R_n]$, defined as follows: $r_1 = N/R_1$ and, for $n \geq 1$,

$$R_{n+1} = \tfrac{1}{2}(R_n + r_n); \quad r_{n+1} = N/R_{n+1}. \tag{1}$$

These sequences converge towards $N^{1/2}$ which is their common limit. Moreover, the approximations R_n and r_n verify the inequalities

$$r_n < N^{1/2} < R_n, \tag{2}$$

so that $[R_n]$ is a decreasing and $[r_n]$ an increasing sequence.

Proof: Since $R_1 > N^{1/2}$ and $r_1 R_1 = N$ we have $r_1 < N^{1/2}$. Suppose that (2) is true for $n = k$, and consider the case $n = k + 1$. Since $r_k < R_k$ it is plain that $2R_{k+1} = R_k + r_k < 2R_k$, so that $R_{k+1} < R_k$. To verify that $R_{k+1} > N^{1/2}$ we form the difference $R_{k+1}^2 - N$:

$$4(R_{k+1}^2 - N) = (R_k + r_k)^2 - 4R_k r_k = (R_k - r_k)^2 > 0.$$

This difference is positive, so that $R_{k+1}^2 > N$ and thus $R_{k+1} > N^{1/2}$.

Multiplying the same inequality $R_k + r_k < 2R_k$ by r_k and again replacing the product $R_k r_k$ by N, we also have $(R_k + r_k) r_k < 2N$, so that

$$r_{k+1} = N/R_{k+1} = 2N/(R_k + r_k) > r_k.$$

Now $r_{k+1} = N/R_{k+1} < N/N^{1/2}$ since $R_{k+1} > N^{1/2}$ and therefore $r_{k+1} < N^{1/2}$ which achieves the proof of the inequalities

$$r_k < r_{k+1} < N^{1/2} < R_{k+1} < R_k. \tag{3}$$

We now compare the lengths of the intervals (r_k, R_k) and (r_{k+1}, R_{k+1}), the second of which is interior to the first. These lengths are equal to $R_k - r_k$ and $R_{k+1} - r_{k+1}$ respectively and we will prove that the length of the next, $(k + 1)$–th, interval is less than half the length of the previous k-th interval. To prove this important point multiply $R_{k+1} - r_{k+1}$ by $4R_{k+1}$:

$$4R_{k+1}(R_{k+1} - r_{k+1}) = 4R_{k+1}^2 - 4R_{k+1}r_{k+1}$$
$$= (R_k + r_k)^2 - 4R_k r_k = (R_k - r_k)^2$$

because $R_{k+1}r_{k+1} = R_k r_k = N$. Dividing both sides by $2R_{k+1} = R_k + r_k$, we obtain

$$2(R_{k+1} - r_{k+1}) = (R_k - r_k)[(R_k - r_k)/(R_k + r_k)] < R_k - r_k$$

because $R_k - r_k < R_k + r_k$. Thus, $R_{k+1} - r_{k+1} < (R_k - r_k)/2$, and the algorithm invented by Hero of Alexandria reduces more than twice the length of the interval containing in its interior the irrational $N^{1/2}$.

If this algorithm is applied n times successively the last interval's length is less than the length of the initial interval divided by 2^n. The divisor 2^n can be made as large as we want by choosing a sufficiently large exponent n and therefore the length of the last interval can be made as small as we want. Since the error made in replacing the interior point $N^{1/2}$ of the approximation's interval (r_n, R_n) by one of its extreme points is less than the length of this interval, we state that the approximations obtained with the aid of Hero's algorithm can be made as accurate as we want, provided that the algorithm be repeated a sufficiently great number of times.

It is important to observe that this algorithm defines an infinite chain of nested intervals and gives, therefore, at each step two approximate values: one, R_n, greater than the irrational $N^{1/2}$, and the other, r_n, smaller than $N^{1/2}$. At each step we can evaluate the upper bound of error made by replacing $N^{1/2}$ by R_n or by r_n. This upper bound is equal to the length $R_n - r_n$ of the interval, that is

$$0 < N^{1/2} - r_n < R_n - r_n; \quad 0 < R_n - N^{1/2} < R_n - r_n.$$

The length $R_{n+1} - r_{n+1}$ of the interval formed by the $(n + 1)$–th approximate values is surely less than the length of the initial interval $R_1 - r_1$ divided by 2^n

$$R_{n+1} - r_{n+1} < (R_1 - r_1)/2^n$$

and therefore it approaches zero when n increases without limit: $\lim_{n=\infty} (R_n - r_n) = 0$. This means that the two limits, $\lim_{n=\infty} R_n$ and $\lim_{n=\infty} r_n$ are equal. Because the irrational number $N^{1/2}$ remains forever between R_n and r_n

$$r_n < N^{1/2} < R_n$$

the two equal limits, $\lim_{n=\infty} R_n$ and $\lim_{n=\infty} r_n$ can become equal only coinciding with the irrational number $N^{1/2}$:

$$\lim_{n=\infty} r_n = \lim_{n=\infty} R_n = N^{1/2}.$$

Thus Hero's algorithm represents a very simple example of two converging rational sequences whose common limit is an irrational number $N^{1/2}$.

Numerical example. To compute the square root $5^{1/2}$ we observe that $2^2 = 4 < 5 < 6.25 = 2.5^2$. Therefore we can choose 2 and 2.5 as r_0 and R_0 and start with them the chain of successive approximation, because $r_0 R_0 = 5$.

Applying the rule (3), we obtain first $R_1 = (2 + 2.5)/2 = 2.25$ and $r_1 = 5/2.25 = 20/9$, so that we already know that $2.22 < \sqrt{5} < 2.25$. Forming the next approximation we obtain $R_2 = (9/4 + 20/9)/2 = 161/72$ and $r_2 = 360/161$. These second approximations give the inequalities

$$2.236111 < 161/72 < \sqrt{5} < 360/161 < 2.236025.$$

The third approximations $r_3 = 115{,}920/51{,}841$ and $R_3 = 51{,}841/23{,}184$ already give the square root $\sqrt{5}$ with eight exact decimals, namely:

$$2.236067977 < r_3 < \sqrt{5} < R_3 < 2.236067979$$

and therefore we obtain 2.23606797 as an approximate value of $\sqrt{5}$.

Hero's method for extracting square roots can be generalized to roots of any order m. Thus, if x is the exact value of the radical $\sqrt[m]{N}$ the rational decreasing sequence $x_1, x_2, x_3, x_4, \ldots$ approximating x is defined by the chain-rule

$$x_{n+1} = [(m - 1) x_n^m + N]/(m x_n^{m-1}) = [(m - 1)/m] \cdot x_n + N/(m x_n^{m-1}).$$

Expansion of a real root of a quadratic equation into a convergent continued fraction

The infinite continued fraction

$$q^|/_|p + q^|/_|p + \cdots + q^|/_|p + \cdots \tag{1}$$

represents a solution of the quadratic equation

$$x^2 + px - q = 0 \tag{2}$$

since this equation can also be written as follows: $x(p + x) = q$ and therefore $x = q/(p + x)$. This leads to the infinite periodic continued fraction (1) by endlessly substituting the equivalent expression $q/(p + x)$ for x in the righthand member.

We study here the convergence of (1) and also establish which of the two roots of (2) is represented by (1) in case the infinite fraction converges. These two questions are easy to answer if the explicit expression of the n-th convergent $C_n = P_n/Q_n$ is known, and it is deduced in terms of two roots x_1 and x_2 of the equation (2).

The partial numerators of (1) are all equal to q and the partial denominators equal to p. Therefore, the recurrent relations between three successive numerators P_n and denominators Q_n of convergents C_n are:

$$P_{n+1} = p \cdot P_n + q \cdot P_{n-1}; \quad Q_{n+1} = p \cdot Q_n + q \cdot Q_{n-1} \tag{3}$$

with the initial values

$$P_1 = q, \quad Q_1 = p, \quad P_2 = pq = q \cdot Q_1, \quad Q_2 = p^2 + q$$

because $C_1 = P_1/Q_1 = q/p$ and $C_2 = P_2/Q_2 = pq/(p^2 + q)$.
Computing P_3 one finds

$$P_3 = p \cdot P_2 + q \cdot P_1 = p^2 q + q^2 = q(p^2 + q) = q \cdot Q_2.$$

Therefore

$$P_4 = p \cdot P_3' + q \cdot P_2 = pq \cdot Q_2 + q^2 Q_1 = q\,(pQ_2 + qQ_1) = q \cdot Q_3$$

and in general, by mathematical induction, for all integral values of the subscript n:

$$P_{n+1} = q \cdot Q_n. \qquad\qquad (n \geqq 1)\ (4)$$

It is sufficient, therefore, to find the expression of Q_n only. The roots x_1, x_2 verify the fundamental relations $p = -(x_1 + x_2)$ and $q = -x_1 x_2$. Using these expressions of p and q, we have:

$$Q_1 = p = -(x_1 + x_2) = -(x_2^2 - x_1^2)/(x_2 - x_1)$$

$$Q_2 = p^2 + q = (x_1 + x_2)^2 - x_1 x_2 = x_2^2 + x_1 x_2 + x_1^2$$

$$= (x_2^3 - x_1^3)/(x_2 - x_1)$$

which suggests that in general

$$Q_n = (-1)^n \cdot (x_2^{n+1} - x_1^{n+1})/(x_2 - x_1). \qquad\qquad (5)$$

To justify (5) we use mathematical induction. Suppose that (5) holds for $n = k - 1$ and $n = k$ because it was already proved for $n \leq k$. If it can be proved for $n = k + 1$, the mathematical induction will justify it for all values of the integer n. Substituting the expressions (5) of Q_{k-1} and Q_k

$$Q_{k-1} = (-1)^{k-1}\,(x_2^k - x_1^k)/(x_2 - x_1);$$

$$Q_k = (-1)^k\,(x_2^{k+1} - x_1^{k+1})/(x_2 - x_1)$$

into the recurrent relation (3)

$$Q_{k+1} = pQ_k + qQ_{k-1} = -(x_1 + x_2)\,Q_k - x_1 x_2 Q_{k-1},$$

and multiplying it by $(x_2 - x_1)$, we obtain:

$$(x_2 - x_1)\,Q_{k+1} = p\,(x_2 - x_1)\,Q_k + q\,(x_2 - x_1)\,Q_{k-1}$$

$$= (-1)^{k+1} \cdot (x_2 + x_1)\,(x_2^{k+1} - x_1^{k+1}) + (-1)^k \cdot x_1 x_2\,(x_2^k - x_1^k)$$

$$= (-1)^{k+1} \cdot (x_2^{k+2} - x_1^{k+2}).$$

This yields the expression (5) for Q_{k+1} and therefore the proof of (5) is achieved.

The relation (4) now yields the corresponding expression of $P_n = qQ_{n-1}$:

$$P_n = (-1)^n x_1 x_2 (x_2^n - x_1^n)/(x_2 - x_1) \tag{6}$$

and thus, dividing member by member (6) by (5), we obtain the expression of the n-th convergent $C_n = P_n/Q_n$ in terms of roots of (2):

$$C_n = x_1 x_2 (x_2^n - x_1^n)/(x_2^{n+1} - x_1^{n+1}). \tag{7}$$

Double root. First let us study the case of double root when the discriminant $D = p^2 + 4q$ vanishes. The expression (7) becomes in this case indeterminate because its numerator and denominator both vanish. But, if we rewrite the expression (5) as follows:

$$Q_n = (-1)^n(x_2^n + x_1 x_2^{n-1} + x_1^2 x_2^{n-2} + \cdots + x_2 x_1^{n-1} + x_1^n), \tag{8}$$

which is obtained by performing the long division indicated in (5) and if we substitute in it $x_2 = x_1 = x_0$, where x_0 is the value of the double root, we find that in the case of a double root the expression (8) of Q_n reduces to

$$Q_n = (-1)^n (n + 1) x_0^n \tag{8'}$$

which also gives

$$P_n = qQ_{n-1} = -x_1 x_2 (-1)^{n-1} \cdot n \cdot x_0^{n-1} = (-1)^n x_0^{n+1} \cdot n$$

Dividing P_n by Q_n, we obtain the following expression of of the n-th convergent C_n

$$C_n = P_n/Q_n = nx_0/(n + 1).$$

Passing now to the limit for $n = \infty$, we see that the sequence $C_1, C_2, \ldots, C_n, \ldots$ of successive convergents does indeed converge towards the double root x_0; that is, $\lim\limits_{n=\infty} C_n = x_0$ because $\lim\limits_{n=\infty} [n/(n + 1)]$ $= 1$. In other words, the periodic continued fraction (1) converges to $-p/2$ if $p^2 + 4q = 0$, so that $q = -p^2/4$:

$$-p/2 = -(p^2/4) \,|/_|p - (p^2/4)|/_|p - \cdots \tag{9}$$

Multiplying both members by $-4/p$ and simplifying the partial fractions which all have common factor p, we see that (9) is equivalent to

$$2 = 1 \,|/_|1 - \tfrac{1}{4}|/_|1 - \tfrac{1}{4}|/_|1 - \cdots \tag{10}$$

The numerical relation (10) holds because, if we denote the value of the continued Periodic fraction in (10) by z, the unknown z must verify the quadratic equation $z = 1/(1 - z/4)$ which has as its unique solution $z = 2$.

Complex roots. Returning to the general case $D \neq 0$, we now consider the case of two complex conjugate roots when D is negative, $D < 0$.

The sequence of convergents $C_1, C_2, ..., C_n, ...$ is a real sequence and therefore, if it converges, it can represent only a real number. On the other hand, we know that if it converges it must represent a root of the equation (2). Since both roots are complex numbers it is plain that the periodic continued fraction (1) cannot converge. Its divergence can be easily proved considering the expression (7) of the nth convergent in the case when $x_1 = Re^{it}$ and $x_2 = Re^{-it}$. Substituting these values of two complex conjugate roots into (7), we have:

$$C_n = R\,(e^{int} - e^{-int})/[e^{i(n+1)t} - e^{-i(n+1)t}] = R \cdot \mathrm{Sin}\,(nt)/\mathrm{Sin}\,[(n+1)\,t]$$

But the two limits $\lim_{n=\infty} \mathrm{Sin}\,(nt)$ and $\lim_{n=\infty} \mathrm{Sin}\,[(n+1)\,t]$ do not exist and therefore there is no limit $\lim_{n=\infty} C_n$ either: the sequence C_n is a divergent sequence.

Therefore, in the case $D > 0$, there is no convergent continued fraction which could represent a complex root of the quadratic equation (2) with real coefficients p and q.

Real roots. In the case $D > 0$ we distinguish between two subcases: $p > 0$ and $p < 0$. Denoting once for all the root of greater absolute value by x_1, so that we always have $|x_1| > |x_2|$, we obtain different formulas for x_1 and x_2 according to the sign of p. If p is positive we must write

$$x_1 = -(p + D^{1/2})/2; \quad x_2 = (-p + D^{1/2})/2 \qquad (p > 0)$$

since, if $p > 0$, $|x_1| = (p + D^{1/2})/2 > |-p + D^{1/2}|/2 = |x_2|$.

But, if p is negative the expressions of the roots change:

$$x_1 = (-p + D^{1/2})/2; \quad x_2 = -(p + D^{1/2})/2 \qquad (p < 0).$$

Indeed, if $p < 0$, we are obliged to write $x_1 = (-p + D^{1/2})/2$ since, for $p < 0$, $(-p + D^{1/2})/2 > |p + D^{1/2}|/2$.

Denoting the sign of p by the sign (p), we can unify both cases into

$$x_1 = -\mathrm{sign}\,(p) \cdot (|p| + D^{1/2})/2; \quad x_2 = \mathrm{sign}\,(p) \cdot (-|p| + D^{1/2})/2.$$

The two roots x_1 and x_2 can have the same or opposite signs. Therefore, their ratio can be positive or negative. Denoting it by $r = x_2/x_1$

we see that the real number r is comprised between -1 and $+1$, since $|x_1| > |x_2|$: $|r| < 1$.

Dividing the numerator and the denominator of the fraction (7) which expresses C_n, by x_1^{n+1} and replacing the ratio x_2/x_1 by r, we obtain

$$C_n = x_2 (r^n - 1)/(r^{n+1} - 1). \qquad (|r| < 1) \ (11)$$

When n increases without limit, r^n and r^{n+1} tend to zero because $|r| < 1$. Thus, at the limit, we obtain

$$\lim_{n=\infty} C_n = x_2(-1)/(-1) = x_2$$

which proves that *the periodic continued fraction* (1) *converges* towards x_2, that is, *towards the root of least absolute value*.

All the foregoing presupposes that p is different from zero. If p is zero, the equation (2) has two roots $\pm q^{1/2}$, which are real if q is positive, but the absolute value of these two real and distinct roots are equal. The fraction (1) is divergent since for $p = 0$ its convergents are equal alternatively to zero and to infinity: $C_{2n+1} = \infty$, but $C_{2n} = 0$.

Expansion of *e* into a continued fraction

Proposition: The successive convergents P_n/Q_n of the continued fraction

$$1^|/_|1 + 1^|/_|2 + 2^|/_|3 + 3^|/_|4 + \cdots + (n - 1)^|/_|n + \cdots$$

form a convergent sequence whose limit is equal to $e - 2$.

Proof: The partial numerators a_n and denominators b_n of the continued fraction are given by $b_n = n$, for $n \geq 1$, and by $a_n = n - 1$ for $n \geq 2$ ($a_1 = 1$), so that the recurrent relation verified by the numerators and denominators of successive convergents is as follows:

$$X_{n+1} = (n + 1) X_n + n \cdot X_{n-1} \qquad (n \geq 2). \ (1)$$

The first and second convergents P_1/Q_1 and P_2/Q_2 are equal to $1/1$ and $2/3$ respectively. Therefore, the initial conditions for the solution P_n of (1) are $P_1 = 1$ and $P_2 = 2$. On the other hand, the second solution Q_n corresponds to another set of initial conditions, namely to $Q_1 = 1$ and $Q_2 = 3$.

Replacing X_n with a new unknown function of the discrete variable n, x_n, related to X_n by $x_n - X_n/n!$, and denoting the particular cases $P_n/n!$ and $Q_n/n!$ of x_n respectively by p_n and q_n

$$x_n = X_n/n!; \quad p_n = P_n/n!; \quad q_n = Q_n/n!,$$

we transform (1) into

$$x_{n+1} = x_n + x_{n-1}/(n + 1), \tag{2}$$

so that p_n and q_n are two particular solutions of (2) defined by the initial conditions $p_1 = p_2 = 1$ and $q_1 = 1$, $q_2 = 3/2$.

These solutions admit of following representations:

$$p_n = n + 2 - 2q_n; \quad q_n = (n + 2) \cdot \sum_{k=0}^{n+2} (-1)^k/k!. \tag{3}$$

To prove this assertion we first have to check that the initial conditions are verified:

$$q_1 = 3\,(1 - 1 + 1/2 - 1/6) = 3\,(1/3) = 1;$$

$$q_2 = 4\,(1 - 1 + 1/2 - 1/6 + 1/24) = 3/2$$

$$p_1 = 3 - 2q_1 = 3 - 2 = 1 \qquad\qquad p_2 = 4 - 2q_2 = 4 - 2\,(3/2) = 1.$$

Substituting the expressions (3) of q_{n-1}, q_n, q_{n+1} in the recurrent relation (2) we can verify the fact that q_n is a particular solution of this relation. First form the quotient $q_{n-1}/(n + 1)$:

$$q_{n-1}/(n + 1) = \sum_{k=0}^{n+1} (-1)^k/k! = \sum_{k=0}^{n+2} (-1)^k/k! + (-1)^{n+3}/(n + 2)!$$

$$= \sum_{k=0}^{n+2} (-1)^k/k! + (n + 3)\,(-1)^{n+3}/(n + 3)!.$$

Adding q_n to $q_{n-1}/(n + 1)$, we obtain

$$q_n + q_{n-1}/(n + 1)$$

$$= (n + 2) \cdot \sum_{k=0}^{n+2} (-1)^k/k! + \sum_{k=0}^{n+2} (-1)^k/k! + (n + 3)\,(-1)^{n+3}/(n + 3)!$$

$$= (n + 3) \cdot \sum_{k=0}^{n+2} (-1)^k/k! + (n + 3)(-1)^{n+3}/(n + 3)!$$

$$= (n + 3) \cdot \sum_{k=0}^{n+3} (-1)^k/k! = q_{n+1},$$

so that q_n does satisfy the recurrent relation (2).

On the other hand, the first term $n + 2$ in the expression of p_n is also a solution of (2) because the direct substitution of $n + 2$ for x_n gives

$$(n + 3) = (n + 2) + (n + 1)/(n + 1) = (n + 2) + 1.$$

Therefore p_n, as a linear combination of two solutions, is also a solution of (2).

Having established that the expressions (3) of p_n and q_n are valid, we observe that a convergent P_n/Q_n can also be represented as p_n/q_n. Therefore

$$P_n/Q_n + 2 = p_n/q_n + 2 = (p_n + 2q_n)\,q_n$$

$$= (n + 2)\Big/\Big[(n + 2) \cdot \sum_{k=0}^{n+2} (-1)^k/k!\Big]$$

that is

$$P_n/Q_n + 2 = \left[\sum_{k=0}^{n+2} (-1)^k/k!\right]^{-1}.$$

The limit of the sum $\sum_{k=0}^{n+2} (-1)^k/k!$ for $n = \infty$ is the reciprocal of e namely e^{-1}, as it can be found from the exponential series if $x = -1$. Therefore,

$$\lim_{n=\infty} (P_n/Q_n + 2) = \lim_{n=\infty} \left[\sum_{k=0}^{n+2} (-1)^k/k!\right]^{-1} = \left[\sum_{k=0}^{\infty} (-1)/k!\right]^{-1}$$

$$= (e^{-1})^{-1} = e,$$

which completes the proof of the proposition.

For a reader who knows the Calculus, it is interesting to see how the solutions (3) were obtained. Here we solve (2) with the aid of the method of generating functions. Let $f(u)$ be the generating function of the infinite sequence $x_1, x_2, ..., x_n, ...$ so that by definition

$$f(u) = \sum_{n=1}^{\infty} x_n u^n.$$

Multiplying (2) by u^{n+1} and summing up from $n = 2$ to $n = \infty$, we deduce an equation verified by the unknown generating function $f(u)$:

$$f(u) - x_1 u - x_2 u^2 = u \cdot [f(u) - x_1 u] + \sum_{n=2}^{\infty} x_{n-1} u^{n+1}/(n + 1). \quad (4)$$

Differentiating (4) with respect to u, we obtain for $f(u)$ the following lincar differential equation

$$f'(u) - x_1 - x_2 \cdot 2u = f(u) - 2x_1 u + uf'(u) + uf(u).$$

Denoting x_1 and $2(x_2 - x_1)$ by A and B respectively, we write it as follows $(A = x_1, B + 2A = 2x_2)$

$$(1 - u)f'(u) - (1 + u)f(u) = A + Bu \quad (5)$$

The homogeneous equation, obtained by replacing the righthand member by zero, is easy to integrate and its general solution is given by the expression

$$K (1 - u)^{-2} e^{-u}$$

where K is a constant of integration. Substituting an auxiliary unknown function $g(u)$ for K, we transform (5) by the substitution:

$$f(u) = g(u) (1 - u)^{-2} e^{-u}. \quad (6)$$

Thus, the auxiliary unknown $g(u)$ is a solution of the differential equation

$$g'(u) = (A + Bu)(1 - u)e^u,$$

and it is obtained without difficulty by a simple integration:

$$g(u) = [2A - 3B + (3B - A)u - Bu^2]e^u + C.$$

Now $f(u)$ satisfies the initial condition $f(0) = 0$. The relation (6) shows that $g(0) = f(0) = 0$ and thus the initial condition is verified if

$$g(0) = 0 = 2A - 3B + C,$$

that is, if the constant of integration C has a special value:

$$C = 3B - 2A.$$

Replacing in (6) $g(u)$ by its expression, we find for $f(u)$ the following final form

$$f(u) = (3B - 2A)(1 - u)^{-2} \cdot e^{-u} + (A - B)(2 - u)(1 - u)^{-2} - B. \quad (7)$$

Expanding the solution (7) into its Maclaurin Series, we finally obtain for the coefficient x_n of u^n the following expression:

$$x_n = (3B - 2A) \cdot \sum_{k=0}^{n} (n - k + 1)(-1)^k/k! + (n + 2)(A - B)$$

$$= (n + 2) \cdot [(3B - 2A) \cdot \sum_{k=0}^{n+2} (-1)^k/k! + A - B]. \quad (8)$$

The parameters A and B depend on initial conditions; that is, on the first two terms x_1 and x_2 of the sequence x_n. For $x_n = p_n$ we have $x_1 = x_2 = 1$, so that $A = 1$; but $B = 0$. In this particular case (8) yields the expression (3) for p_n. If $x_n = q_n$, then $x_1 = 1$ and $x_2 = 3/2$, so that $A = 1$ and $B = 1$ which yields the expression (3) for q_n.

Rigorous proof of Euler's Formula

We have seen that for $x \to 0$, $\operatorname{Sin} x \approx x$ because $\lim\limits_{x=0} \operatorname{Sin} x/x = 1$. From it also follows the limit $\lim\limits_{x=0} [\operatorname{Cos} x/(1 - x^2/2)] = 1$, so that

$$\operatorname{Cos} x \approx 1 - x^2/2 \qquad (x \to 0) \ (1)$$

The approximate formula $\operatorname{Sin} x \approx x$ can be improved, using

$$\operatorname{Sin} x \approx x \cdot (1 + mx + nx^2) \qquad (x \to 0), \ (2)$$

where m and n are two unknown numerical coefficients. To find them we observe that $\operatorname{Sin} 2x = 2 \operatorname{Sin} x \cdot \operatorname{Cos} x$ and, therefore, for $x \to 0$, m and n must verify the condition

$$2x \, (1 + 2mx + 4nx^2) \approx 2x \, (1 + mx + nx^2) \, (1 - x^2/2)$$

obtained by using in $\operatorname{Sin} 2x = 2 \operatorname{Sin} x \operatorname{Cos} x$ the approximate formulas (1) and (2). Performing the multiplication and dropping both sides the common factor $2x$, as well as the terms of order greater than second, we have

$$1 + 2mx + 4nx^2 = 1 + mx + (n - 1/2) \, x^2.$$

Comparing the coefficients of like powers of x in both members, we see that $m = 0$ and $n = -1/6$, so that the formula (2) is replaced by

$$\operatorname{Sin} x \approx x \, (1 - x^2/6) = x - x^3/6 \qquad (x \to 0). \ (3)$$

To prove Euler's Formula $e^{iu} = \operatorname{Cos} u + i \operatorname{Sin} u$ it is sufficient to show that the product $e^{-iu} \cdot (\operatorname{Cos} u + i \operatorname{Sin} u)$ is equal to one. De Moivre's formula shows that $\operatorname{Cos} u + i \operatorname{Sin} u = (\operatorname{Cos} 1 + i \operatorname{Sin} 1)^u$ and on the other hand we have $e^{-iu} = (e^{-i})^u$. Thus we can state that the product $e^{-iu} (\operatorname{Cos} u + i \operatorname{Sin} u)$ is equal to a power with exponent u

$$e^{-iu} (\operatorname{Cos} u + i \operatorname{Sin} u) = [e^{-i} \cdot (\operatorname{Cos} 1 + i \operatorname{Sin} 1)]^u = A^u,$$

the base of the power being equal to a constant number A defined by $A = e^{-i} \cdot (\text{Cos } 1 + i \text{ Sin } 1)$. Euler's Formula will be proved if we show that this constant number A is equal to one.

By definition of e^{-i} we have

$$e^{-i} = \lim_{t=0} [(1 - it)^{1/t}]. \tag{4}$$

Using again De Moivre's Formula $(\text{Cos } t + i \text{ Sin } t)^{1/t} = \text{Cos } 1 + i \text{ Sin } 1$ we can also write

$$\text{Cos } 1 + i \text{ Sin } 1 = \lim_{t=0} [(\text{Cos } t + i \text{ Sin } t)^{1/t}]. \tag{5}$$

Combining (4) and (5), we obtain for A the following limit

$$A = \lim_{t=0} \{[(1 - it)(\text{Cos } t + i \text{ Sin } t)]^{1/t}\}. \tag{6}$$

The product of two complex numbers $1 - it$ and $\text{Cos } t + i \text{ Sin } t$ is again a complex number Re^{is} with absolute value R and amplitude s. Both R and s depend on t and, as functions of t, they may be noted $R(t)$ and $s(t)$.

The absolute value of a product is the product of the absolute values of factors and thus, since the absolute value of $\text{Cos } t + i \text{ Sin } t$ is one, we obtain

$$R(t) = |1 - it| = (1 + t^2)^{1/2}. \tag{7}$$

To find the amplitude $s(t)$ we perform the multiplication and write

$$\text{Cos } t + t \text{ Sin } t + i (\text{Sin } t - t \text{ Cos } t) = R \text{ Cos } s + iR \text{ Sin } s$$

which shows that $R \text{ Cos } s = \text{Cos } t + t \text{ Sin } t$, and $R \text{ Sin } s = \text{Sin } t - t \text{ Cos } t$, so that

$$\text{Sin } s/\text{Cos } s = \text{Tan } s = (\text{Sin } t - t \text{ Cos } t)/(\text{Cos } t + t \text{ Sin } t). \tag{8}$$

If t approaches zero, the righthand member in (8) approaches zero and thus $s \to 0$ since $\tan s \to 0$. The second possibility, namely $s \to 180°$, is excluded: for $t = 0$ the product we are studying becomes equal to one: $R(0) e^{is(0)} = 1$. But $R(0) = 1$, so that $e^{is(0)} = 1$ and so $s(0)$ cannot be equal to $180°$ since $e^{i\pi}$ is equal to minus one. Therefore, $s(t)$ vanishes when t approaches zero.

Replacing in both members of (8) Sin s, Cos s, Sin t, and Cos t by their approximate expressions (1) and (3),

$$s (1 - s^2/6)/(1 - s^2/2) \approx (t - t^3/6 - t + t^3/2)/(1 + t^2/2),$$

and observing that the geometric progressions

$$(1 - s^2/2)^{-1} = 1 + s^2/2 + s^4/4 + s^6/8 + \cdots \approx 1 + s^2/2$$

$$(1 + t^2/2)^{-1} = 1 - t^2/2 + t^4/4 - t^6/8 + \cdots \approx 1 - t^2/2$$

give $1 + s^2/2$ and $1 - t^2/2$ as approximate values of $(1 - s^2/2)^{-1}$ and $(1 + t^2/2)^{-1}$ respectively, we find

$$s(1 - s^2/6)(1 + s^2/2) \approx t^3(1 - t^2/2)/3.$$

This last relation shows that for $t \to 0$, $s \to 0$

$$s = s(t) \approx t^3/3.$$

We now apply these results

$$R(t) = (1 + t^2)^{1/2}; \quad s(t) = t^3(1 + z_t)/3$$

with $\lim_{t=0} z_t = 0$ to the expression (6) of A, that is to

$$A = \lim_{t=0} [R(t)]^{1/t} \cdot \lim_{t=0} e^{is(t)/t}. \tag{9}$$

Since $s(t)/t$ vanishes as $t^2/3$ for $t = 0$, we have $\lim_{t=0} e^{is/t} = e^0 = 1$, and, to achieve the proof of $A = 1$, it remains to prove that

$$\lim_{t=0} [R(t)]^{1/t} = 1.$$

Now, by the definition of e we can write

$$e = \lim_{t=0} [(1 + t^2)^{1/t^2}],$$

where the limit e is reached from below, so that

$$1 < (1 + t^2)^{1/t^2} < e.$$

Raising these inequalities to a power with the exponent $t/2$, we obtain

$$1 < (1 + t^2)^{1/2t} < e^{t/2}$$

At the limit, for $t = 0$, we have therefore $\lim_{t=0} (1 + t^2)^{1/2t} = 1$ since $\lim_{t=0} e^{t/2} = 1$. But $[R(t)]^{1/t} = (1 + t^2)^{1/2t}$ so that $\lim_{t=0} [R(t)^{1/t}] = 1$ which proves with the aid of (9) that $A = 1$.